2020
30TH EDITION

A DESIGN COST DATA COMPANY
DATA YOU CAN TRUST

GENERAL
CONSTRUCTION
COSTBOOK

EDITOR-IN-CHIEF

William D. Mahoney, P.E.

TECHNICAL SERVICES

Tony De Augustine
Joan Hamilton
Anthony Jackson
Eric Mahoney, AIA
Ana Varela

GRAPHIC DESIGN

Robert O. Wright Jr.

BNi Publications, Inc.

VISTA
990 PARK CENTER DRIVE, SUITE E
VISTA, CA 92081

1-888-BNI-BOOK (1-888-264-2665)
www.bnibooks.com

ISBN 978-1-55701-990-5

Table of Contents

Preface

For over 73 years, BNi Building News has been dedicated to providing construction professionals with timely and reliable information. Based on this experience, our staff has researched and compiled thousands of up-to-the-minute costs for the **BNi Costbooks**. This book is an essential reference for contractors, engineers, architects, facility managers — any construction professional who must provide an estimate for any type of building project.

Whether working up a preliminary estimate or submitting a formal bid, the costs listed here can be quickly and easily tailored to your needs. All costs are based on prevailing labor rates. Overhead and profit should be included in all costs. Man-hours are also provided.

All data is categorized according to the CSI division format. This industry standard provides an all-inclusive checklist to ensure that no element of a project is overlooked. In addition, to make specific items even easier to locate, there is a complete alphabetical index.

The "Features of this Book" section presents a clear overview of the many features of this book. Included is an explanation of the data, sample page layout and discussion of how to best use the information in the book.

Of course, all buildings and construction projects are unique. The information provided in this book is based on averages from well-managed projects with good labor productivity under normal working conditions (eight hours a day). Other circumstances affecting costs, such as overtime, unusual working conditions, savings from buying bulk quantities for large projects, and unusual or hidden costs, must be factored in as they arise.

The data provided in this book is for estimating purposes only. Check all applicable federal, state and local codes and regulations for local requirements.

Format

All data is categorized according to the **CSI MASTERFORMAT**. This industry standard provides an all-inclusive checklist to ensure that no element of a project is overlooked.

DIVISION 00 ...PROCUREMENT & CONTRACTING REQUIREMENTS

00 10 00 SOLICITATION
00 20 00 INSTRUCTIONS FOR PROCUREMENT
00 30 00 AVAILABLE INFORMATION
00 40 00 PROCUREMENT FORMS AND SUPPLEMENTS
00 50 00 CONTRACTING FORMS AND SUPPLEMENTS
00 60 00 PROJECT FORMS
00 70 00 CONDITIONS OF THE CONTRACT
00 80 00 Reserved
00 90 00 REVISIONS, CLARIFICATIONS, AND MODIFICATIONS

DIVISION 01 .... GENERAL REQUIREMENTS

01 10 00 SUMMARY
01 20 00 PRICE AND PAYMENT PROCEDURES
01 30 00 ADMINISTRATIVE REQUIREMENTS
01 40 00 QUALITY REQUIREMENTS
01 50 00 TEMPORARY FACILITIES AND CONTROLS
01 60 00 PRODUCT REQUIREMENTS
01 70 00 EXECUTION AND CLOSEOUT REQUIREMENTS
01 80 00 PERFORMANCE REQUIREMENTS
01 90 00 LIFE CYCLE ACTIVITIES

DIVISION 02 .... EXISTING CONDITIONS

02 30 00 SUBSURFACE INVESTIGATION
02 40 00 DEMOLITION AND STRUCTURE MOVING
02 50 00 SITE REMEDIATION
02 60 00 CONTAMINATED SITE MATERIAL REMOVAL
02 70 00 WATER REMEDIATION
02 80 00 FACILITY REMEDIATION

DIVISION 03 .... CONCRETE

03 10 00 CONCRETE FORMING AND ACCESSORIES
03 20 00 CONCRETE REINFORCING
03 30 00 CAST-IN-PLACE CONCRETE
03 40 00 PRECAST CONCRETE
03 50 00 CAST DECKS AND UNDERLAYMENT
03 60 00 GROUTING
03 70 00 MASS CONCRETE
03 80 00 CONCRETE CUTTING AND BORING

DIVISION 04 .... MASONRY

04 20 00 UNIT MASONRY
04 30 00 Reserved
04 40 00 STONE ASSEMBLIES
04 50 00 REFRACTORY MASONRY
04 60 00 CORROSION-RESISTANT MASONRY
04 70 00 MANUFACTURED MASONRY
04 80 00 Reserved
04 90 00 Reserved

DIVISION 05..METALS

05 10 00 STRUCTURAL METAL FRAMING
05 12 00 STRUCTURAL STEEL FRAMING
05 20 00 METAL JOISTS
05 30 00 METAL DECKING
05 40 00 COLD-FORMED METAL FRAMING
05 50 00 METAL FABRICATIONS
05 60 00 Reserved
05 70 00 DECORATIVE METAL
05 80 00 Reserved
05 90 00 Reserved

DIVISION 06...........................WOOD, PLASTICS, AND COMPOSITES

06 10 00 ROUGH CARPENTRY
06 30 00 Reserved
06 40 00 ARCHITECTURAL WOODWORK
06 50 00 STRUCTURAL PLASTICS
06 60 00 PLASTIC FABRICATIONS
06 70 00 STRUCTURAL COMPOSITES
06 80 00 COMPOSITE FABRICATIONS
06 90 00 Reserved

DIVISION 07......................THERMAL AND MOISTURE PROTECTION

07 10 00 DAMPPROOFING AND WATERPROOFING
07 30 00 STEEP SLOPE ROOFING
07 40 00 ROOFING AND SIDING PANELS
07 50 00 MEMBRANE ROOFING
07 60 00 FLASHING AND SHEET METAL
07 70 00 ROOF AND WALL SPECIALTIES AND ACCESSORIES
07 80 00 FIRE AND SMOKE PROTECTION
07 90 00 JOINT PROTECTION

DIVISION 08..OPENINGS

08 10 00 DOORS AND FRAMES
08 20 00 Reserved
08 30 00 SPECIALTY DOORS AND FRAMES
08 40 00 ENTRANCES, STOREFRONTS, AND CURTAIN WALLS
08 50 00 WINDOWS
08 60 00 ROOF WINDOWS AND SKYLIGHTS
08 70 00 HARDWARE
08 80 00 GLAZING
08 90 00 LOUVERS AND VENTS

DIVISION 09..FINISHES

09 20 00 PLASTER AND GYPSUM BOARD
09 30 00 TILING
09 40 00 Reserved
09 50 00 CEILINGS
09 60 00 FLOORING
09 70 00 WALL FINISHES
09 80 00 ACOUSTIC TREATMENT
09 90 00 PAINTING AND COATING

Format *(Continued)*

Format *(Continued)*

Features of this Book

Sample pages with graphic explanations are included before the Costbook pages. These explanations, along with the discussions below, will provide a good understanding of what is included in this book and how it can best be used in construction estimating.

Material Costs

The material costs used in this book represent national averages for prices that a contractor would expect to pay plus an allowance for freight (if applicable) and handling and storage. These costs reflect neither the lowest or highest prices, but rather a typical average cost over time. Periodic fluctuations in availability and in certain commodities (e.g. copper, conduit) can significantly affect local material pricing. In the final estimating and bidding stages of a project when the highest degree of accuracy is required, it is best to check local, current prices.

Labor Costs

Labor costs include the basic wage, plus commonly applicable taxes, insurance and markups for overhead and profit. The labor rates used here to develop the costs are typical average prevailing wage rates. Rates for different trades are used where appropriate for each type of work.

Fixed government rates and average allowances for taxes and insurance are included in the labor costs. These include employer-paid Social Security/Medicare taxes (FICA), Worker's Compensation insurance, state and federal unemployment taxes, and business insurance.

Please note, however, most of these items vary significantly from state to state and within states. For more specific data, local agencies and sources should be consulted.

Man-Hours

These productivities represent typical installation labor for thousands of construction items. The data takes into account all activities involved in normal construction under commonly experienced working conditions such as site movement, material handling, start-up, etc.

Equipment Costs

Costs for various types and pieces of equipment are included in Division 1 - General Requirements and can be included in an estimate when required either as a total "Equipment" category or with specific appropriate trades. Costs for equipment are included when appropriate in the installation costs in the Costbook pages.

Overhead and Profit

Included in the labor costs are allowances for overhead and profit for the contractor/employer whose workers are performing the specific tasks. No cost allowances or fees are included for management of subcontractors by the general contractor or construction manager. These costs, where appropriate, must be added to the costs as listed in the book.

The allowance for overhead is included to account for office overhead, the contractors' typical costs of doing business. These costs normally include in-house office staff salaries and benefits, office rent and operating expenses, professional fees, vehicle costs and other operating costs which are not directly applicable to specific jobs. It should be noted for this book that office overhead as included should be distinguished from project overhead, the General Requirements (Division 1) which are specific to particular projects. Project overhead should be included on an item by item basis for each job.

Depending on the trade, an allowance of 10-15 percent is incorporated into the labor/installation costs to account for typical profit of the installing contractor. See Division 1, General Requirements, for a more detailed review of typical profit allowances.

Features of this Book *(Continued)*

Adjustments to Costs

The costs as presented in this book attempt to represent national averages. Costs, however, vary among regions, states and even between adjacent localities.

In order to more closely approximate the probable costs for specific locations throughout the U.S., a table of Geographic Multipliers is provided. These adjustment factors are used to modify costs obtained from this book to help account for regional variations of construction costs. Whenever local current costs are known, whether material or equipment prices or labor rates, they should be used if more accuracy is required.

Editor's Note: This **Costbook** is intended to provide accurate, reliable, average costs and typical productivities for thousands of common construction components. The data is developed and compiled from various industry sources, including government, manufacturers, suppliers and working professionals. The intent of the information is to provide assistance and guidelines to construction professionals in estimating. The user should be aware that local conditions, material and labor availability and cost variations, economic considerations, weather, local codes and regulations, etc., all affect the actual cost of construction. These and other such factors must be considered and incorporated into any and all construction estimates.

Sample Costbook Page

In order to best use the information in this book, please review this sample page and read the "Features In This Book" section.

Division

Broadscope Category (First 2 Digits)

Mediumscope Category (5 Digits)

Detailed Descriptions
Complete descriptions of items may include information listed above a particular line. Review of the whole category is recommended for a complete description.

Labor Cost
Labor cost represents U.S. prevailing wages plus applicable fringes.

Material Cost
Material cost represents average contractor prices plus an allowance for freight, handling and storage.

Equipment Cost
This cost includes equipment costs only, the wages for the crew operating the equipment are included in the Labor column.

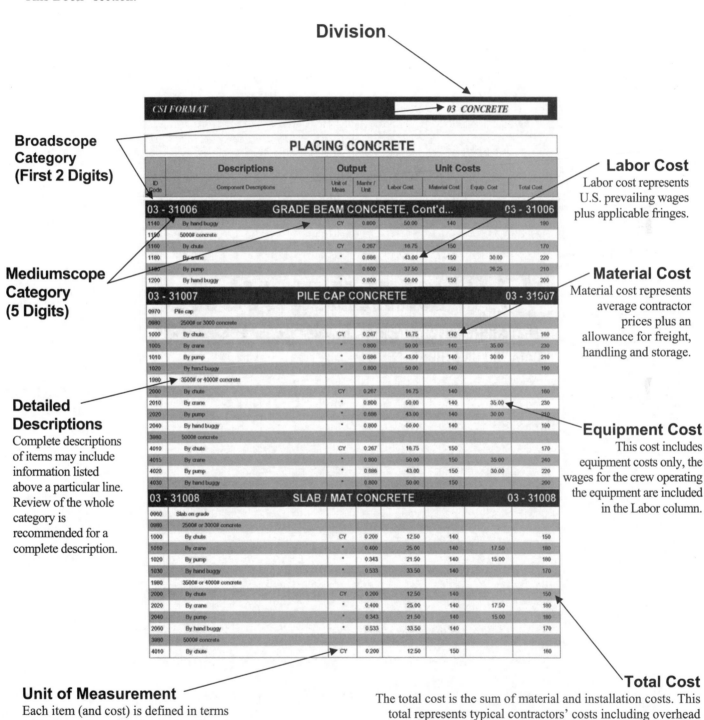

CSI FORMAT — 03 CONCRETE

PLACING CONCRETE

ID Code	Component Descriptions	Unit of Meas	Manhr / Unit	Labor Cost	Material Cost	Equip. Cost	Total Cost
03 - 31006	GRADE BEAM CONCRETE, Cont'd...						03 - 31006
1140	By hand buggy	CY	0.800	50.00	140		190
1150	5000# concrete						
1160	By chute	CY	0.267	16.75	150		170
1180	By crane	"	0.686	43.00	150	30.00	220
1190	By pump	"	0.600	37.50	150	26.25	210
1200	By hand buggy	"	0.800	50.00	150		200
03 - 31007	PILE CAP CONCRETE						03 - 31007
0970	Pile cap						
0980	2500# or 3000 concrete						
1000	By chute	CY	0.267	16.75	140		160
1005	By crane	"	0.800	50.00	140	35.00	230
1010	By pump	"	0.686	43.00	140	30.00	210
1020	By hand buggy	"	0.800	50.00	140		190
1980	3500# or 4000# concrete						
2000	By chute	CY	0.267	16.75	140		160
2010	By crane	"	0.800	50.00	140	35.00	230
2020	By pump	"	0.686	43.00	140	30.00	210
2040	By hand buggy	"	0.800	50.00	140		190
3980	5000# concrete						
4010	By chute	CY	0.267	16.75	150		170
4015	By crane	"	0.800	50.00	150	35.00	240
4020	By pump	"	0.686	43.00	150	30.00	220
4030	By hand buggy	"	0.800	50.00	150		200
03 - 31008	SLAB / MAT CONCRETE						03 - 31008
0960	Slab on grade						
0980	2500# or 3000# concrete						
1000	By chute	CY	0.200	12.50	140		150
1010	By crane	"	0.400	25.00	140	17.50	180
1020	By pump	"	0.343	21.50	140	15.00	180
1030	By hand buggy	"	0.533	33.50	140		170
1980	3500# or 4000# concrete						
2000	By chute	CY	0.200	12.50	140		150
2020	By crane	"	0.400	25.00	140	17.50	180
2040	By pump	"	0.343	21.50	140	15.00	180
2060	By hand buggy	"	0.533	33.50	140		170
3980	5000# concrete						
4010	By chute	CY	0.200	12.50	150		160

Unit of Measurement
Each item (and cost) is defined in terms of the common estimating unit. All costs are listed in dollars per unit.

Total Cost
The total cost is the sum of material and installation costs. This total represents typical contractors' costs including overhead and profit, but does not include markups for the general contractor or construction management fees.

DIVISION 01
GENERAL

REQUIREMENTS

ID Code	Descriptions — Component Descriptions	Output — Unit of Meas.	Output — Manhr / Unit	Unit Costs — Labor Cost	Unit Costs — Material Cost	Unit Costs — Equip. Cost	Unit Costs — Total Cost
01 - 21000	**ALLOWANCES**						**01 - 21000**
0090	Overhead						
1000	$20,000 project						
1020	Minimum	PCT					15.00
1040	Average	"					20.00
1060	Maximum	"					40.00
1080	$100,000 project						
1100	Minimum	PCT					12.00
1120	Average	"					15.00
1140	Maximum	"					25.00
1160	$500,000 project						
1170	Minimum	PCT					10.00
1180	Average	"					12.00
1200	Maximum	"					20.00
1220	$1,000,000 project						
1240	Minimum	PCT					6.00
1260	Average	"					10.00
1280	Maximum	"					12.00
1380	$10,000,000 project						
1385	Minimum	PCT					1.50
1386	Average	"					5.00
1388	Maximum	"					8.00
1480	Profit						
1500	$20,000 project						
1520	Minimum	PCT					10.00
1540	Average	"					15.00
1560	Maximum	"					25.00
1580	$100,000 project						
1600	Minimum	PCT					10.00
1620	Average	"					12.00
1640	Maximum	"					20.00
1660	$500,000 project						
1680	Minimum	PCT					5.00
1700	Average	"					10.00
1720	Maximum	"					15.00
1740	$1,000,000 project						
1760	Minimum	PCT					3.00
1780	Average	"					8.00
1800	Maximum	"					15.00

ALLOWANCES

ID Code	Component Descriptions	Unit of Meas.	Manhr / Unit	Labor Cost	Material Cost	Equip. Cost	Total Cost
		Output		**Unit Costs**			

01 - 21000 ALLOWANCES, Cont'd... **01 - 21000**

ID Code	Component Descriptions	Unit	Manhr	Labor	Material	Equip.	Total
2000	Professional fees						
2100	Architectural						
2120	$100,000 project						
2140	Minimum	PCT					5.00
2160	Average	"					10.00
2180	Maximum	"					20.00
2200	$500,000 project						
2220	Minimum	PCT					5.00
2240	Average	"					8.00
2260	Maximum	"					12.00
2280	$1,000,000 project						
2300	Minimum	PCT					3.50
2320	Average	"					7.00
2340	Maximum	"					10.00
2360	Structural engineering						
2380	Minimum	PCT					2.00
2400	Average	"					3.00
2420	Maximum	"					5.00
2440	Mechanical engineering						
2460	Minimum	PCT					4.00
2480	Average	"					5.00
2500	Maximum	"					15.00
2520	Electrical engineering						
2540	Minimum	PCT					3.00
2560	Average	"					5.00
2580	Maximum	"					12.00
4080	Taxes						
5000	Sales tax						
5020	Minimum	PCT					4.00
5040	Average	"					5.00
5060	Maximum	"					10.00
5080	Unemployment						
5100	Minimum	PCT					3.00
5120	Average	"					6.50
5140	Maximum	"					8.00
5200	Social security (FICA)	"					7.85

PROJECT MANAGEMENT AND COORDINATION

ID Code	Component Descriptions	Unit of Meas.	Manhr / Unit	Labor Cost	Material Cost	Equip. Cost	Total Cost
	Descriptions	**Output**		**Unit Costs**			

01 - 31130 — FIELD STAFF — 01 - 31130

ID Code	Component Descriptions	Unit of Meas.	Manhr / Unit	Labor Cost	Material Cost	Equip. Cost	Total Cost
1000	Superintendent						
1020	Minimum	YEAR					99,141
1040	Average	"					123,943
1060	Maximum	"					148,881
1080	Field engineer						
1100	Minimum	YEAR					97,784
1120	Average	"					112,234
1140	Maximum	"					128,988
1160	Foreman						
1180	Minimum	YEAR					65,895
1200	Average	"					105,383
1220	Maximum	"					123,383
1240	Bookkeeper/timekeeper						
1260	Minimum	YEAR					38,117
1280	Average	"					49,777
1300	Maximum	"					64,401
1320	Watchman						
1340	Minimum	YEAR					28,401
1360	Average	"					37,993
1380	Maximum	"					47,958

CONSTRUCTION PROGRESS DOCUMENTATION

01 - 32130 — SCHEDULING — 01 - 32130

ID Code	Component Descriptions	Unit of Meas.	Manhr / Unit	Labor Cost	Material Cost	Equip. Cost	Total Cost
0090	Scheduling for						
1000	$100,000 project						
1020	Minimum	PCT					1.02
1040	Average	"					2.05
1060	Maximum	"					5.12
1080	$500,000 project						
1100	Minimum	PCT					0.51
1120	Average	"					1.02
1140	Maximum	"					2.05
1160	$1,000,000 project						
1180	Minimum	PCT					0.34
1200	Average	"					0.77
1220	Maximum	"					1.53
4000	Scheduling software						

CONSTRUCTION PROGRESS DOCUMENTATION

ID Code	Component Descriptions	Unit of Meas.	Manhr / Unit	Labor Cost	Material Cost	Equip. Cost	Total Cost
01 - 32130	**SCHEDULING, Cont'd...**						**01 - 32130**
4020	Minimum	EA					690
4040	Average	"					3,970
4060	Maximum	"					79,410
01 - 32230	**SURVEYING**						**01 - 32230**
0080	Surveying						
1000	Small crew	DAY					1,010
1020	Average crew	"					1,520
1040	Large crew	"					2,000
2000	Lot lines and boundaries						
2020	Minimum	ACRE					730
2040	Average	"					1,520
2060	Maximum	"					2,480
01 - 32330	**JOB REQUIREMENTS**						**01 - 32330**
1000	Job photographs, small jobs						
1020	Minimum	EA					130
1040	Average	"					200
1060	Maximum	"					460
1080	Large projects						
1100	Minimum	EA					660
1120	Average	"					990
1140	Maximum	"					3,310

QUALITY CONTROL

ID Code	Component Descriptions	Unit of Meas.	Manhr / Unit	Labor Cost	Material Cost	Equip. Cost	Total Cost
01 - 45230	**TESTING**						**01 - 45230**
1080	Testing concrete, per test						
1100	Minimum	EA					23.50
1120	Average	"					39.25
1140	Maximum	"					78.00
1160	Soil, per test						
1180	Minimum	EA					48.00
1200	Average	"					120
1220	Maximum	"					320
1240	Welding, per test						
1260	Minimum	EA					23.50
1280	Average	"					39.25
1300	Maximum	"					160

CONSTRUCTION FACILITIES

ID Code	Component Descriptions	Unit of Meas.	Manhr / Unit	Labor Cost	Material Cost	Equip. Cost	Total Cost
	Descriptions	**Output**		**Unit Costs**			

ID Code	Component Descriptions	Unit of Meas.	Manhr / Unit	Labor Cost	Material Cost	Equip. Cost	Total Cost
01 - 52190	**SANITARY FACILITIES**						**01 - 52190**
0010	Porta Potty						
0100	Rental per Day Min.	EA					70.00
0120	Rental per Day Max.	"					180
0140	Rental per Month Min.	"					200
0160	Rental per Month Max.	"					350
0180	Specialized, ADA						
0200	Rental per Day Min.	EA					120
0220	Rental per Day Max	"					180
0240	Rental per Month, Min.	"					350
0260	Rental per Month, Max.	"					580
0280	Purchase prices, Min.	"					820

CONSTRUCTION AIDS

ID Code	Component Descriptions	Unit of Meas.	Manhr / Unit	Labor Cost	Material Cost	Equip. Cost	Total Cost
01 - 54001	**CONSTRUCTION AIDS**						**01 - 54001**
1000	Scaffolding/staging, rent per month						
1020	Measured by lineal feet of base						
1040	10' high	LF					14.50
1060	20' high	"					26.50
1080	30' high	"					37.00
1100	40' high	"					42.75
1120	50' high	"					51.00
1140	Measured by square foot of surface						
1160	Minimum	SF					0.64
1180	Average	"					1.11
1200	Maximum	"					1.99
1220	Safety nets, heavy duty, per job						
1240	Minimum	SF					0.43
1260	Average	"					0.52
1280	Maximum	"					1.14
1300	Tarpaulins, fabric, per job						
1320	Minimum	SF					0.30
1340	Average	"					0.51
1360	Maximum	"					1.32

CONSTRUCTION AIDS

ID Code	Descriptions	Output		Unit Costs			
	Component Descriptions	Unit of Meas.	Manhr / Unit	Labor Cost	Material Cost	Equip. Cost	Total Cost
01 - 54008	**MOBILIZATION**						**01 - 54008**
1000	Equipment mobilization						
1020	Bulldozer						
1040	Minimum	EA					220
1060	Average	"					460
1080	Maximum	"					780
1100	Backhoe/front-end loader						
1120	Minimum	EA					130
1140	Average	"					230
1160	Maximum	"					510
1180	Crane, crawler type						
1200	Minimum	EA					2,440
1220	Average	"					6,000
1240	Maximum	"					12,880
1260	Truck crane						
1280	Minimum	EA					560
1300	Average	"					860
1320	Maximum	"					1,490
1340	Pile driving rig						
1360	Minimum	EA					11,100
1380	Average	"					22,210
1400	Maximum	"					39,970
01 - 54009	**EQUIPMENT**						**01 - 54009**
0080	Air compressor						
1000	60 cfm						
1020	By day	EA					110
1030	By week	"					320
1040	By month	"					980
1100	300 cfm						
1120	By day	EA					230
1130	By week	"					700
1140	By month	"					2,140
1200	600 cfm						
1210	By day	EA					620
1220	By week	"					1,860
1230	By month	"					5,630
1300	Air tools, per compressor, per day						
1310	Minimum	EA					44.50

CONSTRUCTION AIDS

ID Code	Component Descriptions	Unit of Meas.	Manhr / Unit	Labor Cost	Material Cost	Equip. Cost	Total Cost
	Descriptions	**Output**		**Unit Costs**			

ID Code	Component Descriptions	Unit of Meas.	Manhr / Unit	Labor Cost	Material Cost	Equip. Cost	Total Cost
01 - 54009	**EQUIPMENT, Cont'd...**						**01 - 54009**
1320	Average	EA					56.00
1330	Maximum	"					78.00
1400	Generators, 5 kw						
1410	By day	EA					110
1420	By week	"					330
1430	By month	"					1,020
1500	Heaters, salamander type, per week						
1510	Minimum	EA					130
1520	Average	"					190
1530	Maximum	"					400
1600	Pumps, submersible						
1605	50 gpm						
1610	By day	EA					89.00
1620	By week	"					270
1630	By month	"					800
1640	100 gpm						
1650	By day	EA					110
1660	By week	"					330
1670	By month	"					1,000
1675	500 gpm						
1680	By day	EA					180
1690	By week	"					530
1700	By month	"					1,600
1900	Diaphragm pump, by week						
1920	Minimum	EA					160
1930	Average	"					270
1940	Maximum	"					550
2000	Pickup truck						
2020	By day	EA					170
2030	By week	"					490
2040	By month	"					1,510
2080	Dump truck						
2100	6 cy truck						
2120	By day	EA					440
2130	By week	"					1,330
2140	By month	"					4,010
2160	10 cy truck						
2170	By day	EA					550

CONSTRUCTION AIDS

ID Code	Component Descriptions	Unit of Meas.	Manhr / Unit	Labor Cost	Material Cost	Equip. Cost	Total Cost
	Descriptions	**Output**		**Unit Costs**			
01 - 54009		**EQUIPMENT, Cont'd...**					**01 - 54009**
2180	By week	EA					1,670
2190	By month	"					5,010
2300	16 cy truck						
2310	By day	EA					890
2320	By week	"					2,670
2340	By month	"					8,020
2400	Backhoe, track mounted						
2420	1/2 cy capacity						
2430	By day	EA					910
2440	By week	"					2,780
2450	By month	"					8,240
2500	1 cy capacity						
2510	By day	EA					1,450
2520	By week	"					4,340
2530	By month	"					13,030
2550	2 cy capacity						
2560	By day	EA					2,450
2570	By week	"					7,350
2580	By month	"					22,050
2600	3 cy capacity						
2620	By day	EA					4,680
2640	By week	"					14,030
2680	By month	"					42,100
3000	Backhoe/loader, rubber tired						
3005	1/2 cy capacity						
3010	By day	EA					550
3020	By week	"					1,670
3030	By month	"					5,010
3035	3/4 cy capacity						
3040	By day	EA					670
3050	By week	"					2,000
3060	By month	"					6,010
3200	Bulldozer						
3205	75 hp						
3210	By day	EA					780
3220	By week	"					2,340
3230	By month	"					7,020
3280	200 hp						

CONSTRUCTION AIDS

ID Code	Component Descriptions	Unit of Meas.	Manhr / Unit	Labor Cost	Material Cost	Equip. Cost	Total Cost
		Descriptions		**Output**		**Unit Costs**	
01 - 54009		**EQUIPMENT, Cont'd...**					**01 - 54009**
3300	By day	EA					2,230
3310	By week	"					6,680
3320	By month	"					20,050
3330	400 hp						
3340	By day	EA					3,310
3350	By week	"					9,920
3360	By month	"					29,780
4000	Cranes, crawler type						
4005	15 ton capacity						
4010	By day	EA					1,000
4020	By week	"					3,010
4030	By month	"					9,020
4035	25 ton capacity						
4040	By day	EA					1,220
4050	By week	"					3,670
4060	By month	"					11,020
4070	50 ton capacity						
4080	By day	EA					2,230
4090	By week	"					6,680
4100	By month	"					20,050
4110	100 ton capacity						
4120	By day	EA					3,340
4130	By week	"					10,020
4140	By month	"					30,170
4145	Truck mounted, hydraulic						
4150	15 ton capacity						
4160	By day	EA					940
4170	By week	"					2,840
4180	By month	"					8,190
5380	Loader, rubber tired						
5385	1 cy capacity						
5390	By day	EA					670
5400	By week	"					2,000
5410	By month	"					6,020
5430	2 cy capacity						
5440	By day	EA					1,000
5450	By week	"					3,900
5460	By month	"					11,690

CONSTRUCTION AIDS

ID Code	Descriptions — Component Descriptions	Output — Unit of Meas.	Output — Manhr / Unit	Unit Costs — Labor Cost	Unit Costs — Material Cost	Unit Costs — Equip. Cost	Unit Costs — Total Cost
01 - 54009	**EQUIPMENT, Cont'd...**						**01 - 54009**
5470	3 cy capacity						
5480	By day	EA					1,780
5490	By week	"					5,350
5500	By month	"					16,040

TEMPORARY BARRIERS AND ENCLOSURES

ID Code	Descriptions — Component Descriptions	Unit of Meas.	Manhr / Unit	Labor Cost	Material Cost	Equip. Cost	Total Cost
01 - 56230	**TEMPORARY FACILITIES**						**01 - 56230**
1000	Barricades, temporary						
1010	Highway						
1020	Concrete	LF	0.080	5.01	14.75		19.75
1040	Wood	"	0.032	2.00	5.10		7.10
1060	Steel	"	0.027	1.67	5.29		6.96
1090	Pedestrian barricades						
1100	Plywood	SF	0.027	1.67	4.54		6.21
1120	Chain link fence	"	0.027	1.67	3.85		5.52
1130	Trailers, general office type, per month						
2020	Minimum	EA					250
2040	Average	"					410
2060	Maximum	"					820
2070	Crew change trailers, per month						
2100	Minimum	EA					150
2120	Average	"					160
2140	Maximum	"					250

PROJECT IDENTIFICATION

ID Code	Descriptions — Component Descriptions	Unit of Meas.	Manhr / Unit	Labor Cost	Material Cost	Equip. Cost	Total Cost
01 - 58130	**SIGNS**						**01 - 58130**
0080	Construction signs, temporary						
1000	Signs, 2' x 4'						
1020	Minimum	EA					41.75
1040	Average	"					100
1060	Maximum	"					350
1080	Signs, 4' x 8'						
1100	Minimum	EA					88.00
1120	Average	"					230
1140	Maximum	"					980
1160	Signs, 8' x 8'						

PROJECT IDENTIFICATION

ID Code	Component Descriptions	Unit of Meas.	Manhr / Unit	Labor Cost	Material Cost	Equip. Cost	Total Cost
01 - 58130	SIGNS, Cont'd...						01 - 58130
1180	Minimum	EA					110
1200	Average	"					350
1220	Maximum	"					3,540

CLOSEOUT SUBMITTALS

ID Code	Component Descriptions	Unit of Meas.	Manhr / Unit	Labor Cost	Material Cost	Equip. Cost	Total Cost
01 - 78330	BONDS						01 - 78330
1000	Performance bonds						
1020	Minimum	PCT					0.62
1040	Average	"					1.93
1060	Maximum	"					3.07

DIVISION 02
SITE CONSTRUCTION

SITE PREPARATION

ID Code	Component Descriptions	Unit of Meas.	Manhr / Unit	Labor Cost	Material Cost	Equip. Cost	Total Cost
	Descriptions	**Output**		**Unit Costs**			
02 - 32130	**SOIL BORING**						**02 - 32130**
1000	Borings, uncased, stable earth						
1022	2-1/2" dia.						
1024	Minimum	LF	0.200	12.50		11.00	23.50
1026	Average	"	0.300	18.75		16.50	35.25
1028	Maximum	"	0.480	29.75		26.50	56.00
1042	4" dia.						
1044	Minimum	LF	0.218	13.50		12.00	25.75
1046	Average	"	0.343	21.25		19.00	40.25
1048	Maximum	"	0.600	37.25		33.25	71.00
1500	Cased, including samples						
1522	2-1/2" dia.						
1524	Minimum	LF	0.240	15.00		13.25	28.25
1526	Average	"	0.400	24.75		22.25	47.00
1528	Maximum	"	0.800	49.75		44.25	94.00
1542	4" dia.						
1544	Minimum	LF	0.480	29.75		26.50	56.00
1546	Average	"	0.686	42.50		38.00	81.00
1548	Maximum	"	0.960	60.00		53.00	110
2000	Drilling in rock						
2022	No sampling						
2024	Minimum	LF	0.436	27.00		24.25	51.00
2026	Average	"	0.632	39.25		35.00	74.00
2028	Maximum	"	0.857	53.00		47.50	100
2042	With casing and sampling						
2044	Minimum	LF	0.600	37.25		33.25	71.00
2046	Average	"	0.800	49.75		44.25	94.00
2048	Maximum	"	1.200	75.00		67.00	140
3000	Test pits						
3022	Light soil						
3024	Minimum	EA	3.000	190		170	350
3026	Average	"	4.000	250		220	470
3028	Maximum	"	8.000	500		440	940
3042	Heavy soil						
3044	Minimum	EA	4.800	300		270	560
3046	Average	"	6.000	370		330	710
3048	Maximum	"	12.000	750		670	1,410

SELECTIVE SITE DEMOLITION

ID Code	Component Descriptions	Unit of Meas.	Manhr / Unit	Labor Cost	Material Cost	Equip. Cost	Total Cost
		Descriptions	**Output**		**Unit Costs**		

02 - 41131	**CATCH BASIN / MANHOLE DEMOLITION**					**02 - 41131**	
0102	Abandon catch basin or manhole (fill with sand)						
0104	Minimum	EA	3.000	190		170	350
0106	Average	"	4.800	300		270	560
0108	Maximum	"	8.000	500		440	940
0202	Remove and reset frame and cover						
0204	Minimum	EA	1.600	99.00		89.00	190
0206	Average	"	2.400	150		130	280
0208	Maximum	"	4.000	250		220	470
0280	Remove catch basin, to 10' deep						
0302	Masonry						
0304	Minimum	EA	4.800	300		270	560
0306	Average	"	6.000	370		330	710
0308	Maximum	"	8.000	500		440	940
0402	Concrete						
0403	Minimum	EA	6.000	370		330	710
0404	Average	"	8.000	500		440	940
0406	Maximum	"	9.600	600		530	1,130

02 - 41132	**FENCE DEMOLITION**					**02 - 41132**	
0060	Remove fencing						
0080	Chain link, 8' high						
0100	For disposal	LF	0.040	2.50			2.50
0200	For reuse	"	0.100	6.26			6.26
0980	Wood						
1000	4' high	SF	0.027	1.67			1.67
1020	6' high	"	0.032	2.00			2.00
1040	8' high	"	0.040	2.50			2.50
1960	Masonry						
1980	8" thick						
2000	4' high	SF	0.080	5.01			5.01
2020	6' high	"	0.100	6.26			6.26
2040	8' high	"	0.114	7.16			7.16
2050	12" thick						
2060	4' high	SF	0.133	8.35			8.35
2080	6' high	"	0.160	10.00			10.00
2100	8' high	"	0.200	12.50			12.50
2120	12' high	"	0.267	16.75			16.75

SELECTIVE SITE DEMOLITION

ID Code	Component Descriptions	Unit of Meas.	Manhr / Unit	Labor Cost	Material Cost	Equip. Cost	Total Cost
	Descriptions	**Output**		**Unit Costs**			

02 - 41133 — CURB & GUTTER DEMOLITION — 02 - 41133

ID Code	Component Descriptions	Unit of Meas.	Manhr / Unit	Labor Cost	Material Cost	Equip. Cost	Total Cost
1000	Curb removal						
1100	Concrete, unreinforced						
1150	Minimum	LF	0.048	2.98		2.66	5.64
1155	Average	"	0.060	3.72		3.32	7.05
1160	Maximum	"	0.075	4.66		4.15	8.81
1200	Reinforced						
1250	Minimum	LF	0.077	4.81		4.29	9.10
1300	Average	"	0.086	5.32		4.75	10.00
1350	Maximum	"	0.096	5.96		5.32	11.25
1450	Combination curb and 2' gutter						
1480	Unreinforced						
1500	Minimum	LF	0.063	3.92		3.50	7.42
1700	Average	"	0.083	5.14		4.58	9.72
1710	Maximum	"	0.120	7.45		6.65	14.00
1720	Reinforced						
1730	Minimum	LF	0.100	6.21		5.54	11.75
2000	Average	"	0.133	8.28		7.38	15.75
2010	Maximum	"	0.240	15.00		13.25	28.25
2020	Granite curb						
2030	Minimum	LF	0.069	4.26		3.80	8.06
2100	Average	"	0.080	4.97		4.43	9.40
2150	Maximum	"	0.092	5.73		5.11	10.75
2160	Asphalt curb						
2170	Minimum	LF	0.040	2.48		2.21	4.70
2180	Average	"	0.048	2.98		2.66	5.64
2190	Maximum	"	0.057	3.55		3.16	6.71

REMOVAL AND SALVAGE OF CONSTRUCTION MATERIALS

02 - 42132 — GUARDRAIL DEMOLITION — 02 - 42132

ID Code	Component Descriptions	Unit of Meas.	Manhr / Unit	Labor Cost	Material Cost	Equip. Cost	Total Cost
0080	Remove standard guardrail						
1000	Steel						
1020	Minimum	LF	0.060	3.72		3.32	7.05
1030	Average	"	0.080	4.97		4.43	9.40
1040	Maximum	"	0.120	7.45		6.65	14.00
2000	Wood						
2020	Minimum	LF	0.052	3.24		2.89	6.13
2040	Average	"	0.062	3.82		3.41	7.23

REMOVAL AND SALVAGE OF CONSTRUCTION MATERIALS

ID Code	Component Descriptions	Unit of Meas.	Manhr / Unit	Labor Cost	Material Cost	Equip. Cost	Total Cost

02 - 42132 GUARDRAIL DEMOLITION, Cont'd... 02 - 42132

| 2060 | Maximum | LF | 0.100 | 6.21 | | 5.54 | 11.75 |

STRUCTURE MOVING

02 - 43133 HYDRANT DEMOLITION 02 - 43133

1002	Remove fire hydrant						
1004	Minimum	EA	3.000	190		170	350
1006	Average	"	4.000	250		220	470
1008	Maximum	"	6.000	370		330	710
5002	Remove and reset fire hydrant						
5004	Minimum	EA	8.000	500		440	940
5006	Average	"	12.000	750		670	1,410
5008	Maximum	"	24.000	1,490		1,330	2,820

PAVEMENT AND SIDEWALK DEMOLITION

02 - 44134 PAVEMENT and SIDEWALK DEMOLITION 02 - 44134

0090	Bituminous pavement, up to 3" thick						
0102	On streets						
0104	Minimum	SY	0.069	4.26		3.80	8.06
0106	Average	"	0.096	5.96		5.32	11.25
0108	Maximum	"	0.160	9.94		8.86	18.75
0202	On pipe trench						
0204	Minimum	SY	0.096	5.96		5.32	11.25
0206	Average	"	0.120	7.45		6.65	14.00
0208	Maximum	"	0.240	15.00		13.25	28.25
0300	Concrete pavement, 6" thick						
0402	No reinforcement						
0404	Minimum	SY	0.120	7.45		6.65	14.00
0406	Average	"	0.160	9.94		8.86	18.75
0408	Maximum	"	0.240	15.00		13.25	28.25
0452	With wire mesh						
0454	Minimum	SY	0.185	11.50		10.25	21.75
0456	Average	"	0.240	15.00		13.25	28.25
0458	Maximum	"	0.300	18.75		16.50	35.25
0552	With rebars						
0554	Minimum	SY	0.240	15.00		13.25	28.25
0556	Average	"	0.300	18.75		16.50	35.25

PAVEMENT AND SIDEWALK DEMOLITION

ID Code	Descriptions — Component Descriptions	Output — Unit of Meas.	Output — Manhr / Unit	Unit Costs — Labor Cost	Unit Costs — Material Cost	Unit Costs — Equip. Cost	Unit Costs — Total Cost
02 - 44134	**PAVEMENT and SIDEWALK DEMOLITION, Cont'd...**					**02 - 44134**	
0558	Maximum	SY	0.400	24.75		22.25	47.00
1380	9" thick						
1402	No reinforcement						
1404	Minimum	SY	0.160	9.94		8.86	18.75
1406	Average	"	0.200	12.50		11.00	23.50
1408	Maximum	"	0.240	15.00		13.25	28.25
1412	With wire mesh						
1414	Minimum	SY	0.253	15.75		14.00	29.75
1416	Average	"	0.300	18.75		16.50	35.25
1418	Maximum	"	0.369	23.00		20.50	43.50
1422	With rebars						
1424	Minimum	SY	0.320	20.00		17.75	37.50
1426	Average	"	0.400	24.75		22.25	47.00
1428	Maximum	"	0.533	33.25		29.50	63.00
1440	12" thick						
1452	No reinforcement						
1454	Minimum	SY	0.200	12.50		11.00	23.50
1456	Average	"	0.240	15.00		13.25	28.25
1458	Maximum	"	0.300	18.75		16.50	35.25
1462	With wire mesh						
1464	Minimum	SY	0.282	17.50		15.75	33.25
1466	Average	"	0.343	21.25		19.00	40.25
1468	Maximum	"	0.436	27.00		24.25	51.00
1472	With rebars						
1474	Minimum	SY	0.400	24.75		22.25	47.00
1476	Average	"	0.480	29.75		26.50	56.00
1478	Maximum	"	0.600	37.25		33.25	71.00
1502	Sidewalk, 4" thick, with disposal						
1504	Minimum	SY	0.057	3.55		3.16	6.71
1506	Average	"	0.080	4.97		4.43	9.40
1508	Maximum	"	0.114	7.10		6.33	13.50
1802	Removal of pavement markings by waterblasting						
1804	Minimum	SF	0.003	0.20			0.20
1806	Average	"	0.004	0.25			0.25
1808	Maximum	"	0.008	0.50			0.50

DRAINAGE AND PIPING DEMOLITION

	Descriptions		Output		Unit Costs			
ID Code	Component Descriptions		Unit of Meas.	Manhr / Unit	Labor Cost	Material Cost	Equip. Cost	Total Cost

02 - 45134	**DRAINAGE PIPING DEMOLITION**							**02 - 45134**
1000	Remove drainage pipe, not including excavation							
1020	12" dia.							
1030	Minimum		LF	0.080	4.97		4.43	9.40
1040	Average		"	0.100	6.21		5.54	11.75
1050	Maximum		"	0.126	7.85		7.00	14.75
1100	18" dia.							
1110	Minimum		LF	0.109	6.78		6.04	12.75
1120	Average		"	0.126	7.85		7.00	14.75
1130	Maximum		"	0.160	9.94		8.86	18.75
1200	24" dia.							
1210	Minimum		LF	0.133	8.28		7.38	15.75
1220	Average		"	0.160	9.94		8.86	18.75
1230	Maximum		"	0.200	12.50		11.00	23.50
1300	36" dia.							
1310	Minimum		LF	0.160	9.94		8.86	18.75
1320	Average		"	0.200	12.50		11.00	23.50
1330	Maximum		"	0.253	15.75		14.00	29.75

GAS PIPING DEMOLITION

02 - 46134	**GAS PIPING DEMOLITION**							**02 - 46134**
0980	Remove welded steel pipe, not including excavation							
1002	4" dia.							
1004	Minimum		LF	0.120	7.45		6.65	14.00
1006	Average		"	0.150	9.32		8.31	17.75
1008	Maximum		"	0.200	12.50		11.00	23.50
2002	5" dia.							
2004	Minimum		LF	0.200	12.50		11.00	23.50
2006	Average		"	0.240	15.00		13.25	28.25
2008	Maximum		"	0.300	18.75		16.50	35.25
2022	6" dia.							
2024	Minimum		LF	0.253	15.75		14.00	29.75
2026	Average		"	0.300	18.75		16.50	35.25
2028	Maximum		"	0.400	24.75		22.25	47.00
2032	8" dia.							
2034	Minimum		LF	0.369	23.00		20.50	43.50
2036	Average		"	0.480	29.75		26.50	56.00
2038	Maximum		"	0.632	39.25		35.00	74.00

GAS PIPING DEMOLITION

ID Code	Descriptions	Output		Unit Costs			
	Component Descriptions	Unit of Meas.	Manhr / Unit	Labor Cost	Material Cost	Equip. Cost	Total Cost
02 - 46134	**GAS PIPING DEMOLITION, Cont'd...**					**02 - 46134**	
2042	10" dia.						
2044	Minimum	LF	0.480	29.75		26.50	56.00
2046	Average	"	0.600	37.25		33.25	71.00
2048	Maximum	"	0.800	49.75		44.25	94.00

SANITARY PIPING DEMOLITION

ID Code	Component Descriptions	Unit of Meas.	Manhr / Unit	Labor Cost	Material Cost	Equip. Cost	Total Cost
02 - 47134	**SANITARY PIPING DEMOLITION**					**02 - 47134**	
0980	Remove sewer pipe, not including excavation						
1002	4" dia.						
1004	Minimum	LF	0.067	4.14		3.69	7.83
1006	Average	"	0.096	5.96		5.32	11.25
1008	Maximum	"	0.160	9.94		8.86	18.75
1022	6" dia.						
1024	Minimum	LF	0.075	4.66		4.15	8.81
1026	Average	"	0.109	6.78		6.04	12.75
1028	Maximum	"	0.200	12.50		11.00	23.50
1042	8" dia.						
1044	Minimum	LF	0.080	4.97		4.43	9.40
1046	Average	"	0.120	7.45		6.65	14.00
1048	Maximum	"	0.240	15.00		13.25	28.25
1062	10" dia.						
1064	Minimum	LF	0.086	5.32		4.75	10.00
1066	Average	"	0.126	7.85		7.00	14.75
1068	Maximum	"	0.267	16.50		14.75	31.25
1082	12" dia.						
1084	Minimum	LF	0.092	5.73		5.11	10.75
1086	Average	"	0.133	8.28		7.38	15.75
1088	Maximum	"	0.300	18.75		16.50	35.25
1102	15" dia.						
1104	Minimum	LF	0.100	6.21		5.54	11.75
1106	Average	"	0.141	8.77		7.82	16.50
1108	Maximum	"	0.343	21.25		19.00	40.25
1122	18" dia.						
1124	Minimum	LF	0.109	6.78		6.04	12.75
1126	Average	"	0.160	9.94		8.86	18.75
1128	Maximum	"	0.400	24.75		22.25	47.00
1142	24" dia.						

SANITARY PIPING DEMOLITION

ID Code	Component Descriptions	Unit of Meas.	Manhr / Unit	Labor Cost	Material Cost	Equip. Cost	Total Cost
	Descriptions	**Output**		**Unit Costs**			
02 - 47134	**SANITARY PIPING DEMOLITION, Cont'd...**					**02 - 47134**	
1144	Minimum	LF	0.120	7.45		6.65	14.00
1146	Average	"	0.200	12.50		11.00	23.50
1148	Maximum	"	0.480	29.75		26.50	56.00
1162	30" dia.						
1164	Minimum	LF	0.133	8.28		7.38	15.75
1166	Average	"	0.240	15.00		13.25	28.25
1168	Maximum	"	0.600	37.25		33.25	71.00
1182	36" dia.						
1184	Minimum	LF	0.160	9.94		8.86	18.75
1186	Average	"	0.300	18.75		16.50	35.25
1188	Maximum	"	0.800	49.75		44.25	94.00

WATER PIPING DEMOLITION

ID Code	Component Descriptions	Unit of Meas.	Manhr / Unit	Labor Cost	Material Cost	Equip. Cost	Total Cost
02 - 48134	**WATER PIPING DEMOLITION**					**02 - 48134**	
0980	Remove water pipe, not including excavation						
1002	4" dia.						
1004	Minimum	LF	0.096	5.96		5.32	11.25
1006	Average	"	0.109	6.78		6.04	12.75
1008	Maximum	"	0.126	7.85		7.00	14.75
1022	6" dia.						
1024	Minimum	LF	0.100	6.21		5.54	11.75
1026	Average	"	0.114	7.10		6.33	13.50
1028	Maximum	"	0.133	8.28		7.38	15.75
1042	8" dia.						
1044	Minimum	LF	0.109	6.78		6.04	12.75
1046	Average	"	0.126	7.85		7.00	14.75
1048	Maximum	"	0.150	9.32		8.31	17.75
1062	10" dia.						
1064	Minimum	LF	0.114	7.10		6.33	13.50
1066	Average	"	0.133	8.28		7.38	15.75
1068	Maximum	"	0.160	9.94		8.86	18.75
1082	12" dia.						
1084	Minimum	LF	0.120	7.45		6.65	14.00
1086	Average	"	0.141	8.77		7.82	16.50
1088	Maximum	"	0.171	10.75		9.50	20.25
1102	14" dia.						
1104	Minimum	LF	0.126	7.85		7.00	14.75

WATER PIPING DEMOLITION

ID Code	Descriptions	Output		Unit Costs			
	Component Descriptions	Unit of Meas.	Manhr / Unit	Labor Cost	Material Cost	Equip. Cost	Total Cost
02 - 48134	**WATER PIPING DEMOLITION, Cont'd...**					**02 - 48134**	
1106	Average	LF	0.150	9.32		8.31	17.75
1108	Maximum	"	0.185	11.50		10.25	21.75
1122	16" dia.						
1124	Minimum	LF	0.133	8.28		7.38	15.75
1126	Average	"	0.160	9.94		8.86	18.75
1128	Maximum	"	0.200	12.50		11.00	23.50
1142	18" dia.						
1144	Minimum	LF	0.141	8.77		7.82	16.50
1146	Average	"	0.171	10.75		9.50	20.25
1148	Maximum	"	0.218	13.50		12.00	25.75
1162	20" dia.						
1164	Minimum	LF	0.150	9.32		8.31	17.75
1166	Average	"	0.185	11.50		10.25	21.75
1168	Maximum	"	0.240	15.00		13.25	28.25
1180	Remove valves						
1200	6"	EA	1.200	75.00		67.00	140
1220	10"	"	1.333	83.00		74.00	160
1240	14"	"	1.500	93.00		83.00	180
1260	18"	"	2.000	120		110	240

SAW CUTTING PAVEMENT

ID Code	Descriptions	Output		Unit Costs			
02 - 49135	**SAW CUTTING PAVEMENT**					**02 - 49135**	
0100	Pavement, bituminous						
0110	2" thick	LF	0.016	0.99		1.20	2.19
0120	3" thick	"	0.020	1.24		1.50	2.74
0130	4" thick	"	0.025	1.52		1.84	3.37
0140	5" thick	"	0.027	1.65		2.00	3.65
0150	6" thick	"	0.029	1.77		2.14	3.91
0200	Concrete pavement, with wire mesh						
0210	4" thick	LF	0.031	1.91		2.30	4.22
0212	5" thick	"	0.033	2.07		2.50	4.57
0215	6" thick	"	0.036	2.26		2.72	4.98
0220	8" thick	"	0.040	2.48		3.00	5.48
0250	10" thick	"	0.044	2.76		3.33	6.09
0300	Plain concrete, unreinforced						
0320	4" thick	LF	0.027	1.65		2.00	3.65
0340	5" thick	"	0.031	1.91		2.30	4.22

SAW CUTTING PAVEMENT

ID Code	Component Descriptions	Unit of Meas.	Manhr / Unit	Labor Cost	Material Cost	Equip. Cost	Total Cost
	Descriptions	**Output**		**Unit Costs**			
02 - 49135	**SAW CUTTING PAVEMENT, Cont'd...**					**02 - 49135**	
0360	6" thick	LF	0.033	2.07		2.50	4.57
0380	8" thick	"	0.036	2.26		2.72	4.98
0390	10" thick	"	0.040	2.48		3.00	5.48
02 - 49298	**WALL, EXTERIOR, DEMOLITION**					**02 - 49298**	
0980	Concrete wall						
0990	Light reinforcing						
1000	6" thick	SF	0.120	7.45		6.65	14.00
1020	8" thick	"	0.126	7.85		7.00	14.75
1040	10" thick	"	0.133	8.28		7.38	15.75
1060	12" thick	"	0.150	9.32		8.31	17.75
1180	Medium reinforcing						
1200	6" thick	SF	0.126	7.85		7.00	14.75
1220	8" thick	"	0.133	8.28		7.38	15.75
1240	10" thick	"	0.150	9.32		8.31	17.75
1260	12" thick	"	0.171	10.75		9.50	20.25
1380	Heavy reinforcing						
1400	6" thick	SF	0.141	8.77		7.82	16.50
1420	8" thick	"	0.150	9.32		8.31	17.75
1440	10" thick	"	0.171	10.75		9.50	20.25
1460	12" thick	"	0.200	12.50		11.00	23.50
1980	Masonry						
1990	No reinforcing						
2000	8" thick	SF	0.053	3.31		2.95	6.27
2020	12" thick	"	0.060	3.72		3.32	7.05
2040	16" thick	. "	0.069	4.26		3.80	8.06
2050	Horizontal reinforcing						
2060	8" thick	SF	0.060	3.72		3.32	7.05
2080	12" thick	"	0.065	4.03		3.59	7.62
2100	16" thick	"	0.077	4.81		4.29	9.10
2110	Vertical reinforcing						
2120	8" thick	SF	0.077	4.81		4.29	9.10
2140	12" thick	"	0.089	5.52		4.92	10.50
2160	16" thick	"	0.109	6.78		6.04	12.75
5000	Remove concrete headwall						
5020	15" pipe	EA	1.714	110		95.00	200
5040	18" pipe	"	2.000	120		110	240
5060	24" pipe	"	2.182	140		120	260

SAW CUTTING PAVEMENT

ID Code	Component Descriptions	Unit of Meas.	Manhr / Unit	Labor Cost	Material Cost	Equip. Cost	Total Cost
	Descriptions	**Output**		**Unit Costs**			

02 - 49298 — WALL, EXTERIOR, DEMOLITION, Cont'd... — 02 - 49298

ID Code	Component Descriptions	Unit of Meas.	Manhr / Unit	Labor Cost	Material Cost	Equip. Cost	Total Cost
5080	30" pipe	EA	2.400	150		130	280
5100	36" pipe	"	2.667	170		150	310
5120	48" pipe	"	3.429	210		190	400
5140	60" pipe	"	4.800	300		270	560

DEMOLITION

02 - 51061 — COMPLETE BUILDING DEMOLITION — 02 - 51061

ID Code	Component Descriptions	Unit of Meas.	Manhr / Unit	Labor Cost	Material Cost	Equip. Cost	Total Cost
0200	Wood frame	CF	0.003	0.16		0.24	0.40
0300	Concrete	"	0.004	0.25		0.36	0.61
0400	Steel frame	"	0.005	0.33		0.48	0.81

02 - 51190 — SELECTIVE BUILDING DEMOLITION — 02 - 51190

ID Code	Component Descriptions	Unit of Meas.	Manhr / Unit	Labor Cost	Material Cost	Equip. Cost	Total Cost
1000	Partition removal						
1100	Concrete block partitions						
1120	4" thick	SF	0.040	2.50			2.50
1140	8" thick	"	0.053	3.34			3.34
1160	12" thick	"	0.073	4.55			4.55
1200	Brick masonry partitions						
1220	4" thick	SF	0.040	2.50			2.50
1240	8" thick	"	0.050	3.13			3.13
1260	12" thick	"	0.067	4.17			4.17
1280	16" thick	"	0.100	6.26			6.26
1380	Cast in place concrete partitions						
1400	Unreinforced						
1421	6" thick	SF	0.160	9.94		8.86	18.75
1423	8" thick	"	0.171	10.75		9.50	20.25
1425	10" thick	"	0.200	12.50		11.00	23.50
1427	12" thick	"	0.240	15.00		13.25	28.25
1440	Reinforced						
1441	6" thick	SF	0.185	11.50		10.25	21.75
1443	8" thick	"	0.240	15.00		13.25	28.25
1445	10" thick	"	0.267	16.50		14.75	31.25
1447	12" thick	"	0.320	20.00		17.75	37.50
1500	Terra cotta						
1520	To 6" thick	SF	0.040	2.50			2.50
1700	Stud partitions						
1720	Metal or wood, with drywall both sides	SF	0.040	2.50			2.50
1740	Metal studs, both sides, lath and plaster	"	0.053	3.34			3.34

DEMOLITION

ID Code	Component Descriptions	Unit of Meas.	Manhr / Unit	Labor Cost	Material Cost	Equip. Cost	Total Cost
	Descriptions	**Output**		**Unit Costs**			
02 - 51190	**SELECTIVE BUILDING DEMOLITION, Cont'd...**						**02 - 51190**
2000	Door and frame removal						
2020	Hollow metal in masonry wall						
2030	Single						
2040	2'6"x6'8"	EA	1.000	63.00			63.00
2060	3'x7'	"	1.333	84.00			84.00
2070	Double						
2080	3'x7'	EA	1.600	100			100
2085	4'x8'	"	1.600	100			100
2140	Wood in framed wall						
2150	Single						
2160	2'6"x6'8"	EA	0.571	35.75			35.75
2180	3'x6'8"	"	0.667	41.75			41.75
2190	Double						
2200	2'6"x6'8"	EA	0.800	50.00			50.00
2220	3'x6'8"	"	0.889	56.00			56.00
2240	Remove for re-use						
2260	Hollow metal	EA	2.000	130			130
2280	Wood	"	1.333	84.00			84.00
2300	Floor removal						
2340	Brick flooring	SF	0.032	2.00			2.00
2360	Ceramic or quarry tile	"	0.018	1.11			1.11
2380	Terrazzo	"	0.036	2.22			2.22
2400	Heavy wood	"	0.021	1.33			1.33
2420	Residential wood	"	0.023	1.43			1.43
2440	Resilient tile or linoleum	"	0.008	0.50			0.50
2500	Ceiling removal						
2520	Acoustical tile ceiling						
2540	Adhesive fastened	SF	0.008	0.50			0.50
2560	Furred and glued	"	0.007	0.41			0.41
2580	Suspended grid	"	0.005	0.31			0.31
2600	Drywall ceiling						
2620	Furred and nailed	SF	0.009	0.55			0.55
2640	Nailed to framing	"	0.008	0.50			0.50
2660	Plastered ceiling						
2680	Furred on framing	SF	0.020	1.25			1.25
2700	Suspended system	"	0.027	1.67			1.67
2800	Roofing removal						
2820	Steel frame						

DEMOLITION

ID Code	Component Descriptions	Unit of Meas.	Manhr / Unit	Labor Cost	Material Cost	Equip. Cost	Total Cost
	Descriptions	**Output**		**Unit Costs**			

02 - 51190 — SELECTIVE BUILDING DEMOLITION, Cont'd... — 02 - 51190

ID Code	Component Descriptions	Unit of Meas.	Manhr / Unit	Labor Cost	Material Cost	Equip. Cost	Total Cost
2840	Corrugated metal roofing	SF	0.016	1.00			1.00
2860	Built-up roof on metal deck	"	0.027	1.67			1.67
2900	Wood frame						
2920	Built up roof on wood deck	SF	0.025	1.54			1.54
2940	Roof shingles	"	0.013	0.83			0.83
2960	Roof tiles	"	0.027	1.67			1.67
8900	Concrete frame	CF	0.053	3.34			3.34
8920	Concrete plank	SF	0.040	2.50			2.50
8940	Built-up roof on concrete	"	0.023	1.43			1.43
9200	Cut-outs						
9230	Concrete, elevated slabs, mesh reinforcing						
9240	Under 5 cf	CF	0.800	50.00			50.00
9260	Over 5 cf	"	0.667	41.75			41.75
9270	Bar reinforcing						
9280	Under 5 cf	CF	1.333	84.00			84.00
9290	Over 5 cf	"	1.000	63.00			63.00
9300	Window removal						
9301	Metal windows, trim included						
9302	2'x3'	EA	0.800	50.00			50.00
9304	2'x4'	"	0.889	56.00			56.00
9306	2'x6'	"	1.000	63.00			63.00
9308	3'x4'	"	1.000	63.00			63.00
9310	3'x6'	"	1.143	72.00			72.00
9312	3'x8'	"	1.333	84.00			84.00
9314	4'x4'	"	1.333	84.00			84.00
9315	4'x6'	"	1.600	100			100
9316	4'x8'	"	2.000	130			130
9317	Wood windows, trim included						
9318	2'x3'	EA	0.444	27.75			27.75
9319	2'x4'	"	0.471	29.50			29.50
9320	2'x6'	"	0.500	31.25			31.25
9321	3'x4'	"	0.533	33.50			33.50
9322	3'x6'	"	0.571	35.75			35.75
9324	3'x8'	"	0.615	38.50			38.50
9325	6'x4'	"	0.667	41.75			41.75
9326	6'x6'	"	0.727	45.50			45.50
9327	6'x8'	"	0.800	50.00			50.00
9329	Walls, concrete, bar reinforcing						

DEMOLITION

ID Code	Component Descriptions	Unit of Meas.	Manhr / Unit	Labor Cost	Material Cost	Equip. Cost	Total Cost
	Descriptions	**Output**		**Unit Costs**			

02 - 51190   **SELECTIVE BUILDING DEMOLITION, Cont'd...**   **02 - 51190**

ID Code	Component Descriptions	Unit of Meas.	Manhr / Unit	Labor Cost	Material Cost	Equip. Cost	Total Cost
9330	Small jobs	CF	0.533	33.50			33.50
9340	Large jobs	"	0.444	27.75			27.75
9360	Brick walls, not including toothing						
9390	4" thick	SF	0.040	2.50			2.50
9400	8" thick	"	0.050	3.13			3.13
9410	12" thick	"	0.067	4.17			4.17
9415	16" thick	"	0.100	6.26			6.26
9420	Concrete block walls, not including toothing						
9440	4" thick	SF	0.044	2.78			2.78
9450	6" thick	"	0.047	2.94			2.94
9460	8" thick	"	0.050	3.13			3.13
9465	10" thick	"	0.057	3.58			3.58
9470	12" thick	"	0.067	4.17			4.17
9500	Rubbish handling						
9519	Load in dumpster or truck						
9520	Minimum	CF	0.018	1.11			1.11
9540	Maximum	"	0.027	1.67			1.67
9550	For use of elevators, add						
9560	Minimum	CF	0.004	0.25			0.25
9570	Maximum	"	0.008	0.50			0.50
9600	Rubbish hauling						
9640	Hand loaded on trucks, 2 mile trip	CY	0.320	20.00		24.00	44.00
9660	Machine loaded on trucks, 2 mile trip	"	0.240	15.00		13.25	28.25

SITE REMEDIATION

02 - 65006   **UNDERGROUND STORAGE TANK REMOVAL**   **02 - 65006**

ID Code	Component Descriptions	Unit of Meas.	Manhr / Unit	Labor Cost	Material Cost	Equip. Cost	Total Cost
1980	Remove underground storage tank, and backfill						
2000	50 to 250 gals	EA	8.000	500		440	940
2050	600 gals	"	8.000	500		440	940
2060	1000 gals	"	12.000	750		670	1,410
2100	4000 gals	"	19.200	1,190		1,060	2,260
2120	5000 gals	"	19.200	1,190		1,060	2,260
2140	10,000 gals	"	32.000	1,990		1,770	3,760
2160	12,000 gals	"	40.000	2,490		2,220	4,700
2180	15,000 gals	"	48.000	2,980		2,660	5,640
2200	20,000 gals	"	60.000	3,730		3,330	7,050

SITE REMEDIATION

ID Code	Component Descriptions	Unit of Meas.	Manhr / Unit	Labor Cost	Material Cost	Equip. Cost	Total Cost
02 - 65007	**SEPTIC TANK REMOVAL**						**02 - 65007**
0980	Remove septic tank						
1000	1000 gals	EA	2.000	120		110	240
1020	2000 gals	"	2.400	150		130	280
1040	5000 gals	"	3.000	190		170	350
1060	15,000 gals	"	24.000	1,490		1,330	2,820
1080	25,000 gals	"	32.000	1,990		1,770	3,760
2000	40,000 gals	"	48.000	2,980		2,660	5,640

HAZARDOUS WASTE

ID Code	Component Descriptions	Unit of Meas.	Manhr / Unit	Labor Cost	Material Cost	Equip. Cost	Total Cost
02 - 82001	**ASBESTOS REMOVAL**						**02 - 82001**
1000	Enclosure using wood studs & poly, install & remove	SF	0.020	1.25	530		530
1020	Trailer (change room)	DAY					120
1100	Disposal suits (4 suits per man day)	"					47.00
1120	Type C respirator mask, includes hose & filters, per man	"					23.50
1130	Respirator mask & filter, light contamination	"					9.39
1980	Air monitoring test, 12 tests per day						
2000	Off job testing	DAY					1,230
2020	On the job testing	"					1,640
6000	Asbestos vacuum with attachments	EA					710
6500	Hydraspray piston pump	"					950
6600	Negative air pressure system	"					950
6800	Grade D breathing air equipment	"					2,140
6900	Glove bag, 44" x 60" x 6 mil plastic	"					6.90
7980	40 CY asbestos dumpster						
8000	Weekly rental	EA					800
8100	Pick up/delivery	"					360
8400	Asbestos dump fee	"					230
02 - 82002	**DUCT INSULATION REMOVAL**						**02 - 82002**
0080	Remove duct insulation, duct size						
1000	6" x 12"	LF	0.044	2.78	240		240
1020	x 18"	"	0.062	3.85	180		180
1040	x 24"	"	0.089	5.56	120		130
1060	8" x 12"	"	0.067	4.17	160		160
1080	x 18"	"	0.073	4.55	150		150
1100	x 24"	"	0.100	6.26	110		120
1120	12" x 12"	"	0.067	4.17	160		160
1140	x 18"	"	0.089	5.56	120		130

HAZARDOUS WASTE

ID Code	Component Descriptions	Unit of Meas.	Manhr / Unit	Labor Cost	Material Cost	Equip. Cost	Total Cost
02 - 82002	**DUCT INSULATION REMOVAL, Cont'd...**						**02 - 82002**
1160	x 24"	LF	0.114	7.16	96.00		100
02 - 82003	**PIPE INSULATION REMOVAL**						**02 - 82003**
0060	Removal, asbestos insulation						
0080	2" thick, pipe						
1000	1" to 3" dia.	LF	0.067	4.17			4.17
1020	4" to 6" dia.	"	0.076	4.77			4.77
1030	3" thick						
1040	7" to 8" dia.	LF	0.080	5.01			5.01
1060	9" to 10" dia.	"	0.084	5.27			5.27
1070	11" to 12" dia.	"	0.089	5.56			5.56
1080	13" to 14" dia.	"	0.094	5.89			5.89
1090	15" to 18" dia.	"	0.100	6.26			6.26

DIVISION 03
CONCRETE

CONCRETE RESTORATION

ID Code	Component Descriptions	Unit of Meas.	Manhr / Unit	Labor Cost	Material Cost	Equip. Cost	Total Cost
03 - 01301		**CONCRETE REPAIR**					**03 - 01301**
0090	Epoxy grout floor patch, 1/4" thick	SF	0.080	5.01	8.59		13.50
0100	Grout, epoxy, 2 component system	CF					420
0110	Epoxy sand	BAG					28.00
0120	Epoxy modifier	GAL					180
0140	Epoxy gel grout	SF	0.800	50.00	4.18		54.00
0150	Injection valve, 1 way, threaded plastic	EA	0.160	10.00	11.50		21.50
0155	Grout crack seal, 2 component	CF	0.800	50.00	970		1,020
0160	Grout, non shrink	"	0.800	50.00	99.00		150
0165	Concrete, epoxy modified						
0170	Sand mix	CF	0.320	20.00	160		180
0180	Gravel mix	"	0.296	18.50	110		130
0190	Concrete repair						
0195	Soffit repair						
0200	16" wide	LF	0.160	10.00	4.90		15.00
0210	18" wide	"	0.167	10.50	5.21		15.75
0220	24" wide	"	0.178	11.25	6.23		17.50
0230	30" wide	"	0.190	12.00	7.01		19.00
0240	32" wide	"	0.200	12.50	7.48		20.00
0245	Edge repair						
0250	2" spall	LF	0.200	12.50	2.33		14.75
0260	3" spall	"	0.211	13.25	2.33		15.50
0270	4" spall	"	0.216	13.50	2.48		16.00
0280	6" spall	"	0.222	14.00	2.57		16.50
0290	8" spall	"	0.235	14.75	2.72		17.50
0300	9" spall	"	0.267	16.75	2.80		19.50
0330	Crack repair, 1/8" crack	"	0.080	5.01	4.59		9.60
5000	Reinforcing steel repair						
5005	1 bar, 4 ft						
5010	#4 bar	LF	0.100	8.16	0.72		8.88
5012	#5 bar	"	0.100	8.16	0.97		9.13
5014	#6 bar	"	0.107	8.70	1.18		9.88
5016	#8 bar	"	0.107	8.70	2.14		10.75
5020	#9 bar	"	0.114	9.33	2.74		12.00
5030	#11 bar	"	0.114	9.33	4.28		13.50
7010	Form fabric, nylon						
7020	18" diameter	LF					18.50
7030	20" diameter	"					18.75
7040	24" diameter	"					31.00

CONCRETE RESTORATION

ID Code	Component Descriptions	Unit of Meas.	Manhr / Unit	Labor Cost	Material Cost	Equip. Cost	Total Cost
	Descriptions	**Output**		**Unit Costs**			

03 - 01301 — CONCRETE REPAIR, Cont'd... — 03 - 01301

ID Code	Component Descriptions	Unit of Meas.	Manhr / Unit	Labor Cost	Material Cost	Equip. Cost	Total Cost
7050	30" diameter	LF					31.75
7060	36" diameter	"					36.50
7100	Pile repairs						
7105	Polyethylene wrap						
7108	30 mil thick						
7110	60" wide	SF	0.267	16.75	20.00		36.75
7120	72" wide	"	0.320	20.00	22.00		42.00
7125	60 mil thick						
7130	60" wide	SF	0.267	16.75	23.75		40.50
7140	80" wide	"	0.364	22.75	27.50		50.00
8010	Pile spall, average repair 3'						
8020	18" x 18"	EA	0.667	41.75	62.00		100
8030	20" x 20"	"	0.800	50.00	83.00		130

CONCRETE FORMING & ACCESSORIES

03 - 10030 — FORMWORK ACCESSORIES — 03 - 10030

ID Code	Component Descriptions	Unit of Meas.	Manhr / Unit	Labor Cost	Material Cost	Equip. Cost	Total Cost
1000	Column clamps						
1010	Small, adjustable, 24"x24"	EA					87.00
1020	Medium 36"x36"	"					90.00
1030	Large 60"x60"	"					91.00
2000	Forming hangers						
2010	Iron 14 ga.	EA					2.81
2020	22 ga.	"					2.81
3000	Snap ties						
3010	Short-end with washers, 6" long	EA					1.73
3020	12" long	"					1.96
4000	18" long	"					2.34
4010	24" long	"					2.52
4020	Long-end with washers, 6' long	"					2.04
4030	12" long	"					2.26
4040	18" long	"					2.56
4050	24" long	"					2.87
5000	Stakes						
5010	Round, pre-drilled holes, 12" long	EA					6.14
5020	18" long	"					6.87
5030	24" long	"					8.90
5040	30" long	"					11.50

CONCRETE FORMING & ACCESSORIES

ID Code	Component Descriptions	Unit of Meas.	Manhr / Unit	Labor Cost	Material Cost	Equip. Cost	Total Cost
	Descriptions	**Output**		**Unit Costs**			

03 - 10030 — FORMWORK ACCESSORIES, Cont'd... — 03 - 10030

ID Code	Component Descriptions	Unit of Meas.	Manhr / Unit	Labor Cost	Material Cost	Equip. Cost	Total Cost
5050	36" long	EA					13.75
5060	48" long	"					18.50
5070	I beam type, 12" long	"					5.05
6000	18" long	"					5.75
6010	24" long	"					8.73
6020	30" long	"					10.25
6030	36" long	"					13.00
7000	48" long	"					16.25
7010	Taper ties						
7020	50K, 1-1/4" to 1", 35" long	EA					85.00
8000	45" long	"					140
8010	55" long	"					170
8020	Walers						
8030	5" deep, 4' long	EA					240
8040	8' long	"					310
8050	12' long	"					510
9000	16' long	"					660
9010	8" deep, 4' long	"					320
9020	8' long	"					580
9030	12' long	"					840
9040	16' long	"					1,330

FORMWORK

03 - 11130 — BEAM FORMWORK — 03 - 11130

ID Code	Component Descriptions	Unit of Meas.	Manhr / Unit	Labor Cost	Material Cost	Equip. Cost	Total Cost
1000	Beam forms, job built						
1020	Beam bottoms						
1040	1 use	SF	0.133	10.75	5.15		16.00
1060	2 uses	"	0.127	10.25	3.03		13.25
1080	3 uses	"	0.123	9.84	2.32		12.25
1100	4 uses	"	0.118	9.41	1.92		11.25
1120	5 uses	"	0.114	9.14	1.75		11.00
2000	Beam sides						
2020	1 use	SF	0.089	7.11	3.68		10.75
2040	2 uses	"	0.084	6.73	2.18		8.91
2060	3 uses	"	0.080	6.40	1.92		8.32
2080	4 uses	"	0.076	6.09	1.77		7.86
2100	5 uses	"	0.073	5.81	1.56		7.37

FORMWORK

ID Code	Component Descriptions	Unit of Meas.	Manhr / Unit	Labor Cost	Material Cost	Equip. Cost	Total Cost
03 - 11131	**BOX CULVERT FORMWORK**						**03 - 11131**
1000	Box culverts, job built						
1010	6' x 6'						
1020	1 use	SF	0.080	6.40	3.75		10.25
1040	2 uses	"	0.076	6.09	2.04		8.13
1060	3 uses	"	0.073	5.81	1.69		7.50
1080	4 uses	"	0.070	5.56	1.43		6.99
1100	5 uses	"	0.067	5.33	1.25		6.58
1110	8' x 12'						
1120	1 use	SF	0.067	5.33	3.75		9.08
1130	2 uses	"	0.064	5.12	2.04		7.16
1150	3 uses	"	0.062	4.92	1.69		6.61
1170	4 uses	"	0.059	4.74	1.43		6.17
1200	5 uses	"	0.057	4.57	1.25		5.82
03 - 11132	**COLUMN FORMWORK**						**03 - 11132**
1000	Column, square forms, job built						
1020	8" x 8" columns						
1040	1 use	SF	0.160	12.75	4.33		17.00
1060	2 uses	"	0.154	12.25	2.33		14.50
1080	3 uses	"	0.148	11.75	1.97		13.75
1100	4 uses	"	0.143	11.50	1.79		13.25
1120	5 uses	"	0.138	11.00	1.53		12.50
1200	12" x 12" columns						
1220	1 use	SF	0.145	11.75	3.95		15.75
1240	2 uses	"	0.140	11.25	2.19		13.50
1260	3 uses	"	0.136	10.75	1.75		12.50
1280	4 uses	"	0.131	10.50	1.53		12.00
1290	5 uses	"	0.127	10.25	1.29		11.50
1300	16" x 16" columns						
1320	1 use	SF	0.133	10.75	3.77		14.50
1340	2 uses	"	0.129	10.25	1.99		12.25
1360	3 uses	"	0.125	10.00	1.59		11.50
1380	4 uses	"	0.121	9.69	1.45		11.25
1390	5 uses	"	0.118	9.41	1.19		10.50
1400	24" x 24" columns						
1420	1 use	SF	0.123	9.84	3.77		13.50
1440	2 uses	"	0.119	9.55	1.75		11.25
1460	3 uses	"	0.116	9.27	1.46		10.75

FORMWORK

ID Code	Component Descriptions	Unit of Meas.	Manhr / Unit	Labor Cost	Material Cost	Equip. Cost	Total Cost
	Descriptions	**Output**		**Unit Costs**			

03 - 11132 — COLUMN FORMWORK, Cont'd... — 03 - 11132

ID Code	Component Descriptions	Unit of Meas.	Manhr / Unit	Labor Cost	Material Cost	Equip. Cost	Total Cost
1480	4 uses	SF	0.113	9.01	1.19		10.25
1490	5 uses	"	0.110	8.76	1.09		9.85
1500	36" x 36" columns						
1520	1 use	SF	0.114	9.14	3.80		13.00
1540	2 uses	"	0.111	8.88	1.78		10.75
1560	3 uses	"	0.108	8.64	1.46		10.00
1580	4 uses	"	0.105	8.42	1.26		9.68
1590	5 uses	"	0.103	8.20	1.18		9.38
2000	Round fiber forms, 1 use						
2040	10" dia.	LF	0.160	12.75	5.65		18.50
2060	12" dia.	"	0.163	13.00	6.95		20.00
2080	14" dia.	"	0.170	13.50	9.14		22.75
2100	16" dia.	"	0.178	14.25	12.00		26.25
2120	18" dia.	"	0.190	15.25	19.50		34.75
2140	24" dia.	"	0.205	16.50	24.00		40.50
2160	30" dia.	"	0.222	17.75	36.00		54.00
2180	36" dia.	"	0.242	19.50	44.50		64.00
2200	42" dia.	"	0.267	21.25	81.00		100

03 - 11133 — CURB FORMWORK — 03 - 11133

ID Code	Component Descriptions	Unit of Meas.	Manhr / Unit	Labor Cost	Material Cost	Equip. Cost	Total Cost
0980	Curb forms						
0990	Straight, 6" high						
1000	1 use	LF	0.080	6.40	2.58		8.98
1020	2 uses	"	0.076	6.09	1.55		7.64
1040	3 uses	"	0.073	5.81	1.16		6.97
1060	4 uses	"	0.070	5.56	1.04		6.60
1080	5 uses	"	0.067	5.33	0.94		6.27
1090	Curved, 6" high						
2000	1 use	LF	0.100	8.00	2.79		10.75
2020	2 uses	"	0.094	7.52	1.75		9.27
2040	3 uses	"	0.089	7.11	1.34		8.45
2060	4 uses	"	0.085	6.80	1.22		8.02
2080	5 uses	"	0.082	6.53	1.13		7.66

FORMWORK

ID Code	Component Descriptions	Unit of Meas.	Manhr / Unit	Labor Cost	Material Cost	Equip. Cost	Total Cost
	Descriptions	**Output**		**Unit Costs**			
03 - 11134	**ELEVATED SLAB FORMWORK**						**03 - 11134**
0100	Elevated slab formwork						
1000	Slab, with drop panels						
1020	1 use	SF	0.064	5.12	4.63		9.75
1040	2 uses	"	0.062	4.92	2.69		7.61
1060	3 uses	"	0.059	4.74	2.08		6.82
1080	4 uses	"	0.057	4.57	1.85		6.42
1100	5 uses	"	0.055	4.41	1.66		6.07
2000	Floor slab, hung from steel beams						
2020	1 use	SF	0.062	4.92	3.73		8.65
2040	2 uses	"	0.059	4.74	2.04		6.78
2060	3 uses	"	0.057	4.57	1.86		6.43
2080	4 uses	"	0.055	4.41	1.60		6.01
2100	5 uses	"	0.053	4.26	1.37		5.63
3000	Floor slab, with pans or domes						
3020	1 use	SF	0.073	5.81	6.65		12.50
3040	2 uses	"	0.070	5.56	4.32		9.88
3060	3 uses	"	0.067	5.33	4.03		9.36
3080	4 uses	"	0.064	5.12	3.76		8.88
3100	5 uses	"	0.062	4.92	3.33		8.25
9030	Equipment curbs, 12" high						
9035	1 use	LF	0.080	6.40	3.43		9.83
9040	2 uses	"	0.076	6.09	2.20		8.29
9060	3 uses	"	0.073	5.81	1.92		7.73
9080	4 uses	"	0.070	5.56	1.72		7.28
9100	5 uses	"	0.067	5.33	1.49		6.82
03 - 11135	**EQUIPMENT PAD FORMWORK**						**03 - 11135**
1000	Equipment pad, job built						
1020	1 use	SF	0.100	8.00	4.50		12.50
1040	2 uses	"	0.094	7.52	2.70		10.25
1060	3 uses	"	0.089	7.11	2.16		9.27
1080	4 uses	"	0.084	6.73	1.68		8.41
1100	5 uses	"	0.080	6.40	1.34		7.74

FORMWORK

ID Code	Component Descriptions	Unit of Meas.	Manhr / Unit	Labor Cost	Material Cost	Equip. Cost	Total Cost
	Descriptions	**Output**		**Unit Costs**			
03 - 11136	**FOOTING FORMWORK**						**03 - 11136**
2000	Wall footings, job built, continuous						
2040	1 use	SF	0.080	6.40	2.09		8.49
2050	2 uses	"	0.076	6.09	1.47		7.56
2060	3 uses	"	0.073	5.81	1.21		7.02
2080	4 uses	"	0.070	5.56	1.08		6.64
2090	5 uses	"	0.067	5.33	0.93		6.26
3000	Column footings, spread						
3020	1 use	SF	0.100	8.00	2.21		10.25
3040	2 uses	"	0.094	7.52	1.64		9.16
3060	3 uses	"	0.089	7.11	1.17		8.28
3080	4 uses	"	0.084	6.73	0.98		7.71
3100	5 uses	"	0.080	6.40	0.90		7.30
03 - 11137	**GRADE BEAM FORMWORK**						**03 - 11137**
1000	Grade beams, job built						
1020	1 use	SF	0.080	6.40	3.29		9.69
1040	2 uses	"	0.076	6.09	1.85		7.94
1060	3 uses	"	0.073	5.81	1.44		7.25
1080	4 uses	"	0.070	5.56	1.20		6.76
1100	5 uses	"	0.067	5.33	1.00		6.33
03 - 11138	**PILE CAP FORMWORK**						**03 - 11138**
1500	Pile cap forms, job built						
1510	Square						
1520	1 use	SF	0.100	8.00	3.74		11.75
1540	2 uses	"	0.094	7.52	2.16		9.68
1560	3 uses	"	0.089	7.11	1.71		8.82
1580	4 uses	"	0.084	6.73	1.51		8.24
1600	5 uses	"	0.080	6.40	1.25		7.65
2000	Triangular						
2020	1 use	SF	0.114	9.14	3.97		13.00
2040	2 uses	"	0.107	8.53	2.62		11.25
2060	3 uses	"	0.100	8.00	2.09		10.00
2080	4 uses	"	0.094	7.52	1.71		9.23
2100	5 uses	"	0.089	7.11	1.36		8.47

FORMWORK

ID Code	Descriptions	Output		Unit Costs			
	Component Descriptions	Unit of Meas.	Manhr / Unit	Labor Cost	Material Cost	Equip. Cost	Total Cost
03 - 11139	**SLAB / MAT FORMWORK**						**03 - 11139**
3000	Mat foundations, job built						
3020	1 use	SF	0.100	8.00	3.27		11.25
3040	2 uses	"	0.094	7.52	1.89		9.41
3060	3 uses	"	0.089	7.11	1.39		8.50
3080	4 uses	"	0.084	6.73	1.17		7.90
3100	5 uses	"	0.080	6.40	0.94		7.34
3980	Edge forms						
3990	6" high						
4000	1 use	LF	0.073	5.81	3.30		9.11
4001	2 uses	"	0.070	5.56	1.90		7.46
4002	3 uses	"	0.067	5.33	1.39		6.72
4003	4 uses	"	0.064	5.12	1.18		6.30
4004	5 uses	"	0.062	4.92	0.95		5.87
4006	12" high						
4010	1 use	LF	0.080	6.40	3.11		9.51
4011	2 uses	"	0.076	6.09	1.76		7.85
4012	3 uses	"	0.073	5.81	1.29		7.10
4013	4 uses	"	0.070	5.56	1.07		6.63
4014	5 uses	"	0.067	5.33	0.86		6.19
5000	Formwork for openings						
5020	1 use	SF	0.160	12.75	4.45		17.25
5040	2 uses	"	0.145	11.75	2.56		14.25
5060	3 uses	"	0.133	10.75	2.14		13.00
5080	4 uses	"	0.123	9.84	1.65		11.50
5100	5 uses	"	0.114	9.14	1.38		10.50
03 - 11140	**STAIR FORMWORK**						**03 - 11140**
1000	Stairway forms, job built						
1020	1 use	SF	0.160	12.75	5.14		18.00
1030	2 uses	"	0.145	11.75	2.88		14.75
1040	3 uses	"	0.133	10.75	2.24		13.00
1050	4 uses	"	0.123	9.84	2.05		12.00
1060	5 uses	"	0.114	9.14	1.72		10.75
2000	Stairs, elevated						
2020	1 use	SF	0.160	12.75	6.20		19.00
2040	2 uses	"	0.133	10.75	3.30		14.00
2060	3 uses	"	0.114	9.14	2.88		12.00
2080	4 uses	"	0.107	8.53	2.48		11.00

FORMWORK

ID Code	Component Descriptions	Unit of Meas.	Manhr / Unit	Labor Cost	Material Cost	Equip. Cost	Total Cost
		Output		**Unit Costs**			
03 - 11140	**STAIR FORMWORK, Cont'd...**						**03 - 11140**
2100	5 uses	SF	0.100	8.00	2.05		10.00
03 - 11141	**WALL FORMWORK**						**03 - 11141**
2980	Wall forms, exterior, job built						
3000	Up to 8' high wall						
3120	1 use	SF	0.080	6.40	3.52		9.92
3140	2 uses	"	0.076	6.09	1.94		8.03
3160	3 uses	"	0.073	5.81	1.71		7.52
3180	4 uses	"	0.070	5.56	1.47		7.03
3190	5 uses	"	0.067	5.33	1.29		6.62
3200	Over 8' high wall						
3220	1 use	SF	0.100	8.00	3.87		11.75
3230	2 uses	"	0.094	7.52	2.21		9.73
3240	3 uses	"	0.089	7.11	2.01		9.12
3280	4 uses	"	0.084	6.73	1.83		8.56
3290	5 uses	"	0.080	6.40	1.58		7.98
3300	Over 16' high wall						
3320	1 use	SF	0.114	9.14	4.06		13.25
3340	2 uses	"	0.107	8.53	2.43		11.00
3360	3 uses	"	0.100	8.00	2.21		10.25
3380	4 uses	"	0.094	7.52	2.01		9.53
3400	5 uses	"	0.089	7.11	1.83		8.94
4000	Radial wall forms						
4020	1 use	SF	0.123	9.84	3.78		13.50
4040	2 uses	"	0.114	9.14	2.27		11.50
4060	3 uses	"	0.107	8.53	2.10		10.75
4080	4 uses	"	0.100	8.00	1.90		9.90
4090	5 uses	"	0.094	7.52	1.71		9.23
4591	Retaining wall forms						
4592	1 use	SF	0.089	7.11	3.27		10.50
4593	2 uses	"	0.084	6.73	1.74		8.47
4594	3 uses	"	0.080	6.40	1.50		7.90
4595	4 uses	"	0.076	6.09	1.30		7.39
4596	5 uses	"	0.073	5.81	1.11		6.92
4600	Radial retaining wall forms						
4620	1 use	SF	0.133	10.75	3.46		14.25
4640	2 uses	"	0.123	9.84	2.13		12.00
4660	3 uses	"	0.114	9.14	1.82		11.00

FORMWORK

ID Code	Component Descriptions	Unit of Meas.	Manhr / Unit	Labor Cost	Material Cost	Equip. Cost	Total Cost
	Descriptions	**Output**		**Unit Costs**			

03 - 11141   **WALL FORMWORK, Cont'd...**   **03 - 11141**

ID Code	Component Descriptions	Unit of Meas.	Manhr / Unit	Labor Cost	Material Cost	Equip. Cost	Total Cost
4680	4 uses	SF	0.107	8.53	1.72		10.25
4690	5 uses	"	0.100	8.00	1.49		9.49
5000	Column pier and pilaster						
5020	1 use	SF	0.160	12.75	3.87		16.50
5040	2 uses	"	0.145	11.75	2.28		14.00
5060	3 uses	"	0.133	10.75	2.13		13.00
5080	4 uses	"	0.123	9.84	1.94		11.75
5090	5 uses	"	0.114	9.14	1.74		11.00
6980	Interior wall forms						
7000	Up to 8' high						
7020	1 use	SF	0.073	5.81	3.52		9.33
7040	2 uses	"	0.070	5.56	1.96		7.52
7060	3 uses	"	0.067	5.33	1.74		7.07
7080	4 uses	"	0.064	5.12	1.49		6.61
7100	5 uses	"	0.062	4.92	1.25		6.17
7200	Over 8' high						
7220	1 use	SF	0.089	7.11	3.87		11.00
7240	2 uses	"	0.084	6.73	2.21		8.94
7260	3 uses	"	0.080	6.40	2.01		8.41
7280	4 uses	"	0.076	6.09	1.83		7.92
7290	5 uses	"	0.073	5.81	1.60		7.41
7300	Over 16' high						
7320	1 use	SF	0.100	8.00	4.05		12.00
7340	2 uses	"	0.094	7.52	2.43		9.95
7360	3 uses	"	0.089	7.11	2.21		9.32
7380	4 uses	"	0.084	6.73	2.01		8.74
7390	5 uses	"	0.080	6.40	1.83		8.23
7400	Radial wall forms						
7420	1 use	SF	0.107	8.53	3.78		12.25
7440	2 uses	"	0.100	8.00	2.27		10.25
7460	3 uses	"	0.094	7.52	2.10		9.62
7480	4 uses	"	0.089	7.11	1.90		9.01
7490	5 uses	"	0.084	6.73	1.71		8.44
7500	Curved wall forms, 24" sections						
7520	1 use	SF	0.160	12.75	3.62		16.25
7540	2 uses	"	0.145	11.75	2.15		14.00
7560	3 uses	"	0.133	10.75	2.00		12.75
7580	4 uses	"	0.123	9.84	1.82		11.75

FORMWORK

ID Code	Component Descriptions	Unit of Meas.	Manhr / Unit	Labor Cost	Material Cost	Equip. Cost	Total Cost
	Descriptions	**Output**		**Unit Costs**			
03 - 11141	**WALL FORMWORK, Cont'd...**						**03 - 11141**
7590	5 uses	SF	0.114	9.14	1.62		10.75
9000	PVC form liner, per side, smooth finish						
9010	1 use	SF	0.067	5.33	9.09		14.50
9020	2 uses	"	0.064	5.12	4.99		10.00
9030	3 uses	"	0.062	4.92	4.22		9.14
9040	4 uses	"	0.057	4.57	3.26		7.83
9050	5 uses	"	0.053	4.26	2.60		6.86
03 - 11242	**MISCELLANEOUS FORMWORK**						**03 - 11242**
1200	Keyway forms (5 uses)						
1220	2 x 4	LF	0.040	3.20	0.30		3.50
1240	2 x 6	"	0.044	3.55	0.43		3.98
1500	Bulkheads						
1510	Walls, with keyways						
1515	2 piece	LF	0.073	5.81	4.97		10.75
1520	3 piece	"	0.080	6.40	6.28		12.75
1560	Elevated slab, with keyway						
1570	2 piece	LF	0.067	5.33	5.69		11.00
1580	3 piece	"	0.073	5.81	8.39		14.25
1600	Ground slab, with keyway						
1620	2 piece	LF	0.057	4.57	5.88		10.50
1640	3 piece	"	0.062	4.92	7.19		12.00
2000	Chamfer strips						
2020	Wood						
2040	1/2" wide	LF	0.018	1.42	0.28		1.70
2060	3/4" wide	"	0.018	1.42	0.36		1.78
2070	1" wide	"	0.018	1.42	0.49		1.91
2100	PVC						
2120	1/2" wide	LF	0.018	1.42	1.26		2.68
2140	3/4" wide	"	0.018	1.42	1.36		2.78
2160	1" wide	"	0.018	1.42	1.98		3.40
2170	Radius						
2180	1"	LF	0.019	1.52	1.47		2.99
2200	1-1/2"	"	0.019	1.52	2.67		4.19
3000	Reglets						
3020	Galvanized steel, 24 ga.	LF	0.032	2.56	1.91		4.47
5000	Metal formwork						
5020	Straight edge forms						

FORMWORK

ID Code	Component Descriptions	Unit of Meas.	Manhr / Unit	Labor Cost	Material Cost	Equip. Cost	Total Cost
	Descriptions	**Output**		**Unit Costs**			

03 - 11242 MISCELLANEOUS FORMWORK, Cont'd... 03 - 11242

ID Code	Component Descriptions	Unit of Meas.	Manhr / Unit	Labor Cost	Material Cost	Equip. Cost	Total Cost
5040	4" high	LF	0.050	4.00	23.50		27.50
5060	6" high	"	0.053	4.26	25.75		30.00
5080	8" high	"	0.057	4.57	35.25		39.75
5100	12" high	"	0.062	4.92	41.00		46.00
5120	16" high	"	0.067	5.33	48.25		54.00
5300	Curb form, S-shape						
5310	12" x						
5320	1'-6"	LF	0.114	9.14	52.00		61.00
5340	2'	"	0.107	8.53	57.00		66.00
5360	2'-6"	"	0.100	8.00	62.00		70.00
5380	3'	"	0.089	7.11	67.00		74.00

ACCESSORIES

03 - 15001 CONCRETE ACCESSORIES 03 - 15001

ID Code	Component Descriptions	Unit of Meas.	Manhr / Unit	Labor Cost	Material Cost	Equip. Cost	Total Cost
1000	Expansion joint, poured						
1010	Asphalt						
1020	1/2" x 1"	LF	0.016	1.00	0.88		1.88
1040	1" x 2"	"	0.017	1.08	2.76		3.84
1060	Liquid neoprene, cold applied						
1080	1/2" x 1"	LF	0.016	1.02	3.45		4.47
1100	1" x 2"	"	0.018	1.11	14.25		15.25
1110	Polyurethane, 2 parts						
1120	1/2" x 1"	LF	0.027	1.67	3.31		4.98
1140	1" x 2"	"	0.029	1.82	13.00		14.75
1150	Rubberized asphalt, cold						
1160	1/2" x 1"	LF	0.016	1.00	0.84		1.84
1180	1" x 2"	"	0.017	1.08	2.54		3.62
1190	Hot, fuel resistant						
1200	1/2" x 1"	LF	0.016	1.00	1.53		2.53
1220	1" x 2"	"	0.017	1.08	7.38		8.46
1300	Expansion joint, premolded, in slabs						
1310	Asphalt						
1320	1/2" x 6"	LF	0.020	1.25	0.98		2.23
1340	1" x 12"	"	0.027	1.67	1.64		3.31
1350	Cork						
1360	1/2" x 6"	LF	0.020	1.25	1.95		3.20
1380	1" x 12"	"	0.027	1.67	7.41		9.08

ACCESSORIES

ID Code	Component Descriptions	Unit of Meas.	Manhr / Unit	Labor Cost	Material Cost	Equip. Cost	Total Cost
	Descriptions	**Output**		**Unit Costs**			
03 - 15001	**CONCRETE ACCESSORIES, Cont'd...**						**03 - 15001**
1390	Neoprene sponge						
1400	1/2" x 6"	LF	0.020	1.25	2.87		4.12
1420	1" x 12"	"	0.027	1.67	10.50		12.25
1430	Polyethylene foam						
1440	1/2" x 6"	LF	0.020	1.25	1.11		2.36
1460	1" x 12"	"	0.027	1.67	5.11		6.78
1560	Polyurethane foam						
1580	1/2" x 6"	LF	0.020	1.25	1.46		2.71
1600	1" x 12"	"	0.027	1.67	3.22		4.89
1610	Polyvinyl chloride foam						
1620	1/2" x 6"	LF	0.020	1.25	3.13		4.38
1640	1" x 12"	"	0.027	1.67	6.75		8.42
1650	Rubber, gray sponge						
1660	1/2" x 6"	LF	0.020	1.25	4.87		6.12
1680	1" x 12"	"	0.027	1.67	21.25		23.00
1700	Asphalt felt control joints or bond breaker, screed joints						
1780	4" slab	LF	0.016	1.00	1.32		2.32
1800	6" slab	"	0.018	1.11	1.65		2.76
1820	8" slab	"	0.020	1.25	2.15		3.40
1840	10" slab	"	0.023	1.43	3.03		4.46
1900	Keyed cold expansion and control joints, 24 ga.						
1940	4" slab	LF	0.050	3.13	1.07		4.20
1960	5" slab	"	0.050	3.13	1.43		4.56
1980	6" slab	"	0.053	3.34	1.65		4.99
1990	8" slab	"	0.057	3.58	2.00		5.58
2000	10" slab	"	0.062	3.85	2.20		6.05
2100	Waterstops						
2120	Polyvinyl chloride						
2125	Ribbed						
2130	3/16" thick x						
2140	4" wide	LF	0.040	2.50	1.57		4.07
2160	6" wide	"	0.044	2.78	2.38		5.16
2165	1/2" thick x						
2170	9" wide	LF	0.050	3.13	6.32		9.45
2178	Ribbed with center bulb						
2180	3/16" thick x 9" wide	LF	0.050	3.13	5.31		8.44
2200	3/8" thick x 9" wide	"	0.050	3.13	6.24		9.37
2240	Dumbbell type, 3/8" thick x 6" wide	"	0.044	2.78	6.32		9.10

ACCESSORIES

ID Code	Descriptions — Component Descriptions	Output — Unit of Meas.	Output — Manhr / Unit	Unit Costs — Labor Cost	Unit Costs — Material Cost	Unit Costs — Equip. Cost	Unit Costs — Total Cost
03 - 15001	**CONCRETE ACCESSORIES, Cont'd...**						**03 - 15001**
2260	Plain, 3/8" thick x 9" wide	LF	0.050	3.13	8.39		11.50
2280	Center bulb, 3/8" thick x 9" wide	"	0.050	3.13	10.00		13.25
2300	Rubber						
2310	Flat dumbbell						
2315	3/8" thick x						
2320	6" wide	LF	0.044	2.78	7.77		10.50
2340	9" wide	"	0.050	3.13	8.39		11.50
2350	Center bulb						
2355	3/8" thick x						
2360	6" wide	LF	0.044	2.78	8.72		11.50
2380	9" wide	"	0.050	3.13	11.00		14.25
5060	Vapor barrier						
5090	4 mil polyethylene	SF	0.003	0.16	0.05		0.21
5094	6 mil polyethylene	"	0.003	0.16	0.08		0.24
5200	Gravel porous fill, under floor slabs, 3/4" stone	CY	1.333	84.00	21.75		110
6000	Reinforcing accessories						
6010	Beam bolsters						
6020	1-1/2" high, plain	LF	0.008	0.65	0.58		1.23
6030	Galvanized	"	0.008	0.65	1.27		1.92
6035	3" high						
6040	Plain	LF	0.010	0.81	0.83		1.64
6050	Galvanized	"	0.010	0.81	2.05		2.86
6080	Slab bolsters						
6090	1" high						
6100	Plain	LF	0.004	0.32	0.62		0.94
6110	Galvanized	"	0.004	0.32	1.25		1.57
6115	2" high						
6120	Plain	LF	0.004	0.36	0.69		1.05
6130	Galvanized	"	0.004	0.36	1.46		1.82
6210	Chairs, high chairs						
6215	3" high						
6220	Plain	EA	0.020	1.63	1.67		3.30
6230	Galvanized	"	0.020	1.63	1.84		3.47
6235	5" high						
6240	Plain	EA	0.021	1.71	1.72		3.43
6250	Galvanized	"	0.021	1.71	3.46		5.17
6255	8" high						
6260	Plain	EA	0.023	1.86	2.82		4.68

ACCESSORIES

ID Code	Component Descriptions	Unit of Meas.	Manhr / Unit	Labor Cost	Material Cost	Equip. Cost	Total Cost
	Descriptions	**Output**		**Unit Costs**			

03 - 15001	CONCRETE ACCESSORIES, Cont'd...						03 - 15001
6270	Galvanized	EA	0.023	1.86	4.79		6.65
6275	12" high						
6280	Plain	EA	0.027	2.17	5.11		7.28
6290	Galvanized	"	0.027	2.17	9.75		12.00
6295	Continuous, high chair						
6299	3" high						
6300	Plain	LF	0.005	0.43	2.32		2.75
6310	Galvanized	"	0.005	0.43	2.87		3.30
6315	5" high						
6320	Plain	LF	0.006	0.46	2.49		2.95
6330	Galvanized	"	0.006	0.46	3.51		3.97
6335	8" high						
6340	Plain	LF	0.006	0.50	2.87		3.37
6350	Galvanized	"	0.006	0.50	3.73		4.23
6355	12" high						
6360	Plain	LF	0.007	0.54	3.69		4.23
6370	Galvanized	"	0.007	0.54	4.79		5.33

REINFORCEMENT

03 - 21001	BEAM REINFORCING						03 - 21001
0980	Beam-girders						
1000	#3 - #4	TON	20.000	1,630	1,980		3,610
1010	#5 - #6	"	16.000	1,310	1,740		3,050
1011	#7 - #8	"	13.333	1,090	1,650		2,740
1012	#9 - #10	"	11.429	930	1,650		2,580
1013	#11	"	10.667	870	1,650		2,520
1014	#14	"	10.000	820	1,650		2,470
1018	Galvanized						
1020	#3 - #4	TON	20.000	1,630	3,360		4,990
1030	#5 - #6	"	16.000	1,310	3,180		4,490
1031	#7 - #8	"	13.333	1,090	3,060		4,150
1032	#9 - #10	"	11.429	930	3,060		3,990
1033	#11	"	10.667	870	3,060		3,930
1034	#14	"	10.000	820	3,060		3,880
1100	Epoxy coated						
1200	#3 - #4	TON	22.857	1,870	2,910		4,780
1210	#5 - #6	"	17.778	1,450	2,730		4,180

REINFORCEMENT

ID Code	Component Descriptions	Unit of Meas.	Manhr / Unit	Labor Cost	Material Cost	Equip. Cost	Total Cost
03 - 21001	**BEAM REINFORCING, Cont'd...**						**03 - 21001**
1220	#7 - #8	TON	14.545	1,190	2,640		3,830
1230	#9 - #10	"	12.308	1,000	2,640		3,640
1240	#11	"	11.429	930	2,640		3,570
1250	#14	"	10.667	870	2,640		3,510
2000	Bond Beams						
2100	#3 - #4	TON	26.667	2,180	1,980		4,160
2110	#5 - #6	"	20.000	1,630	1,740		3,370
2120	#7 - #8	"	17.778	1,450	1,650		3,100
2200	Galvanized						
2210	#3 - #4	TON	26.667	2,180	3,220		5,400
2220	#5 - #6	"	20.000	1,630	3,180		4,810
2230	#7 - #8	"	17.778	1,450	3,060		4,510
2400	Epoxy coated						
2410	#3 - #4	TON	32.000	2,610	2,910		5,520
2420	#5 - #6	"	22.857	1,870	2,730		4,600
2430	#7 - #8	"	20.000	1,630	2,640		4,270
03 - 21002	**BOX CULVERT REINFORCING**						**03 - 21002**
0980	Box culverts						
1000	#3 - #4	TON	10.000	820	1,980		2,800
1020	#5 - #6	"	8.889	730	1,740		2,470
1040	#7 - #8	"	8.000	650	1,650		2,300
1060	#9 - #10	"	7.273	590	1,650		2,240
1080	#11	"	6.667	540	1,650		2,190
1180	Galvanized						
1200	#3 - #4	TON	10.000	820	3,220		4,040
1220	#5 - #6	"	8.889	730	3,180		3,910
1240	#7 - #8	"	8.000	650	3,060		3,710
1260	#9 - #10	"	7.273	590	3,060		3,650
1280	#11	"	6.667	540	3,060		3,600
2000	Epoxy coated						
2100	#3 - #4	TON	10.667	870	2,910		3,780
2110	#5 - #6	"	9.412	770	2,730		3,500
2120	#7 - #8	"	8.421	690	2,640		3,330
2130	#9 - #10	"	7.619	620	2,640		3,260
2140	#11	"	6.957	570	2,640		3,210

REINFORCEMENT

ID Code	Component Descriptions	Unit of Meas.	Manhr / Unit	Labor Cost	Material Cost	Equip. Cost	Total Cost
03 - 21003	**COLUMN REINFORCING**						**03 - 21003**
0980	Columns						
1000	#3 - #4	TON	22.857	1,870	1,980		3,850
1010	#5 - #6	"	17.778	1,450	1,740		3,190
1015	#7 - #8	"	16.000	1,310	1,650		2,960
1020	#9 - #10	"	14.545	1,190	1,650		2,840
1025	#11	"	13.333	1,090	1,650		2,740
1030	#14	"	12.308	1,000	1,650		2,650
1040	#18	"	11.429	930	1,650		2,580
1100	Galvanized						
1200	#3 - #4	TON	22.857	1,870	3,360		5,230
1300	#5 - #6	"	17.778	1,450	3,180		4,630
1320	#7 - #8	"	16.000	1,310	3,060		4,370
1340	#9 - #10	"	14.545	1,190	3,060		4,250
1360	#11	"	13.333	1,090	3,060		4,150
1380	#14	"	12.308	1,000	3,060		4,060
1400	#18	"	11.429	930	3,060		3,990
1500	Epoxy coated						
1510	#3 - #4	TON	26.667	2,180	2,910		5,090
1520	#5 - #6	"	20.000	1,630	2,730		4,360
1530	#7 - #8	"	17.778	1,450	2,640		4,090
1540	#9 - #10	"	16.000	1,310	2,640		3,950
1550	#11	"	14.545	1,190	2,640		3,830
1560	#14	"	13.333	1,090	2,640		3,730
1570	#18	"	12.308	1,000	2,640		3,640
1980	Spirals						
2000	8" to 24" dia.	TON	20.000	1,630	3,050		4,680
2020	24" to 48" dia.	"	17.778	1,450	3,050		4,500
2040	48" to 84" dia.	"	16.000	1,310	3,360		4,670
03 - 21004	**ELEVATED SLAB REINFORCING**						**03 - 21004**
0980	Elevated slab						
1000	#3 - #4	TON	10.000	820	1,980		2,800
1020	#5 - #6	"	8.889	730	1,740		2,470
1040	#7 - #8	"	8.000	650	1,650		2,300
1060	#9 - #10	"	7.273	590	1,650		2,240
1080	#11	"	6.667	540	1,650		2,190
1980	Galvanized						
2000	#3 - #4	TON	10.000	820	3,220		4,040

REINFORCEMENT

ID Code	Component Descriptions	Unit of Meas.	Manhr / Unit	Labor Cost	Material Cost	Equip. Cost	Total Cost
	Descriptions	**Output**		**Unit Costs**			

ID Code	Component Descriptions	Unit of Meas.	Manhr / Unit	Labor Cost	Material Cost	Equip. Cost	Total Cost
03 - 21004	**ELEVATED SLAB REINFORCING, Cont'd...**						**03 - 21004**
2020	#5 - #6	TON	8.889	730	3,180		3,910
2040	#7 - #8	"	8.000	650	3,060		3,710
2060	#9 - #10	"	7.273	590	3,060		3,650
2100	#11	"	6.667	540	3,060		3,600
3000	Epoxy coated						
3100	#3 - #4	TON	10.667	870	2,910		3,780
3110	#5 - #6	"	9.412	770	2,730		3,500
3120	#7 - #8	"	8.421	690	2,640		3,330
3130	#9 - #10	"	7.619	620	2,640		3,260
3140	#11	"	6.957	570	2,640		3,210
03 - 21005	**EQUIP. PAD REINFORCING**						**03 - 21005**
0980	Equipment pad						
1000	#3 - #4	TON	16.000	1,310	1,980		3,290
1020	#5 - #6	"	14.545	1,190	1,740		2,930
1040	#7 - #8	"	13.333	1,090	1,650		2,740
1060	#9 - #10	"	12.308	1,000	1,650		2,650
1080	#11	"	11.429	930	1,650		2,580
03 - 21006	**FOOTING REINFORCING**						**03 - 21006**
1000	Footings						
1010	Grade 50						
1020	#3 - #4	TON	13.333	1,090	1,980		3,070
1030	#5 - #6	"	11.429	930	1,740		2,670
1040	#7 - #8	"	10.000	820	1,650		2,470
1050	#9 - #10	"	8.889	730	1,650		2,380
1055	Grade 60						
1060	#3 - #4	TON	13.333	1,090	1,980		3,070
1072	#5 - #6	"	11.429	930	1,740		2,670
1074	#7 - #8	"	10.000	820	1,650		2,470
1080	#9 - #10	"	8.889	730	1,650		2,380
1090	Grade 70						
1100	#3 - #4	TON	13.333	1,090	1,980		3,070
1110	#5 - #6	"	11.429	930	1,740		2,670
1120	#7 - #8	"	10.000	820	1,650		2,470
1140	#9 - #10	"	8.889	730	1,650		2,380
1160	#11	"	8.000	650	1,650		2,300
4980	Straight dowels, 24" long						
5000	1" dia. (#8)	EA	0.080	6.53	6.13		12.75

REINFORCEMENT

ID Code	Component Descriptions	Unit of Meas.	Manhr / Unit	Labor Cost	Material Cost	Equip. Cost	Total Cost
03 - 21006	**FOOTING REINFORCING, Cont'd...**						**03 - 21006**
5040	3/4" dia. (#6)	EA	0.080	6.53	5.51		12.00
5050	5/8" dia. (#5)	"	0.067	5.44	4.76		10.25
5060	1/2" dia. (#4)	"	0.057	4.66	3.59		8.25
03 - 21007	**FOUNDATION REINFORCING**						**03 - 21007**
0980	Foundations						
1000	#3 - #4	TON	13.333	1,090	1,980		3,070
1020	#5 - #6	"	11.429	930	1,740		2,670
1040	#7 - #8	"	10.000	820	1,650		2,470
1060	#9 - #10	"	8.889	730	1,650		2,380
1080	#11	"	8.000	650	1,650		2,300
1380	Galvanized						
1400	#3 - #4	TON	13.333	1,090	3,370		4,460
1410	#5 - #6	"	11.429	930	3,190		4,120
1420	#7 - #8	"	10.000	820	3,070		3,890
1430	#9 - #10	"	8.889	730	3,070		3,800
1440	#11	"	8.000	650	3,070		3,720
2000	Epoxy Coated						
2100	#3 - #4	TON	14.545	1,190	2,920		4,110
2110	#5 - #6	"	12.308	1,000	2,740		3,740
2120	#7 - #8	"	10.667	870	2,650		3,520
2130	#9 - #10	"	9.412	770	2,650		3,420
2140	#11	"	8.421	690	2,650		3,340
03 - 21008	**GRADE BEAM REINFORCING**						**03 - 21008**
0980	Grade beams						
1000	#3 - #4	TON	12.308	1,000	1,980		2,980
1020	#5 - #6	"	10.667	870	1,740		2,610
1040	#7 - #8	"	9.412	770	1,650		2,420
1060	#9 - #10	"	8.421	690	1,650		2,340
1080	#11	"	7.619	620	1,650		2,270
1090	Galvanized						
1100	#3 - #4	TON	12.308	1,000	3,370		4,370
1120	#5 - #6	"	10.667	870	3,190		4,060
1140	#7 - #8	"	9.412	770	3,070		3,840
1160	#9 - #10	"	8.421	690	3,070		3,760
1180	#11	"	7.619	620	3,070		3,690
2000	Epoxy coated						
2100	#3 - #4	TON	13.333	1,090	2,920		4,010

REINFORCEMENT

ID Code	Component Descriptions	Unit of Meas.	Manhr / Unit	Labor Cost	Material Cost	Equip. Cost	Total Cost
	Descriptions	**Output**		**Unit Costs**			
03 - 21008	**GRADE BEAM REINFORCING, Cont'd...**						**03 - 21008**
2110	#5 - #6	TON	11.429	930	2,740		3,670
2120	#7 - #8	"	10.000	820	2,650		3,470
2130	#9 - #10	"	8.889	730	2,650		3,380
2140	#11	"	8.000	650	2,650		3,300
03 - 21009	**SLAB / MAT REINFORCING**						**03 - 21009**
0900	Bars, slabs						
1000	#3 - #4	TON	13.333	1,090	1,980		3,070
1020	#5 - #6	"	11.429	930	1,740		2,670
1040	#7 - #8	"	10.000	820	1,650		2,470
1060	#9 - #10	"	8.889	730	1,650		2,380
1080	#11	"	8.000	650	1,650		2,300
1090	Galvanized						
2000	#3 - #4	TON	13.333	1,090	3,370		4,460
2020	#5 - #6	"	11.429	930	3,190		4,120
2040	#7 - #8	"	10.000	820	3,070		3,890
2060	#9 - #10	"	8.889	730	3,070		3,800
2080	#11	"	8.000	650	3,070		3,720
2090	Epoxy coated						
3100	#3 - #4	TON	14.545	1,190	2,920		4,110
3110	#5 - #6	"	12.308	1,000	2,740		3,740
3120	#7 - #8	"	10.667	870	2,650		3,520
3130	#9 - #10	"	9.412	770	2,650		3,420
3140	#11	"	8.421	690	2,650		3,340
4990	Wire mesh, slabs						
5000	Galvanized						
5010	4x4						
5020	W1.4xW1.4	SF	0.005	0.43	0.49		0.92
5040	W2.0xW2.0	"	0.006	0.46	0.63		1.09
5060	W2.9xW2.9	"	0.006	0.50	0.89		1.39
5080	W4.0xW4.0	"	0.007	0.54	1.32		1.86
5090	6x6						
5100	W1.4xW1.4	SF	0.004	0.32	0.45		0.77
5120	W2.0xW2.0	"	0.004	0.36	0.63		0.99
5140	W2.9xW2.9	"	0.005	0.38	0.86		1.24
5150	W4.0xW4.0	"	0.005	0.43	0.93		1.36
5160	Standard						
5170	2x2						

REINFORCEMENT

ID Code	Component Descriptions	Unit of Meas.	Manhr / Unit	Labor Cost	Material Cost	Equip. Cost	Total Cost
03 - 21009	**SLAB / MAT REINFORCING, Cont'd...**						**03 - 21009**
5180	W.9xW.9	SF	0.005	0.43	0.49		0.92
5190	4x4						
5200	W1.4xW1.4	SF	0.005	0.43	0.32		0.75
5300	W2.0xW2.0	"	0.006	0.46	0.42		0.88
5400	W2.9xW2.9	"	0.006	0.50	0.58		1.08
5500	W4.0xW4.0	"	0.007	0.54	0.89		1.43
5600	6x6						
5700	W1.4xW1.4	SF	0.004	0.32	0.21		0.53
5800	W2.0xW2.0	"	0.004	0.36	0.29		0.65
6000	W2.9xW2.9	"	0.005	0.38	0.42		0.80
6020	W4.0xW4.0	"	0.005	0.43	0.60		1.03
03 - 21010	**STAIR REINFORCING**						**03 - 21010**
0980	Stairs						
1000	#3 - #4	TON	16.000	1,310	1,980		3,290
1020	#5 - #6	"	13.333	1,090	1,740		2,830
1040	#7 - #8	"	11.429	930	1,650		2,580
1060	#9 - #10	"	10.000	820	1,650		2,470
1980	Galvanized						
2000	#3 - #4	TON	16.000	1,310	3,370		4,680
2020	#5 - #6	"	13.333	1,090	3,190		4,280
2040	#7 - #8	"	11.429	930	3,070		4,000
2060	#9 - #10	"	10.000	820	3,070		3,890
3000	Epoxy coated						
3100	#3 - #4	TON	17.778	1,450	2,920		4,370
3110	#5 - #6	"	14.545	1,190	2,740		3,930
3120	#7 - #8	"	12.308	1,000	2,650		3,650
3130	#9 - #10	"	10.667	870	2,650		3,520
03 - 21011	**WALL REINFORCING**						**03 - 21011**
0980	Walls						
1000	#3 - #4	TON	11.429	930	1,980		2,910
1020	#5 - #6	"	10.000	820	1,740		2,560
1040	#7 - #8	"	8.889	730	1,650		2,380
1060	#9 - #10	"	8.000	650	1,650		2,300
1980	Galvanized						
2000	#3 - #4	TON	11.429	930	3,370		4,300
2020	#5 - #6	"	10.000	820	3,190		4,010
2040	#7 - #8	"	8.889	730	3,070		3,800

REINFORCEMENT

ID Code	Component Descriptions	Unit of Meas.	Manhr / Unit	Labor Cost	Material Cost	Equip. Cost	Total Cost
03 - 21011	**WALL REINFORCING, Cont'd...**						**03 - 21011**
2060	#9 - #10	TON	8.000	650	3,070		3,720
3000	Epoxy coated						
3100	#3 - #4	TON	12.308	1,000	2,920		3,920
3110	#5 - #6	"	10.667	870	2,740		3,610
3120	#7 - #8	"	9.412	770	2,650		3,420
3130	#9 - #10	"	8.421	690	2,650		3,340
8980	Masonry wall (horizontal)						
9000	#3 - #4	TON	32.000	2,610	1,980		4,590
9020	#5 - #6	"	26.667	2,180	1,740		3,920
9030	Galvanized						
9040	#3 - #4	TON	32.000	2,610	3,370		5,980
9060	#5 - #6	"	26.667	2,180	3,190		5,370
9180	Masonry wall (vertical)						
9200	#3 - #4	TON	40.000	3,270	1,980		5,250
9220	#5 - #6	"	32.000	2,610	1,740		4,350
9230	Galvanized						
9240	#3 - #4	TON	40.000	3,270	3,370		6,640
9260	#5 - #6	"	32.000	2,610	3,190		5,800
03 - 21016	**PILE CAP REINFORCING**						**03 - 21016**
0980	Pile caps						
1000	#3 - #4	TON	20.000	1,630	1,980		3,610
1020	#5 - #6	"	17.778	1,450	1,740		3,190
1040	#7 - #8	"	16.000	1,310	1,650		2,960
1060	#9 - #10	"	14.545	1,190	1,650		2,840
1080	#11	"	13.333	1,090	1,650		2,740
1090	Galvanized						
1100	#3 - #4	TON	20.000	1,630	3,370		5,000
1120	#5 - #6	"	17.778	1,450	3,190		4,640
1140	#7 - #8	"	16.000	1,310	3,070		4,380
1160	#9 - #10	"	14.545	1,190	3,070		4,260
1180	#11	"	13.333	1,090	3,070		4,160
2000	Epoxy coated						
2100	#3 - #4	TON	22.857	1,870	2,920		4,790
2110	#5 - #6	"	20.000	1,630	2,740		4,370
2120	#7 - #8	"	17.778	1,450	2,650		4,100
2130	#9 - #10	"	16.000	1,310	2,650		3,960
2140	#11	"	14.545	1,190	2,650		3,840

CAST-IN-PLACE CONCRETE

ID Code	Component Descriptions	Unit of Meas.	Manhr / Unit	Labor Cost	Material Cost	Equip. Cost	Total Cost
	Descriptions	**Output**		**Unit Costs**			

03 - 30531 — CONCRETE ADMIXTURES — 03 - 30531

ID Code	Component Descriptions	Unit of Meas.	Manhr / Unit	Labor Cost	Material Cost	Equip. Cost	Total Cost
1000	Concrete admixtures						
1020	Water reducing admixture	GAL					12.00
1040	Set retarder	"					25.75
1060	Air entraining agent	"					11.25

PLACING CONCRETE

03 - 31001 — BEAM CONCRETE — 03 - 31001

ID Code	Component Descriptions	Unit of Meas.	Manhr / Unit	Labor Cost	Material Cost	Equip. Cost	Total Cost
0960	Beams and girders						
0980	2500# or 3000# concrete						
1000	By crane	CY	0.960	60.00	130	42.00	230
1010	By pump	"	0.873	55.00	130	38.25	220
1020	By hand buggy	"	0.800	50.00	130		180
2480	3500# or 4000# concrete						
2500	By crane	CY	0.960	60.00	140	42.00	240
2520	By pump	"	0.873	55.00	140	38.25	230
2540	By hand buggy	"	0.800	50.00	140		190
4000	5000# concrete						
4010	By crane	CY	0.960	60.00	150	42.00	250
4020	By pump	"	0.873	55.00	150	38.25	240
4040	By hand buggy	"	0.800	50.00	150		200
9460	Bond beam, 3000# concrete						
9470	By pump						
9480	8" high						
9500	4" wide	LF	0.019	1.20	0.36	0.84	2.40
9520	6" wide	"	0.022	1.36	0.89	0.95	3.21
9530	8" wide	"	0.024	1.50	1.13	1.05	3.68
9540	10" wide	"	0.027	1.67	1.51	1.16	4.34
9550	12" wide	"	0.030	1.87	2.03	1.31	5.22
9555	16" high						
9560	8" wide	LF	0.030	1.87	2.79	1.31	5.98
9570	10" wide	"	0.034	2.14	3.74	1.50	7.38
9580	12" wide	"	0.040	2.50	4.97	1.75	9.22
9585	By crane						
9590	8" high						
9600	4" wide	LF	0.021	1.30	0.46	0.91	2.68
9620	6" wide	"	0.023	1.43	0.84	1.00	3.27
9640	8" wide	"	0.024	1.50	1.08	1.05	3.63

PLACING CONCRETE

ID Code	Component Descriptions	Unit of Meas.	Manhr / Unit	Labor Cost	Material Cost	Equip. Cost	Total Cost

Descriptions / **Output** / **Unit Costs**

03 - 31001 — BEAM CONCRETE, Cont'd... — 03 - 31001

ID	Desc						
9650	10" wide	LF	0.027	1.67	1.41	1.16	4.24
9660	12" wide	"	0.030	1.87	1.91	1.31	5.10
9665	16" high						
9670	8" wide	LF	0.030	1.87	2.64	1.31	5.83
9680	10" wide	"	0.032	2.00	3.53	1.40	6.93
9690	12" wide	"	0.037	2.31	4.69	1.61	8.61

03 - 31002 — COLUMN CONCRETE — 03 - 31002

ID	Desc						
0980	Columns						
0990	2500# or 3000# concrete						
1000	By crane	CY	0.873	55.00	140	38.25	230
1010	By pump	"	0.800	50.00	140	35.00	230
1980	3500# or 4000# concrete						
2000	By crane	CY	0.873	55.00	140	38.25	230
2020	By pump	"	0.800	50.00	140	35.00	230
3980	5000# concrete						
4010	By crane	CY	0.873	55.00	150	38.25	240
4020	By pump	"	0.800	50.00	150	35.00	240

03 - 31003 — ELEVATED SLAB CONCRETE — 03 - 31003

ID	Desc						
0980	Elevated slab						
0990	2500# or 3000# concrete						
1000	By crane	CY	0.480	30.00	140	21.00	190
1010	By pump	"	0.369	23.25	140	16.25	180
1020	By hand buggy	"	0.800	50.00	140		190
1980	3500# or 4000# concrete						
2000	By crane	CY	0.480	30.00	140	21.00	190
2020	By pump	"	0.369	23.25	140	16.25	180
2040	By hand buggy	"	0.800	50.00	140		190
4000	5000# concrete						
4010	By crane	CY	0.480	30.00	150	21.00	200
4020	By pump	"	0.369	23.25	150	16.25	190
4040	By hand buggy	"	0.800	50.00	150		200
8980	Topping						
8990	2500# or 3000# concrete						
9010	By crane	CY	0.480	30.00	140	21.00	190
9020	By pump	"	0.369	23.25	140	16.25	180
9040	By hand buggy	"	0.800	50.00	140		190
9080	3500# or 4000# concrete						

PLACING CONCRETE

ID Code	Component Descriptions	Unit of Meas.	Manhr / Unit	Labor Cost	Material Cost	Equip. Cost	Total Cost
	Descriptions	**Output**		**Unit Costs**			

03 - 31003 — ELEVATED SLAB CONCRETE, Cont'd... — 03 - 31003

ID Code	Component Descriptions	Unit of Meas.	Manhr / Unit	Labor Cost	Material Cost	Equip. Cost	Total Cost
9100	By crane	CY	0.480	30.00	140	21.00	190
9120	By pump	"	0.369	23.25	140	16.25	180
9140	By hand buggy	"	0.800	50.00	140		190
9180	5000# concrete						
9200	By crane	CY	0.480	30.00	150	21.00	200
9210	By pump	"	0.369	23.25	150	16.25	190
9220	By hand buggy	"	0.800	50.00	150		200

03 - 31004 — EQUIPMENT PAD CONCRETE — 03 - 31004

ID Code	Component Descriptions	Unit of Meas.	Manhr / Unit	Labor Cost	Material Cost	Equip. Cost	Total Cost
0960	Equipment pad						
0980	2500# or 3000# concrete						
1000	By chute	CY	0.267	16.75	140		160
1020	By pump	"	0.686	43.00	140	30.00	210
1040	By crane	"	0.800	50.00	140	35.00	230
1050	3500# or 4000# concrete						
1060	By chute	CY	0.267	16.75	140		160
1080	By pump	"	0.686	43.00	140	30.00	210
1100	By crane	"	0.800	50.00	140	35.00	230
1110	5000# concrete						
1120	By chute	CY	0.267	16.75	150		170
1140	By pump	"	0.686	43.00	150	30.00	220
1160	By crane	"	0.800	50.00	150	35.00	240

03 - 31005 — FOOTING CONCRETE — 03 - 31005

ID Code	Component Descriptions	Unit of Meas.	Manhr / Unit	Labor Cost	Material Cost	Equip. Cost	Total Cost
0980	Continuous footing						
0990	2500# or 3000# concrete						
1000	By chute	CY	0.267	16.75	140		160
1010	By pump	"	0.600	37.50	140	26.25	200
1020	By crane	"	0.686	43.00	140	30.00	210
1980	3500# or 4000# concrete						
2000	By chute	CY	0.267	16.75	140		160
2020	By pump	"	0.600	37.50	140	26.25	200
2040	By crane	"	0.686	43.00	140	30.00	210
4000	5000# concrete						
4010	By chute	CY	0.267	16.75	150		170
4020	By pump	"	0.600	37.50	150	26.25	210
4030	By crane	"	0.686	43.00	150	30.00	220
4980	Spread footing						
5000	2500# or 3000# concrete						

PLACING CONCRETE

ID Code	Component Descriptions	Unit of Meas.	Manhr / Unit	Labor Cost	Material Cost	Equip. Cost	Total Cost
	Descriptions	**Output**		**Unit Costs**			
03 - 31005	**FOOTING CONCRETE, Cont'd...**						**03 - 31005**
5010	Under 5 cy						
5020	By chute	CY	0.267	16.75	130		150
5040	By pump	"	0.640	40.00	130	28.00	200
5060	By crane	"	0.738	46.25	130	32.25	210
6980	Over 5 cy						
7000	By chute	CY	0.200	12.50	130		140
7020	By pump	"	0.565	35.25	130	24.75	190
7040	By crane	"	0.640	40.00	130	28.00	200
7060	3500# or 4000# concrete						
7070	Under 5 c.y.						
7080	By chute	CY	0.267	16.75	140		160
7100	By pump	"	0.640	40.00	140	28.00	210
7120	By crane	"	0.738	46.25	140	32.25	220
7130	Over 5 c.y.						
7140	By chute	CY	0.200	12.50	140		150
7160	By pump	"	0.565	35.25	140	24.75	200
7180	By crane	"	0.640	40.00	140	28.00	210
7200	5000# concrete						
7205	Under 5 c.y.						
7210	By chute	CY	0.267	16.75	150		170
7220	By pump	"	0.640	40.00	150	28.00	220
7230	By crane	"	0.738	46.25	150	32.25	230
7235	Over 5 c.y.						
7240	By chute	CY	0.200	12.50	150		160
7250	By pump	"	0.565	35.25	150	24.75	210
7260	By crane	"	0.640	40.00	150	28.00	220
03 - 31006	**GRADE BEAM CONCRETE**						**03 - 31006**
0960	Grade beam						
0980	2500# or 3000# concrete						
1000	By chute	CY	0.267	16.75	130		150
1020	By crane	"	0.686	43.00	130	30.00	200
1040	By pump	"	0.600	37.50	130	26.25	190
1060	By hand buggy	"	0.800	50.00	130		180
1070	3500# or 4000# concrete						
1080	By chute	CY	0.267	16.75	140		160
1100	By crane	"	0.686	43.00	140	30.00	210
1120	By pump	"	0.600	37.50	140	26.25	200

PLACING CONCRETE

ID Code	Component Descriptions	Unit of Meas.	Manhr / Unit	Labor Cost	Material Cost	Equip. Cost	Total Cost
03 - 31006	**GRADE BEAM CONCRETE, Cont'd...**						**03 - 31006**
1140	By hand buggy	CY	0.800	50.00	140		190
1150	5000# concrete						
1160	By chute	CY	0.267	16.75	150		170
1180	By crane	"	0.686	43.00	150	30.00	220
1190	By pump	"	0.600	37.50	150	26.25	210
1200	By hand buggy	"	0.800	50.00	150		200
03 - 31007	**PILE CAP CONCRETE**						**03 - 31007**
0970	Pile cap						
0980	2500# or 3000 concrete						
1000	By chute	CY	0.267	16.75	140		160
1005	By crane	"	0.800	50.00	140	35.00	230
1010	By pump	"	0.686	43.00	140	30.00	210
1020	By hand buggy	"	0.800	50.00	140		190
1980	3500# or 4000# concrete						
2000	By chute	CY	0.267	16.75	140		160
2010	By crane	"	0.800	50.00	140	35.00	230
2020	By pump	"	0.686	43.00	140	30.00	210
2040	By hand buggy	"	0.800	50.00	140		190
3980	5000# concrete						
4010	By chute	CY	0.267	16.75	150		170
4015	By crane	"	0.800	50.00	150	35.00	240
4020	By pump	"	0.686	43.00	150	30.00	220
4030	By hand buggy	"	0.800	50.00	150		200
03 - 31008	**SLAB / MAT CONCRETE**						**03 - 31008**
0960	Slab on grade						
0980	2500# or 3000# concrete						
1000	By chute	CY	0.200	12.50	140		150
1010	By crane	"	0.400	25.00	140	17.50	180
1020	By pump	"	0.343	21.50	140	15.00	180
1030	By hand buggy	"	0.533	33.50	140		170
1980	3500# or 4000# concrete						
2000	By chute	CY	0.200	12.50	140		150
2020	By crane	"	0.400	25.00	140	17.50	180
2040	By pump	"	0.343	21.50	140	15.00	180
2060	By hand buggy	"	0.533	33.50	140		170
3980	5000# concrete						
4010	By chute	CY	0.200	12.50	150		160

PLACING CONCRETE

ID Code	Component Descriptions	Unit of Meas.	Manhr / Unit	Labor Cost	Material Cost	Equip. Cost	Total Cost
	Descriptions	**Output**		**Unit Costs**			

ID Code	Component Descriptions	Unit of Meas.	Manhr / Unit	Labor Cost	Material Cost	Equip. Cost	Total Cost
03 - 31008	**SLAB / MAT CONCRETE, Cont'd...**						**03 - 31008**
4020	By crane	CY	0.400	25.00	150	17.50	190
4030	By pump	"	0.343	21.50	150	15.00	190
4040	By hand buggy	"	0.533	33.50	150		180
5000	Foundation mat						
5010	2500# or 3000# concrete, over 20 cy						
5020	By chute	CY	0.160	10.00	140		150
5040	By crane	"	0.343	21.50	140	15.00	180
5060	By pump	"	0.300	18.75	140	13.00	170
5080	By hand buggy	"	0.400	25.00	140		160
03 - 31009	**WALL CONCRETE**						**03 - 31009**
0940	Walls						
0960	2500# or 3000# concrete						
0980	To 4'						
1000	By chute	CY	0.229	14.25	140		150
1005	By crane	"	0.800	50.00	140	35.00	230
1010	By pump	"	0.738	46.25	140	32.25	220
1020	To 8'						
1030	By crane	CY	0.873	55.00	140	38.25	230
1040	By pump	"	0.800	50.00	140	35.00	230
1045	To 16'						
1050	By crane	CY	0.960	60.00	140	42.00	240
1060	By pump	"	0.873	55.00	140	38.25	230
1065	Over 16'						
1070	By crane	CY	1.067	67.00	140	46.75	250
1080	By pump	"	0.960	60.00	140	42.00	240
2960	3500# or 4000# concrete						
2980	To 4'						
3000	By chute	CY	0.229	14.25	140		150
3020	By crane	"	0.800	50.00	140	35.00	230
3030	By pump	"	0.738	46.25	140	32.25	220
3060	To 8'						
3080	By crane	CY	0.873	55.00	140	38.25	230
3100	By pump	"	0.800	50.00	140	35.00	230
3105	To 16'						
3110	By crane	CY	0.960	60.00	140	42.00	240
3130	By pump	"	0.873	55.00	140	38.25	230
3135	Over 16'						

PLACING CONCRETE

ID Code	Component Descriptions	Unit of Meas.	Manhr / Unit	Labor Cost	Material Cost	Equip. Cost	Total Cost
		Descriptions	**Output**		**Unit Costs**		
03 - 31009	**WALL CONCRETE, Cont'd...**						**03 - 31009**
3140	By crane	CY	1.067	67.00	140	46.75	250
3150	By pump	"	0.960	60.00	140	42.00	240
3960	5000# concrete						
3980	To 4'						
4010	By chute	CY	0.229	14.25	150		160
4015	By crane	"	0.800	50.00	150	35.00	240
4020	By pump	"	0.738	46.25	150	32.25	230
4030	To 8'						
4050	By crane	CY	0.873	55.00	150	38.25	240
4070	By pump	"	0.800	50.00	150	35.00	240
4100	To 16'						
4110	By crane	CY	0.960	60.00	150	42.00	250
4150	By pump	"	0.873	55.00	150	38.25	240
8480	Filled block (CMU)						
8490	3000# concrete, by pump						
8500	4" wide	SF	0.034	2.14	0.51	1.50	4.15
8510	6" wide	"	0.040	2.50	1.15	1.75	5.40
8520	8" wide	"	0.048	3.00	1.80	2.10	6.90
8530	10" wide	"	0.056	3.53	2.41	2.47	8.41
8540	12" wide	"	0.069	4.29	3.10	3.00	10.50
8560	Pilasters, 3000# concrete	CF	0.960	60.00	7.04	42.00	110
8700	Wall cavity, 2" thick, 3000# concrete	SF	0.032	2.00	1.31	1.40	4.71
03 - 31011	**STAIR CONCRETE**						**03 - 31011**
0960	Stairs						
0980	2500# or 3000# concrete						
1000	By chute	CY	0.267	16.75	140		160
1020	By crane	"	0.800	50.00	140	35.00	230
1030	By pump	"	0.686	43.00	140	30.00	210
1040	By hand buggy	"	0.800	50.00	140		190
2100	3500# or 4000# concrete						
2120	By chute	CY	0.267	16.75	140		160
2140	By crane	"	0.800	50.00	140	35.00	230
2160	By pump	"	0.686	43.00	140	30.00	210
2180	By hand buggy	"	0.800	50.00	140		190
4000	5000# concrete						
4010	By chute	CY	0.267	16.75	150		170
4020	By crane	"	0.800	50.00	150	35.00	240

PLACING CONCRETE

ID Code	Component Descriptions	Unit of Meas.	Manhr / Unit	Labor Cost	Material Cost	Equip. Cost	Total Cost
	Descriptions	**Output**		**Unit Costs**			

03 - 31011   STAIR CONCRETE, Cont'd...   03 - 31011

ID Code	Component Descriptions	Unit of Meas.	Manhr / Unit	Labor Cost	Material Cost	Equip. Cost	Total Cost
4030	By pump	CY	0.686	43.00	150	30.00	220
4040	By hand buggy	"	0.800	50.00	150		200

CONCRETE FINISHING

03 - 35001   CONCRETE FINISHES   03 - 35001

ID Code	Component Descriptions	Unit of Meas.	Manhr / Unit	Labor Cost	Material Cost	Equip. Cost	Total Cost
0980	Floor finishes						
1000	Broom	SF	0.011	0.71			0.71
1020	Screed	"	0.010	0.62			0.62
1040	Darby	"	0.010	0.62			0.62
1060	Steel float	"	0.013	0.83			0.83
2000	Granolithic topping						
2020	1/2" thick	SF	0.036	2.27	0.47		2.74
2040	1" thick	"	0.040	2.50	0.85		3.35
2060	2" thick	"	0.044	2.78	1.03		3.81
4000	Wall finishes						
4020	Burlap rub, with cement paste	SF	0.013	0.83	0.12		0.95
4040	Float finish	"	0.020	1.25	0.12		1.37
4060	Etch with acid	"	0.013	0.83	0.40		1.23
4070	Sandblast						
4080	Minimum	SF	0.016	1.00	0.14	0.34	1.48
4100	Maximum	"	0.016	1.00	0.51	0.34	1.85
4110	Bush hammer						
4120	Green concrete	SF	0.040	2.50			2.50
4140	Cured concrete	"	0.062	3.85			3.85
4160	Break ties and patch holes	"	0.016	1.00			1.00
4170	Carborundum						
4180	Dry rub	SF	0.027	1.67			1.67
4200	Wet rub	"	0.040	2.50			2.50
5000	Floor hardeners						
5010	Metallic						
5020	Light service	SF	0.010	0.62	0.43		1.05
5040	Heavy service	"	0.013	0.83	1.30		2.13
5050	Non-metallic						
5060	Light service	SF	0.010	0.62	0.21		0.83
5080	Heavy service	"	0.013	0.83	0.90		1.73
5200	Rusticated concrete finish						
5220	Beveled edge	LF	0.044	2.78	0.42		3.20

CONCRETE FINISHING

ID Code	Component Descriptions	Unit of Meas.	Manhr / Unit	Labor Cost	Material Cost	Equip. Cost	Total Cost
	Descriptions	**Output**		**Unit Costs**			

03 - 35001 — CONCRETE FINISHES, Cont'd... — 03 - 35001

ID Code	Component Descriptions	Unit of Meas.	Manhr / Unit	Labor Cost	Material Cost	Equip. Cost	Total Cost
5240	Square edge	LF	0.057	3.58	0.59		4.17
5400	Solid board concrete finish						
5420	Standard	SF	0.067	4.17	1.07		5.24
5440	Rustic	"	0.080	5.01	0.99		6.00

SPECIALTY PLACED CONCRETE

03 - 37190 — PNEUMATIC CONCRETE — 03 - 37190

ID Code	Component Descriptions	Unit of Meas.	Manhr / Unit	Labor Cost	Material Cost	Equip. Cost	Total Cost
0100	Pneumatic applied concrete (gunite)						
1035	2" thick	SF	0.030	1.86	6.33	1.66	9.85
1040	3" thick	"	0.040	2.48	7.77	2.21	12.50
1060	4" thick	"	0.048	2.98	9.48	2.66	15.00
1980	Finish surface						
2000	Minimum	SF	0.040	3.20			3.20
2020	Maximum	"	0.080	6.40			6.40

CONCRETE CURING

03 - 39001 — CURING CONCRETE — 03 - 39001

ID Code	Component Descriptions	Unit of Meas.	Manhr / Unit	Labor Cost	Material Cost	Equip. Cost	Total Cost
1000	Sprayed membrane						
1010	Slabs	SF	0.002	0.10	0.06		0.16
1020	Walls	"	0.002	0.12	0.08		0.20
1025	Curing paper						
1030	Slabs	SF	0.002	0.13	0.08		0.21
2000	Walls	"	0.002	0.14	0.08		0.22
2010	Burlap						
2020	7.5 oz.	SF	0.003	0.16	0.07		0.23
2500	12 oz.	"	0.003	0.17	0.10		0.27

PRECAST CONCRETE

03 - 41001 — PRECAST BEAMS — 03 - 41001

ID Code	Component Descriptions	Unit of Meas.	Manhr / Unit	Labor Cost	Material Cost	Equip. Cost	Total Cost
0060	Prestressed, double tee, 24" deep, 8' wide						
0080	35' span						
0100	115 psf	SF	0.008	0.64	13.50	0.76	15.00
0120	140 psf	"	0.008	0.64	14.25	0.76	15.75
0130	40' span						
0140	80 psf	SF	0.009	0.68	13.00	0.82	14.50

PRECAST CONCRETE

ID Code	Component Descriptions	Unit of Meas.	Manhr / Unit	Labor Cost	Material Cost	Equip. Cost	Total Cost
	Descriptions	**Output**		**Unit Costs**			

03 - 41001   PRECAST BEAMS, Cont'd...   03 - 41001

ID Code	Component Descriptions	Unit of Meas.	Manhr / Unit	Labor Cost	Material Cost	Equip. Cost	Total Cost
0180	143 psf	SF	0.009	0.68	13.50	0.82	15.00
0185	45' span						
0190	50 psf	SF	0.007	0.59	12.25	0.70	13.50
0200	70 psf	"	0.007	0.59	13.00	0.70	14.25
0220	100 psf	"	0.007	0.59	13.25	0.70	14.50
0230	130 psf	"	0.007	0.59	15.00	0.70	16.25
0235	50' span						
0240	75 psf	SF	0.007	0.53	12.25	0.63	13.50
0250	100 psf	"	0.007	0.53	13.25	0.63	14.50
3000	Precast beams, girders and joists						
3020	1000 lb/lf live load						
3040	10' span	LF	0.160	12.75	110	15.25	140
3060	20' span	"	0.096	7.68	120	9.20	140
3080	30' span	"	0.080	6.40	150	7.66	160
3200	3000 lb/lf live load						
3220	10' span	LF	0.160	12.75	120	15.25	150
3240	20' span	"	0.096	7.68	130	9.20	150
3260	30' span	"	0.080	6.40	180	7.66	190
3300	5000 lb/lf live load						
3320	10' span	LF	0.160	12.75	120	15.25	150
3340	20' span	"	0.096	7.68	160	9.20	180
3360	30' span	"	0.080	6.40	200	7.66	210

03 - 41002   PRECAST COLUMNS   03 - 41002

ID Code	Component Descriptions	Unit of Meas.	Manhr / Unit	Labor Cost	Material Cost	Equip. Cost	Total Cost
0060	Prestressed concrete columns						
0080	10" x 10"						
0100	10' long	EA	0.960	77.00	320	92.00	490
0120	15' long	"	1.000	80.00	490	96.00	670
0140	20' long	"	1.067	85.00	650	100	840
0160	25' long	"	1.143	91.00	840	110	1,040
0180	30' long	"	1.200	96.00	1,000	110	1,210
0220	12" x 12"						
0240	20' long	EA	1.200	96.00	890	110	1,100
0300	25' long	"	1.297	100	1,090	120	1,320
0320	30' long	"	1.371	110	1,380	130	1,620
0980	16" x 16"						
1000	20' long	EA	1.200	96.00	1,380	110	1,590
1002	25' long	"	1.297	100	2,040	120	2,270

PRECAST CONCRETE

ID Code	Component Descriptions	Unit of Meas.	Manhr / Unit	Labor Cost	Material Cost	Equip. Cost	Total Cost
03 - 41002	**PRECAST COLUMNS, Cont'd...**						**03 - 41002**
1003	30' long	EA	1.371	110	2,410	130	2,650
1010	20" x 20"						
1020	20' long	EA	1.263	100	2,480	120	2,700
1022	25' long	"	1.333	110	3,390	130	3,620
1023	30' long	"	1.412	110	3,890	140	4,140
1030	24" x 24"						
1040	20' long	EA	1.333	110	3,800	130	4,030
1042	25' long	"	1.412	110	4,620	140	4,870
1043	30' long	"	1.500	120	5,700	140	5,960
1060	28" x 28"						
1080	20' long	EA	1.500	120	5,160	140	5,420
1082	25' long	"	1.600	130	6,240	150	6,520
1083	30' long	"	1.714	140	7,740	160	8,040
1089	32" x 32"						
1100	20' long	EA	1.600	130	6,510	150	6,790
1102	25' long	"	1.714	140	8,420	160	8,720
1103	30' long	"	1.846	150	9,640	180	9,960
1110	36" x 36"						
1120	20' long	EA	1.714	140	8,140	160	8,440
1122	25' long	"	1.846	150	10,180	180	10,500
1123	30' long	"	2.000	160	12,220	190	12,570
03 - 41003	**PRECAST SLABS**						**03 - 41003**
0040	Prestressed flat slab						
0060	6" thick, 4' wide						
0080	20' span						
0100	80 psf	SF	0.020	1.60	19.75	1.91	23.25
0110	110 psf	"	0.020	1.60	19.75	1.91	23.25
0120	25' span						
0130	80 psf	SF	0.019	1.53	20.25	1.84	23.50
0940	Cored slab						
0960	6" thick, 4' wide						
0980	20' span						
2000	80 psf	SF	0.020	1.60	10.50	1.91	14.00
2030	100 psf	"	0.020	1.60	10.75	1.91	14.25
2050	130 psf	"	0.020	1.60	10.75	1.91	14.25
2060	8" thick, 4' wide						
2070	25' span						

PRECAST CONCRETE

	Descriptions	Output		Unit Costs			
ID Code	Component Descriptions	Unit of Meas.	Manhr / Unit	Labor Cost	Material Cost	Equip. Cost	Total Cost
03 - 41003	**PRECAST SLABS, Cont'd...**						**03 - 41003**
2090	70 psf	SF	0.019	1.53	10.25	1.84	13.50
2100	125 psf	"	0.019	1.53	11.00	1.84	14.25
2110	170 psf	"	0.019	1.53	11.00	1.84	14.25
2115	30' span						
2120	70 psf	SF	0.016	1.28	10.25	1.53	13.00
2140	90 psf	"	0.016	1.28	10.75	1.53	13.50
2170	35' span						
2180	70 psf	SF	0.015	1.20	10.75	1.43	13.50
2190	10" thick, 4' wide						
2195	30' span						
2200	75 psf	SF	0.016	1.28	10.75	1.53	13.50
2220	100 psf	"	0.016	1.28	11.00	1.53	13.75
2240	130 psf	"	0.016	1.28	11.25	1.53	14.00
2260	35' span						
2280	60 psf	SF	0.015	1.20	11.00	1.43	13.75
2290	80 psf	"	0.015	1.20	11.25	1.43	14.00
2300	120 psf	"	0.015	1.20	11.75	1.43	14.50
2310	40' span						
2320	65 psf	SF	0.012	0.96	12.00	1.15	14.00
7000	Slabs, roof and floor members, 4' wide						
7020	6" thick, 25' span	SF	0.019	1.53	9.49	1.84	12.75
7040	8" thick, 30' span	"	0.015	1.16	10.75	1.39	13.25
7060	10" thick, 40' span	"	0.013	1.03	13.25	1.24	15.50
7100	Tee members						
7120	Multiple tee, roof and floor						
7140	Minimum	SF	0.012	0.96	12.25	1.15	14.25
7160	Maximum	"	0.024	1.92	15.50	2.30	19.75
7200	Double tee wall member						
7220	Minimum	SF	0.014	1.09	11.25	1.31	13.75
7240	Maximum	"	0.027	2.13	14.25	2.55	19.00
7280	Single tee						
7290	Short span, roof members						
7300	Minimum	SF	0.015	1.16	12.75	1.39	15.25
7320	Maximum	"	0.030	2.40	15.50	2.87	20.75
7400	Long span, roof members						
7420	Minimum	SF	0.012	0.96	16.00	1.15	18.00
7440	Maximum	"	0.024	1.92	19.25	2.30	23.50

PRECAST ARCHITECTURAL CONCRETE

ID Code	Component Descriptions	Unit of Meas.	Manhr / Unit	Labor Cost	Material Cost	Equip. Cost	Total Cost
		Output		Unit Costs			

03 - 45001 PRECAST WALLS 03 - 45001

ID Code	Component Descriptions	Unit of Meas.	Manhr / Unit	Labor Cost	Material Cost	Equip. Cost	Total Cost
0060	Wall panel, 8' x 20'						
0070	Gray cement						
0080	Liner finish						
0100	4" wall	SF	0.014	1.09	15.00	1.31	17.50
0120	5" wall	"	0.014	1.12	16.25	1.35	18.75
0140	6" wall	"	0.015	1.16	18.75	1.39	21.25
0160	8" wall	"	0.015	1.20	18.75	1.43	21.50
0180	Sandblast finish						
0200	4" wall	SF	0.014	1.09	17.50	1.31	20.00
0210	5" wall	"	0.014	1.12	19.25	1.35	21.75
0220	6" wall	"	0.015	1.16	21.00	1.39	23.50
0230	8" wall	"	0.015	1.20	22.00	1.43	24.75
0280	White cement						
0290	Liner finish						
0300	4" wall	SF	0.014	1.09	18.50	1.31	21.00
0310	5" wall	"	0.014	1.12	19.50	1.35	22.00
0320	6" wall	"	0.015	1.16	21.50	1.39	24.00
0330	8" wall	"	0.015	1.20	22.75	1.43	25.50
2000	Sandblast finish						
2010	4" wall	SF	0.014	1.09	19.75	1.31	22.25
2011	5" wall	"	0.014	1.12	21.00	1.35	23.50
2012	6" wall	"	0.015	1.16	21.50	1.39	24.00
2013	8" wall	"	0.015	1.20	23.75	1.43	26.50
2015	Double tee wall panel, 24" deep						
2018	Gray cement						
2020	Liner finish	SF	0.016	1.28	10.75	1.53	13.50
2030	Sandblast finish	"	0.016	1.28	13.25	1.53	16.00
2035	White cement						
2040	Form liner finish	SF	0.016	1.28	15.00	1.53	17.75
2050	Sandblast finish	"	0.016	1.28	19.25	1.53	22.00
3000	Partition panels						
3020	4" wall	SF	0.016	1.28	16.00	1.53	18.75
3040	5" wall	"	0.016	1.28	17.25	1.53	20.00
3060	6" wall	"	0.016	1.28	19.00	1.53	21.75
3080	8" wall	"	0.016	1.28	20.75	1.53	23.50
3200	Cladding panels						
3220	4" wall	SF	0.017	1.37	15.75	1.64	18.75
3240	5" wall	"	0.017	1.37	17.25	1.64	20.25

PRECAST ARCHITECTURAL CONCRETE

ID Code	Component Descriptions	Unit of Meas.	Manhr / Unit	Labor Cost	Material Cost	Equip. Cost	Total Cost
	Descriptions	**Output**		**Unit Costs**			

03 - 45001   **PRECAST WALLS, Cont'd...**   **03 - 45001**

ID Code	Component Descriptions	Unit of Meas.	Manhr / Unit	Labor Cost	Material Cost	Equip. Cost	Total Cost
3260	6" wall	SF	0.017	1.37	19.25	1.64	22.25
3280	8" wall	"	0.017	1.37	20.75	1.64	23.75
3400	Sandwich panel, 2.5" cladding panel, 2" insulation						
3440	5" wall	SF	0.017	1.37	23.50	1.64	26.50
3460	6" wall	"	0.017	1.37	24.50	1.64	27.50
3480	8" wall	"	0.017	1.37	26.00	1.64	29.00

PRECAST CONCRETE SPECIALTIES

03 - 48001   **PRECAST SPECIALTIES**   **03 - 48001**

ID Code	Component Descriptions	Unit of Meas.	Manhr / Unit	Labor Cost	Material Cost	Equip. Cost	Total Cost
0980	Precast concrete, coping, 4' to 8' long						
1000	12" wide	LF	0.060	3.72	10.75	3.32	17.75
1010	10" wide	"	0.069	4.26	9.52	3.80	17.50
1520	Splash block, 30"x12"x4"	EA	0.400	24.75	16.25	22.25	63.00
2000	Stair unit, per riser	"	0.400	24.75	100	22.25	150
4000	Sun screen and trellis, 8' long, 12" high						
4020	4" thick blades	EA	0.300	18.75	110	16.50	150
4040	5" thick blades	"	0.300	18.75	140	16.50	180
4060	6" thick blades	"	0.320	20.00	170	17.75	210
4080	8" thick blades	"	0.320	20.00	230	17.75	270
8000	Bearing pads for precast members, 2" wide strips						
8040	1/8" thick	LF	0.003	0.20	0.38		0.58
8060	1/4" thick	"	0.003	0.20	0.50		0.70
8080	1/2" thick	"	0.003	0.20	0.57		0.77
8100	3/4" thick	"	0.004	0.22	1.12		1.34
8120	1" thick	"	0.004	0.25	1.16		1.41
8140	1-1/2" thick	"	0.004	0.25	1.48		1.73

CEMENTITIOUS TOPPINGS

03 - 53001   **CONCRETE TOPPINGS**   **03 - 53001**

ID Code	Component Descriptions	Unit of Meas.	Manhr / Unit	Labor Cost	Material Cost	Equip. Cost	Total Cost
1000	Gypsum fill						
1020	2" thick	SF	0.005	0.31	2.11	0.21	2.63
1040	2-1/2" thick	"	0.005	0.31	2.40	0.22	2.93
1060	3" thick	"	0.005	0.32	2.96	0.22	3.51
1080	3-1/2" thick	"	0.005	0.33	3.38	0.23	3.94
1100	4" thick	"	0.006	0.37	3.95	0.26	4.58
2000	Formboard						

CEMENTITIOUS TOPPINGS

ID Code	Component Descriptions	Unit of Meas.	Manhr / Unit	Labor Cost	Material Cost	Equip. Cost	Total Cost
03 - 53001	**CONCRETE TOPPINGS, Cont'd...**						**03 - 53001**
2020	Mineral fiber board						
2040	1" thick	SF	0.020	1.25	1.89		3.14
2060	1-1/2" thick	"	0.023	1.43	4.96		6.39
2070	Cement fiber board						
2080	1" thick	SF	0.027	1.67	1.47		3.14
2100	1-1/2" thick	"	0.031	1.92	1.89		3.81
2110	Glass fiber board						
2120	1" thick	SF	0.020	1.25	2.32		3.57
2140	1-1/2" thick	"	0.023	1.43	3.15		4.58
4000	Poured deck						
4010	Vermiculite or perlite						
4020	1 to 4 mix	CY	0.800	50.00	200	35.00	290
4040	1 to 6 mix	"	0.738	46.25	180	32.25	260
4050	Vermiculite or perlite						
4060	2" thick						
4080	1 to 4 mix	SF	0.005	0.31	1.89	0.22	2.42
4100	1 to 6 mix	"	0.005	0.28	1.38	0.20	1.86
4200	3" thick						
4220	1 to 4 mix	SF	0.007	0.46	2.58	0.32	3.36
4240	1 to 6 mix	"	0.007	0.42	2.04	0.30	2.76
6000	Concrete plank, lightweight						
6020	2" thick	SF	0.024	1.92	10.25	2.30	14.50
6040	2-1/2" thick	"	0.024	1.92	10.50	2.30	14.75
6080	3-1/2" thick	"	0.027	2.13	11.00	2.55	15.75
6100	4" thick	"	0.027	2.13	11.25	2.55	16.00
6500	Channel slab, lightweight, straight						
6520	2-3/4" thick	SF	0.024	1.92	8.28	2.30	12.50
6540	3-1/2" thick	"	0.024	1.92	8.52	2.30	12.75
6560	3-3/4" thick	"	0.024	1.92	9.20	2.30	13.50
6580	4-3/4" thick	"	0.027	2.13	11.75	2.55	16.50
7000	Gypsum plank						
7020	2" thick	SF	0.024	1.92	3.83	2.30	8.05
7040	3" thick	"	0.024	1.92	4.02	2.30	8.24
8000	Cement fiber, T and G planks						
8020	1" thick	SF	0.022	1.74	2.11	2.09	5.94
8040	1-1/2" thick	"	0.022	1.74	2.24	2.09	6.07
8060	2" thick	"	0.024	1.92	2.68	2.30	6.90
8080	2-1/2" thick	"	0.024	1.92	2.84	2.30	7.06

CEMENTITIOUS TOPPINGS

ID Code	Component Descriptions	Unit of Meas.	Manhr / Unit	Labor Cost	Material Cost	Equip. Cost	Total Cost
	Descriptions	**Output**		**Unit Costs**			
03 - 53001	**CONCRETE TOPPINGS, Cont'd...**						**03 - 53001**
8100	3" thick	SF	0.024	1.92	3.69	2.30	7.91
8120	3-1/2" thick	"	0.027	2.13	4.26	2.55	8.94
8140	4" thick	"	0.027	2.13	4.68	2.55	9.36

GROUT

ID Code	Component Descriptions	Unit of Meas.	Manhr / Unit	Labor Cost	Material Cost	Equip. Cost	Total Cost
03 - 61001	**GROUTING**						**03 - 61001**
1000	Grouting for bases						
1010	Nonshrink						
1020	Metallic grout						
1040	1" deep	SF	0.160	10.00	8.58	3.40	22.00
1060	2" deep	"	0.178	11.25	16.25	3.77	31.25
2000	Non-metallic grout						
2020	1" deep	SF	0.160	10.00	6.46	3.40	20.00
2040	2" deep	"	0.178	11.25	12.25	3.77	27.25
2480	Fluid type						
2500	Non-metallic						
2520	1" deep	SF	0.160	10.00	6.61	3.40	20.00
2540	2" deep	"	0.178	11.25	11.75	3.77	26.75
3000	Grouting for joints						
3020	Portland cement grout (1 cement to 3 sand)						
3040	1/2" joint thickness						
3080	6" wide joints	LF	0.027	1.67	0.22	0.56	2.45
3100	8" wide joints	"	0.032	2.00	0.24	0.68	2.92
3200	1" joint thickness						
3220	4" wide joints	LF	0.025	1.56	0.24	0.53	2.33
3240	6" wide joints	"	0.028	1.72	0.40	0.58	2.71
3260	8" wide joints	"	0.033	2.08	0.49	0.70	3.28
3400	Nonshrink, nonmetallic grout						
3420	1/2" joint thickness						
3440	4" wide joint	LF	0.023	1.43	1.16	0.48	3.07
3460	6" wide joint	"	0.027	1.67	1.53	0.56	3.76
3480	8" wide joint	"	0.032	2.00	2.00	0.68	4.68
3600	1" joint thickness						
3620	4" wide joint	LF	0.025	1.56	2.00	0.53	4.09
3640	6" wide joint	"	0.028	1.72	3.02	0.58	5.33
3660	8" wide joint	"	0.033	2.08	4.09	0.70	6.88

CONCRETE BORING

ID Code	Component Descriptions	Unit of Meas.	Manhr / Unit	Labor Cost	Material Cost	Equip. Cost	Total Cost
	Descriptions	**Output**		**Unit Costs**			
03 - 82131	**CORE DRILLING**						**03 - 82131**
0100	Concrete						
0110	6" thick						
0120	3" dia.	EA	0.571	35.75		12.25	48.00
0140	4" dia.	"	0.667	41.75		14.25	56.00
0160	6" dia.	"	0.800	50.00		17.00	67.00
0180	8" dia.	"	1.333	84.00		28.25	110
0300	8" thick						
0320	3" dia.	EA	0.800	50.00		17.00	67.00
0360	4" dia.	"	1.000	63.00		21.25	84.00
0380	6" dia.	"	1.143	72.00		24.25	96.00
0400	8" dia.	"	1.600	100		34.00	130
0420	10" thick						
0440	3" dia.	EA	1.000	63.00		21.25	84.00
0460	4" dia.	"	1.143	72.00		24.25	96.00
0480	6" dia.	"	1.333	84.00		28.25	110
0490	8" dia.	"	2.000	130		42.50	170
0520	12" thick						
0540	3" dia.	EA	1.333	84.00		28.25	110
0560	4" dia.	"	1.600	100		34.00	130
0580	6" dia.	"	2.000	130		42.50	170
0600	8" dia.	"	2.667	170		57.00	220

DIVISION 04
MASONRY

MASONRY RESTORATION

ID Code	Descriptions — Component Descriptions	Output — Unit of Meas.	Output — Manhr / Unit	Unit Costs — Labor Cost	Unit Costs — Material Cost	Unit Costs — Equip. Cost	Unit Costs — Total Cost
04 - 01201	**RESTORATION AND CLEANING**						**04 - 01201**
1080	Masonry cleaning						
1090	Washing brick						
1120	Smooth surface	SF	0.013	1.01	0.25		1.26
1130	Rough surface	"	0.018	1.35	0.35		1.70
1140	Steam clean masonry						
1150	Smooth face						
1220	Minimum	SF	0.010	0.62	0.53	0.21	1.36
1240	Maximum	"	0.015	0.91	0.86	0.30	2.08
1250	Rough face						
1260	Minimum	SF	0.013	0.83	0.78	0.28	1.89
1270	Maximum	"	0.020	1.25	1.15	0.42	2.82
1300	Sandblast masonry						
1320	Minimum	SF	0.016	1.00	0.48	0.34	1.82
1340	Maximum	"	0.027	1.67	0.72	0.56	2.95
1360	Pointing masonry						
1420	Brick	SF	0.032	2.44	1.30		3.74
1430	Concrete block	"	0.023	1.74	0.58		2.32
1450	Cut and repoint						
1470	Brick						
2020	Minimum	SF	0.040	3.05	0.44		3.49
2030	Maximum	"	0.080	6.10	0.77		6.87
2040	Stone work	LF	0.062	4.69	1.18		5.87
2060	Cut and recaulk						
3020	Oil base caulks	LF	0.053	4.06	1.59		5.65
3030	Butyl caulks	"	0.053	4.06	1.40		5.46
3040	Polysulfides and acrylics	"	0.053	4.06	2.71		6.77
3050	Silicones	"	0.053	4.06	3.17		7.23
4000	Cement and sand grout on walls, to 1/8" thick						
4020	Minimum	SF	0.032	2.44	0.78		3.22
4040	Maximum	"	0.040	3.05	1.98		5.03
8010	Brick removal and replacement						
8020	Minimum	EA	0.100	7.62	0.82		8.44
8040	Average	"	0.133	10.25	1.07		11.25
8060	Maximum	"	0.400	30.50	2.17		32.75

MORTAR, GROUT AND ACCESSORIES

ID Code	Component Descriptions	Unit of Meas.	Manhr / Unit	Labor Cost	Material Cost	Equip. Cost	Total Cost
04 - 05161	**MASONRY GROUT**						**04 - 05161**
0100	Grout, non shrink, non-metallic, trowelable	CF	0.016	0.99	5.94	0.88	7.82
2110	Grout door frame, hollow metal						
2120	Single	EA	0.600	37.25	14.50	33.25	86.00
2140	Double	"	0.632	39.25	20.50	35.00	95.00
2980	Grout-filled concrete block (CMU)						
3000	4" wide	SF	0.020	1.24	0.43	1.10	2.78
3020	6" wide	"	0.022	1.35	1.12	1.20	3.68
3040	8" wide	"	0.024	1.49	1.65	1.33	4.47
3060	12" wide	"	0.025	1.57	2.71	1.40	5.68
3070	Grout-filled individual CMU cells						
3090	4" wide	LF	0.012	0.74	0.36	0.66	1.77
3100	6" wide	"	0.012	0.74	0.48	0.66	1.89
3120	8" wide	"	0.012	0.74	0.64	0.66	2.05
3140	10" wide	"	0.014	0.85	0.80	0.76	2.41
3160	12" wide	"	0.014	0.85	0.97	0.76	2.58
4000	Bond beams or lintels, 8" deep						
4010	6" thick	LF	0.022	1.36	0.97	0.95	3.29
4020	8" thick	"	0.024	1.50	1.28	1.05	3.83
4040	10" thick	"	0.027	1.67	1.61	1.16	4.44
4060	12" thick	"	0.030	1.87	1.93	1.31	5.12
5000	Cavity walls						
5020	2" thick	SF	0.032	2.00	1.07	1.40	4.47
5040	3" thick	"	0.032	2.00	1.61	1.40	5.01
5060	4" thick	"	0.034	2.14	2.14	1.50	5.78
5080	6" thick	"	0.040	2.50	3.21	1.75	7.46
04 - 05231	**MASONRY ACCESSORIES**						**04 - 05231**
0200	Foundation vents	EA	0.320	24.50	26.25		51.00
1010	Bar reinforcing						
1015	Horizontal						
1020	#3 - #4	LB	0.032	2.44	0.60		3.04
1030	#5 - #6	"	0.027	2.03	0.60		2.63
1035	Vertical						
1040	#3 - #4	LB	0.040	3.05	0.60		3.65
1050	#5 - #6	"	0.032	2.44	0.60		3.04
1100	Horizontal joint reinforcing						
1105	Truss type						
1110	4" wide, 6" wall	LF	0.003	0.24	0.20		0.44

MORTAR, GROUT AND ACCESSORIES

ID Code	Component Descriptions	Unit of Meas.	Manhr / Unit	Labor Cost	Material Cost	Equip. Cost	Total Cost
	Descriptions	**Output**		**Unit Costs**			
04 - 05231	**MASONRY ACCESSORIES, Cont'd...**						**04 - 05231**
1120	6" wide, 8" wall	LF	0.003	0.25	0.20		0.45
1130	8" wide, 10" wall	"	0.003	0.26	0.25		0.51
1140	10" wide, 12" wall	"	0.004	0.27	0.25		0.52
1150	12" wide, 14" wall	"	0.004	0.29	0.30		0.59
1155	Ladder type						
1160	4" wide, 6" wall	LF	0.003	0.24	0.15		0.39
1170	6" wide, 8" wall	"	0.003	0.25	0.17		0.42
1180	8" wide, 10" wall	"	0.003	0.26	0.18		0.44
1190	10" wide, 12" wall	"	0.003	0.26	0.22		0.48
2000	Rectangular wall ties						
2005	3/16" dia., galvanized						
2010	2" x 6"	EA	0.013	1.01	0.38		1.39
2020	2" x 8"	"	0.013	1.01	0.40		1.41
2040	2" x 10"	"	0.013	1.01	0.47		1.48
2050	2" x 12"	"	0.013	1.01	0.53		1.54
2060	4" x 6"	"	0.016	1.22	0.44		1.66
2070	4" x 8"	"	0.016	1.22	0.49		1.71
2080	4" x 10"	"	0.016	1.22	0.63		1.85
2090	4" x 12"	"	0.016	1.22	0.73		1.95
2095	1/4" dia., galvanized						
2100	2" x 6"	EA	0.013	1.01	0.71		1.72
2110	2" x 8"	"	0.013	1.01	0.80		1.81
2120	2" x 10"	"	0.013	1.01	0.91		1.92
2130	2" x 12"	"	0.013	1.01	1.04		2.05
2140	4" x 6"	"	0.016	1.22	0.82		2.04
2150	4" x 8"	"	0.016	1.22	0.91		2.13
2160	4" x 10"	"	0.016	1.22	1.04		2.26
2170	4" x 12"	"	0.016	1.22	1.08		2.30
2200	"Z" type wall ties, galvanized						
2215	6" long						
2220	1/8" dia.	EA	0.013	1.01	0.34		1.35
2230	3/16" dia.	"	0.013	1.01	0.36		1.37
2240	1/4" dia.	"	0.013	1.01	0.38		1.39
2245	8" long						
2250	1/8" dia.	EA	0.013	1.01	0.36		1.37
2260	3/16" dia.	"	0.013	1.01	0.38		1.39
2270	1/4" dia.	"	0.013	1.01	0.40		1.41
2275	10" long						

MORTAR, GROUT AND ACCESSORIES

ID Code	Component Descriptions	Unit of Meas.	Manhr / Unit	Labor Cost	Material Cost	Equip. Cost	Total Cost
	Descriptions	**Output**		**Unit Costs**			
04 - 05231	**MASONRY ACCESSORIES, Cont'd...**						**04 - 05231**
2280	1/8" dia.	EA	0.013	1.01	0.38		1.39
2290	3/16" dia.	"	0.013	1.01	0.44		1.45
2300	1/4" dia.	"	0.013	1.01	0.49		1.50
3000	Dovetail anchor slots						
3015	Galvanized steel, filled						
3020	24 ga.	LF	0.020	1.52	1.17		2.69
3040	20 ga.	"	0.020	1.52	2.46		3.98
3060	16 oz. copper, foam filled	"	0.020	1.52	3.53		5.05
3100	Dovetail anchors						
3115	16 ga.						
3120	3-1/2" long	EA	0.013	1.01	0.39		1.40
3140	5-1/2" long	"	0.013	1.01	0.48		1.49
3150	12 ga.						
3160	3-1/2" long	EA	0.013	1.01	0.52		1.53
3180	5-1/2" long	"	0.013	1.01	0.86		1.87
3200	Dovetail, triangular galvanized ties, 12 ga.						
3220	3" x 3"	EA	0.013	1.01	0.88		1.89
3240	5" x 5"	"	0.013	1.01	0.95		1.96
3260	7" x 7"	"	0.013	1.01	1.07		2.08
3280	7" x 9"	"	0.013	1.01	1.14		2.15
3400	Brick anchors						
3420	Corrugated, 3-1/2" long						
3440	16 ga.	EA	0.013	1.01	0.57		1.58
3460	12 ga.	"	0.013	1.01	0.66		1.67
3500	Non-corrugated, 3-1/2" long						
3520	16 ga.	EA	0.013	1.01	0.47		1.48
3540	12 ga.	"	0.013	1.01	0.85		1.86
3580	Cavity wall anchors, corrugated, galvanized						
3600	5" long						
3620	16 ga.	EA	0.013	1.01	0.95		1.96
3640	12 ga.	"	0.013	1.01	1.43		2.44
3660	7" long						
3680	28 ga.	EA	0.013	1.01	1.05		2.06
3700	24 ga.	"	0.013	1.01	1.33		2.34
3720	22 ga.	"	0.013	1.01	1.36		2.37
3740	16 ga.	"	0.013	1.01	1.55		2.56
3800	Mesh ties, 16 ga., 3" wide						
3820	8" long	EA	0.013	1.01	1.28		2.29

MORTAR, GROUT AND ACCESSORIES

ID Code	Component Descriptions	Unit of Meas.	Manhr / Unit	Labor Cost	Material Cost	Equip. Cost	Total Cost
	Descriptions	**Output**		**Unit Costs**			

04 - 05231 — MASONRY ACCESSORIES, Cont'd... — 04 - 05231

ID Code	Component Descriptions	Unit of Meas.	Manhr / Unit	Labor Cost	Material Cost	Equip. Cost	Total Cost
3840	12" long	EA	0.013	1.01	1.43		2.44
3860	20" long	"	0.013	1.01	1.96		2.97
3900	24" long	"	0.013	1.01	2.16		3.17

04 - 05232 — MASONRY CONTROL JOINTS — 04 - 05232

ID Code	Component Descriptions	Unit of Meas.	Manhr / Unit	Labor Cost	Material Cost	Equip. Cost	Total Cost
1000	Control joint, cross shaped PVC	LF	0.020	1.52	2.38		3.90
1010	Closed cell joint filler						
1020	1/2"	LF	0.020	1.52	0.41		1.93
1040	3/4"	"	0.020	1.52	0.85		2.37
1070	Rubber, for						
1080	4" wall	LF	0.020	1.52	2.75		4.27
1090	6" wall	"	0.021	1.60	3.40		5.00
1100	8" wall	"	0.022	1.69	4.10		5.79
1110	PVC, for						
1120	4" wall	LF	0.020	1.52	1.43		2.95
1140	6" wall	"	0.021	1.60	2.41		4.01
1160	8" wall	"	0.022	1.69	3.65		5.34

04 - 05235 — MASONRY FLASHING — 04 - 05235

ID Code	Component Descriptions	Unit of Meas.	Manhr / Unit	Labor Cost	Material Cost	Equip. Cost	Total Cost
0080	Through-wall flashing						
1000	5 oz. coated copper	SF	0.067	5.08	4.18		9.26
1020	0.030" elastomeric	"	0.053	4.06	1.32		5.38

UNIT MASONRY

04 - 21131 — BRICK MASONRY — 04 - 21131

ID Code	Component Descriptions	Unit of Meas.	Manhr / Unit	Labor Cost	Material Cost	Equip. Cost	Total Cost
0100	Standard size brick, running bond						
1000	Face brick, red (6.4/sf)						
1020	Veneer	SF	0.133	10.25	5.66		16.00
1030	Cavity wall	"	0.114	8.71	5.66		14.25
1040	9" solid wall	"	0.229	17.50	11.25		28.75
1200	Common brick (6.4/sf)						
1210	Select common for veneers	SF	0.133	10.25	3.69		14.00
1215	Back-up						
1220	4" thick	SF	0.100	7.62	3.32		11.00
1230	8" thick	"	0.160	12.25	6.65		19.00
1235	Firewall						
1240	12" thick	SF	0.267	20.25	10.75		31.00
1250	16" thick	"	0.364	27.75	14.25		42.00

UNIT MASONRY

ID Code	Component Descriptions	Unit of Meas.	Manhr / Unit	Labor Cost	Material Cost	Equip. Cost	Total Cost
	Descriptions	**Output**		**Unit Costs**			

04 - 21131 — BRICK MASONRY, Cont'd... — 04 - 21131

ID Code	Component Descriptions	Unit of Meas.	Manhr / Unit	Labor Cost	Material Cost	Equip. Cost	Total Cost
1300	Glazed brick (7.4/sf)						
1310	Veneer	SF	0.145	11.00	15.25		26.25
1400	Buff or gray face brick (6.4/sf)						
1410	Veneer	SF	0.133	10.25	6.58		16.75
1420	Cavity wall	"	0.114	8.71	6.58		15.25
1500	Jumbo or oversize brick (3/sf)						
1510	4" veneer	SF	0.080	6.10	4.76		10.75
1530	4" back-up	"	0.067	5.08	4.76		9.84
1540	8" back-up	"	0.114	8.71	5.52		14.25
1550	12" firewall	"	0.200	15.25	7.42		22.75
1560	16" firewall	"	0.267	20.25	10.50		30.75
1600	Norman brick, red face, (4.5/sf)						
1620	4" veneer	SF	0.100	7.62	7.88		15.50
1640	Cavity wall	"	0.089	6.77	7.88		14.75
3000	Chimney, standard brick, including flue						
3020	16" x 16"	LF	0.800	61.00	32.00		93.00
3040	16" x 20"	"	0.800	61.00	54.00		110
3060	16" x 24"	"	0.800	61.00	58.00		120
3080	20" x 20"	"	1.000	76.00	45.00		120
3100	20" x 24"	"	1.000	76.00	61.00		140
3120	20" x 32"	"	1.143	87.00	68.00		160
4000	Window sill, face brick on edge	"	0.200	15.25	3.59		18.75

04 - 21231 — STRUCTURAL TILE — 04 - 21231

ID Code	Component Descriptions	Unit of Meas.	Manhr / Unit	Labor Cost	Material Cost	Equip. Cost	Total Cost
5000	Structural glazed tile						
5010	6T series, 5-1/2" x 12"						
5020	Glazed on one side						
5040	2" thick	SF	0.080	6.10	11.00		17.00
5060	4" thick	"	0.080	6.10	13.25		19.25
5080	6" thick	"	0.089	6.77	20.75		27.50
5100	8" thick	"	0.100	7.62	25.50		33.00
5200	Glazed on two sides						
5220	4" thick	SF	0.100	7.62	19.25		26.75
5240	6" thick	"	0.114	8.71	26.50		35.25
5500	Special shapes						
5510	Group 1	SF	0.160	12.25	11.25		23.50
5520	Group 2	"	0.160	12.25	14.25		26.50
5530	Group 3	"	0.160	12.25	18.75		31.00

UNIT MASONRY

ID Code	Component Descriptions	Unit of Meas.	Manhr / Unit	Labor Cost	Material Cost	Equip. Cost	Total Cost
	Descriptions	**Output**		**Unit Costs**			

04 - 21231 — STRUCTURAL TILE, Cont'd... — 04 - 21231

ID Code	Component Descriptions	Unit of Meas.	Manhr / Unit	Labor Cost	Material Cost	Equip. Cost	Total Cost
5540	Group 4	SF	0.160	12.25	37.75		50.00
5550	Group 5	"	0.160	12.25	46.00		58.00
5600	Fire rated						
5620	4" thick, 1 hr rating	SF	0.080	6.10	18.00		24.00
5640	6" thick, 2 hr rating	"	0.089	6.77	25.25		32.00
6000	8W series, 8" x 16"						
6010	Glazed on one side						
6020	2" thick	SF	0.053	4.06	12.50		16.50
6040	4" thick	"	0.053	4.06	13.25		17.25
6060	6" thick	"	0.062	4.69	22.00		26.75
6080	8" thick	"	0.062	4.69	24.00		28.75
6100	Glazed on two sides						
6120	4" thick	SF	0.067	5.08	21.00		26.00
6140	6" thick	"	0.080	6.10	29.25		35.25
6160	8" thick	"	0.080	6.10	35.50		41.50
6200	Special shapes						
6220	Group 1	SF	0.114	8.71	18.75		27.50
6230	Group 2	"	0.114	8.71	23.00		31.75
6240	Group 3	"	0.114	8.71	25.25		34.00
6250	Group 4	"	0.114	8.71	42.00		51.00
6260	Group 5	"	0.114	8.71	53.00		62.00
6270	Fire rated						
6290	4" thick, 1 hr rating	SF	0.114	8.71	31.50		40.25
6300	6" thick, 2 hr rating	"	0.114	8.71	43.25		52.00

CONCRETE UNIT MASONRY

04 - 22001 — CONCRETE MASONRY UNITS — 04 - 22001

ID Code	Component Descriptions	Unit of Meas.	Manhr / Unit	Labor Cost	Material Cost	Equip. Cost	Total Cost
0110	Hollow, load bearing						
0120	4"	SF	0.059	4.51	1.62		6.13
0140	6"	"	0.062	4.69	2.38		7.07
0160	8"	"	0.067	5.08	2.73		7.81
0180	10"	"	0.073	5.54	3.77		9.31
0190	12"	"	0.080	6.10	4.34		10.50
0280	Solid, load bearing						
0300	4"	SF	0.059	4.51	2.55		7.06
0320	6"	"	0.062	4.69	2.86		7.55
0340	8"	"	0.067	5.08	3.91		8.99

CONCRETE UNIT MASONRY

ID Code	Component Descriptions	Unit of Meas.	Manhr / Unit	Labor Cost	Material Cost	Equip. Cost	Total Cost
	Descriptions	**Output**		**Unit Costs**			

ID Code	Component Descriptions	Unit of Meas.	Manhr / Unit	Labor Cost	Material Cost	Equip. Cost	Total Cost
04 - 22001	**CONCRETE MASONRY UNITS, Cont'd...**						**04 - 22001**
0360	10"	SF	0.073	5.54	4.16		9.70
0380	12"	"	0.080	6.10	6.19		12.25
0480	Back-up block, 8" x 16"						
0490	2"	SF	0.046	3.48	1.70		5.18
0540	4"	"	0.047	3.58	1.78		5.36
0560	6"	"	0.050	3.81	2.60		6.41
0580	8"	"	0.053	4.06	2.99		7.05
0600	10"	"	0.057	4.35	4.13		8.48
0620	12"	"	0.062	4.69	4.75		9.44
0980	Foundation wall, 8" x 16"						
1000	6"	SF	0.057	4.35	2.60		6.95
1030	8"	"	0.062	4.69	2.99		7.68
1040	10"	"	0.067	5.08	4.13		9.21
1050	12"	"	0.073	5.54	4.76		10.25
1055	Solid						
1060	6"	SF	0.062	4.69	3.15		7.84
1070	8"	"	0.067	5.08	4.30		9.38
1080	10"	"	0.073	5.54	4.57		10.00
1100	12"	"	0.080	6.10	6.79		13.00
1480	Exterior, styrofoam inserts, std weight, 8" x 16"						
1500	6"	SF	0.062	4.69	4.57		9.26
1530	8"	"	0.067	5.08	4.93		10.00
1540	10"	"	0.073	5.54	6.40		12.00
1550	12"	"	0.080	6.10	8.77		14.75
1580	Lightweight						
1600	6"	SF	0.062	4.69	5.09		9.78
1660	8"	"	0.067	5.08	5.73		10.75
1680	10"	"	0.073	5.54	6.08		11.50
1700	12"	"	0.080	6.10	8.04		14.25
1980	Acoustical slotted block						
2000	4"	SF	0.073	5.54	5.31		10.75
2020	6"	"	0.073	5.54	5.56		11.00
2040	8"	"	0.080	6.10	6.94		13.00
2050	Filled cavities						
2060	4"	SF	0.089	6.77	5.69		12.50
2070	6"	"	0.094	7.17	6.55		13.75
2080	8"	"	0.100	7.62	8.40		16.00
4000	Hollow, split face						

CONCRETE UNIT MASONRY

ID Code	Component Descriptions	Unit of Meas.	Manhr / Unit	Labor Cost	Material Cost	Equip. Cost	Total Cost
				Descriptions → Output → Unit Costs			

ID Code	Component Descriptions	Unit of Meas.	Manhr / Unit	Labor Cost	Material Cost	Equip. Cost	Total Cost
04 - 22001	**CONCRETE MASONRY UNITS, Cont'd...**						**04 - 22001**
4020	4"	SF	0.059	4.51	3.64		8.15
4030	6"	"	0.062	4.69	4.21		8.90
4040	8"	"	0.067	5.08	4.42		9.50
4080	10"	"	0.073	5.54	4.95		10.50
4100	12"	"	0.080	6.10	5.28		11.50
4480	Split rib profile						
4500	4"	SF	0.073	5.54	4.42		9.96
4520	6"	"	0.073	5.54	5.13		10.75
4540	8"	"	0.080	6.10	5.58		11.75
4560	10"	"	0.080	6.10	6.12		12.25
4580	12"	"	0.080	6.10	6.63		12.75
4980	High strength block, 3500 psi						
5000	2"	SF	0.059	4.51	1.71		6.22
5020	4"	"	0.062	4.69	2.14		6.83
5030	6"	"	0.062	4.69	2.56		7.25
5040	8"	"	0.067	5.08	2.90		7.98
5050	10"	"	0.073	5.54	3.38		8.92
5060	12"	"	0.080	6.10	4.00		10.00
5500	Solar screen concrete block						
5505	4" thick						
5510	6" x 6"	SF	0.178	13.50	4.29		17.75
5520	8" x 8"	"	0.160	12.25	5.12		17.25
5530	12" x 12"	"	0.123	9.38	5.24		14.50
5540	8" thick						
5550	8" x 16"	SF	0.114	8.71	5.24		14.00
7000	Glazed block						
7020	Cove base, glazed 1 side, 2"	LF	0.089	6.77	11.00		17.75
7030	4"	"	0.089	6.77	11.25		18.00
7040	6"	"	0.100	7.62	11.50		19.00
7050	8"	"	0.100	7.62	12.50		20.00
7055	Single face						
7060	2"	SF	0.067	5.08	11.50		16.50
7080	4"	"	0.067	5.08	14.25		19.25
7090	6"	"	0.073	5.54	15.25		20.75
7100	8"	"	0.080	6.10	16.00		22.00
7105	10"	"	0.089	6.77	18.00		24.75
7110	12"	"	0.094	7.17	19.25		26.50
7115	Double face						

CONCRETE UNIT MASONRY

ID Code	Component Descriptions	Unit of Meas.	Manhr / Unit	Labor Cost	Material Cost	Equip. Cost	Total Cost
	Descriptions	**Output**		**Unit Costs**			

04 - 22001 — CONCRETE MASONRY UNITS, Cont'd... — 04 - 22001

ID Code	Component Descriptions	Unit of Meas.	Manhr / Unit	Labor Cost	Material Cost	Equip. Cost	Total Cost
7120	4"	SF	0.084	6.42	17.25		23.75
7140	6"	"	0.089	6.77	20.25		27.00
7160	8"	"	0.100	7.62	21.25		28.75
7180	Corner or bullnose						
7200	2"	EA	0.100	7.62	18.25		25.75
7240	4"	"	0.114	8.71	23.50		32.25
7260	6"	"	0.114	8.71	28.75		37.50
7280	8"	"	0.133	10.25	31.25		41.50
7290	10"	"	0.145	11.00	34.00		45.00
7300	12"	"	0.160	12.25	36.50		48.75
9500	Gypsum unit masonry						
9510	Partition blocks (12"x30")						
9515	Solid						
9520	2"	SF	0.032	2.44	1.41		3.85
9525	Hollow						
9530	3"	SF	0.032	2.44	1.42		3.86
9540	4"	"	0.033	2.54	1.63		4.17
9550	6"	"	0.036	2.77	1.74		4.51
9900	Vertical reinforcing						
9920	4' o.c., add 5% to labor						
9940	2'8" o.c., add 15% to labor						
9960	Interior partitions, add 10% to labor						

04 - 22009 — BOND BEAMS & LINTELS — 04 - 22009

ID Code	Component Descriptions	Unit of Meas.	Manhr / Unit	Labor Cost	Material Cost	Equip. Cost	Total Cost
0980	Bond beam, no grout or reinforcement						
0990	8" x 16" x						
1000	4" thick	LF	0.062	4.69	1.85		6.54
1040	6" thick	"	0.064	4.88	2.83		7.71
1060	8" thick	"	0.067	5.08	3.24		8.32
1080	10" thick	"	0.070	5.30	4.01		9.31
1100	12" thick	"	0.073	5.54	4.56		10.00
6000	Beam lintel, no grout or reinforcement						
6010	8" x 16" x						
6020	10" thick	LF	0.080	6.10	8.85		15.00
6040	12" thick	"	0.089	6.77	9.42		16.25
6080	Precast masonry lintel						
7000	6 lf, 8" high x						
7020	4" thick	LF	0.133	10.25	7.80		18.00

CONCRETE UNIT MASONRY

ID Code	Component Descriptions	Unit of Meas.	Manhr / Unit	Labor Cost	Material Cost	Equip. Cost	Total Cost
04 - 22009	**BOND BEAMS & LINTELS, Cont'd...**						**04 - 22009**
7040	6" thick	LF	0.133	10.25	9.96		20.25
7060	8" thick	"	0.145	11.00	11.25		22.25
7080	10" thick	"	0.145	11.00	13.50		24.50
7090	10 lf, 8" high x						
7100	4" thick	LF	0.080	6.10	9.80		16.00
7120	6" thick	"	0.080	6.10	12.00		18.00
7140	8" thick	"	0.089	6.77	13.50		20.25
7160	10" thick	"	0.089	6.77	18.25		25.00
8000	Steel angles and plates						
8010	Minimum	LB	0.011	0.87	1.33		2.20
8020	Maximum	"	0.020	1.52	1.95		3.47
8200	Various size angle lintels						
8205	1/4" stock						
8210	3" x 3"	LF	0.050	3.81	6.85		10.75
8220	3" x 3-1/2"	"	0.050	3.81	7.54		11.25
8225	3/8" stock						
8230	3" x 4"	LF	0.050	3.81	12.00		15.75
8240	3-1/2" x 4"	"	0.050	3.81	12.50		16.25
8250	4" x 4"	"	0.050	3.81	13.75		17.50
8260	5" x 3-1/2"	"	0.050	3.81	14.50		18.25
8262	6" x 3-1/2"	"	0.050	3.81	16.25		20.00
8265	1/2" stock						
8280	6" x 4"	LF	0.050	3.81	18.00		21.75

GLASS UNIT MASONRY

ID Code	Component Descriptions	Unit of Meas.	Manhr / Unit	Labor Cost	Material Cost	Equip. Cost	Total Cost
04 - 23001	**GLASS BLOCK**						**04 - 23001**
1000	Glass block, 4" thick						
1040	6" x 6"	SF	0.267	20.25	38.25		59.00
1060	8" x 8"	"	0.200	15.25	24.25		39.50
1080	12" x 12"	"	0.160	12.25	30.75		43.00

ADOBE UNIT MASONRY

ID Code	Component Descriptions	Unit of Meas.	Manhr / Unit	Labor Cost	Material Cost	Equip. Cost	Total Cost
	Descriptions	**Output**		**Unit Costs**			
04 - 24001		**CLAY TILE**					**04 - 24001**
0100	Hollow clay tile, for back-up, 12" x 12"						
1000	Scored face						
1010	Load bearing						
1020	4" thick	SF	0.057	4.35	7.22		11.50
1040	6" thick	"	0.059	4.51	8.42		13.00
1060	8" thick	"	0.062	4.69	10.50		15.25
1080	10" thick	"	0.064	4.88	13.00		18.00
1100	12" thick	"	0.067	5.08	22.00		27.00
2000	Non-load bearing						
2020	3" thick	SF	0.055	4.20	5.85		10.00
2040	4" thick	"	0.057	4.35	6.77		11.00
2060	6" thick	"	0.059	4.51	7.84		12.25
2080	8" thick	"	0.062	4.69	9.99		14.75
2100	12" thick	"	0.067	5.08	17.75		22.75
4100	Partition, 12" x 12"						
4150	In walls						
4201	3" thick	SF	0.067	5.08	5.85		11.00
4210	4" thick	"	0.067	5.08	6.78		11.75
4220	6" thick	"	0.070	5.30	7.48		12.75
4230	8" thick	"	0.073	5.54	9.81		15.25
4240	10" thick	"	0.076	5.80	11.75		17.50
4250	12" thick	"	0.080	6.10	17.00		23.00
4300	Clay tile floors						
4320	4" thick	SF	0.044	3.38	6.77		10.25
4330	6" thick	"	0.047	3.58	8.42		12.00
4340	8" thick	"	0.050	3.81	10.50		14.25
4350	10" thick	"	0.053	4.06	13.00		17.00
4360	12" thick	"	0.057	4.35	19.25		23.50
6000	Terra cotta						
6020	Coping, 10" or 12" wide, 3" thick	LF	0.160	12.25	16.00		28.25

STONE

ID Code	Component Descriptions	Unit of Meas.	Manhr / Unit	Labor Cost	Material Cost	Equip. Cost	Total Cost
		Output		**Unit Costs**			
04 - 43001	**STONE**						**04 - 43001**
0160	Rubble stone						
0180	Walls set in mortar						
0200	8" thick	SF	0.200	15.25	17.50		32.75
0220	12" thick	"	0.320	24.50	21.00		45.50
0420	18" thick	"	0.400	30.50	28.00		59.00
0440	24" thick	"	0.533	40.75	35.00		76.00
0445	Dry set wall						
0450	8" thick	SF	0.133	10.25	19.50		29.75
0455	12" thick	"	0.200	15.25	22.25		37.50
0460	18" thick	"	0.267	20.25	30.50		51.00
0465	24" thick	"	0.320	24.50	37.25		62.00
0480	Cut stone						
0490	Imported marble						
0510	Facing panels						
0520	3/4" thick	SF	0.320	24.50	45.25		70.00
0530	1-1/2" thick	"	0.364	27.75	64.00		92.00
0540	2-1/4" thick	"	0.444	34.00	77.00		110
0600	Base						
0610	1" thick						
0620	4" high	LF	0.400	30.50	20.50		51.00
0640	6" high	"	0.400	30.50	24.75		55.00
0700	Columns, solid						
0720	Plain faced	CF	5.333	410	150		560
0740	Fluted	"	5.333	410	420		830
0780	Flooring, travertine, minimum	SF	0.123	9.38	20.75		30.25
0800	Average	"	0.160	12.25	27.75		40.00
0820	Maximum	"	0.178	13.50	51.00		65.00
1000	Domestic marble						
1020	Facing panels						
1040	7/8" thick	SF	0.320	24.50	42.50		67.00
1060	1-1/2" thick	"	0.364	27.75	64.00		92.00
1080	2-1/4" thick	"	0.444	34.00	77.00		110
1500	Stairs						
1510	12" treads	LF	0.400	30.50	38.00		69.00
1520	6" risers	"	0.267	20.25	28.25		48.50
1525	Thresholds, 7/8" thick, 3' long, 4" to 6" wide						
1530	Plain	EA	0.667	51.00	34.50		86.00
1540	Beveled	"	0.667	51.00	38.25		89.00

STONE

ID Code	Component Descriptions	Unit of Meas.	Manhr / Unit	Labor Cost	Material Cost	Equip. Cost	Total Cost
	Descriptions	**Output**		**Unit Costs**			

04 - 43001 — STONE, Cont'd... — 04 - 43001

ID Code	Component Descriptions	Unit of Meas.	Manhr / Unit	Labor Cost	Material Cost	Equip. Cost	Total Cost
1545	Window sill						
1550	6" wide, 2" thick	LF	0.320	24.50	19.25		43.75
1555	Stools						
1560	5" wide, 7/8" thick	LF	0.320	24.50	25.75		50.00
1620	Limestone panels up to 12' x 5', smooth finish						
1630	2" thick	SF	0.096	5.96	29.50	5.32	40.75
1650	3" thick	"	0.096	5.96	34.50	5.32	45.75
1660	4" thick	"	0.096	5.96	49.25	5.32	61.00
1760	Miscellaneous limestone items						
1770	Steps, 14" wide, 6" deep	LF	0.533	40.75	63.00		100
1780	Coping, smooth finish	CF	0.267	20.25	88.00		110
1790	Sills, lintels, jambs, smooth finish	"	0.320	24.50	88.00		110
1800	Granite veneer facing panels, polished						
1810	7/8" thick						
1820	Black	SF	0.320	24.50	48.25		73.00
1840	Gray	"	0.320	24.50	38.00		63.00
1850	Base						
1860	4" high	LF	0.160	12.25	20.25		32.50
1870	6" high	"	0.178	13.50	24.50		38.00
1880	Curbing, straight, 6" x 16"	"	0.400	24.75	22.50	22.25	70.00
1890	Radius curbs, radius over 5'	"	0.533	33.25	27.50	29.50	91.00
1900	Ashlar veneer						
1905	4" thick, random	SF	0.320	24.50	34.00		59.00
1910	Pavers, 4" x 4" split						
1915	Gray	SF	0.160	12.25	33.25		45.50
1920	Pink	"	0.160	12.25	32.75		45.00
1930	Black	"	0.160	12.25	32.25		44.50
2000	Slate, panels						
2010	1" thick	SF	0.320	24.50	27.50		52.00
2020	2" thick	"	0.364	27.75	37.25		65.00
2030	Sills or stools						
2040	1" thick						
2060	6" wide	LF	0.320	24.50	12.75		37.25
2080	10" wide	"	0.348	26.50	20.75		47.25
2100	2" thick						
2120	6" wide	LF	0.364	27.75	21.00		48.75
2140	10" wide	"	0.400	30.50	34.75		65.00

STONE

ID Code	Component Descriptions	Unit of Meas.	Manhr / Unit	Labor Cost	Material Cost	Equip. Cost	Total Cost
		Output		**Unit Costs**			

04 - 51001　FLUE LINERS　04 - 51001

ID	Description	UM	Manhr	Labor	Material	Equip	Total
1000	Flue liners						
1020	Rectangular						
1040	8" x 12"	LF	0.133	10.25	10.50		20.75
1060	12" x 12"	"	0.145	11.00	13.25		24.25
1080	12" x 18"	"	0.160	12.25	23.25		35.50
1100	16" x 16"	"	0.178	13.50	25.00		38.50
1120	18" x 18"	"	0.190	14.50	31.00		45.50
1140	20" x 20"	"	0.200	15.25	52.00		67.00
1170	24" x 24"	"	0.229	17.50	62.00		80.00
1200	Round						
1220	18" dia.	LF	0.190	14.50	47.75		62.00
1240	24" dia.	"	0.229	17.50	94.00		110

MANUFACTURED MASONRY

04 - 71001　SIMULATED BRICK AND STONE　04 - 71001

ID	Description	UM	Manhr	Labor	Material	Equip	Total
1010	Brick Veneer Panel 48" x 33"						
1020	Antique	EA	0.400	30.50	140		170
1030	Baked Clay	"	0.400	30.50	120		150
1040	Brick Cream Caramel	"	0.400	30.50	140		170
1050	Dusky Evening	"	0.400	30.50	140		170
1060	Glacier	"	0.400	30.50	120		150
1070	Merlot	"	0.400	30.50	140		170
1080	Mixed Twilight	"	0.400	30.50	120		150
1090	Mocha	"	0.400	30.50	140		170
1100	Spiced	"	0.400	30.50	120		150
1200	Cast stone						
1220	6" Window/Door Molding	LF	0.080	6.10	20.75		26.75
1240	12" Dia. Column	"	0.200	15.25	88.00		100
1260	12" x 12" Quoins	EA	0.100	7.62	61.00		69.00
1280	6" Base Molding	LF	0.080	6.10	16.50		22.50
1300	10" Wallcap	"	0.080	6.10	18.75		24.75
1320	3 Piece baluster system	"	0.100	7.62	100		110
1340	24" x 24" x 1-1/2" Paver	SF	0.020	1.52	11.00		12.50
1360	Simulated Stone						
1380	Slate, 43-1/4" Wide × 8-1/2" High × approx. 1-3/4" Thick						
1400	Arizona Red	EA	0.027	2.03	29.50		31.50
1420	Brunswick Brown	"	0.027	2.03	29.50		31.50

MANUFACTURED MASONRY

ID Code	Component Descriptions	Unit of Meas.	Manhr / Unit	Labor Cost	Material Cost	Equip. Cost	Total Cost
	Descriptions	**Output**		**Unit Costs**			
04 - 71001	**SIMULATED BRICK AND STONE, Cont'd...**					**04 - 71001**	
1440	Midnight Ash	EA	0.027	2.03	29.50		31.50
1460	Onyx	"	0.027	2.03	29.50		31.50
1480	Pewter	"	0.027	2.03	29.50		31.50
1500	Rocky Mountain Graphite	"	0.027	2.03	29.50		31.50
1520	Sahara	"	0.027	2.03	29.50		31.50
1540	Stacked Stone 49-1/4" Wide x 25" High 2" Thick						
1560	Birchwood	EA	0.400	30.50	110		140
1580	Earth	"	0.400	30.50	110		140
1600	Honey	"	0.400	30.50	110		140
1620	Espresso	"	0.400	30.50	110		140
1640	Spice	"	0.400	30.50	110		140
1660	Potomac	"	0.400	30.50	110		140
1680	Ponderosa	"	0.400	30.50	110		140
1700	Tudor	"	0.400	30.50	110		140
1720	Riviera	"	0.400	30.50	110		140
1740	White	"	0.400	30.50	110		140
1760	Corners 15-1/2 x 14-1/2 x 25" High x 2-1/4" Thick						
1780	Birchwood	EA	0.100	7.62	65.00		73.00
1800	Earth	"	0.100	7.62	65.00		73.00
1820	Honey	"	0.100	7.62	65.00		73.00
1840	Espresso	"	0.100	7.62	65.00		73.00
1860	Spice	"	0.100	7.62	65.00		73.00
1880	Potomac	"	0.100	7.62	65.00		73.00
1900	Ponderosa	"	0.100	7.62	65.00		73.00
1920	Tudor	"	0.100	7.62	65.00		73.00
1940	Riviera	"	0.100	7.62	65.00		73.00
1960	White	"	0.100	7.62	65.00		73.00
1980	Ledgers 48" Wide x 3-1/2" Deep x 3-5/8" High						
2000	Birchwood	EA	0.267	20.25	33.00		53.00
2020	Earth	"	0.267	20.25	33.00		53.00
2040	Honey	"	0.267	20.25	33.00		53.00
2060	Espresso	"	0.267	20.25	33.00		53.00
2080	Spice	"	0.267	20.25	33.00		53.00
2100	Potomac	"	0.267	20.25	33.00		53.00
2120	Ponderosa	"	0.267	20.25	33.00		53.00
2140	Tudor	"	0.267	20.25	33.00		53.00
2160	Riviera	"	0.267	20.25	33.00		53.00
2180	White	"	0.267	20.25	33.00		53.00

DIVISION 05
METALS

METAL FASTENING

ID Code	Component Descriptions	Unit of Meas.	Manhr / Unit	Labor Cost	Material Cost	Equip. Cost	Total Cost
	Descriptions	**Output**		**Unit Costs**			

05 - 05231	**STRUCTURAL WELDING**						**05 - 05231**
0080	Welding						
0100	Single pass						
0120	1/8"	LF	0.040	3.53	0.33		3.86
0140	3/16"	"	0.053	4.70	0.55		5.25
0160	1/4"	"	0.067	5.88	0.77		6.65
0180	Miscellaneous steel shapes						
0190	Plain	LB	0.002	0.14	1.44		1.58
0200	Galvanized	"	0.003	0.23	1.80		2.03
0210	Plates						
0220	Plain	LB	0.002	0.17	1.29		1.46
0240	Galvanized	"	0.003	0.28	1.66		1.94

05 - 05239	**METAL FASTENINGS**						**05 - 05239**
0050	Powder Actuated Anchors						
0100	Loads						
0120	Single Shot						
0140	.22 Cal Green	EA					0.07
0160	.22 Cal Yellow	"					0.11
0180	.22 Cal Red	"					0.12
0200	Strip						
0220	.27 Cal Green	EA					0.18
0240	.27 Cal Yellow	"					0.17
0260	.27 Cal Red	"					0.17
0280	Pins						
0300	.145 Dia. X Length 300 Head						
0320	1/2"	EA					0.18
0340	5/8"	"					0.25
0360	3/4"	"					0.29
0380	1"	"					0.37
0400	1-1/4"	"					0.38
0420	1-1/2"	"					0.44
0440	2"	"					0.46
0460	2-1/2"	"					0.49
0480	3"	"					0.52
1000	Anchor bolts, material only						
1020	3/8" x						
1040	8" long	EA					1.11
1060	10" long	"					1.21

METAL FASTENING

ID Code	Descriptions	Output		Unit Costs			
	Component Descriptions	Unit of Meas.	Manhr / Unit	Labor Cost	Material Cost	Equip. Cost	Total Cost
05 - 05239	**METAL FASTENINGS, Cont'd...**						**05 - 05239**
1080	12" long	EA					1.31
1090	1/2" x						
1100	8" long	EA					1.65
1120	10" long	"					1.76
1140	12" long	"					1.93
1160	18" long	"					2.10
1170	5/8" x						
1180	8" long	EA					1.54
1200	10" long	"					1.70
1220	12" long	"					1.81
1240	18" long	"					1.93
1260	24" long	"					2.10
1270	3/4" x						
1280	8" long	EA					2.20
1300	12" long	"					2.48
1320	18" long	"					3.41
1340	24" long	"					4.52
1350	7/8" x						
1360	8" long	EA					2.20
1380	12" long	"					2.48
1400	18" long	"					3.41
1420	24" long	"					4.52
1430	1" x						
1440	12" long	EA					4.41
1460	18" long	"					5.51
1480	24" long	"					6.61
1500	36" long	"					9.93
3980	Expansion shield						
4000	1/4"	EA					0.68
4020	3/8"	"					1.14
4040	1/2"	"					2.25
4060	5/8"	"					3.26
4080	3/4"	"					3.99
4100	1"	"					5.40
4480	Non-drilling anchor						
4500	1/4"	EA					0.71
4540	3/8"	"					0.88
4560	1/2"	"					1.35

METAL FASTENING

	Descriptions	Output		Unit Costs			
ID Code	Component Descriptions	Unit of Meas.	Manhr / Unit	Labor Cost	Material Cost	Equip. Cost	Total Cost
05 - 05239	**METAL FASTENINGS, Cont'd...**						**05 - 05239**
4580	5/8"	EA					2.22
4600	3/4"	"					3.81
7000	Self-drilling anchor						
7020	1/4"	EA					1.79
7040	5/16"	"					2.23
7060	3/8"	"					2.68
7080	1/2"	"					3.58
7100	5/8"	"					6.80
7120	3/4"	"					8.92
7140	7/8"	"					12.50
8020	Add 25% for galvanized anchor bolts						
8040	Channel door frame, with anchors	LB	0.009	0.78	1.96		2.74
8060	Corner guard angle, with anchors	"	0.013	1.17	1.75		2.92
05 - 05240	**METAL LINTELS**						**05 - 05240**
0080	Lintels, steel						
0100	Plain	LB	0.020	1.76	1.33		3.09
0120	Galvanized	"	0.020	1.76	2.00		3.76

STRUCTURAL METAL FRAMING

	BEAMS, GIRDERS, COLUMNS, TRUSSES						
05 - 12001							**05 - 12001**
0100	Beams and girders, A-36						
0120	Welded	TON	4.800	380	3,160	460	4,000
0140	Bolted	"	4.364	350	3,070	420	3,840
0180	Columns						
0185	Pipe						
0190	6" dia.	LB	0.005	0.38	1.61	0.46	2.45
0200	12" dia.	"	0.004	0.32	1.37	0.38	2.07
0220	Purlins and girts						
0230	Welded	TON	8.000	640	3,010	770	4,420
0240	Bolted	"	6.857	550	2,960	660	4,170
1000	Column base plates						
1020	Up to 150 lb each	LB	0.005	0.47	1.73		2.20
1040	Over 150 lb each	"	0.007	0.58	1.41		1.99
1200	Structural pipe						
1220	3" to 5" o.d.	TON	9.600	770	3,250	920	4,940
1240	6" to 12" o.d.	"	6.857	550	3,010	660	4,220
1300	Structural tube						

STRUCTURAL METAL FRAMING

ID Code	Component Descriptions	Unit of Meas.	Manhr / Unit	Labor Cost	Material Cost	Equip. Cost	Total Cost
	Descriptions	**Output**		**Unit Costs**			

05 - 12001 — BEAMS, GIRDERS, COLUMNS, TRUSSES, Cont'd... — 05 - 12001

ID Code	Component Descriptions	Unit	Manhr/Unit	Labor	Material	Equip.	Total
1310	6" square						
1320	Light sections	TON	9.600	770	3,770	920	5,460
1340	Heavy sections	"	6.857	550	3,530	660	4,740
1350	6" wide rectangular						
1360	Light sections	TON	8.000	640	3,770	770	5,180
1380	Heavy sections	"	6.000	480	3,530	580	4,590
1390	Greater than 6" wide rectangular						
1400	Light sections	TON	8.000	640	4,010	770	5,420
1420	Heavy sections	"	6.000	480	3,780	580	4,840
1500	Miscellaneous structural shapes						
1520	Steel angle	TON	12.000	960	2,680	1,150	4,790
1540	Steel plate	"	8.000	640	3,040	770	4,450
5980	Trusses, field welded						
6000	60 lb/lf	TON	6.000	480	4,090	580	5,150
6020	100 lb/lf	"	4.800	380	3,580	460	4,420
6040	150 lb/lf	"	4.000	320	3,370	380	4,070
6050	Bolted						
6060	60 lb/lf	TON	5.333	430	4,040	510	4,980
6080	100 lb/lf	"	4.364	350	3,530	420	4,300
6100	150 lb/lf	"	3.692	300	3,350	350	4,000
9100	Add for galvanizing	"					830

WIRE ROPE ASSEMBLIES

05 - 15011 — WIRE ROPE — 05 - 15011

ID Code	Description	Unit					Total
0100	Galvanized Cable						
0120	1/16"	LF					0.30
0130	1/8"	"					1.01
0140	3/16"	"					1.33
0160	1/4"	"					1.67
0180	5/16"	"					2.33
0200	3/8"	"					2.78
0220	1/2"	"					3.03
0240	5/8"	"					3.41
0260	3/4"	"					5.62
0280	1-1/4"	"					14.75
0300	Stainless						
0320	1/16"	LF					0.34

WIRE ROPE ASSEMBLIES

ID Code	Component Descriptions	Unit of Meas.	Manhr / Unit	Labor Cost	Material Cost	Equip. Cost	Total Cost
		Output		**Unit Costs**			
05 - 15011	**WIRE ROPE, Cont'd...**						**05 - 15011**
0340	1/8"	LF					1.12
0360	3/16"	"					1.47
0380	1/4"	"					1.85
0400	5/16"	"					2.58
0420	3/8"	"					3.09
0440	1/2"	"					3.36
0460	5/8"	"					4.11
0480	3/4"	"					6.23
0490	1-1/4"	"					16.25
0520	Coated						
0540	1/16"	LF					0.58
0560	1/8"	"					1.25
0580	3/16"	"					2.00
1300	Clips						
1320	1/16"	EA					1.37
1340	1/8"	"					1.52
1360	3/16"	"					1.57
1380	1/4"	"					1.56
1400	5/16"	"					2.68
1420	3/8"	"					1.89
1440	1/2"	"					2.32
1460	5/8"	"					4.04
1480	3/4"	"					6.30
1500	1-1/4"	"					10.50
1520	Thimbles						
1580	3/16"	EA					0.75
1600	1/4"	"					1.00
1620	5/16"	"					1.07
1640	3/8"	"					1.47
1660	1/2"	"					1.83
1680	5/8"	"					4.95
1700	3/4"	"					4.85
1720	1-1/4"	"					13.50
1740	Sleeves (Swage type)						
1760	1/16"	EA					0.29
1780	1/8"	"					0.74
1800	3/16"	"					0.69
1820	1/4"	"					0.85

WIRE ROPE ASSEMBLIES

ID Code	Descriptions	Output		Unit Costs			
	Component Descriptions	Unit of Meas.	Manhr / Unit	Labor Cost	Material Cost	Equip. Cost	Total Cost
05 - 15011	**WIRE ROPE, Cont'd...**						**05 - 15011**
1840	5/16"	EA					1.76
1860	3/8"	"					1.90
1880	1/2"	"					1.95
1900	5/8"	"					2.11
1920	3/4"	"					2.21
1940	1-1/4"	"					2.32

STEEL JOIST FRAMING

ID Code	Descriptions	Output		Unit Costs			
05 - 21001	**METAL JOISTS**						**05 - 21001**
0090	Joist						
0100	DLH series	TON	3.200	260	1,960	310	2,520
0120	K series	"	3.200	260	2,030	310	2,590
0140	LH series	"	3.200	260	1,960	310	2,520

STEEL DECKING

ID Code	Descriptions	Output		Unit Costs			
05 - 31001	**METAL DECKING**						**05 - 31001**
0090	Roof, 1-1/2" deep, non-composite						
0095	16 ga.						
0100	Primed	SF	0.008	0.64	4.46	0.76	5.86
0120	Galvanized	"	0.008	0.64	4.68	0.76	6.08
0130	18 ga.						
0140	Primed	SF	0.008	0.64	3.49	0.76	4.89
0200	Galvanized	"	0.008	0.64	3.83	0.76	5.23
0210	20 ga.						
0220	Primed	SF	0.008	0.64	2.57	0.76	3.97
0240	Galvanized	"	0.008	0.64	3.05	0.76	4.45
0250	22 ga.						
0260	Primed	SF	0.008	0.64	2.09	0.76	3.49
0270	Galvanized	"	0.008	0.64	2.33	0.76	3.73
1000	Open type decking, galvanized						
1010	1-1/2" deep						
1020	18 ga.	SF	0.008	0.64	3.35	0.76	4.75
1040	20 ga.	"	0.008	0.64	2.57	0.76	3.97
1060	22 ga.	"	0.008	0.64	2.21	0.76	3.61
1070	3" deep						
1080	16 ga.	SF	0.009	0.69	5.21	0.83	6.74

STEEL DECKING

ID Code	Component Descriptions	Unit of Meas.	Manhr / Unit	Labor Cost	Material Cost	Equip. Cost	Total Cost
05 - 31001	**METAL DECKING, Cont'd...**					**05 - 31001**	
1100	18 ga.	SF	0.009	0.69	4.90	0.83	6.43
1120	20 ga.	"	0.009	0.69	3.71	0.83	5.24
1140	22 ga.	"	0.009	0.69	3.60	0.83	5.13
1150	4-1/2" deep						
1160	16 ga.	SF	0.010	0.76	7.72	0.92	9.40
1180	18 ga.	"	0.010	0.76	6.39	0.92	8.07
1200	6" deep						
1220	16 ga.	SF	0.011	0.85	10.75	1.02	12.50
1240	18 ga.	"	0.011	0.85	9.29	1.02	11.25
1250	7-1/2" deep						
1260	16 ga.	SF	0.011	0.89	11.50	1.06	13.50
1280	18 ga.	"	0.011	0.89	11.00	1.06	13.00
2480	Cellular type						
2500	1-1/2" deep, galvanized						
2520	18-18 ga.	SF	0.010	0.76	9.22	0.92	11.00
2530	22-18 ga.	"	0.010	0.76	8.39	0.92	10.00
2535	3" deep, galvanized						
2540	16-16 ga.	SF	0.011	0.85	13.25	1.02	15.00
2550	18-16 ga.	"	0.011	0.85	12.25	1.02	14.00
2560	18-18 ga.	"	0.011	0.85	11.25	1.02	13.00
2570	20-18 ga.	"	0.011	0.85	10.00	1.02	11.75
2575	4-1/2" deep, galvanized						
2580	16-16 ga.	SF	0.011	0.91	19.75	1.09	21.75
2590	18-16 ga.	"	0.011	0.91	18.25	1.09	20.25
2600	18-18 ga.	"	0.011	0.91	17.25	1.09	19.25
2610	20-18 ga.	"	0.011	0.91	15.75	1.09	17.75
3500	Composite deck, non-cellular, galvanized						
3520	1-1/2" deep						
3530	18 ga.	SF	0.009	0.69	3.10	0.83	4.63
3540	20 ga.	"	0.009	0.69	2.82	0.83	4.35
3550	22 ga.	"	0.009	0.69	2.29	0.83	3.82
3560	3" deep						
3570	18 ga.	SF	0.009	0.73	4.37	0.88	5.99
3580	20 ga.	"	0.009	0.73	2.82	0.88	4.44
3590	22 ga.	"	0.009	0.73	2.29	0.88	3.91
3600	Slab form floor deck						
3610	9/16" deep						
3620	28 ga.	SF	0.009	0.69	1.39	0.83	2.92

STEEL DECKING

ID Code	Component Descriptions	Unit of Meas.	Manhr / Unit	Labor Cost	Material Cost	Equip. Cost	Total Cost
			Descriptions / **Output** / **Unit Costs**				

05 - 31001 — METAL DECKING, Cont'd... — 05 - 31001

ID Code	Component Descriptions	Unit of Meas.	Manhr / Unit	Labor Cost	Material Cost	Equip. Cost	Total Cost
3630	1-5/16" deep						
3640	24 ga.	SF	0.009	0.72	2.04	0.86	3.63
3650	22 ga.	"	0.009	0.72	2.45	0.86	4.04

COLD FORMED FRAMING

05 - 41001 — METAL FRAMING — 05 - 41001

ID Code	Component Descriptions	Unit of Meas.	Manhr / Unit	Labor Cost	Material Cost	Equip. Cost	Total Cost
0100	Furring channel, galvanized						
0110	Beams and columns, 3/4"						
0120	12" o.c.	SF	0.080	7.06	0.44		7.50
0140	16" o.c.	"	0.073	6.42	0.34		6.76
0150	Walls, 3/4"						
0160	12" o.c.	SF	0.040	3.53	0.44		3.97
0170	16" o.c.	"	0.033	2.94	0.34		3.28
0172	24" o.c.	"	0.027	2.35	0.24		2.59
0173	1-1/2"						
0174	12" o.c.	SF	0.040	3.53	0.72		4.25
0175	16" o.c.	"	0.033	2.94	0.55		3.49
0176	24" o.c.	"	0.027	2.35	0.37		2.72
0177	Stud, load bearing						
0178	16" o.c.						
0179	16 ga.						
0180	2-1/2"	SF	0.036	3.13	1.33		4.46
0190	3-5/8"	"	0.036	3.13	1.57		4.70
0200	4"	"	0.036	3.13	1.63		4.76
0220	6"	"	0.040	3.53	2.05		5.58
0280	18 ga.						
0300	2-1/2"	SF	0.036	3.13	1.08		4.21
0310	3-5/8"	"	0.036	3.13	1.33		4.46
0320	4"	"	0.036	3.13	1.39		4.52
0330	6"	"	0.040	3.53	1.76		5.29
0350	8"	"	0.040	3.53	2.12		5.65
0360	20 ga.						
0370	2-1/2"	SF	0.036	3.13	0.60		3.73
0390	3-5/8"	"	0.036	3.13	0.72		3.85
0400	4"	"	0.036	3.13	0.79		3.92
0420	6"	"	0.040	3.53	0.96		4.49
0450	8"	"	0.040	3.53	1.15		4.68

COLD FORMED FRAMING

ID Code	Component Descriptions	Unit of Meas.	Manhr / Unit	Labor Cost	Material Cost	Equip. Cost	Total Cost
		Descriptions	**Output**		**Unit Costs**		
05 - 41001	**METAL FRAMING, Cont'd...**						**05 - 41001**
0460	24" o.c.						
0470	16 ga.						
0480	2-1/2"	SF	0.031	2.71	0.91		3.62
0510	3-5/8"	"	0.031	2.71	1.08		3.79
0520	4"	"	0.031	2.71	1.15		3.86
0530	6"	"	0.033	2.94	1.39		4.33
0540	8"	"	0.033	2.94	1.76		4.70
0545	18 ga.						
0550	2-1/2"	SF	0.031	2.71	0.72		3.43
0560	3-5/8"	"	0.031	2.71	0.84		3.55
0570	4"	"	0.031	2.71	0.91		3.62
0580	6"	"	0.033	2.94	1.15		4.09
0590	8"	"	0.033	2.94	1.39		4.33
0595	20 ga.						
0600	2-1/2"	SF	0.031	2.71	0.44		3.15
0610	3-5/8"	"	0.031	2.71	0.49		3.20
0620	4"	"	0.031	2.71	0.55		3.26
0630	6"	"	0.033	2.94	0.71		3.65
0640	8"	"	0.033	2.94	0.88		3.82

METAL FABRICATIONS

ID Code	Component Descriptions	Unit of Meas.	Manhr / Unit	Labor Cost	Material Cost	Equip. Cost	Total Cost
05 - 51001	**STAIRS**						**05 - 51001**
1000	Stock unit, steel, complete, per riser						
1010	Tread						
1020	3'-6" wide	EA	1.000	88.00	240		330
1040	4' wide	"	1.143	100	280		380
1060	5' wide	"	1.333	120	330		450
1200	Metal pan stair, cement filled, per riser						
1220	3'-6" wide	EA	0.800	71.00	260		330
1240	4' wide	"	0.889	78.00	300		380
1260	5' wide	"	1.000	88.00	340		430
1280	Landing, steel pan	SF	0.200	17.75	100		120
1300	Cast iron tread, steel stringers, stock units, per riser						
1310	Tread						
1320	3'-6" wide	EA	1.000	88.00	460		550
1340	4' wide	"	1.143	100	530		630
1360	5' wide	"	1.333	120	640		760

METAL FABRICATIONS

ID Code	Component Descriptions	Unit of Meas.	Manhr / Unit	Labor Cost	Material Cost	Equip. Cost	Total Cost
05 - 51001	**STAIRS, Cont'd...**						**05 - 51001**
1400	Stair treads, abrasive, 12" x 3'-6"						
1410	Cast iron						
1420	3/8"	EA	0.400	35.25	220		260
1440	1/2"	"	0.400	35.25	280		320
1450	Cast aluminum						
1460	5/16"	EA	0.400	35.25	250		290
1480	3/8"	"	0.400	35.25	270		310
1500	1/2"	"	0.400	35.25	320		360
05 - 51331	**LADDERS**						**05 - 51331**
0100	Ladder, 18" wide						
0110	With cage	LF	0.533	47.00	110		160
0120	Without cage	"	0.400	35.25	70.00		110

METAL RAILINGS

ID Code	Component Descriptions	Unit of Meas.	Manhr / Unit	Labor Cost	Material Cost	Equip. Cost	Total Cost
05 - 52131	**RAILINGS**						**05 - 52131**
0080	Railing, pipe						
0090	1-1/4" diameter, welded steel						
0095	2-rail						
0100	Primed	LF	0.160	14.00	31.75		45.75
0120	Galvanized	"	0.160	14.00	40.75		55.00
0130	3-rail						
0140	Primed	LF	0.200	17.75	40.75		59.00
0160	Galvanized	"	0.200	17.75	53.00		71.00
0170	Wall mounted, single rail, welded steel						
0180	Primed	LF	0.123	10.75	21.25		32.00
0200	Galvanized	"	0.123	10.75	27.50		38.25
0210	1-1/2" diameter, welded steel						
0215	2-rail						
0220	Primed	LF	0.160	14.00	34.50		48.50
0240	Galvanized	"	0.160	14.00	44.75		59.00
0245	3-rail						
0250	Primed	LF	0.200	17.75	43.25		61.00
0260	Galvanized	"	0.200	17.75	56.00		74.00
0270	Wall mounted, single rail, welded steel						
0280	Primed	LF	0.123	10.75	21.75		32.50
0300	Galvanized	"	0.123	10.75	28.50		39.25
0960	2" diameter, welded steel						

METAL RAILINGS

ID Code	Component Descriptions	Unit of Meas.	Manhr / Unit	Labor Cost	Material Cost	Equip. Cost	Total Cost
			Descriptions →		**Output** →	**Unit Costs** →	

ID Code	Component Descriptions	Unit of Meas.	Manhr / Unit	Labor Cost	Material Cost	Equip. Cost	Total Cost
05 - 52131	**RAILINGS, Cont'd...**						**05 - 52131**
0980	2-rail						
1000	Primed	LF	0.178	15.75	41.25		57.00
1020	Galvanized	"	0.178	15.75	54.00		70.00
1030	3-rail						
1040	Primed	LF	0.229	20.25	52.00		72.00
1070	Galvanized	"	0.229	20.25	68.00		88.00
1075	Wall mounted, single rail, welded steel						
1080	Primed	LF	0.133	11.75	23.75		35.50
1100	Galvanized	"	0.133	11.75	30.75		42.50

METAL GRATINGS

ID Code	Component Descriptions	Unit of Meas.	Manhr / Unit	Labor Cost	Material Cost	Equip. Cost	Total Cost
05 - 53001	**METAL GRATING**						**05 - 53001**
0200	Floor plate, checkered, steel						
0220	1/4"						
0240	Primed	SF	0.011	1.00	11.75		12.75
0260	Galvanized	"	0.011	1.00	18.00		19.00
0270	3/8"						
0280	Primed	SF	0.012	1.08	17.25		18.25
0300	Galvanized	"	0.012	1.08	27.25		28.25
1000	Aluminum grating, pressure-locked bearing bars						
1020	3/4" x 1/8"	SF	0.020	1.76	28.75		30.50
1030	1" x 1/8"	"	0.020	1.76	32.25		34.00
1040	1-1/4" x 1/8"	"	0.020	1.76	46.00		47.75
1050	1-1/4" x 3/16"	"	0.020	1.76	48.25		50.00
1060	1-1/2" x 1/8"	"	0.020	1.76	63.00		65.00
1070	1-3/4" x 3/16"	"	0.020	1.76	35.75		37.50
2000	Miscellaneous expenses						
2010	Cutting						
2020	Minimum	LF	0.053	4.70			4.70
2040	Maximum	"	0.080	7.06			7.06
2050	Banding						
2060	Minimum	LF	0.133	11.75			11.75
2080	Maximum	"	0.160	14.00			14.00
2090	Toe plates						
2100	Minimum	LF	0.160	14.00			14.00
2120	Maximum	"	0.200	17.75			17.75
3000	Steel grating, primed						

METAL GRATINGS

ID Code	Component Descriptions	Unit of Meas.	Manhr / Unit	Labor Cost	Material Cost	Equip. Cost	Total Cost
	Descriptions	**Output**		**Unit Costs**			
05 - 53001	**METAL GRATING, Cont'd...**						**05 - 53001**
3020	3/4" x 1/8"	SF	0.027	2.35	9.98		12.25
3040	1" x 1/8"	"	0.027	2.35	10.25		12.50
3060	1-1/4" x 1/8"	"	0.027	2.35	11.50		13.75
3080	1-1/4" x 3/16"	"	0.027	2.35	15.25		17.50
3100	1-1/2" x 1/8"	"	0.027	2.35	14.00		16.25
3120	1-3/4" x 3/16"	"	0.027	2.35	20.00		22.25
3140	Galvanized						
3160	3/4" x 1/8"	SF	0.027	2.35	12.50		14.75
3180	1" x 1/8"	"	0.027	2.35	13.00		15.25
3200	1-1/4" x 1/8"	"	0.027	2.35	14.25		16.50
3220	1-1/4" x 3/16"	"	0.027	2.35	19.00		21.25
3240	1-1/2" x 1/8"	"	0.027	2.35	17.50		19.75
3320	1-3/4" x 3/16"	"	0.027	2.35	24.75		27.00
3400	Miscellaneous expenses						
3410	Cutting						
3420	Minimum	LF	0.057	5.04			5.04
3440	Maximum	"	0.089	7.84			7.84
3450	Banding						
3460	Minimum	LF	0.145	12.75			12.75
3480	Maximum	"	0.178	15.75			15.75
3490	Toe plates						
3500	Minimum	LF	0.178	15.75			15.75
3520	Maximum	"	0.229	20.25			20.25

METAL CASTINGS

ID Code	Component Descriptions	Unit of Meas.	Manhr / Unit	Labor Cost	Material Cost	Equip. Cost	Total Cost
05 - 56001	**CASTINGS**						**05 - 56001**
1000	Miscellaneous castings						
1020	Light sections	LB	0.016	1.41	8.04		9.45
1040	Heavy sections	"	0.011	1.00	5.88		6.88
1060	Manhole covers and frames						
1080	Regular, city type						
1090	18" dia.						
1100	100 lb	EA	1.600	140	410		550
1110	24" dia.						
1120	200 lb	EA	1.600	140	380		520
1130	300 lb	"	1.778	160	390		550
1140	400 lb	"	1.778	160	410		570

METAL CASTINGS

ID Code	Component Descriptions	Unit of Meas.	Manhr / Unit	Labor Cost	Material Cost	Equip. Cost	Total Cost
	Descriptions	**Output**		**Unit Costs**			
05 - 56001	**CASTINGS, Cont'd...**						**05 - 56001**
1160	26" dia., 475 lb	EA	2.000	180	500		680
1180	30" dia., 600 lb	"	2.286	200	640		840
1200	8" square, 75 lb	"	0.320	28.25	180		210
1210	24" square						
1220	126 lb	EA	1.600	140	400		540
1240	500 lb	"	2.000	180	640		820
1400	Watertight type						
1420	20" dia., 200 lb	EA	2.000	180	330		510
1440	24" dia., 350 lb	"	2.667	240	570		810
1500	Steps, cast iron						
1520	7" x 9"	EA	0.160	14.00	18.75		32.75
1540	8" x 9"	"	0.178	15.75	26.50		42.25
1600	Manhole covers and frames, aluminum						
1620	12" x 12"	EA	0.320	28.25	91.00		120
1640	18" x 18"	"	0.320	28.25	94.00		120
1660	24" x 24"	"	0.400	35.25	100		140
1800	Corner protection						
1820	Steel angle guard with anchors						
1840	2" x 2" x 3/16"	LF	0.114	10.00	17.50		27.50
1860	2" x 3" x 1/4"	"	0.114	10.00	19.75		29.75
1880	3" x 3" x 5/16"	"	0.114	10.00	23.00		33.00
1900	3" x 4" x 5/16"	"	0.123	10.75	27.75		38.50
1920	4" x 4" x 5/16"	"	0.123	10.75	28.75		39.50

MISC. FABRICATIONS

ID Code	Component Descriptions	Unit of Meas.	Manhr / Unit	Labor Cost	Material Cost	Equip. Cost	Total Cost
05 - 59001	**METAL SPECIALTIES**						**05 - 59001**
0060	Kick plate						
0080	4" high x 1/4" thick						
0100	Primed	LF	0.160	14.00	8.47		22.50
0120	Galvanized	"	0.160	14.00	9.62		23.50
0130	6" high x 1/4" thick						
0140	Primed	LF	0.178	15.75	9.58		25.25
0160	Galvanized	"	0.178	15.75	11.50		27.25

DECORATIVE METAL RAILINGS

ID Code	Component Descriptions	Unit of Meas.	Manhr / Unit	Labor Cost	Material Cost	Equip. Cost	Total Cost
	Descriptions	**Output**		**Unit Costs**			
05 - 73001	**ORNAMENTAL METAL**						**05 - 73001**
1030	Railings, square bars, 6" o.c., shaped top rails						
1040	Steel	LF	0.400	35.25	92.00		130
1060	Aluminum	"	0.400	35.25	110		150
1080	Bronze	"	0.533	47.00	230		280
1100	Stainless steel	"	0.533	47.00	240		290
1200	Laminated metal or wood handrails						
1220	2-1/2" round or oval shape	LF	0.400	35.25	280		320

DIVISION 06
WOOD AND PLASTICS

FASTENERS AND ADHESIVES

ID Code	Descriptions	Output		Unit Costs			
	Component Descriptions	Unit of Meas.	Manhr / Unit	Labor Cost	Material Cost	Equip. Cost	Total Cost
06 - 05231	**ACCESSORIES**						**06 - 05231**
0080	Column/post base, cast aluminum						
0100	4" x 4"	EA	0.200	16.00	19.00		35.00
0120	6" x 6"	"	0.200	16.00	26.75		42.75
0130	Bridging, metal, per pair						
0140	12" o.c.	EA	0.080	6.40	2.59		8.99
0160	16" o.c.	"	0.073	5.81	2.39		8.20
1000	Anchors						
1020	Bolts, threaded two ends, with nuts and washers						
1030	1/2" dia.						
1040	4" long	EA	0.050	4.00	3.02		7.02
1060	7-1/2" long	"	0.050	4.00	3.52		7.52
1070	3/4" dia.						
1080	7-1/2" long	EA	0.050	4.00	6.68		10.75
1100	15" long	"	0.050	4.00	10.00		14.00
1200	Framing anchors						
1202	10 gauge	EA	0.067	5.33	1.19		6.52
1210	Bolts, carriage						
1212	1/4 x 4	EA	0.080	6.40	0.79		7.19
1214	5/16 x 6	"	0.084	6.73	1.78		8.51
1216	3/8 x 6	"	0.084	6.73	3.60		10.25
1218	1/2 x 6	"	0.084	6.73	5.02		11.75
1240	Joist and beam hangers						
1250	18 ga.						
1260	2 x 4	EA	0.080	6.40	1.45		7.85
1280	2 x 6	"	0.080	6.40	1.74		8.14
1282	2 x 8	"	0.080	6.40	2.03		8.43
1284	2 x 10	"	0.089	7.11	2.18		9.29
1286	2 x 12	"	0.100	8.00	2.83		10.75
1288	16 ga.						
1290	3 x 6	EA	0.089	7.11	5.09		12.25
1292	3 x 8	"	0.089	7.11	6.18		13.25
1300	3 x 10	"	0.094	7.52	6.98		14.50
1302	3 x 12	"	0.107	8.53	7.86		16.50
1304	3 x 14	"	0.114	9.14	8.50		17.75
1320	4 x 6	"	0.089	7.11	8.72		15.75
1322	4 x 8	"	0.089	7.11	10.25		17.25
1324	4 x 10	"	0.094	7.52	11.75		19.25
1326	4 x 12	"	0.107	8.53	15.00		23.50

FASTENERS AND ADHESIVES

ID Code	Component Descriptions	Unit of Meas.	Manhr / Unit	Labor Cost	Material Cost	Equip. Cost	Total Cost
	Descriptions	**Output**		**Unit Costs**			
06 - 05231	**ACCESSORIES, Cont'd...**					**06 - 05231**	
1328	4 x 14	EA	0.114	9.14	15.75		25.00
1520	Rafter anchors, 18 ga., 1-1/2" wide						
1540	5-1/4" long	EA	0.067	5.33	1.10		6.43
1560	10-3/4" long	"	0.067	5.33	1.62		6.95
1600	Shear plates						
1620	2-5/8" dia.	EA	0.062	4.92	3.89		8.81
1640	4" dia.	"	0.067	5.33	8.09		13.50
1700	Sill anchors						
1720	Embedded in concrete	EA	0.080	6.40	2.86		9.26
1800	Split rings						
1820	2-1/2" dia.	EA	0.089	7.11	2.35		9.46
1840	4" dia.	"	0.100	8.00	4.33		12.25
1900	Strap ties, 14 ga., 1-3/8" wide						
1920	12" long	EA	0.067	5.33	2.94		8.27
1940	18" long	"	0.073	5.81	3.16		8.97
1960	24" long	"	0.080	6.40	4.70		11.00
1980	36" long	"	0.089	7.11	6.47		13.50
2000	Toothed rings						
2020	2-5/8" dia.	EA	0.133	10.75	2.72		13.50
2040	4" dia.	"	0.160	12.75	3.16		16.00
06 - 05731	**WOOD TREATMENT**					**06 - 05731**	
1000	Creosote preservative treatment						
1020	8 lb/cf	BF					0.74
1040	10 lb/cf	"					0.89
1060	Salt preservative treatment						
1070	Oil borne						
1080	Minimum	BF					0.68
1100	Maximum	"					0.96
1120	Water borne						
1140	Minimum	BF					0.48
1150	Maximum	"					0.74
1200	Fire retardant treatment						
1220	Minimum	BF					0.96
1240	Maximum	"					1.16
1300	Kiln dried, softwood, add to framing costs						
1320	1" thick	BF					0.34
1340	2" thick	"					0.48

FASTENERS AND ADHESIVES

ID Code	Descriptions Component Descriptions	Output Unit of Meas.	Manhr / Unit	Unit Costs Labor Cost	Material Cost	Equip. Cost	Total Cost
06 - 05731	**WOOD TREATMENT, Cont'd...**						**06 - 05731**
1360	3" thick	BF					0.61
1380	4" thick	"					0.74

ROUGH CARPENTRY

06 - 11001	**BLOCKING**						**06 - 11001**
1100	Steel construction						
1105	Walls						
1110	2x4	LF	0.053	4.26	0.54		4.80
1120	2x6	"	0.062	4.92	0.82		5.74
1130	2x8	"	0.067	5.33	1.08		6.41
1140	2x10	"	0.073	5.81	1.44		7.25
1150	2x12	"	0.080	6.40	1.86		8.26
1160	Ceilings						
1170	2x4	LF	0.062	4.92	0.54		5.46
1180	2x6	"	0.073	5.81	0.82		6.63
1190	2x8	"	0.080	6.40	1.08		7.48
1200	2x10	"	0.089	7.11	1.44		8.55
1210	2x12	"	0.100	8.00	1.86		9.86
1215	Wood construction						
1220	Walls						
1230	2x4	LF	0.044	3.55	0.60		4.15
1240	2x6	"	0.050	4.00	0.92		4.92
1250	2x8	"	0.053	4.26	1.21		5.47
1260	2x10	"	0.057	4.57	1.62		6.19
1270	2x12	"	0.062	4.92	2.09		7.01
1280	Ceilings						
1290	2x4	LF	0.050	4.00	0.60		4.60
1300	2x6	"	0.057	4.57	0.92		5.49
1310	2x8	"	0.062	4.92	1.21		6.13
1320	2x10	"	0.067	5.33	1.62		6.95
1330	2x12	"	0.073	5.81	2.09		7.90

ROUGH CARPENTRY

ID Code	Component Descriptions	Unit of Meas.	Manhr / Unit	Labor Cost	Material Cost	Equip. Cost	Total Cost
06 - 11002	**CEILING FRAMING**						**06 - 11002**
1000	Ceiling joists						
1010	12" o.c.						
1020	2x4	SF	0.019	1.52	0.90		2.42
1030	2x6	"	0.020	1.60	1.30		2.90
1040	2x8	"	0.021	1.68	1.91		3.59
1050	2x10	"	0.022	1.77	2.17		3.94
1060	2x12	"	0.024	1.88	4.00		5.88
1070	16" o.c.						
1080	2x4	SF	0.015	1.23	0.73		1.96
1090	2x6	"	0.016	1.28	1.09		2.37
1100	2x8	"	0.017	1.33	1.55		2.88
1110	2x10	"	0.017	1.39	1.74		3.13
1120	2x12	"	0.018	1.45	3.26		4.71
1130	24" o.c.						
1140	2x4	SF	0.013	1.01	0.52		1.53
1150	2x6	"	0.013	1.06	0.87		1.93
1160	2x8	"	0.014	1.12	1.30		2.42
1170	2x10	"	0.015	1.18	1.55		2.73
1180	2x12	"	0.016	1.25	3.92		5.17
1200	Headers and nailers						
1210	2x4	LF	0.026	2.06	0.60		2.66
1220	2x6	"	0.027	2.13	0.92		3.05
1230	2x8	"	0.029	2.28	1.21		3.49
1240	2x10	"	0.031	2.46	1.62		4.08
1250	2x12	"	0.033	2.66	1.99		4.65
1300	Sister joists for ceilings						
1310	2x4	LF	0.057	4.57	0.60		5.17
1320	2x6	"	0.067	5.33	0.92		6.25
1330	2x8	"	0.080	6.40	1.21		7.61
1340	2x10	"	0.100	8.00	1.62		9.62
1350	2x12	"	0.133	10.75	1.99		12.75
06 - 11003	**FLOOR FRAMING**						**06 - 11003**
1000	Floor joists						
1010	12" o.c.						
1020	2x6	SF	0.016	1.28	1.10		2.38
1030	2x8	"	0.016	1.30	1.63		2.93
1040	2x10	"	0.017	1.33	2.25		3.58

ROUGH CARPENTRY

ID Code	Descriptions — Component Descriptions	Output — Unit of Meas.	Output — Manhr / Unit	Unit Costs — Labor Cost	Unit Costs — Material Cost	Unit Costs — Equip. Cost	Unit Costs — Total Cost
06 - 11003	**FLOOR FRAMING, Cont'd...**						**06 - 11003**
1050	2x12	SF	0.017	1.39	3.31		4.70
1060	2x14	"	0.017	1.33	5.04		6.37
1070	3x6	"	0.017	1.36	3.73		5.09
1080	3x8	"	0.017	1.39	4.87		6.26
1090	3x10	"	0.018	1.45	6.09		7.54
1100	3x12	"	0.019	1.52	7.31		8.83
1120	3x14	"	0.020	1.60	8.35		9.95
1130	4x6	"	0.017	1.33	4.87		6.20
1140	4x8	"	0.017	1.39	6.26		7.65
1150	4x10	"	0.018	1.45	8.00		9.45
1160	4x12	"	0.019	1.52	9.73		11.25
1170	4x14	"	0.020	1.60	11.25		12.75
1180	16" o.c.						
1190	2x6	SF	0.013	1.06	0.95		2.01
1200	2x8	"	0.014	1.08	1.34		2.42
1220	2x10	"	0.014	1.10	1.63		2.73
1230	2x12	"	0.014	1.14	2.03		3.17
1240	2x14	"	0.015	1.18	4.52		5.70
1250	3x6	"	0.014	1.10	3.13		4.23
1260	3x8	"	0.014	1.14	4.00		5.14
1270	3x10	"	0.015	1.18	5.04		6.22
1280	3x12	"	0.015	1.23	6.09		7.32
1290	3x14	"	0.016	1.28	7.21		8.49
1300	4x6	"	0.014	1.10	4.00		5.10
1310	4x8	"	0.014	1.14	5.48		6.62
1320	4x10	"	0.015	1.18	6.78		7.96
1330	4x12	"	0.015	1.23	8.00		9.23
1340	4x14	"	0.016	1.28	9.57		10.75
2000	Sister joists for floors						
2010	2x4	LF	0.050	4.00	0.60		4.60
2020	2x6	"	0.057	4.57	0.92		5.49
2030	2x8	"	0.067	5.33	1.21		6.54
2040	2x10	"	0.080	6.40	1.62		8.02
2050	2x12	"	0.100	8.00	2.09		10.00
2060	3x6	"	0.080	6.40	3.04		9.44
2070	3x8	"	0.089	7.11	3.73		10.75
2080	3x10	"	0.100	8.00	4.95		13.00
2090	3x12	"	0.114	9.14	5.99		15.25

ROUGH CARPENTRY

ID Code	Component Descriptions	Unit of Meas.	Manhr / Unit	Labor Cost	Material Cost	Equip. Cost	Total Cost
	Descriptions	**Output**		**Unit Costs**			
06 - 11003	**FLOOR FRAMING, Cont'd...**					**06 - 11003**	
2100	4x6	LF	0.080	6.40	3.92		10.25
2110	4x8	"	0.089	7.11	5.22		12.25
2120	4x10	"	0.100	8.00	6.78		14.75
2130	4x12	"	0.114	9.14	7.56		16.75
3000	Plywood Web Joists, 16" o.c.						
3010	3/8" plywood web and 1-3/4" top & bottom chord						
3020	9-1/2" depth	SF	0.014	1.10	1.80		2.90
3030	11-7/8" depth	"	0.016	1.28	1.85		3.13
3040	14" depth	"	0.018	1.42	2.28		3.70
3050	16" depth	"	0.020	1.60	3.43		5.03
3100	Wood Trussed Floor Joists						
3110	2" x 4" chord and truss members						
3130	11-1/4" depth	SF	0.016	1.28	5.79		7.07
3140	14" depth	"	0.018	1.42	6.21		7.63
3150	16" depth	"	0.020	1.60	6.38		7.98
3160	18" depth	"	0.023	1.82	6.69		8.51
06 - 11004	**FURRING**					**06 - 11004**	
1100	Furring, wood strips						
1102	Walls						
1105	On masonry or concrete walls						
1107	1x2 furring						
1110	12" o.c.	SF	0.025	2.00	0.48		2.48
1120	16" o.c.	"	0.023	1.82	0.41		2.23
1130	24" o.c.	"	0.021	1.68	0.40		2.08
1135	1x3 furring						
1140	12" o.c.	SF	0.025	2.00	0.60		2.60
1150	16" o.c.	"	0.023	1.82	0.55		2.37
1160	24" o.c.	"	0.021	1.68	0.42		2.10
1165	On wood walls						
1167	1x2 furring						
1170	12" o.c.	SF	0.018	1.42	0.48		1.90
1180	16" o.c.	"	0.016	1.28	0.41		1.69
1190	24" o.c.	"	0.015	1.16	0.38		1.54
1195	1x3 furring						
1200	12" o.c.	SF	0.018	1.42	0.62		2.04
1210	16" o.c.	"	0.016	1.28	0.52		1.80
1220	24" o.c.	"	0.015	1.16	0.42		1.58

ROUGH CARPENTRY

ID Code	Component Descriptions	Unit of Meas.	Manhr / Unit	Labor Cost	Material Cost	Equip. Cost	Total Cost
	Descriptions	**Output**		**Unit Costs**			

06 - 11004 — FURRING, Cont'd... — 06 - 11004

ID Code	Component Descriptions	Unit of Meas.	Manhr / Unit	Labor Cost	Material Cost	Equip. Cost	Total Cost
1224	Ceilings						
1226	On masonry or concrete ceilings						
1228	1x2 furring						
1230	12" o.c.	SF	0.044	3.55	0.48		4.03
1240	16" o.c.	"	0.040	3.20	0.41		3.61
1250	24" o.c.	"	0.036	2.90	0.38		3.28
1254	1x3 furring						
1260	12" o.c.	SF	0.044	3.55	0.60		4.15
1270	16" o.c.	"	0.040	3.20	0.52		3.72
1280	24" o.c.	"	0.036	2.90	0.42		3.32
1286	On wood ceilings						
1288	1x2 furring						
1290	12" o.c.	SF	0.030	2.37	0.48		2.85
1300	16" o.c.	"	0.027	2.13	0.41		2.54
1310	24" o.c.	"	0.024	1.93	0.38		2.31
1316	1x3						
1320	12" o.c.	SF	0.030	2.37	0.60		2.97
1330	16" o.c.	"	0.027	2.13	0.52		2.65
1340	24" o.c.	"	0.024	1.93	0.42		2.35

06 - 11005 — ROOF FRAMING — 06 - 11005

ID Code	Component Descriptions	Unit of Meas.	Manhr / Unit	Labor Cost	Material Cost	Equip. Cost	Total Cost
1000	Roof framing						
1005	Rafters, gable end						
1008	0-2 pitch (flat to 2-in-12)						
1010	12" o.c.						
1020	2x4	SF	0.017	1.33	0.87		2.20
1030	2x6	"	0.017	1.39	1.21		2.60
1040	2x8	"	0.018	1.45	1.74		3.19
1050	2x10	"	0.019	1.52	2.17		3.69
1060	2x12	"	0.020	1.60	4.00		5.60
1070	16" o.c.						
1080	2x6	SF	0.014	1.14	1.09		2.23
1090	2x8	"	0.015	1.18	1.53		2.71
1100	2x10	"	0.015	1.23	1.74		2.97
1110	2x12	"	0.016	1.28	3.21		4.49
1120	24" o.c.						
1130	2x6	SF	0.012	0.96	0.60		1.56
1140	2x8	"	0.013	1.00	1.27		2.27

ROUGH CARPENTRY

ID Code	Component Descriptions	Unit of Meas.	Manhr / Unit	Labor Cost	Material Cost	Equip. Cost	Total Cost
06 - 11005	**ROOF FRAMING, Cont'd...**						**06 - 11005**
1150	2x10	SF	0.013	1.03	1.48		2.51
1160	2x12	"	0.013	1.06	2.60		3.66
1165	4-6 pitch (4-in-12 to 6-in-12)						
1170	12" o.c.						
1175	2x4	SF	0.017	1.39	0.87		2.26
1180	2x6	"	0.018	1.45	1.30		2.75
1190	2x8	"	0.019	1.52	1.99		3.51
1200	2x10	"	0.020	1.60	2.25		3.85
1210	2x12	"	0.021	1.68	3.47		5.15
1220	16" o.c.						
1230	2x6	SF	0.015	1.18	1.09		2.27
1240	2x8	"	0.015	1.23	1.74		2.97
1250	2x10	"	0.016	1.28	1.99		3.27
1260	2x12	"	0.017	1.33	2.96		4.29
1270	24" o.c.						
1280	2x6	SF	0.013	1.00	0.87		1.87
1290	2x8	"	0.013	1.03	1.48		2.51
1300	2x10	"	0.014	1.10	1.56		2.66
1310	2x12	"	0.015	1.23	2.43		3.66
1315	8-12 pitch (8-in-12 to 12-in-12)						
1320	12" o.c.						
1330	2x4	SF	0.018	1.45	0.95		2.40
1340	2x6	"	0.019	1.52	1.48		3.00
1350	2x8	"	0.020	1.60	2.09		3.69
1360	2x10	"	0.021	1.68	2.43		4.11
1370	2x12	"	0.022	1.77	3.73		5.50
1380	16" o.c.						
1390	2x6	SF	0.015	1.23	1.21		2.44
1400	2x8	"	0.016	1.28	1.95		3.23
1410	2x10	"	0.017	1.33	2.17		3.50
1420	2x12	"	0.017	1.39	3.13		4.52
1430	24" o.c.						
1440	2x6	SF	0.013	1.03	0.95		1.98
1450	2x8	"	0.013	1.06	1.55		2.61
1460	2x10	"	0.014	1.10	1.74		2.84
1470	2x12	"	0.014	1.14	2.78		3.92
2000	Ridge boards						
2010	2x6	LF	0.040	3.20	0.92		4.12

ROUGH CARPENTRY

ID Code	Component Descriptions	Unit of Meas.	Manhr / Unit	Labor Cost	Material Cost	Equip. Cost	Total Cost
	Descriptions	**Output**		**Unit Costs**			
06 - 11005	**ROOF FRAMING, Cont'd...**						**06 - 11005**
2020	2x8	LF	0.044	3.55	1.21		4.76
2030	2x10	"	0.050	4.00	1.62		5.62
2040	2x12	"	0.057	4.57	2.09		6.66
3000	Hip rafters						
3010	2x6	LF	0.029	2.28	0.92		3.20
3020	2x8	"	0.030	2.37	1.21		3.58
3030	2x10	"	0.031	2.46	1.62		4.08
3040	2x12	"	0.032	2.56	2.09		4.65
3180	Jack rafters						
3190	4-6 pitch (4-in-12 to 6-in-12)						
3200	16" o.c.						
3210	2x6	SF	0.024	1.88	1.13		3.01
3220	2x8	"	0.024	1.93	1.74		3.67
3230	2x10	"	0.026	2.06	1.99		4.05
3240	2x12	"	0.027	2.13	2.96		5.09
3250	24" o.c.						
3260	2x6	SF	0.018	1.45	0.87		2.32
3270	2x8	"	0.019	1.48	1.48		2.96
3280	2x10	"	0.020	1.56	1.74		3.30
3290	2x12	"	0.020	1.60	2.52		4.12
3295	8-12 pitch (8-in-12 to 12-in-12)						
3300	16" o.c.						
3310	2x6	SF	0.025	2.00	1.74		3.74
3320	2x8	"	0.026	2.06	2.17		4.23
3330	2x10	"	0.027	2.13	3.13		5.26
3340	2x12	"	0.028	2.20	4.34		6.54
3350	24" o.c.						
3360	2x6	SF	0.019	1.52	1.38		2.90
3370	2x8	"	0.020	1.56	1.74		3.30
3380	2x10	"	0.020	1.60	2.78		4.38
3390	2x12	"	0.021	1.64	4.00		5.64
4980	Sister rafters						
5000	2x4	LF	0.057	4.57	0.60		5.17
5010	2x6	"	0.067	5.33	0.92		6.25
5020	2x8	"	0.080	6.40	1.21		7.61
5030	2x10	"	0.100	8.00	1.62		9.62
5040	2x12	"	0.133	10.75	2.09		12.75
5050	Fascia boards						

ROUGH CARPENTRY

ID Code	Component Descriptions	Unit of Meas.	Manhr / Unit	Labor Cost	Material Cost	Equip. Cost	Total Cost
	Descriptions	**Output**		**Unit Costs**			
06 - 11005	**ROOF FRAMING, Cont'd...**						**06 - 11005**
5060	2x4	LF	0.040	3.20	0.60		3.80
5070	2x6	"	0.040	3.20	0.92		4.12
5080	2x8	"	0.044	3.55	1.21		4.76
5090	2x10	"	0.044	3.55	1.62		5.17
5100	2x12	"	0.050	4.00	2.09		6.09
7980	Cant strips						
7985	Fiber						
8000	3x3	LF	0.023	1.82	0.48		2.30
8020	4x4	"	0.024	1.93	0.67		2.60
8030	Wood						
8040	3x3	LF	0.024	1.93	2.52		4.45
06 - 11006	**SLEEPERS**						**06 - 11006**
0960	Sleepers, over concrete						
0980	12" o.c.						
1000	1x2	SF	0.018	1.45	0.29		1.74
1020	1x3	"	0.019	1.52	0.43		1.95
1060	2x4	"	0.022	1.77	0.95		2.72
1080	2x6	"	0.024	1.88	1.39		3.27
1090	16" o.c.						
1100	1x2	SF	0.016	1.28	0.26		1.54
1120	1x3	"	0.016	1.28	0.37		1.65
1140	2x4	"	0.019	1.52	0.79		2.31
1160	2x6	"	0.020	1.60	1.17		2.77
06 - 11007	**SOFFITS**						**06 - 11007**
0980	Soffit framing						
1000	2x3	LF	0.057	4.57	0.41		4.98
1020	2x4	"	0.062	4.92	0.51		5.43
1030	2x6	"	0.067	5.33	0.75		6.08
1040	2x8	"	0.073	5.81	1.06		6.87
06 - 11008	**WALL FRAMING**						**06 - 11008**
0960	Framing wall, studs						
0980	12" o.c.						
1000	2x3	SF	0.015	1.18	0.53		1.71
1040	2x4	"	0.015	1.18	0.75		1.93
1080	2x6	"	0.016	1.28	1.09		2.37
1100	2x8	"	0.017	1.33	1.46		2.79

ROUGH CARPENTRY

ID Code	Component Descriptions	Unit of Meas.	Manhr / Unit	Labor Cost	Material Cost	Equip. Cost	Total Cost
	Descriptions	**Output**		**Unit Costs**			
06 - 11008	**WALL FRAMING, Cont'd...**						**06 - 11008**
1110	16" o.c.						
1120	2x3	SF	0.013	1.00	0.43		1.43
1140	2x4	"	0.013	1.00	0.61		1.61
1150	2x6	"	0.013	1.06	0.87		1.93
1160	2x8	"	0.014	1.10	1.37		2.47
1165	24" o.c.						
1170	2x3	SF	0.011	0.86	0.34		1.20
1180	2x4	"	0.011	0.86	0.46		1.32
1190	2x6	"	0.011	0.91	0.73		1.64
1200	2x8	"	0.012	0.94	0.95		1.89
1480	Plates, top or bottom						
1500	2x3	LF	0.024	1.88	0.41		2.29
1510	2x4	"	0.025	2.00	0.51		2.51
1520	2x6	"	0.027	2.13	0.75		2.88
1530	2x8	"	0.029	2.28	1.06		3.34
2000	Headers, door or window						
2005	2x6						
2008	Single						
2010	3' long	EA	0.400	32.00	2.46		34.50
2020	6' long	"	0.500	40.00	4.92		45.00
2025	Double						
2030	3' long	EA	0.444	35.50	4.94		40.50
2040	6' long	"	0.571	45.75	9.89		56.00
2044	2x8						
2046	Single						
2050	4' long	EA	0.500	40.00	4.51		44.50
2060	8' long	"	0.615	49.25	9.01		58.00
2065	Double						
2070	4' long	EA	0.571	45.75	9.01		55.00
2080	8' long	"	0.727	58.00	18.00		76.00
2085	2x10						
2088	Single						
2090	5' long	EA	0.615	49.25	6.82		56.00
2100	10' long	"	0.800	64.00	13.75		78.00
2110	Double						
2120	5' long	EA	0.667	53.00	13.75		67.00
2130	10' long	"	0.800	64.00	27.25		91.00
2134	2x12						

ROUGH CARPENTRY

ID Code	Component Descriptions	Unit of Meas.	Manhr / Unit	Labor Cost	Material Cost	Equip. Cost	Total Cost
		Descriptions	**Output**		**Unit Costs**		

06 - 11008 — WALL FRAMING, Cont'd... — 06 - 11008

ID Code	Component Descriptions	Unit of Meas.	Manhr / Unit	Labor Cost	Material Cost	Equip. Cost	Total Cost
2138	Single						
2140	6' long	EA	0.615	49.25	9.89		59.00
2150	12' long	"	0.800	64.00	19.50		84.00
2155	Double						
2160	6' long	EA	0.727	58.00	19.50		78.00
2170	12' long	"	0.889	71.00	38.75		110

TIMBER

06 - 13001 — HEAVY TIMBER — 06 - 13001

ID Code	Component Descriptions	Unit of Meas.	Manhr / Unit	Labor Cost	Material Cost	Equip. Cost	Total Cost
1000	Mill framed structures						
1010	Beams to 20' long						
1020	Douglas fir						
1040	6x8	LF	0.080	5.01	8.36	3.50	16.75
1042	6x10	"	0.083	5.18	9.87	3.62	18.75
1044	6x12	"	0.089	5.56	11.75	3.88	21.25
1046	6x14	"	0.092	5.78	14.25	4.03	24.00
1048	6x16	"	0.096	6.01	15.50	4.20	25.75
1060	8x10	"	0.083	5.18	13.00	3.62	21.75
1070	8x12	"	0.089	5.56	15.50	3.88	25.00
1080	8x14	"	0.092	5.78	17.75	4.03	27.50
1090	8x16	"	0.096	6.01	20.25	4.20	30.50
1200	Southern yellow pine						
1220	6x8	LF	0.080	5.01	6.63	3.50	15.25
1222	6x10	"	0.083	5.18	8.05	3.62	16.75
1224	6x12	"	0.089	5.56	10.25	3.88	19.75
1226	6x14	"	0.092	5.78	11.75	4.03	21.50
1228	6x16	"	0.096	6.01	13.00	4.20	23.25
1240	8x10	"	0.083	5.18	11.00	3.62	19.75
1242	8x12	"	0.089	5.56	13.25	3.88	22.75
1244	8x14	"	0.092	5.78	15.25	4.03	25.00
1246	8x16	"	0.096	6.01	17.50	4.20	27.75
1380	Columns to 12' high						
1400	Douglas fir						
1420	6x6	LF	0.120	7.51	6.01	5.25	18.75
1440	8x8	"	0.120	7.51	10.25	5.25	23.00
1460	10x10	"	0.133	8.35	18.00	5.83	32.25
1480	12x12	"	0.133	8.35	22.25	5.83	36.50

TIMBER

ID Code	Component Descriptions	Unit of Meas.	Manhr / Unit	Labor Cost	Material Cost	Equip. Cost	Total Cost
	Descriptions	**Output**		**Unit Costs**			

06 - 13001　　HEAVY TIMBER, Cont'd...　　06 - 13001

ID Code	Component Descriptions	Unit of Meas.	Manhr / Unit	Labor Cost	Material Cost	Equip. Cost	Total Cost
1500	Southern yellow pine						
1520	6x6	LF	0.120	7.51	5.17	5.25	18.00
1540	8x8	"	0.120	7.51	8.70	5.25	21.50
1560	10x10	"	0.133	8.35	13.50	5.83	27.75
1580	12x12	"	0.133	8.35	18.75	5.83	33.00
2000	Posts, treated						
2100	4x4	LF	0.032	2.56	2.07		4.63
2120	6x6	"	0.040	3.20	6.01		9.21

WOOD DECKING

06 - 15001　　WOOD DECKING　　06 - 15001

ID Code	Component Descriptions	Unit of Meas.	Manhr / Unit	Labor Cost	Material Cost	Equip. Cost	Total Cost
0090	Decking, T&G solid						
0095	Cedar						
0100	3" thick	SF	0.020	1.60	11.75		13.25
0120	4" thick	"	0.021	1.70	14.50		16.25
1030	Fir						
1040	3" thick	SF	0.020	1.60	5.10		6.70
1060	4" thick	"	0.021	1.70	6.19		7.89
1080	Southern yellow pine						
2000	3" thick	SF	0.023	1.82	5.10		6.92
2020	4" thick	"	0.025	1.96	5.39		7.35
3120	White pine						
3140	3" thick	SF	0.020	1.60	6.19		7.79
3160	4" thick	"	0.021	1.70	8.38		10.00

SHEATHING

06 - 16001　　FLOOR SHEATHING　　06 - 16001

ID Code	Component Descriptions	Unit of Meas.	Manhr / Unit	Labor Cost	Material Cost	Equip. Cost	Total Cost
1980	Sub-flooring, plywood, CDX						
2000	1/2" thick	SF	0.010	0.80	0.61		1.41
2020	5/8" thick	"	0.011	0.91	0.88		1.79
2080	3/4" thick	"	0.013	1.06	1.62		2.68
2090	Structural plywood						
2100	1/2" thick	SF	0.010	0.80	0.96		1.76
2120	5/8" thick	"	0.011	0.91	1.54		2.45
2140	3/4" thick	"	0.012	0.98	1.62		2.60
3100	Board type subflooring						

SHEATHING

	Descriptions	Output		Unit Costs			
ID Code	Component Descriptions	Unit of Meas.	Manhr / Unit	Labor Cost	Material Cost	Equip. Cost	Total Cost
06 - 16001	**FLOOR SHEATHING, Cont'd...**						**06 - 16001**
3105	1x6						
3110	Minimum	SF	0.018	1.42	1.46		2.88
3115	Maximum	"	0.020	1.60	1.86		3.46
3117	1x8						
3120	Minimum	SF	0.017	1.34	1.62		2.96
3140	Maximum	"	0.019	1.50	1.90		3.40
3150	1x10						
3160	Minimum	SF	0.016	1.28	2.27		3.55
3180	Maximum	"	0.018	1.42	2.43		3.85
5990	Underlayment						
6000	Hardboard, 1/4" tempered	SF	0.010	0.80	0.90		1.70
6010	Plywood, CDX						
6020	3/8" thick	SF	0.010	0.80	0.94		1.74
6040	1/2" thick	"	0.011	0.85	1.12		1.97
6060	5/8" thick	"	0.011	0.91	1.30		2.21
6080	3/4" thick	"	0.012	0.98	1.62		2.60
06 - 16002	**ROOF SHEATHING**						**06 - 16002**
0080	Sheathing						
0090	Plywood, CDX						
1000	3/8" thick	SF	0.010	0.82	0.94		1.76
1020	1/2" thick	"	0.011	0.85	1.12		1.97
1040	5/8" thick	"	0.011	0.91	1.30		2.21
1060	3/4" thick	"	0.012	0.98	1.62		2.60
1080	Structural plywood						
2040	3/8" thick	SF	0.010	0.82	0.59		1.41
2060	1/2" thick	"	0.011	0.85	0.77		1.62
2080	5/8" thick	"	0.011	0.91	0.94		1.85
2100	3/4" thick	"	0.012	0.98	1.13		2.11
06 - 16003	**WALL SHEATHING**						**06 - 16003**
0980	Sheathing						
0990	Plywood, CDX						
1000	3/8" thick	SF	0.012	0.94	0.94		1.88
1020	1/2" thick	"	0.012	0.98	1.12		2.10
1040	5/8" thick	"	0.013	1.06	1.30		2.36
1060	3/4" thick	"	0.015	1.16	1.62		2.78
3000	Waferboard						
3020	3/8" thick	SF	0.012	0.94	0.59		1.53

SHEATHING

ID Code	Component Descriptions	Unit of Meas.	Manhr / Unit	Labor Cost	Material Cost	Equip. Cost	Total Cost
	Descriptions	**Output**		**Unit Costs**			

06 - 16003 — WALL SHEATHING, Cont'd... — 06 - 16003

ID Code	Component Descriptions	Unit of Meas.	Manhr / Unit	Labor Cost	Material Cost	Equip. Cost	Total Cost
3040	1/2" thick	SF	0.012	0.98	0.77		1.75
3060	5/8" thick	"	0.013	1.06	0.94		2.00
3080	3/4" thick	"	0.015	1.16	1.03		2.19
4100	Structural plywood						
4120	3/8" thick	SF	0.012	0.94	0.94		1.88
4140	1/2" thick	"	0.012	0.98	1.12		2.10
4160	5/8" thick	"	0.013	1.06	1.30		2.36
4180	3/4" thick	"	0.015	1.16	1.12		2.28
7000	Gypsum, 1/2" thick	"	0.012	0.98	0.59		1.57
8000	Asphalt impregnated fiberboard, 1/2" thick	"	0.012	0.98	1.03		2.01

TRUSSES

06 - 17531 — WOOD TRUSSES — 06 - 17531

ID Code	Component Descriptions	Unit of Meas.	Manhr / Unit	Labor Cost	Material Cost	Equip. Cost	Total Cost
0960	Truss, fink, 2x4 members						
0980	3-in-12 slope						
1000	24' span	EA	0.686	43.00	120	30.00	190
1020	26' span	"	0.686	43.00	130	30.00	200
1021	28' span	"	0.727	45.50	140	31.75	220
1022	30' span	"	0.727	45.50	150	31.75	230
1024	34' span	"	0.774	48.50	150	33.75	230
1025	38' span	"	0.774	48.50	150	33.75	230
1030	5-in-12 slope						
1040	24' span	EA	0.706	44.25	130	31.00	200
1050	28' span	"	0.727	45.50	140	31.75	220
1055	30' span	"	0.750	47.00	150	32.75	230
1060	32' span	"	0.750	47.00	160	32.75	240
1070	40' span	"	0.800	50.00	210	35.00	300
1074	Gable, 2x4 members						
1078	5-in-12 slope						
1080	24' span	EA	0.706	44.25	150	31.00	230
1090	26' span	"	0.706	44.25	160	31.00	240
1100	28' span	"	0.727	45.50	180	31.75	260
1120	30' span	"	0.750	47.00	190	32.75	270
1140	32' span	"	0.750	47.00	200	32.75	280
1160	36' span	"	0.774	48.50	210	33.75	290
1180	40' span	"	0.800	50.00	230	35.00	310
1190	King post type, 2x4 members						

TRUSSES

ID Code	Descriptions	Output		Unit Costs			
	Component Descriptions	Unit of Meas.	Manhr / Unit	Labor Cost	Material Cost	Equip. Cost	Total Cost

06 - 17531 — WOOD TRUSSES, Cont'd... — 06 - 17531

ID Code	Component Descriptions	Unit of Meas.	Manhr / Unit	Labor Cost	Material Cost	Equip. Cost	Total Cost
2000	4-in-12 slope						
2040	16' span	EA	0.649	40.75	91.00	28.25	160
2060	18' span	"	0.667	41.75	98.00	29.25	170
2080	24' span	"	0.706	44.25	110	31.00	190
2100	26' span	"	0.706	44.25	110	31.00	190
2120	30' span	"	0.750	47.00	140	32.75	220
2140	34' span	"	0.750	47.00	150	32.75	230
2160	38' span	"	0.774	48.50	180	33.75	260
2180	42' span	"	0.828	52.00	220	36.25	310

GLUED-LAMINATED CONSTRUCTION

06 - 18131 — LAMINATED BEAMS — 06 - 18131

ID Code	Component Descriptions	Unit of Meas.	Manhr / Unit	Labor Cost	Material Cost	Equip. Cost	Total Cost
0010	Parallel strand beams 3-1/2" wide x						
0020	9-1/2"	LF	0.034	2.14	12.25	1.50	16.00
0030	11-1/4"	"	0.036	2.22	13.00	1.55	16.75
0040	11-7/8"	"	0.037	2.31	13.75	1.61	17.75
0050	14"	"	0.044	2.73	17.50	1.90	22.25
0060	16"	"	0.048	3.00	20.75	2.10	25.75
0070	18"	"	0.053	3.34	24.50	2.33	30.25
1000	Laminated veneer beams, 1-3/4" wide x						
1010	11-7/8"	LF	0.037	2.31	8.36	1.61	12.25
1020	14"	"	0.044	2.73	10.50	1.90	15.25
1030	16"	"	0.048	3.00	10.25	2.10	15.25
1040	18"	"	0.053	3.34	13.00	2.33	18.75
2000	Laminated strand beams, 1-3/4" wide x						
2010	9-1/2"	LF	0.034	2.14	5.36	1.50	9.00
2020	11-7/8"	"	0.037	2.31	6.13	1.61	10.00
2030	14"	"	0.044	2.73	7.21	1.90	11.75
2040	16"	"	0.048	3.00	8.27	2.10	13.25
2050	3-1/2" wide x						
2060	9-1/2"	LF	0.034	2.14	9.43	1.50	13.00
2070	11-7/8"	"	0.037	2.31	12.25	1.61	16.25
2080	14"	"	0.044	2.73	14.50	1.90	19.25
2090	16"	"	0.048	3.00	17.25	2.10	22.25
3000	Gluelam beam, 3-1/2" wide x						
3010	10"	LF	0.034	2.14	14.25	1.50	18.00
3020	12"	"	0.040	2.50	16.75	1.75	21.00

GLUED-LAMINATED CONSTRUCTION

ID Code	Component Descriptions	Unit of Meas.	Manhr / Unit	Labor Cost	Material Cost	Equip. Cost	Total Cost
	Descriptions	**Output**		**Unit Costs**			

06 - 18131	LAMINATED BEAMS, Cont'd...						06 - 18131
3030	15"	LF	0.046	2.86	20.00	2.00	24.75
3040	5-1/2" wide x						
3050	10"	LF	0.034	2.14	23.00	1.50	26.75
3060	16"	"	0.048	3.00	36.00	2.10	41.00
3070	20"	"	0.056	3.53	42.50	2.47	48.50

FINISH CARPENTRY

06 - 20231	FINISH CARPENTRY						06 - 20231
0070	Mouldings and trim						
0980	Apron, flat						
1000	9/16 x 2	LF	0.040	3.20	1.99		5.19
1010	9/16 x 3-1/2	"	0.042	3.36	4.59		7.95
1015	Base						
1020	Colonial						
1022	7/16 x 2-1/4	LF	0.040	3.20	2.37		5.57
1024	7/16 x 3	"	0.040	3.20	3.07		6.27
1026	7/16 x 3-1/4	"	0.040	3.20	3.14		6.34
1028	9/16 x 3	"	0.042	3.36	3.07		6.43
1030	9/16 x 3-1/4	"	0.042	3.36	3.21		6.57
1034	11/16 x 2-1/4	"	0.044	3.55	3.37		6.92
1035	Ranch						
1036	7/16 x 2-1/4	LF	0.040	3.20	2.60		5.80
1038	7/16 x 3-1/4	"	0.040	3.20	3.07		6.27
1039	9/16 x 2-1/4	"	0.042	3.36	2.83		6.19
1041	9/16 x 3	"	0.042	3.36	3.07		6.43
1043	9/16 x 3-1/4	"	0.042	3.36	3.14		6.50
1050	Casing						
1060	11/16 x 2-1/2	LF	0.036	2.90	2.44		5.34
1070	11/16 x 3-1/2	"	0.038	3.04	2.76		5.80
1180	Chair rail						
1200	9/16 x 2-1/2	LF	0.040	3.20	2.60		5.80
1210	9/16 x 3-1/2	"	0.040	3.20	3.60		6.80
1250	Closet pole						
1300	1-1/8" dia.	LF	0.053	4.26	1.76		6.02
1310	1-5/8" dia.	"	0.053	4.26	2.60		6.86
1340	Cove						
1500	9/16 x 1-3/4	LF	0.040	3.20	1.99		5.19

FINISH CARPENTRY

ID Code	Descriptions	Output		Unit Costs			
	Component Descriptions	Unit of Meas.	Manhr / Unit	Labor Cost	Material Cost	Equip. Cost	Total Cost
06 - 20231	**FINISH CARPENTRY, Cont'd...**					**06 - 20231**	
1510	11/16 x 2-3/4	LF	0.040	3.20	3.07		6.27
1550	Crown						
1600	9/16 x 1-5/8	LF	0.053	4.26	2.60		6.86
1610	9/16 x 2-5/8	"	0.062	4.92	2.83		7.75
1620	11/16 x 3-5/8	"	0.067	5.33	3.07		8.40
1630	11/16 x 4-1/4	"	0.073	5.81	4.59		10.50
1640	11/16 x 5-1/4	"	0.080	6.40	5.14		11.50
1680	Drip cap						
1700	1-1/16 x 1-5/8	LF	0.040	3.20	2.76		5.96
1780	Glass bead						
1800	3/8 x 3/8	LF	0.050	4.00	0.99		4.99
1820	1/2 x 9/16	"	0.050	4.00	1.22		5.22
1840	5/8 x 5/8	"	0.050	4.00	1.30		5.30
1860	3/4 x 3/4	"	0.050	4.00	1.53		5.53
1880	Half round						
1900	1/2	LF	0.032	2.56	1.15		3.71
1910	5/8	"	0.032	2.56	1.53		4.09
1920	3/4	"	0.032	2.56	2.07		4.63
1980	Lattice						
2000	1/4 x 7/8	LF	0.032	2.56	0.92		3.48
2010	1/4 x 1-1/8	"	0.032	2.56	0.99		3.55
2020	1/4 x 1-3/8	"	0.032	2.56	1.06		3.62
2030	1/4 x 1-3/4	"	0.032	2.56	1.19		3.75
2040	1/4 x 2	"	0.032	2.56	1.38		3.94
2080	Ogee molding						
2100	5/8 x 3/4	LF	0.040	3.20	1.83		5.03
2110	11/16 x 1-1/8	"	0.040	3.20	4.30		7.50
2120	11/16 x 1-3/8	"	0.040	3.20	3.37		6.57
2180	Parting bead						
2200	3/8 x 7/8	LF	0.050	4.00	1.53		5.53
2300	Quarter round						
2301	1/4 x 1/4	LF	0.032	2.56	0.54		3.10
2303	3/8 x 3/8	"	0.032	2.56	0.76		3.32
2305	1/2 x 1/2	"	0.032	2.56	0.99		3.55
2307	11/16 x 11/16	"	0.035	2.78	0.99		3.77
2309	3/4 x 3/4	"	0.035	2.78	1.83		4.61
2311	1-1/16 x 1-1/16	"	0.036	2.90	1.45		4.35
2380	Railings, balusters						

FINISH CARPENTRY

ID Code	Component Descriptions	Unit of Meas.	Manhr / Unit	Labor Cost	Material Cost	Equip. Cost	Total Cost
06 - 20231	**FINISH CARPENTRY, Cont'd...**						**06 - 20231**
2400	1-1/8 x 1-1/8	LF	0.080	6.40	4.91		11.25
2410	1-1/2 x 1-1/2	"	0.073	5.81	5.75		11.50
2480	Screen moldings						
2500	1/4 x 3/4	LF	0.067	5.33	1.22		6.55
2510	5/8 x 5/16	"	0.067	5.33	1.53		6.86
2580	Shoe						
2600	7/16 x 11/16	LF	0.032	2.56	1.53		4.09
2605	Sash beads						
2610	1/2 x 3/4	LF	0.067	5.33	1.76		7.09
2620	1/2 x 7/8	"	0.067	5.33	1.99		7.32
2630	1/2 x 1-1/8	"	0.073	5.81	2.15		7.96
2640	5/8 x 7/8	"	0.073	5.81	2.15		7.96
2760	Stop						
2780	5/8 x 1-5/8						
2800	Colonial	LF	0.050	4.00	1.06		5.06
2810	Ranch	"	0.050	4.00	1.06		5.06
2880	Stools						
2900	11/16 x 2-1/4	LF	0.089	7.11	4.68		11.75
2910	11/16 x 2-1/2	"	0.089	7.11	4.91		12.00
2920	11/16 x 5-1/4	"	0.100	8.00	5.06		13.00
4000	Exterior trim, casing, select pine, 1x3	"	0.040	3.20	3.37		6.57
4010	Douglas fir						
4020	1x3	LF	0.040	3.20	1.60		4.80
4040	1x4	"	0.040	3.20	1.99		5.19
4060	1x6	"	0.044	3.55	2.60		6.15
4100	1x8	"	0.050	4.00	3.60		7.60
5000	Cornices, white pine, #2 or better						
5020	1x2	LF	0.040	3.20	0.99		4.19
5040	1x4	"	0.040	3.20	1.22		4.42
5060	1x6	"	0.044	3.55	1.99		5.54
5080	1x8	"	0.047	3.76	2.44		6.20
5100	1x10	"	0.050	4.00	3.14		7.14
5120	1x12	"	0.053	4.26	3.91		8.17
8600	Shelving, pine						
8620	1x8	LF	0.062	4.92	1.76		6.68
8640	1x10	"	0.064	5.12	2.30		7.42
8660	1x12	"	0.067	5.33	2.91		8.24
8800	Plywood shelf, 3/4", with edge band, 12" wide	"	0.080	6.40	3.14		9.54

FINISH CARPENTRY

ID Code	Component Descriptions	Unit of Meas.	Manhr / Unit	Labor Cost	Material Cost	Equip. Cost	Total Cost
	Descriptions	**Output**		**Unit Costs**			

06 - 20231 — FINISH CARPENTRY, Cont'd... — 06 - 20231

ID Code	Component Descriptions	Unit of Meas.	Manhr / Unit	Labor Cost	Material Cost	Equip. Cost	Total Cost
8840	Adjustable shelf, and rod, 12" wide						
8860	3' to 4' long	EA	0.200	16.00	25.00		41.00
8880	5' to 8' long	"	0.267	21.25	47.00		68.00
8900	Prefinished wood shelves with brackets and supports						
8905	8" wide						
8910	3' long	EA	0.200	16.00	74.00		90.00
8922	4' long	"	0.200	16.00	85.00		100
8924	6' long	"	0.200	16.00	120		140
8930	10" wide						
8940	3' long	EA	0.200	16.00	81.00		97.00
8942	4' long	"	0.200	16.00	120		140
8946	6' long	"	0.200	16.00	130		150

MILLWORK

06 - 22001 — MILLWORK — 06 - 22001

ID Code	Component Descriptions	Unit of Meas.	Manhr / Unit	Labor Cost	Material Cost	Equip. Cost	Total Cost
0070	Countertop, laminated plastic						
0080	25" x 7/8" thick						
0099	Minimum	LF	0.200	16.00	18.75		34.75
0100	Average	"	0.267	21.25	35.50		57.00
0110	Maximum	"	0.320	25.50	52.00		78.00
0115	25" x 1-1/4" thick						
0120	Minimum	LF	0.267	21.25	22.75		44.00
0130	Average	"	0.320	25.50	45.50		71.00
0140	Maximum	"	0.400	32.00	68.00		100
0160	Add for cutouts	EA	0.500	40.00			40.00
0165	Backsplash, 4" high, 7/8" thick	LF	0.160	12.75	25.00		37.75
2000	Plywood, sanded, A-C						
2020	1/4" thick	SF	0.027	2.13	1.61		3.74
2040	3/8" thick	"	0.029	2.28	1.75		4.03
2060	1/2" thick	"	0.031	2.46	1.98		4.44
2070	A-D						
2080	1/4" thick	SF	0.027	2.13	1.53		3.66
2090	3/8" thick	"	0.029	2.28	1.75		4.03
2100	1/2" thick	"	0.031	2.46	1.90		4.36
2500	Base cabinet, 34-1/2" high, 24" deep, hardwood						
2540	Minimum	LF	0.320	25.50	250		280
2560	Average	"	0.400	32.00	280		310

MILLWORK

ID Code	Component Descriptions	Unit of Meas.	Manhr / Unit	Labor Cost	Material Cost	Equip. Cost	Total Cost
	Descriptions	**Output**		**Unit Costs**			

06 - 22001　　　MILLWORK, Cont'd...　　　06 - 22001

ID Code	Component Descriptions	Unit of Meas.	Manhr / Unit	Labor Cost	Material Cost	Equip. Cost	Total Cost
2580	Maximum	LF	0.533	42.75	310		350
2600	Wall cabinets						
2640	Minimum	LF	0.267	21.25	75.00		96.00
2660	Average	"	0.320	25.50	100		130
2680	Maximum	"	0.400	32.00	130		160

ARCHITECTURAL WOODWORK

06 - 26001　　　PANEL WORK　　　06 - 26001

ID Code	Component Descriptions	Unit of Meas.	Manhr / Unit	Labor Cost	Material Cost	Equip. Cost	Total Cost
1020	Hardboard, tempered, 1/4" thick						
1040	Natural faced	SF	0.020	1.60	1.16		2.76
1060	Plastic faced	"	0.023	1.82	1.75		3.57
1080	Pegboard, natural	"	0.020	1.60	1.46		3.06
1100	Plastic faced	"	0.023	1.82	1.75		3.57
1200	Untempered, 1/4" thick						
1220	Natural faced	SF	0.020	1.60	1.10		2.70
1240	Plastic faced	"	0.023	1.82	1.90		3.72
1260	Pegboard, natural	"	0.020	1.60	1.16		2.76
1280	Plastic faced	"	0.023	1.82	1.68		3.50
1300	Plywood unfinished, 1/4" thick						
1320	Birch						
1330	Natural	SF	0.027	2.13	1.25		3.38
1340	Select	"	0.027	2.13	1.83		3.96
1400	Knotty pine	"	0.027	2.13	2.41		4.54
1500	Cedar (closet lining)						
1520	Standard boards T&G	SF	0.027	2.13	3.00		5.13
1540	Particle board	"	0.027	2.13	1.83		3.96
2000	Plywood, prefinished, 1/4" thick, premium grade						
2020	Birch veneer	SF	0.032	2.56	4.39		6.95
2040	Cherry veneer	"	0.032	2.56	5.12		7.68
2060	Chestnut veneer	"	0.032	2.56	9.89		12.50
2080	Lauan veneer	"	0.032	2.56	1.90		4.46
2100	Mahogany veneer	"	0.032	2.56	5.05		7.61
2120	Oak veneer (red)	"	0.032	2.56	5.05		7.61
2140	Pecan veneer	"	0.032	2.56	6.37		8.93
2160	Rosewood veneer	"	0.032	2.56	9.89		12.50
2180	Teak veneer	"	0.032	2.56	6.52		9.08
2200	Walnut veneer	"	0.032	2.56	5.64		8.20

WOOD STAIRS AND RAILINGS

ID Code	Descriptions — Component Descriptions	Output — Unit of Meas.	Manhr / Unit	Unit Costs — Labor Cost	Material Cost	Equip. Cost	Total Cost
06 - 43131	**STAIRWORK**						**06 - 43131**
0080	Risers, 1x8, 42" wide						
0100	White oak	EA	0.400	32.00	53.00		85.00
0120	Pine	"	0.400	32.00	47.00		79.00
0130	Treads, 1-1/16" x 9-1/2" x 42"						
0140	White oak	EA	0.500	40.00	63.00		100

ORNAMENTAL WOODWORK

ID Code	COLUMNS	Unit of Meas.	Manhr / Unit	Labor Cost	Material Cost	Equip. Cost	Total Cost
06 - 44001	**COLUMNS**						**06 - 44001**
0980	Column, hollow, round wood						
0990	12" diameter						
1000	10' high	EA	0.800	49.75	940	44.25	1,030
1040	12' high	"	0.857	53.00	1,150	47.50	1,250
1060	14' high	"	0.960	60.00	1,380	53.00	1,490
1080	16' high	"	1.200	75.00	1,710	67.00	1,850
2000	24" diameter						
2020	16' high	EA	1.200	75.00	3,900	67.00	4,040
2040	18' high	"	1.263	79.00	4,440	70.00	4,590
2060	20' high	"	1.263	79.00	5,460	70.00	5,610
2080	22' high	"	1.333	83.00	5,750	74.00	5,910
2100	24' high	"	1.333	83.00	6,270	74.00	6,430

DIVISION 07
THERMAL AND
MOISTURE

MOISTURE PROTECTION

ID Code	Component Descriptions	Unit of Meas.	Manhr / Unit	Labor Cost	Material Cost	Equip. Cost	Total Cost
		Descriptions	**Output**	**Unit Costs**			

07 - 11001	**DAMPPROOFING**						**07 - 11001**
1000	Silicone dampproofing, sprayed on						
1020	Concrete surface						
1040	1 coat	SF	0.004	0.27	0.64		0.91
1060	2 coats	"	0.006	0.38	1.06		1.44
1070	Concrete block						
1080	1 coat	SF	0.005	0.33	0.64		0.97
1100	2 coats	"	0.007	0.45	1.06		1.51
1110	Brick						
1120	1 coat	SF	0.006	0.38	0.64		1.02
1140	2 coats	"	0.008	0.50	1.06		1.56

07 - 11131	**BITUMINOUS DAMPPROOFING**						**07 - 11131**
0100	Building paper, asphalt felt						
0120	15 lb	SF	0.032	2.00	0.19		2.19
0140	30 lb	"	0.033	2.08	0.37		2.45
1000	Asphalt, troweled, cold, primer plus						
1020	1 coat	SF	0.027	1.67	0.68		2.35
1040	2 coats	"	0.040	2.50	1.43		3.93
1060	3 coats	"	0.050	3.13	2.04		5.17
1200	Fibrous asphalt, hot troweled, primer plus						
1220	1 coat	SF	0.032	2.00	0.68		2.68
1240	2 coats	"	0.044	2.78	1.43		4.21
1260	3 coats	"	0.057	3.58	2.04		5.62
1400	Asphaltic paint dampproofing, per coat						
1420	Brush on	SF	0.011	0.71	0.35		1.06
1440	Spray on	"	0.009	0.55	0.49		1.04

07 - 11161	**PARGING / MASONRY PLASTER**						**07 - 11161**
0080	Parging						
0100	1/2" thick	SF	0.053	4.06	0.44		4.50
0200	3/4" thick	"	0.067	5.08	0.48		5.56
0300	1" thick	"	0.080	6.10	0.63		6.73

SHEET WATERPROOFING

ID Code	Component Descriptions	Unit of Meas.	Manhr / Unit	Labor Cost	Material Cost	Equip. Cost	Total Cost
	Descriptions	**Output**		**Unit Costs**			
07 - 13001	**WATERPROOFING**						**07 - 13001**
1000	Membrane waterproofing, elastomeric						
1020	Butyl						
1040	1/32" thick	SF	0.032	2.00	1.47		3.47
1060	1/16" thick	"	0.033	2.08	1.91		3.99
1080	Butyl with nylon						
1100	1/32" thick	SF	0.032	2.00	1.71		3.71
1120	1/16" thick	"	0.033	2.08	2.07		4.15
1140	Neoprene						
1160	1/32" thick	SF	0.032	2.00	2.51		4.51
1180	1/16" thick	"	0.033	2.08	3.60		5.68
1190	Neoprene with nylon						
1220	1/32" thick	SF	0.032	2.00	2.61		4.61
1240	1/16" thick	"	0.033	2.08	4.21		6.29
1420	Bituminous membrane, asphalt felt, 15 lb.						
1440	One ply	SF	0.020	1.25	0.87		2.12
1460	Two ply	"	0.024	1.51	1.03		2.54
1480	Three ply	"	0.029	1.79	1.27		3.06
1500	Four ply	"	0.033	2.08	1.46		3.54
1520	Five ply	"	0.042	2.63	1.56		4.19
1620	Modified asphalt membrane, fibrous asphalt						
1630	One ply	SF	0.033	2.08	0.55		2.63
1640	Two ply	"	0.040	2.50	1.12		3.62
1650	Three ply	"	0.044	2.78	1.73		4.51
1669	Four ply	"	0.053	3.34	2.31		5.65
1670	Five ply	"	0.064	4.00	2.77		6.77
1700	Asphalt coated protective board						
1710	1/8" thick	SF	0.020	1.25	0.51		1.76
1720	1/4" thick	"	0.020	1.25	0.70		1.95
1730	3/8" thick	"	0.020	1.25	0.78		2.03
1740	1/2" thick	"	0.021	1.31	0.94		2.25
1800	Cement protective board						
1820	3/8" thick	SF	0.027	1.67	1.45		3.12
1840	1/2" thick	"	0.027	1.67	2.03		3.70
2000	Fluid applied, neoprene						
2040	50 mil	SF	0.027	1.67	2.03		3.70
2060	90 mil	"	0.027	1.67	3.36		5.03
2100	Tab extended polyurethane						
2120	.050" thick	SF	0.020	1.25	1.88		3.13

SHEET WATERPROOFING

ID Code	Component Descriptions	Unit of Meas.	Manhr / Unit	Labor Cost	Material Cost	Equip. Cost	Total Cost
	Descriptions	**Output**		**Unit Costs**			

07 - 13001   WATERPROOFING, Cont'd...   07 - 13001

ID Code	Component Descriptions	Unit of Meas.	Manhr / Unit	Labor Cost	Material Cost	Equip. Cost	Total Cost
2140	Fluid applied rubber based polyurethane						
2160	6 mil	SF	0.025	1.56	1.20		2.76
2200	15 mil	"	0.020	1.25	2.28		3.53
2300	Bentonite waterproofing, panels						
2320	3/16" thick	SF	0.020	1.25	2.04		3.29
2330	1/4" thick	"	0.020	1.25	2.32		3.57
2340	5/8" thick	"	0.021	1.31	3.45		4.76
2350	Granular admixtures, trowel on, 3/8" thick	"	0.020	1.25	1.91		3.16
2410	Metallic oxide, iron compound, troweled						
2420	5/8" thick	SF	0.020	1.25	1.73		2.98
2440	3/4" thick	"	0.023	1.43	2.10		3.53

INSULATION

07 - 21131   BOARD INSULATION   07 - 21131

ID Code	Component Descriptions	Unit of Meas.	Manhr / Unit	Labor Cost	Material Cost	Equip. Cost	Total Cost
1000	Insulation, rigid						
1010	Fiberglass, roof						
1020	0.75" thick, R2.78	SF	0.007	0.45	0.55		1.00
1040	1.06" thick, R4.17	"	0.008	0.47	0.84		1.31
1060	1.31" thick, R5.26	"	0.008	0.50	1.13		1.63
1080	1.63" thick, R6.67	"	0.008	0.52	1.39		1.91
1100	2.25" thick, R8.33	"	0.009	0.55	1.53		2.08
2000	Composite board, roof						
2020	1-1/2" thick, R6.67	SF	0.008	0.50	1.20		1.70
2040	1-5/8" thick, R7.69	"	0.008	0.52	1.27		1.79
2060	2" thick, R10.0	"	0.009	0.55	2.29		2.84
2080	2-1/4" thick, R12.50	"	0.009	0.58	2.54		3.12
2100	2-1/2" thick, R14.29	"	0.010	0.62	2.76		3.38
2120	2-3/4" thick, R16.67	"	0.011	0.66	3.03		3.69
2140	3-1/4" thick, R20.00	"	0.011	0.71	3.90		4.61
2200	Perlite board, roof						
2220	1.00" thick, R2.78	SF	0.007	0.41	0.57		0.98
2240	1.50" thick, R4.17	"	0.007	0.43	0.90		1.33
2260	2.00" thick, R5.92	"	0.007	0.45	1.10		1.55
2280	2.50" thick, R6.67	"	0.008	0.47	1.35		1.82
2290	3.00" thick, R8.33	"	0.008	0.50	1.69		2.19
2300	4.00" thick, R10.00	"	0.008	0.52	1.88		2.40
2320	5.25" thick, R14.29	"	0.009	0.55	2.07		2.62

INSULATION

ID Code	Descriptions	Output		Unit Costs			
	Component Descriptions	Unit of Meas.	Manhr / Unit	Labor Cost	Material Cost	Equip. Cost	Total Cost
07 - 21131	**BOARD INSULATION, Cont'd...**						**07 - 21131**
2580	Rigid urethane						
2590	Roof						
2600	1" thick, R6.67	SF	0.007	0.41	1.09		1.50
2620	1.20" thick, R8.33	"	0.007	0.42	1.25		1.67
2640	1.50" thick, R11.11	"	0.007	0.43	1.49		1.92
2660	2" thick, R14.29	"	0.007	0.45	1.92		2.37
2680	2.25" thick, R16.67	"	0.008	0.47	2.52		2.99
2685	Wall						
2690	1" thick, R6.67	SF	0.008	0.52	1.09		1.61
2700	1.5" thick, R11.11	"	0.009	0.55	1.49		2.04
2720	2" thick, R14.29	"	0.009	0.58	1.97		2.55
2780	Polystyrene						
2790	Roof						
2800	1.0" thick, R4.17	SF	0.007	0.41	0.41		0.82
2820	1.5" thick, R6.26	"	0.007	0.43	0.63		1.06
2840	2.0" thick, R8.33	"	0.007	0.45	0.78		1.23
2880	Wall						
2900	1.0" thick, R4.17	SF	0.008	0.52	0.41		0.93
2920	1.5" thick, R6.26	"	0.009	0.55	0.63		1.18
2940	2.0" thick, R8.33	"	0.009	0.58	0.78		1.36
4020	Rigid board insulation, deck						
4025	Mineral fiberboard						
4030	1" thick, R3.0	SF	0.007	0.41	0.60		1.01
4040	2" thick, R5.26	"	0.007	0.45	1.33		1.78
4045	Fiberglass						
4050	1" thick, R4.3	SF	0.007	0.41	1.03		1.44
4060	2" thick, R8.5	"	0.007	0.45	1.52		1.97
4065	Polystyrene						
4070	1" thick, R5.4	SF	0.007	0.41	0.41		0.82
4080	2" thick, R10.8	"	0.007	0.45	1.05		1.50
4090	Urethane						
4100	.75" thick, R5.4	SF	0.007	0.41	0.95		1.36
4120	1" thick, R6.4	"	0.007	0.41	1.13		1.54
4140	1.5" thick, R10.7	"	0.007	0.43	1.36		1.79
4160	2" thick, R14.3	"	0.007	0.45	1.55		2.00
4170	Foamglass						
4180	1" thick, R1.8	SF	0.007	0.41	1.54		1.95
4220	2" thick, R5.26	"	0.007	0.45	1.96		2.41

INSULATION

ID Code	Descriptions — Component Descriptions	Output — Unit of Meas.	Output — Manhr / Unit	Unit Costs — Labor Cost	Unit Costs — Material Cost	Unit Costs — Equip. Cost	Unit Costs — Total Cost
07 - 21131	**BOARD INSULATION, Cont'd...**						**07 - 21131**
4230	Wood fiber						
4240	1" thick, R3.85	SF	0.007	0.41	1.74		2.15
4260	2" thick, R7.7	"	0.007	0.45	2.10		2.55
4270	Particle board						
4280	3/4" thick, R2.08	SF	0.007	0.41	0.92		1.33
4300	1" thick, R2.77	"	0.007	0.41	0.96		1.37
4320	2" thick, R5.50	"	0.007	0.45	1.27		1.72
07 - 21161	**BATT INSULATION**						**07 - 21161**
0980	Ceiling, fiberglass, unfaced						
1000	3-1/2" thick, R11	SF	0.009	0.58	0.42		1.00
1020	6" thick, R19	"	0.011	0.66	0.56		1.22
1030	9" thick, R30	"	0.012	0.77	1.10		1.87
1035	Suspended ceiling, unfaced						
1040	3-1/2" thick, R11	SF	0.009	0.55	0.42		0.97
1060	6" thick, R19	"	0.010	0.62	0.56		1.18
1070	9" thick, R30	"	0.011	0.71	1.10		1.81
1075	Crawl space, unfaced						
1080	3-1/2" thick, R11	SF	0.012	0.77	0.42		1.19
1100	6" thick, R19	"	0.013	0.83	0.56		1.39
1120	9" thick, R30	"	0.015	0.91	1.10		2.01
2000	Wall, fiberglass						
2010	Paper backed						
2020	2" thick, R7	SF	0.008	0.52	0.33		0.85
2040	3" thick, R8	"	0.009	0.55	0.36		0.91
2060	4" thick, R11	"	0.009	0.58	0.59		1.17
2080	6" thick, R19	"	0.010	0.62	0.88		1.50
2090	Foil backed, 1 side						
2100	2" thick, R7	SF	0.008	0.52	0.63		1.15
2120	3" thick, R11	"	0.009	0.55	0.68		1.23
2140	4" thick, R14	"	0.009	0.58	0.71		1.29
2160	6" thick, R21	"	0.010	0.62	0.93		1.55
2170	Foil backed, 2 sides						
2180	2" thick, R7	SF	0.009	0.58	0.72		1.30
2200	3" thick, R11	"	0.010	0.62	0.92		1.54
2220	4" thick, R14	"	0.011	0.66	1.08		1.74
2240	6" thick, R21	"	0.011	0.71	1.17		1.88
2250	Unfaced						

INSULATION

ID Code	Component Descriptions	Unit of Meas.	Manhr / Unit	Labor Cost	Material Cost	Equip. Cost	Total Cost
	Descriptions	**Output**		**Unit Costs**			

07 - 21161 — BATT INSULATION, Cont'd... — 07 - 21161

ID Code	Component Descriptions	Unit of Meas.	Manhr / Unit	Labor Cost	Material Cost	Equip. Cost	Total Cost
2260	2" thick, R7	SF	0.008	0.52	0.40		0.92
2280	3" thick, R9	"	0.009	0.55	0.46		1.01
2300	4" thick, R11	"	0.009	0.58	0.49		1.07
2320	6" thick, R19	"	0.010	0.62	0.63		1.25
2400	Mineral wool batts						
2410	Paper backed						
2420	2" thick, R6	SF	0.008	0.52	0.35		0.87
2440	4" thick, R12	"	0.009	0.55	0.79		1.34
2460	6" thick, R19	"	0.010	0.62	0.99		1.61
8980	Fasteners, self adhering, attached to ceiling deck						
9000	2-1/2" long	EA	0.013	0.83	0.26		1.09
9020	4-1/2" long	"	0.015	0.91	0.29		1.20
9060	Capped, self-locking washers	"	0.008	0.50	0.26		0.76

07 - 21231 — LOOSE FILL INSULATION — 07 - 21231

ID Code	Component Descriptions	Unit of Meas.	Manhr / Unit	Labor Cost	Material Cost	Equip. Cost	Total Cost
1000	Blown-in type						
1010	Fiberglass						
1020	5" thick, R11	SF	0.007	0.41	0.41		0.82
1040	6" thick, R13	"	0.008	0.50	0.48		0.98
1060	9" thick, R19	"	0.011	0.71	0.58		1.29
2000	Rockwool, attic application						
2040	6" thick, R13	SF	0.008	0.50	0.38		0.88
2060	8" thick, R19	"	0.010	0.62	0.45		1.07
2080	10" thick, R22	"	0.012	0.77	0.53		1.30
2100	12" thick, R26	"	0.013	0.83	0.68		1.51
2120	15" thick, R30	"	0.016	1.00	0.82		1.82
6200	Poured type						
6210	Fiberglass						
6220	1" thick, R4	SF	0.005	0.31	0.45		0.76
6222	2" thick, R8	"	0.006	0.35	0.84		1.19
6224	3" thick, R12	"	0.007	0.41	1.24		1.65
6226	4" thick, R16	"	0.008	0.50	1.63		2.13
6230	Mineral wool						
6240	1" thick, R3	SF	0.005	0.31	0.50		0.81
6242	2" thick, R6	"	0.006	0.35	0.92		1.27
6244	3" thick, R9	"	0.007	0.41	1.40		1.81
6246	4" thick, R12	"	0.008	0.50	1.63		2.13
6300	Vermiculite or perlite						

INSULATION

ID Code	Descriptions — Component Descriptions	Output — Unit of Meas.	Manhr / Unit	Unit Costs — Labor Cost	Material Cost	Equip. Cost	Total Cost
07 - 21231	**LOOSE FILL INSULATION, Cont'd...**						**07 - 21231**
6310	2" thick, R4.8	SF	0.006	0.35	0.98		1.33
6320	3" thick, R7.2	"	0.007	0.41	1.39		1.80
6330	4" thick, R9.6	"	0.008	0.50	1.81		2.31
8000	Masonry, poured vermiculite or perlite						
8020	4" block	SF	0.004	0.25	0.57		0.82
8040	6" block	"	0.005	0.31	0.86		1.17
8060	8" block	"	0.006	0.35	1.25		1.60
8100	10" block	"	0.006	0.38	1.65		2.03
8120	12" block	"	0.007	0.41	2.05		2.46
07 - 21291	**SPRAYED INSULATION**						**07 - 21291**
1000	Foam, sprayed on						
1010	Polystyrene						
1020	1" thick, R4	SF	0.008	0.50	0.69		1.19
1040	2" thick, R8	"	0.011	0.66	1.34		2.00
1050	Urethane						
1060	1" thick, R4	SF	0.008	0.50	0.65		1.15
1080	2" thick, R8	"	0.011	0.66	1.24		1.90

EXTERIOR INSULATION AND FINISH SYSTEMS

ID Code	Component Descriptions	Unit of Meas.	Manhr / Unit	Labor Cost	Material Cost	Equip. Cost	Total Cost
07 - 24001	**AGGREGATE COATED PANELS**						**07 - 24001**
0980	Dryvit type system						
1000	1" thick	SF	0.027	2.35	3.31		5.66
1020	1-1/2" thick	"	0.029	2.52	3.45		5.97
1040	2" thick	"	0.033	2.94	3.91		6.85
07 - 24011	**EXTERIOR INSULATION FINISH SYSTEM, EIFS**						**07 - 24011**
1000	3" Thick	SF	0.010	0.62	5.08		5.70
2000	For Base & Finish Only	"					1.83

VAPOR RETARDERS

ID Code	Descriptions — Component Descriptions	Output — Unit of Meas.	Output — Manhr / Unit	Unit Costs — Labor Cost	Unit Costs — Material Cost	Unit Costs — Equip. Cost	Unit Costs — Total Cost

07 - 26001   VAPOR BARRIERS   07 - 26001

ID Code	Component Descriptions	Unit of Meas.	Manhr / Unit	Labor Cost	Material Cost	Equip. Cost	Total Cost
0980	Vapor barrier, polyethylene						
1000	2 mil	SF	0.004	0.25	0.02		0.27
1010	6 mil	"	0.004	0.25	0.07		0.32
1020	8 mil	"	0.004	0.27	0.08		0.35
1040	10 mil	"	0.004	0.27	0.09		0.36

SHINGLES AND TILES

07 - 31131   ASPHALT SHINGLES   07 - 31131

ID Code	Component Descriptions	Unit of Meas.	Manhr / Unit	Labor Cost	Material Cost	Equip. Cost	Total Cost
1000	Standard asphalt shingles, strip shingles						
1020	210 lb/square	SQ	0.800	61.00	90.00		150
1040	235 lb/square	"	0.889	68.00	95.00		160
1060	240 lb/square	"	1.000	76.00	99.00		180
1080	260 lb/square	"	1.143	87.00	140		230
1100	300 lb/square	"	1.333	100	150		250
1120	385 lb/square	"	1.600	120	210		330
5980	Roll roofing, mineral surface						
6000	90 lb	SQ	0.571	43.50	55.00		99.00
6020	110 lb	"	0.667	51.00	92.00		140
6040	140 lb	"	0.800	61.00	95.00		160

07 - 31161   METAL SHINGLES   07 - 31161

ID Code	Component Descriptions	Unit of Meas.	Manhr / Unit	Labor Cost	Material Cost	Equip. Cost	Total Cost
0980	Aluminum, .020" thick						
1000	Plain	SQ	1.600	120	280		400
1020	Colors	"	1.600	120	310		430
1960	Steel, galvanized						
1980	26 ga.						
2000	Plain	SQ	1.600	120	350		470
2020	Colors	"	1.600	120	440		560
2030	24 ga.						
2040	Plain	SQ	1.600	120	400		520
2060	Colors	"	1.600	120	510		630
2960	Porcelain enamel, 22 ga.						
3000	Minimum	SQ	2.000	150	870		1,020
3020	Average	"	2.000	150	1,000		1,150
3040	Maximum	"	2.000	150	1,120		1,270

SHINGLES AND TILES

ID Code	Component Descriptions	Unit of Meas.	Manhr / Unit	Labor Cost	Material Cost	Equip. Cost	Total Cost
		Output		**Unit Costs**			

07 - 31261   **SLATE SHINGLES**   **07 - 31261**

ID Code	Component Descriptions	Unit of Meas.	Manhr / Unit	Labor Cost	Material Cost	Equip. Cost	Total Cost
0960	Slate shingles						
0980	Pennsylvania						
1000	Ribbon	SQ	4.000	310	600		910
1020	Clear	"	4.000	310	770		1,080
1030	Vermont						
1040	Black	SQ	4.000	310	710		1,020
1060	Gray	"	4.000	310	780		1,090
1070	Green	"	4.000	310	800		1,110
1080	Red	"	4.000	310	1,440		1,750
1980	Replacement shingles						
2000	Small jobs	EA	0.267	20.25	12.75		33.00
2020	Large jobs	SF	0.133	10.25	9.94		20.25

07 - 31291   **WOOD SHINGLES**   **07 - 31291**

ID Code	Component Descriptions	Unit of Meas.	Manhr / Unit	Labor Cost	Material Cost	Equip. Cost	Total Cost
1000	Wood shingles, on roofs						
1010	White cedar, #1 shingles						
1020	4" exposure	SQ	2.667	200	270		470
1040	5" exposure	"	2.000	150	240		390
1050	#2 shingles						
1060	4" exposure	SQ	2.667	200	190		390
1080	5" exposure	"	2.000	150	160		310
1090	Resquared and rebutted						
1100	4" exposure	SQ	2.667	200	240		440
1120	5" exposure	"	2.000	150	200		350
1140	On walls						
1150	White cedar, #1 shingles						
1160	4" exposure	SQ	4.000	310	270		580
1180	5" exposure	"	3.200	240	240		480
1200	6" exposure	"	2.667	200	200		400
1210	#2 shingles						
1220	4" exposure	SQ	4.000	310	190		500
1240	5" exposure	"	3.200	240	160		400
1260	6" exposure	"	2.667	200	130		330
1300	Add for fire retarding	"					120

SHINGLES AND TILES

ID Code	Descriptions — Component Descriptions	Output — Unit of Meas.	Output — Manhr / Unit	Unit Costs — Labor Cost	Unit Costs — Material Cost	Unit Costs — Equip. Cost	Unit Costs — Total Cost

07 - 31292 — WOOD SHAKES — 07 - 31292

ID Code	Component Descriptions	Unit of Meas.	Manhr / Unit	Labor Cost	Material Cost	Equip. Cost	Total Cost
2010	Shakes, hand split, 24" red cedar, on roofs						
2020	5" exposure	SQ	4.000	310	300		610
2040	7" exposure	"	3.200	240	280		520
2060	9" exposure	"	2.667	200	260		460
2080	On walls						
2100	6" exposure	SQ	4.000	310	280		590
2120	8" exposure	"	3.200	240	270		510
2140	10" exposure	"	2.667	200	260		460
3000	Add for fire retarding	"					78.00

ROOF TILES

07 - 32161 — CONCRETE ROOF TILE — 07 - 32161

ID Code	Component Descriptions	Unit of Meas.	Manhr / Unit	Labor Cost	Material Cost	Equip. Cost	Total Cost
0100	Concrete Roof Tile, Corrugated						
0120	13"x16-1/2", 90/SQ, 950 LB/SQ Earthtone Colors	SQ	4.000	310	180		490
0140	Custom Blues	"	4.000	310	390		700
0160	Custom Greens	"	4.000	310	230		540
0180	Concrete Roof Tile, Shakes						
0200	13"x16-1/2", 90/SQ,950 LB/SQ,Colors	SQ	4.000	310	240		550

ROOFING AND SIDING

07 - 41001 — MANUFACTURED ROOFS — 07 - 41001

ID Code	Component Descriptions	Unit of Meas.	Manhr / Unit	Labor Cost	Material Cost	Equip. Cost	Total Cost
1020	Aluminum roof panels, for steel framing						
1040	Corrugated						
1045	Unpainted finish						
1050	.024"	SF	0.020	1.52	2.06		3.58
1060	.030"	"	0.020	1.52	3.35		4.87
1065	Painted finish						
1070	.024"	SF	0.020	1.52	2.61		4.13
1080	.030"	"	0.020	1.52	3.52		5.04
1100	V-beam						
1110	Unpainted finish						
1120	.032"	SF	0.020	1.52	2.96		4.48
1140	.040"	"	0.020	1.52	3.56		5.08
1160	.050"	"	0.020	1.52	4.48		6.00
1170	Painted finish						
1180	.032"	SF	0.020	1.52	3.85		5.37

ROOFING AND SIDING

ID Code	Component Descriptions	Unit of Meas.	Manhr / Unit	Labor Cost	Material Cost	Equip. Cost	Total Cost
	Descriptions	**Output**		**Unit Costs**			

07 - 41001   MANUFACTURED ROOFS, Cont'd...   07 - 41001

ID Code	Component Descriptions	Unit of Meas.	Manhr / Unit	Labor Cost	Material Cost	Equip. Cost	Total Cost
1200	.040"	SF	0.020	1.52	4.61		6.13
1240	.050"	"	0.020	1.52	5.51		7.03
2020	Steel roof panels, for structural steel framing						
2040	Corrugated, painted						
2100	18 ga.	SF	0.020	1.52	4.26		5.78
2120	20 ga.	"	0.020	1.52	3.97		5.49
2140	22 ga.	"	0.020	1.52	3.50		5.02
2160	Box rib, painted						
2180	18 ga.	SF	0.021	1.60	4.97		6.57
2200	20 ga.	"	0.021	1.60	4.09		5.69
2220	22 ga.	"	0.021	1.60	3.64		5.24
2240	4" rib, painted						
2250	18 ga.	SF	0.022	1.69	5.73		7.42
2260	20 ga.	"	0.022	1.69	4.85		6.54
2280	22 ga.	"	0.022	1.69	4.34		6.03
2300	Standing seam roof						
2320	2" high seam, painted						
2360	22 ga.	SF	0.032	2.44	5.55		7.99
2380	24 ga.	"	0.032	2.44	5.43		7.87
2400	26 ga.	"	0.032	2.44	5.26		7.70

WALL PANELS

07 - 42003   MANUFACTURED WALLS   07 - 42003

ID Code	Component Descriptions	Unit of Meas.	Manhr / Unit	Labor Cost	Material Cost	Equip. Cost	Total Cost
2090	Sandwich panels with 1-1/2" fiberglass insulation						
2091	Galvanized 18 ga. steel interior panels						
2095	Exterior panels						
2100	16 ga. aluminum	SF	0.107	9.41	7.26		16.75
2120	18 ga. galvanized steel	"	0.107	9.41	10.25		19.75
2140	20 ga. painted steel	"	0.107	9.41	10.50		20.00
2160	20 ga. stainless steel	"	0.107	9.41	10.75		20.25
3000	Metal liner panels, 1-3/8" thick, 24" wide						
3020	Galvanized						
3040	22 ga.	SF	0.027	2.35	3.64		5.99
3060	20 ga.	"	0.027	2.35	4.01		6.36
3080	18 ga.	"	0.027	2.35	4.93		7.28
3100	Primed						
3120	22 ga.	SF	0.027	2.35	2.83		5.18

WALL PANELS

ID Code	Descriptions — Component Descriptions	Output — Unit of Meas.	Output — Manhr / Unit	Unit Costs — Labor Cost	Unit Costs — Material Cost	Unit Costs — Equip. Cost	Unit Costs — Total Cost
07 - 42003	**MANUFACTURED WALLS, Cont'd...**						**07 - 42003**
3140	20 ga.	SF	0.027	2.35	3.26		5.61
3160	18 ga.	"	0.027	2.35	4.01		6.36
07 - 42005	**METAL SIDING PANELS**						**07 - 42005**
1000	Aluminum siding panels						
1020	Corrugated						
1030	Plain finish						
1040	.024"	SF	0.032	2.82	2.23		5.05
1060	.032"	"	0.032	2.82	2.62		5.44
1070	Painted finish						
1080	.024"	SF	0.032	2.82	2.78		5.60
1100	.032"	"	0.032	2.82	3.19		6.01
1120	V. beam						
1130	Plain finish						
1140	.032"	SF	0.032	2.82	3.21		6.03
1160	.040"	"	0.032	2.82	3.70		6.52
1180	.050"	"	0.032	2.82	4.69		7.51
1190	Painted finish						
1200	.032"	SF	0.032	2.82	3.96		6.78
1220	.040"	"	0.032	2.82	4.67		7.49
1240	.050"	"	0.032	2.82	6.64		9.46
1260	4" rib						
1270	Plain finish						
1280	.032"	SF	0.036	3.21	2.94		6.15
1300	.040"	"	0.036	3.21	3.27		6.48
1320	.050"	"	0.036	3.21	3.99		7.20
1330	Painted finish						
1340	.032"	SF	0.036	3.21	3.82		7.03
1360	.040"	"	0.036	3.21	3.98		7.19
1380	.050"	"	0.036	3.21	4.55		7.76
2000	Steel siding panels						
2040	Corrugated						
2080	22 ga.	SF	0.053	4.70	2.73		7.43
2100	24 ga.	"	0.053	4.70	2.49		7.19
2120	26 ga.	"	0.053	4.70	2.26		6.96
2140	Box rib						
2160	20 ga.	SF	0.053	4.70	4.08		8.78
2180	22 ga.	"	0.053	4.70	3.42		8.12

WALL PANELS

	Descriptions		Output		Unit Costs			
ID Code	Component Descriptions		Unit of Meas.	Manhr / Unit	Labor Cost	Material Cost	Equip. Cost	Total Cost

07 - 42005   METAL SIDING PANELS, Cont'd...   07 - 42005

ID Code	Component Descriptions	Unit of Meas.	Manhr / Unit	Labor Cost	Material Cost	Equip. Cost	Total Cost
2200	24 ga.	SF	0.053	4.70	3.01		7.71
2220	26 ga.	"	0.053	4.70	2.46		7.16
3000	Ribbed, sheets, galvanized						
3020	22 ga.	SF	0.032	2.82	3.42		6.24
3040	24 ga.	"	0.032	2.82	3.01		5.83
3060	26 ga.	"	0.032	2.82	2.46		5.28
3080	28 ga.	"	0.032	2.82	2.25		5.07
3200	Primed						
3220	24 ga.	SF	0.032	2.82	3.01		5.83
3240	26 ga.	"	0.032	2.82	2.46		5.28
3260	28 ga.	"	0.032	2.82	2.25		5.07

SIDING

07 - 46231   WOOD SIDING   07 - 46231

ID Code	Component Descriptions	Unit of Meas.	Manhr / Unit	Labor Cost	Material Cost	Equip. Cost	Total Cost
1000	Beveled siding, cedar						
1010	A grade						
1020	1/2 x 6	SF	0.040	3.20	4.89		8.09
1040	1/2 x 8	"	0.032	2.56	5.00		7.56
1060	3/4 x 10	"	0.027	2.13	6.43		8.56
1070	Clear						
1080	1/2 x 6	SF	0.040	3.20	5.44		8.64
1100	1/2 x 8	"	0.032	2.56	5.56		8.12
1120	3/4 x 10	"	0.027	2.13	7.45		9.58
1130	B grade						
1140	1/2 x 6	SF	0.040	3.20	5.26		8.46
1160	1/2 x 8	"	0.032	2.56	5.94		8.50
1180	3/4 x 10	"	0.027	2.13	5.60		7.73
2000	Board and batten						
2010	Cedar						
2020	1x6	SF	0.040	3.20	6.84		10.00
2040	1x8	"	0.032	2.56	6.22		8.78
2060	1x10	"	0.029	2.28	5.62		7.90
2080	1x12	"	0.026	2.06	5.04		7.10
2090	Pine						
2100	1x6	SF	0.040	3.20	1.73		4.93
2120	1x8	"	0.032	2.56	1.69		4.25
2140	1x10	"	0.029	2.28	1.62		3.90

SIDING

ID Code	Component Descriptions	Unit of Meas.	Manhr / Unit	Labor Cost	Material Cost	Equip. Cost	Total Cost
		Descriptions		**Output**		**Unit Costs**	

07 - 46231	**WOOD SIDING, Cont'd...**						**07 - 46231**
2160	1x12	SF	0.026	2.06	1.49		3.55
2170	Redwood						
2180	1x6	SF	0.040	3.20	7.44		10.75
2200	1x8	"	0.032	2.56	6.93		9.49
2220	1x10	"	0.029	2.28	6.43		8.71
2240	1x12	"	0.026	2.06	5.93		7.99
3000	Tongue and groove						
3010	Cedar						
3020	1x4	SF	0.044	3.55	6.43		9.98
3040	1x6	"	0.042	3.36	6.18		9.54
3060	1x8	"	0.040	3.20	5.80		9.00
3080	1x10	"	0.038	3.04	5.69		8.73
3090	Pine						
3100	1x4	SF	0.044	3.55	1.93		5.48
3120	1x6	"	0.042	3.36	1.82		5.18
3140	1x8	"	0.040	3.20	1.70		4.90
3160	1x10	"	0.038	3.04	1.62		4.66
3170	Redwood						
3180	1x4	SF	0.044	3.55	6.80		10.25
3200	1x6	"	0.042	3.36	6.55		9.91
3220	1x8	"	0.040	3.20	6.33		9.53
3240	1x10	"	0.038	3.04	6.04		9.08

07 - 46291	**PLYWOOD SIDING**						**07 - 46291**
1000	Rough sawn cedar, 3/8" thick	SF	0.027	2.13	2.16		4.29
1020	Fir, 3/8" thick	"	0.027	2.13	1.19		3.32
1980	Texture 1-11, 5/8" thick						
2000	Cedar	SF	0.029	2.28	2.92		5.20
2020	Fir	"	0.029	2.28	2.04		4.32
2040	Redwood	"	0.029	2.18	3.14		5.32
2060	Southern Yellow Pine	"	0.029	2.28	1.66		3.94

07 - 46331	**PLASTIC SIDING**						**07 - 46331**
1000	Horizontal vinyl siding, solid						
1010	8" wide						
1020	Standard	SF	0.031	2.46	1.35		3.81
1040	Insulated	"	0.031	2.46	1.64		4.10
1050	10" wide						
1060	Standard	SF	0.029	2.28	1.40		3.68

SIDING

ID Code	Component Descriptions	Unit of Meas.	Manhr / Unit	Labor Cost	Material Cost	Equip. Cost	Total Cost
	Descriptions	**Output**		**Unit Costs**			
07 - 46331	**PLASTIC SIDING, Cont'd...**						**07 - 46331**
1080	Insulated	SF	0.029	2.28	1.68		3.96
8500	Vinyl moldings for doors and windows	LF	0.032	2.56	0.87		3.43
07 - 46461	**WOOD FIBER CEMENT SIDING**						**07 - 46461**
1000	Lap siding 5/16" x 8.25 x 12', 7" exposure	SF	0.031	2.46	1.32		3.78
2000	Panel siding 4' x 8'	"	0.029	2.28	0.99		3.27
3000	Shingle siding 14-5/8" x 25-5/32" (per bundle)	EA					130

MEMBRANE ROOFING

ID Code	Component Descriptions	Unit of Meas.	Manhr / Unit	Labor Cost	Material Cost	Equip. Cost	Total Cost
07 - 51131	**BUILT-UP ASPHALT ROOFING**						**07 - 51131**
0980	Built-up roofing, asphalt felt, including gravel						
1000	2 ply	SQ	2.000	150	88.00		240
1500	3 ply	"	2.667	200	120		320
2000	4 ply	"	3.200	240	170		410
2090	Walkway, for built-up roofs						
2095	3' x 3' x						
2100	1/2" thick	SF	0.027	2.03	2.46		4.49
2110	3/4" thick	"	0.027	2.03	3.81		5.84
2120	1" thick	"	0.027	2.03	4.12		6.15
2150	Roof bonds						
2155	10 yrs	SQ					37.25
2160	20 yrs	"					42.50
2195	Cant strip, 4" x 4"						
2200	Treated wood	LF	0.023	1.74	2.56		4.30
2260	Foamglass	"	0.020	1.52	2.20		3.72
2280	Mineral fiber	"	0.020	1.52	0.43		1.95
8000	New gravel for built-up roofing, 400 lb/sq	SQ	1.600	120	44.50		160
8220	Roof gravel (ballast)	CY	4.000	310	32.75		340
9000	Aluminum coating, top surfacing, for built-up roofing	SQ	1.333	100	49.00		150
9500	Remove 4-ply built-up roof (includes gravel)	"	4.000	310			310
9600	Remove & replace gravel, includes flood coat	"	2.667	200	59.00		260

ELASTOMERIC MEMBRANE ROOFING

ID Code	Component Descriptions	Unit of Meas.	Manhr / Unit	Labor Cost	Material Cost	Equip. Cost	Total Cost
		Descriptions		**Output**		**Unit Costs**	
07 - 53001	**SINGLE-PLY ROOFING**						**07 - 53001**
2000	Elastic sheet roofing						
2060	Neoprene, 1/16" thick	SF	0.010	0.76	2.83		3.59
2080	EPDM rubber						
2100	45 mil	SF	0.010	0.76	1.78		2.54
2110	60 mil	"	0.010	0.76	2.44		3.20
2115	PVC						
2120	45 mil	SF	0.010	0.76	2.34		3.10
2140	60 mil	"	0.010	0.76	2.78		3.54
2200	Flashing						
2220	Pipe flashing, 90 mil thick						
2260	1" pipe	EA	0.200	15.25	34.00		49.25
2280	2" pipe	"	0.200	15.25	36.50		52.00
2290	3" pipe	"	0.211	16.00	36.75		53.00
2300	4" pipe	"	0.211	16.00	40.00		56.00
2310	5" pipe	"	0.222	17.00	42.75		60.00
2320	6" pipe	"	0.222	17.00	46.50		64.00
2330	8" pipe	"	0.235	18.00	53.00		71.00
2340	10" pipe	"	0.267	20.25	61.00		81.00
2350	12" pipe	"	0.267	20.25	74.00		94.00
2360	Neoprene flashing, 60 mil thick strip						
2380	6" wide	LF	0.067	5.09	1.72		6.81
2390	12" wide	"	0.100	7.63	3.38		11.00
2400	18" wide	"	0.133	10.25	4.98		15.25
2420	24" wide	"	0.200	15.25	6.55		21.75
2500	Adhesives						
2520	Mastic sealer, applied at joints only						
2540	1/4" bead	LF	0.004	0.30	0.19		0.49
3000	Fluid applied roofing						
3100	Urethane, 2 part, elastomeric membrane						
3101	1" thick	SF	0.013	1.01	4.97		5.98
3200	Vinyl liquid roofing, 2 coats, 2 mils per coat	"	0.011	0.87	7.07		7.94
3300	Silicone roofing, 2 coats sprayed, 16 mil per coat	"	0.013	1.01	5.28		6.29
3400	Inverted roof system						
3420	Insulated membrane with coarse gravel ballast						
3421	3 ply with 2" polystyrene	SF	0.013	1.01	8.47		9.48
8000	Ballast, 3/4" through 1-1/2" gravel, 100lb/sf	"	0.008	0.61	0.52		1.13
8100	Walkway for membrane roofs, 1/2" thick	"	0.027	2.03	2.69		4.72

FLASHING AND SHEET METAL

ID Code	Component Descriptions	Unit of Meas.	Manhr / Unit	Labor Cost	Material Cost	Equip. Cost	Total Cost
	Descriptions	**Output**		**Unit Costs**			

07 - 61001 — METAL ROOFING — 07 - 61001

ID Code	Component Descriptions	Unit of Meas.	Manhr / Unit	Labor Cost	Material Cost	Equip. Cost	Total Cost
1000	Sheet metal roofing, copper, 16 oz, batten seam	SQ	5.333	410	1,800		2,210
1020	Standing seam	"	5.000	380	1,760		2,140
2000	Aluminum roofing, natural finish						
2005	Corrugated, on steel frame						
2010	.0175" thick	SQ	2.286	170	140		310
2040	.0215" thick	"	2.286	170	180		350
2060	.024" thick	"	2.286	170	210		380
2080	.032" thick	"	2.286	170	260		430
2100	V-beam, on steel frame						
2120	.032" thick	SQ	2.286	170	270		440
2130	.040" thick	"	2.286	170	290		460
2140	.050" thick	"	2.286	170	370		540
2200	Ridge cap						
2220	.019" thick	LF	0.027	2.03	4.25		6.28
2500	Corrugated galvanized steel roofing, on steel frame						
2520	28 ga.	SQ	2.286	170	230		400
2540	26 ga.	"	2.286	170	270		440
2550	24 ga.	"	2.286	170	300		470
2560	22 ga.	"	2.286	170	330		500
2580	26 ga., factory insulated with 1" polystyrene	"	3.200	240	510		750
2600	Ridge roll						
2620	10" wide	LF	0.027	2.03	2.31		4.34
2640	20" wide	"	0.032	2.44	4.70		7.14

SHEET METAL FLASHING AND TRIM

07 - 62001 — FLASHING AND TRIM — 07 - 62001

ID Code	Component Descriptions	Unit of Meas.	Manhr / Unit	Labor Cost	Material Cost	Equip. Cost	Total Cost
0050	Counter flashing						
0060	Aluminum, .032"	SF	0.080	6.10	2.09		8.19
0100	Stainless steel, .015"	"	0.080	6.10	6.69		12.75
0105	Copper						
0110	16 oz.	SF	0.080	6.10	9.36		15.50
0112	20 oz.	"	0.080	6.10	11.00		17.00
0114	24 oz.	"	0.080	6.10	13.50		19.50
0116	32 oz.	"	0.080	6.10	16.50		22.50
0118	Valley flashing						
0120	Aluminum, .032"	SF	0.050	3.81	1.74		5.55
0130	Stainless steel, .015	"	0.050	3.81	5.56		9.37

SHEET METAL FLASHING AND TRIM

ID Code	Component Descriptions	Unit of Meas.	Manhr / Unit	Labor Cost	Material Cost	Equip. Cost	Total Cost
	Descriptions	**Output**		**Unit Costs**			
07 - 62001	**FLASHING AND TRIM, Cont'd...**						**07 - 62001**
0135	Copper						
0140	16 oz.	SF	0.050	3.81	9.36		13.25
0160	20 oz.	"	0.067	5.09	11.00		16.00
0180	24 oz.	"	0.050	3.81	13.50		17.25
0200	32 oz.	"	0.050	3.81	16.50		20.25
0380	Base flashing						
0400	Aluminum, .040"	SF	0.067	5.09	2.60		7.69
0410	Stainless steel, .018"	"	0.067	5.09	6.65		11.75
0415	Copper						
0420	16 oz.	SF	0.067	5.09	9.36		14.50
0422	20 oz.	"	0.050	3.81	11.00		14.75
0424	24 oz.	"	0.067	5.09	13.50		18.50
0426	32 oz.	"	0.067	5.09	16.50		21.50
2040	Waterstop, "T" section, 22 ga.						
2050	1-1/2" x 3"	LF	0.040	3.05	3.25		6.30
2060	2" x 2"	"	0.040	3.05	3.60		6.65
2070	4" x 3"	"	0.040	3.05	4.41		7.46
2080	6" x 4"	"	0.040	3.05	4.67		7.72
2090	8" x 4"	"	0.040	3.05	5.79		8.84
2500	Scupper outlets						
2520	10" x 10" x 4"	EA	0.200	15.25	58.00		73.00
2530	22" x 4" x 4"	"	0.200	15.25	62.00		77.00
2540	8" x 8" x 5"	"	0.200	15.25	57.00		72.00
3201	Flashing and trim, aluminum						
3221	.019" thick	SF	0.057	4.36	1.28		5.64
3231	.032" thick	"	0.057	4.36	1.57		5.93
3241	.040" thick	"	0.062	4.69	2.69		7.38
3310	Neoprene sheet flashing, .060" thick	"	0.050	3.81	2.14		5.95
3320	Copper, paper backed						
3330	2 oz.	SF	0.080	6.10	2.75		8.85
3340	5 oz.	"	0.080	6.10	3.55		9.65
3400	Drainage boots, roof, cast iron						
3420	2 x 3	LF	0.100	7.63	110		120
3430	3 x 4	"	0.100	7.63	140		150
3440	4 x 5	"	0.107	8.14	150		160
3450	4 x 6	"	0.107	8.14	160		170
3460	5 x 7	"	0.114	8.72	180		190
7980	Pitch pocket, copper, 16 oz.						

SHEET METAL FLASHING AND TRIM

ID Code	Descriptions Component Descriptions	Output Unit of Meas.	Output Manhr / Unit	Unit Costs Labor Cost	Unit Costs Material Cost	Unit Costs Equip. Cost	Unit Costs Total Cost
07 - 62001	**FLASHING AND TRIM, Cont'd...**						**07 - 62001**
8120	4 x 4	EA	0.200	15.25	130		150
8140	6 x 6	"	0.200	15.25	140		160
8160	8 x 8	"	0.200	15.25	190		210
8180	8 x 10	"	0.200	15.25	220		240
8200	8 x 12	"	0.200	15.25	260		280
8400	Reglets, copper 10 oz.	LF	0.053	4.07	7.39		11.50
8420	Stainless steel, .020"	"	0.053	4.07	3.35		7.42
8480	Gravel stop						
8500	Aluminum, .032"						
8600	4"	LF	0.027	2.03	1.95		3.98
8620	6"	"	0.027	2.03	2.87		4.90
8640	8"	"	0.031	2.34	3.85		6.19
8660	10"	"	0.031	2.34	4.81		7.15
8670	Copper, 16 oz.						
8680	4"	LF	0.027	2.03	6.21		8.24
8700	6"	"	0.027	2.03	9.26		11.25
8720	8"	"	0.031	2.34	12.50		14.75
8740	10"	"	0.031	2.34	15.50		17.75

ROOFING SPECIALTIES

ID Code	Descriptions Component Descriptions	Output Unit of Meas.	Output Manhr / Unit	Unit Costs Labor Cost	Unit Costs Material Cost	Unit Costs Equip. Cost	Unit Costs Total Cost
07 - 71001	**MANUFACTURED SPECIALTIES**						**07 - 71001**
0080	Moisture relief vent						
0100	Aluminum	EA	0.114	8.72	23.25		32.00
0120	Copper	"	0.114	8.72	63.00		72.00
0130	Expansion joint						
0135	Aluminum						
0140	Opening to 2.5"	LF	0.057	4.36	17.75		22.00
0160	Opening to 3.5"	"	0.062	4.69	17.50		22.25
0170	Copper, 16 oz.						
0180	Opening to 2.5"	LF	0.057	4.36	33.25		37.50
0200	Opening to 3.5"	"	0.062	4.69	41.25		46.00
0210	Butyl or neoprene						
0215	4" wide						
0220	16 oz. copper bellows	LF	0.067	5.09	32.00		37.00
0240	28 ga. stainless steel bellows	"	0.067	5.09	20.00		25.00
0260	6" wide						
0280	Copper bellows	LF	0.073	5.55	35.25		40.75

ROOFING SPECIALTIES

ID Code	Component Descriptions	Unit of Meas.	Manhr / Unit	Labor Cost	Material Cost	Equip. Cost	Total Cost
	Descriptions	**Output**		**Unit Costs**			
07 - 71001	**MANUFACTURED SPECIALTIES, Cont'd...**						**07 - 71001**
0290	Stainless steel						
0300	Opening to 2.5"	LF	0.057	4.36	20.50		24.75
0320	Opening to 3.5"	"	0.062	4.69	26.00		30.75
0800	Smoke vent, 48" x 48"						
0820	Aluminum	EA	2.000	150	2,310		2,460
0860	Galvanized steel	"	2.000	150	2,030		2,180
0900	Heat/smoke vent, 48" x 96"						
1000	Aluminum	EA	2.667	200	3,240		3,440
1020	Galvanized steel	"	2.667	200	2,760		2,960
2020	Ridge vent strips						
2040	Mill finish	LF	0.053	4.07	3.90		7.97
2050	Connectors	EA	0.200	15.25	3.85		19.00
2060	End cap	"	0.229	17.50	1.92		19.50
2080	Soffit vents						
2085	Mill finish						
2090	2-1/2" wide	LF	0.032	2.44	0.49		2.93
2100	3" wide	"	0.032	2.44	0.60		3.04
2125	6" wide	"	0.032	2.44	1.04		3.48
3000	Roof hatches						
3020	Steel, plain, primed						
3040	2'6" x 3'0"	EA	2.000	150	800		950
3060	2'6" x 4'6"	"	2.667	200	1,180		1,380
3080	2'6" x 8'0"	"	4.000	310	1,820		2,130
3100	Galvanized steel						
3120	2'6" x 3'0"	EA	2.000	150	820		970
3140	2'6" x 4'6"	"	2.667	200	1,240		1,440
3160	2'6" x 8'0"	"	4.000	310	1,940		2,250
3180	Aluminum						
3200	2'6" x 3'0"	EA	2.000	150	950		1,100
3220	2'6" x 4'6"	"	2.667	200	1,430		1,630
3240	2'6" x 8'0"	"	4.000	310	2,660		2,970
3520	Ceiling access doors						
3540	Swing up model, metal frame						
3550	Steel door						
3560	2'6" x 2'6"	EA	0.800	61.00	690		750
3580	2'6" x 3'0"	"	0.800	61.00	740		800
3590	Aluminum door						
3600	2'6" x 2'6"	EA	0.800	61.00	850		910

ROOFING SPECIALTIES

ID Code	Component Descriptions	Unit of Meas.	Manhr / Unit	Labor Cost	Material Cost	Equip. Cost	Total Cost
	Descriptions	**Output**		**Unit Costs**			
07 - 71001	**MANUFACTURED SPECIALTIES, Cont'd...**						**07 - 71001**
3620	2'6" x 3'0"	EA	0.800	61.00	920		980
3640	Swing down model, metal frame						
3650	Steel door						
3660	2'6" x 2'6"	EA	0.800	61.00	1,040		1,100
3670	2'6" x 3'0"	"	0.800	61.00	1,120		1,180
3680	Aluminum door						
3690	2'6" x 2'6"	EA	0.800	61.00	1,240		1,300
3700	2'6" x 3'0"	"	0.800	61.00	1,330		1,390
3800	Gravity ventilators, with curb, base, damper and screen						
3820	Stationary siphon						
3830	6" dia.	EA	0.533	40.75	51.00		92.00
3840	12" dia.	"	0.533	40.75	89.00		130
3850	24" dia.	"	0.800	61.00	330		390
3860	36" dia.	"	0.800	61.00	690		750
3900	Wind driven spinner						
3920	6" dia.	EA	0.533	40.75	78.00		120
3940	12" dia.	"	0.533	40.75	100		140
3960	24" dia.	"	0.800	61.00	390		450
3980	36" dia.	"	0.800	61.00	800		860
4000	Stationary mushroom						
4020	16" dia.	EA	0.800	61.00	640		700
4060	30" dia.	"	1.000	76.00	1,430		1,510
4080	36" dia.	"	1.333	100	1,850		1,950
4100	42" dia.	"	1.600	120	2,760		2,880
07 - 71231	**GUTTERS AND DOWNSPOUTS**						**07 - 71231**
1500	Copper gutter and downspout						
1520	Downspouts, 16 oz. copper						
1530	Round						
1540	3" dia.	LF	0.053	4.07	12.50		16.50
1550	4" dia.	"	0.053	4.07	15.50		19.50
1560	Rectangular, corrugated						
1570	2" x 3"	LF	0.050	3.81	12.00		15.75
1580	3" x 4"	"	0.050	3.81	14.75		18.50
1585	Rectangular, flat surface						
1590	2" x 3"	LF	0.053	4.07	13.75		17.75
1600	3" x 4"	"	0.053	4.07	19.50		23.50
1620	Lead-coated copper downspouts						

ROOFING SPECIALTIES

ID Code	Component Descriptions	Unit of Meas.	Manhr / Unit	Labor Cost	Material Cost	Equip. Cost	Total Cost
07 - 71231	**GUTTERS AND DOWNSPOUTS, Cont'd...**						**07 - 71231**
1625	Round						
1630	3" dia.	LF	0.050	3.81	16.25		20.00
1650	4" dia.	"	0.057	4.36	19.75		24.00
1670	Rectangular, corrugated						
1680	2" x 3"	LF	0.053	4.07	16.25		20.25
1690	3" x 4"	"	0.053	4.07	19.50		23.50
1695	Rectangular, plain						
1700	2" x 3"	LF	0.053	4.07	11.25		15.25
1750	3" x 4"	"	0.053	4.07	13.25		17.25
1800	Gutters, 16 oz. copper						
1810	Half round						
1820	4" wide	LF	0.080	6.10	11.25		17.25
1840	5" wide	"	0.089	6.78	13.75		20.50
1860	Type K						
1880	4" wide	LF	0.080	6.10	12.50		18.50
1890	5" wide	"	0.089	6.78	13.00		19.75
1900	Lead-coated copper gutters						
1905	Half round						
1910	4" wide	LF	0.080	6.10	13.50		19.50
1920	6" wide	"	0.089	6.78	18.50		25.25
1925	Type K						
1930	4" wide	LF	0.080	6.10	14.75		20.75
1940	5" wide	"	0.089	6.78	19.25		26.00
3000	Aluminum gutter and downspout						
3005	Downspouts						
3010	2" x 3"	LF	0.053	4.07	1.45		5.52
3030	3" x 4"	"	0.057	4.36	2.00		6.36
3035	4" x 5"	"	0.062	4.69	2.31		7.00
3038	Round						
3040	3" dia.	LF	0.053	4.07	2.44		6.51
3050	4" dia.	"	0.057	4.36	3.13		7.49
3240	Gutters, stock units						
3260	4" wide	LF	0.084	6.42	2.26		8.68
3270	5" wide	"	0.089	6.78	2.69		9.47
4101	Galvanized steel gutter and downspout						
4111	Downspouts, round corrugated						
4121	3" dia.	LF	0.053	4.07	2.09		6.16
4131	4" dia.	"	0.053	4.07	2.80		6.87

ROOFING SPECIALTIES

ID Code	Component Descriptions	Unit of Meas.	Manhr / Unit	Labor Cost	Material Cost	Equip. Cost	Total Cost
07 - 71231	**GUTTERS AND DOWNSPOUTS, Cont'd...**						**07 - 71231**
4141	5" dia.	LF	0.057	4.36	4.18		8.54
4151	6" dia.	"	0.057	4.36	5.54		9.90
4161	Rectangular						
4171	2" x 3"	LF	0.053	4.07	1.89		5.96
4191	3" x 4"	"	0.050	3.81	2.70		6.51
4201	4" x 4"	"	0.050	3.81	3.38		7.19
4300	Gutters, stock units						
4310	5" wide						
4320	Plain	LF	0.089	6.78	1.82		8.60
4330	Painted	"	0.089	6.78	1.98		8.76
4335	6" wide						
4340	Plain	LF	0.094	7.18	2.55		9.73
4360	Painted	"	0.094	7.18	2.86		10.00

FIREPROOFING

ID Code	Component Descriptions	Unit of Meas.	Manhr / Unit	Labor Cost	Material Cost	Equip. Cost	Total Cost
07 - 81001	**FIREPROOFING**						**07 - 81001**
0980	Sprayed on						
1000	1" thick						
1020	On beams	SF	0.018	1.11	0.89		2.00
1040	On columns	"	0.016	1.00	0.91		1.91
1050	On decks						
1060	Flat surface	SF	0.008	0.50	0.91		1.41
1080	Fluted surface	"	0.010	0.62	1.15		1.77
1100	1-1/2" thick						
1120	On beams	SF	0.023	1.43	1.60		3.03
1140	On columns	"	0.020	1.25	1.81		3.06
1150	On decks						
1160	Flat surface	SF	0.010	0.62	1.36		1.98
1170	Fluted surface	"	0.013	0.83	1.60		2.43

JOINT SEALANTS

	Descriptions	Output		Unit Costs			
ID Code	Component Descriptions	Unit of Meas.	Manhr / Unit	Labor Cost	Material Cost	Equip. Cost	Total Cost
07 - 92001	**CAULKING**						**07 - 92001**
0100	Caulk exterior, two component						
0120	1/4 x 1/2	LF	0.040	3.20	0.43		3.63
0140	3/8 x 1/2	"	0.044	3.55	0.66		4.21
0160	1/2 x 1/2	"	0.050	4.00	0.90		4.90
0220	Caulk interior, single component						
0240	1/4 x 1/2	LF	0.038	3.04	0.29		3.33
0260	3/8 x 1/2	"	0.042	3.36	0.41		3.77
0280	1/2 x 1/2	"	0.047	3.76	0.54		4.30
1000	Butyl rubber fillers						
1010	1/4" x 1/4"	LF	0.016	1.28	0.83		2.11
1020	1/2" x 1/2"	"	0.027	2.13	1.21		3.34
1030	1/2" x 3/4"	"	0.032	2.56	1.85		4.41
1040	3/4" x 3/4"	"	0.032	2.56	2.43		4.99
1060	1" x 1"	"	0.036	2.84	2.85		5.69
1400	Seals, "O" ring type cord						
1410	1/4" dia.	LF	0.020	1.60	0.91		2.51
1420	1/2" dia.	"	0.021	1.68	2.72		4.40
1440	1" dia.	"	0.022	1.77	9.64		11.50
1450	1-1/4" dia.	"	0.024	1.88	12.25		14.25
1460	1-1/2" dia.	"	0.025	2.00	16.25		18.25
1470	1-3/4" dia.	"	0.026	2.06	24.00		26.00
1480	2" dia.	"	0.027	2.13	31.00		33.25
1500	Polyvinyl chloride, closed cell						
1520	1/4" x 2"	LF	0.029	2.28	0.62		2.90
1540	1/4" x 6"	"	0.036	2.90	1.96		4.86
1600	Silicon foam penetration seal						
1620	1/4" x 1/2"	LF	0.010	0.80	0.22		1.02
1640	1/2" x 1/2"	"	0.013	1.06	0.39		1.45
1660	1/2" x 3/4"	"	0.016	1.28	0.61		1.89
1680	3/4" x 3/4"	"	0.020	1.60	0.91		2.51
1700	1/8" x 1"	"	0.010	0.80	0.22		1.02
1720	1/8" x 3"	"	0.016	1.28	0.61		1.89
1740	1/4" x 3"	"	0.020	1.60	1.21		2.81
1760	1/4" x 6"	"	0.027	2.13	2.49		4.62
1780	1/2" x 6"	"	0.062	4.92	4.90		9.82
1800	1/2" x 9"	"	0.100	8.00	7.35		15.25
1820	1/2" x 12"	"	0.145	11.75	9.75		21.50
2020	Oil base sealants and caulking						

JOINT SEALANTS

ID Code	Component Descriptions	Unit of Meas.	Manhr / Unit	Labor Cost	Material Cost	Equip. Cost	Total Cost
	Descriptions	**Output**		**Unit Costs**			
07 - 92001		**CAULKING, Cont'd...**					**07 - 92001**
2040	1/4" x 1/4"	LF	0.020	1.60	0.04		1.64
2060	1/4" x 3/8"	"	0.021	1.66	0.10		1.76
2080	1/4" x 1/2"	"	0.022	1.72	0.12		1.84
2100	3/8" x 3/8"	"	0.023	1.82	0.14		1.96
2120	3/8" x 1/2"	"	0.024	1.93	0.16		2.09
2140	3/8" x 5/8"	"	0.026	2.06	0.30		2.36
2160	3/8" x 3/4"	"	0.028	2.20	0.33		2.53
2180	1/2" x 1/2"	"	0.031	2.46	0.30		2.76
2200	1/2" x 5/8"	"	0.035	2.78	0.37		3.15
2220	1/2" x 3/4"	"	0.040	3.20	0.43		3.63
2240	1/2" x 7/8"	"	0.041	3.28	0.50		3.78
2260	1/2" x 1"	"	0.042	3.36	0.55		3.91
2280	3/4" x 3/4"	"	0.043	3.45	0.65		4.10
2300	1" x 1"	"	0.044	3.55	1.13		4.68
2400	Polyurethane compounds						
2420	1/4" x 1/4"	LF	0.020	1.60	0.22		1.82
2440	1/4" x 3/8"	"	0.021	1.66	0.41		2.07
2460	1/4" x 1/2"	"	0.022	1.72	0.52		2.24
2480	3/8" x 3/8"	"	0.023	1.82	0.58		2.40
2500	3/8" x 1/2"	"	0.024	1.93	0.73		2.66
2520	3/8" x 5/8"	"	0.026	2.06	0.91		2.97
2540	3/8" x 3/4"	"	0.028	2.20	1.11		3.31
2560	1/2" x 1/2"	"	0.031	2.46	1.06		3.52
2580	1/2" x 5/8"	"	0.035	2.78	1.16		3.94
2590	1/2" x 3/4"	"	0.040	3.20	1.33		4.53
2600	1/2" x 7/8"	"	0.041	3.28	1.69		4.97
2620	1/2" x 1"	"	0.044	3.55	2.14		5.69
2640	3/4" x 3/4"	"	0.043	3.45	2.17		5.62
2660	3/4" x 1"	"	0.044	3.55	2.37		5.92
4000	Backer rod, polyethylene						
4100	1/4"	LF	0.020	1.60	0.06		1.66
4120	1/2"	"	0.021	1.68	0.10		1.78
4140	3/4"	"	0.022	1.77	0.13		1.90
4160	1"	"	0.024	1.88	0.19		2.07

EXPANSION CONTROL

ID Code	Component Descriptions	Unit of Meas.	Manhr / Unit	Labor Cost	Material Cost	Equip. Cost	Total Cost
		Output		**Unit Costs**			

07 - 95001	**EXPANSION JOINTS**						**07 - 95001**
1000	Expansion joints with covers, floor assembly type						
1040	With 1" space						
1060	Aluminum	LF	0.133	11.75	31.25		43.00
1080	Bronze	"	0.133	11.75	65.00		77.00
1100	Stainless steel	"	0.133	11.75	51.00		63.00
1200	With 2" space						
1210	Aluminum	LF	0.133	11.75	33.75		45.50
1220	Bronze	"	0.133	11.75	60.00		72.00
1240	Stainless steel	"	0.133	11.75	53.00		65.00
1400	Ceiling and wall assembly type						
1420	With 1" space						
1430	Aluminum	LF	0.160	14.00	17.50		31.50
1440	Bronze	"	0.160	14.00	60.00		74.00
1450	Stainless steel	"	0.160	14.00	54.00		68.00
1500	With 2" space						
1520	Aluminum	LF	0.160	14.00	19.25		33.25
1540	Bronze	"	0.160	14.00	65.00		79.00
1560	Stainless steel	"	0.160	14.00	57.00		71.00
1600	Exterior roof and wall, aluminum						
1640	Roof to roof						
1660	With 1" space	LF	0.133	11.75	51.00		63.00
1680	With 2" space	"	0.133	11.75	55.00		67.00
1700	Roof to wall						
1720	With 1" space	LF	0.145	12.75	39.75		53.00
1740	With 2" space	"	0.145	12.75	47.25		60.00
1760	Flat wall to wall						
1780	With 1" space	LF	0.133	11.75	19.25		31.00
1790	With 2" space	"	0.133	11.75	21.00		32.75
1800	Corner to flat wall						
1820	With 1" space	LF	0.160	14.00	23.25		37.25
1840	With 2" in space	"	0.160	14.00	23.50		37.50

DIVISION 08
DOORS AND WINDOWS

METAL DOORS & TRANSOMS

ID Code	Descriptions — Component Descriptions	Output — Unit of Meas.	Output — Manhr / Unit	Unit Costs — Labor Cost	Unit Costs — Material Cost	Unit Costs — Equip. Cost	Unit Costs — Total Cost
08 - 11131	**METAL DOORS**						**08 - 11131**
1000	Flush hollow metal, std. duty, 20 ga., 1-3/8" thick						
1020	2-6 x 6-8	EA	0.889	71.00	350		420
1040	2-8 x 6-8	"	0.889	71.00	390		460
1080	3-0 x 6-8	"	0.889	71.00	420		490
1090	1-3/4" thick						
1100	2-6 x 6-8	EA	0.889	71.00	410		480
1120	2-8 x 6-8	"	0.889	71.00	510		580
1150	3-0 x 6-8	"	0.889	71.00	470		540
1200	2-6 x 7-0	"	0.889	71.00	450		520
1210	2-8 x 7-0	"	0.889	71.00	470		540
1240	3-0 x 7-0	"	0.889	71.00	500		570
2110	Heavy duty, 20 ga., unrated, 1-3/4"						
2130	2-8 x 6-8	EA	0.889	71.00	450		520
2135	3-0 x 6-8	"	0.889	71.00	490		560
2140	2-8 x 7-0	"	0.889	71.00	520		590
2150	3-0 x 7-0	"	0.889	71.00	500		570
2170	3-4 x 7-0	"	0.889	71.00	520		590
2200	18 ga., 1-3/4", unrated door						
2210	2-0 x 7-0	EA	0.889	71.00	480		550
2230	2-4 x 7-0	"	0.889	71.00	480		550
2235	2-6 x 7-0	"	0.889	71.00	480		550
2240	2-8 x 7-0	"	0.889	71.00	530		600
2260	3-0 x 7-0	"	0.889	71.00	540		610
2270	3-4 x 7-0	"	0.889	71.00	560		630
2310	2", unrated door						
2320	2-0 x 7-0	EA	1.000	80.00	530		610
2330	2-4 x 7-0	"	1.000	80.00	530		610
2340	2-6 x 7-0	"	1.000	80.00	530		610
2350	2-8 x 7-0	"	1.000	80.00	580		660
2360	3-0 x 7-0	"	1.000	80.00	600		680
2370	3-4 x 7-0	"	1.000	80.00	610		690
2400	Galvanized metal door						
2410	3-0 x 7-0	EA	1.000	80.00	620		700
2450	For lead lining in doors	"					1,120
2460	For sound attenuation	"					100
4280	Vision glass						
4300	8" x 8"	EA	1.000	80.00	130		210
4320	8" x 48"	"	1.000	80.00	200		280

METAL DOORS & TRANSOMS

ID Code	Component Descriptions	Unit of Meas.	Manhr / Unit	Labor Cost	Material Cost	Equip. Cost	Total Cost
	Descriptions	**Output**		**Unit Costs**			
08 - 11131	**METAL DOORS, Cont'd...**						**08 - 11131**
4340	Fixed metal louver	EA	0.800	64.00	290		350
4350	For fire rating, add						
4370	3 hr door	EA					490
4380	1-1/2 hr door	"					220
4400	3/4 hr door	"					110
4430	1' extra height, add to material, 20%						
4440	1'6" extra height, add to material, 60%						
4470	For dutch doors with shelf, add to material, 100%						
08 - 11134	**METAL DOOR FRAMES**						**08 - 11134**
1000	Hollow metal, stock, 18 ga., 4-3/4" x 1-3/4"						
1020	2-0 x 7-0	EA	1.000	80.00	160		240
1040	2-4 x 7-0	"	1.000	80.00	190		270
1060	2-6 x 7-0	"	1.000	80.00	190		270
1080	2-8 x 7-0	"	1.000	80.00	190		270
1100	3-0 x 7-0	"	1.000	80.00	190		270
1120	4-0 x 7-0	"	1.333	110	210		320
1140	5-0 x 7-0	"	1.333	110	220		330
1160	6-0 x 7-0	"	1.333	110	260		370
1500	16 ga., 6-3/4" x 1-3/4"						
1520	2-0 x 7-0	EA	1.000	88.00	190		280
1530	2-4 x 7-0	"	1.000	88.00	180		270
1535	2-6 x 7-0	"	1.000	88.00	180		270
1540	2-8 x 7-0	"	1.000	88.00	180		270
1550	3-0 x 7-0	"	1.000	88.00	200		290
1560	4-0 x 7-0	"	1.333	120	230		350
1580	6-0 x 7-0	"	1.333	120	260		380
1600	Transom frame						
1620	3-4 x 1-6	EA	1.000	88.00	130		220
1640	3-8 x 1-6	"	1.000	88.00	130		220
1660	6-4 x 1-6	"	1.000	88.00	190		280
1680	Transom sash						
1690	3-0 x 1-4	EA	1.000	88.00	120		210
1700	3-4 x 1-4	"	1.000	88.00	130		220
1720	6-0 x 1-4	"	1.000	88.00	190		280
1760	1' extension of frame, add	"					24.75
1770	14 ga. frame, add	"					24.75
1775	For fire rating, add						

METAL DOORS & TRANSOMS

ID Code	Component Descriptions	Unit of Meas.	Manhr / Unit	Labor Cost	Material Cost	Equip. Cost	Total Cost
	Descriptions	**Output**		**Unit Costs**			

ID Code	Component Descriptions	Unit of Meas.	Manhr / Unit	Labor Cost	Material Cost	Equip. Cost	Total Cost
08 - 11134	**METAL DOOR FRAMES, Cont'd...**						**08 - 11134**
1780	3 hour	EA					67.00
1790	1-1/2 hour	"					54.00
1800	3/4 hour	"					47.00
1810	Lead lining in frame, add	"					140
1900	Sidelights, complete						
1920	1-0 x 7-2	EA	1.000	88.00	460		550
1940	1-4 x 7-2	"	1.000	88.00	510		600
1960	1-0 x 8-8	"	1.000	88.00	540		630
1970	1-6 x 8-8	"	1.000	88.00	560		650
2000	16 ga., 4-3/4" x 1-3/4"						
2020	2-0 x 7-0	EA	1.000	88.00	170		260
2030	2-4 x 7-0	"	1.000	88.00	170		260
2035	2-6 x 7-0	"	1.000	88.00	170		260
2040	2-8 x 7-0	"	1.000	88.00	170		260
2050	3-0 x 7-0	"	1.000	88.00	180		270
2060	4-0 x 7-0	"	1.333	120	180		300
2070	6-0 x 7-0	"	1.333	120	190		310
2100	Transom frame						
2120	3-4 x 1-6	EA	1.000	88.00	120		210
2140	3-8 x 1-6	"	1.000	88.00	120		210
2160	6-4 x 1-6	"	1.000	88.00	160		250
2180	Transom sash						
2200	3-0 x 1-4	EA	1.000	88.00	100		190
2220	3-4 x 1-4	"	1.000	88.00	110		200
2240	6-0 x 1-4	"	1.000	88.00	160		250
2320	1' extension of door frame, add	"					24.75
2330	14 ga., metal frame, add	"					24.75
2335	For fire rating, add						
2340	3 hour	EA					64.00
2360	1-1/2 hour	"					51.00
2380	3/4 hour	"					44.75
2390	Lead lining in frame, add	"					140
2400	Sidelights, complete						
2420	1-0 x 7-2	EA	1.000	88.00	440		530
2440	1-4 x 7-2	"	1.000	88.00	460		550
2460	1-0 x 8-8	"	1.000	88.00	500		590
2480	1-4 x 8-8	"	1.000	88.00	510		600
2500	16 ga., 5-3/4" x 1-3/4"						

METAL DOORS & TRANSOMS

ID Code	Component Descriptions	Unit of Meas.	Manhr / Unit	Labor Cost	Material Cost	Equip. Cost	Total Cost
	Descriptions	**Output**		**Unit Costs**			

08 - 11134 — METAL DOOR FRAMES, Cont'd... — 08 - 11134

ID Code	Component Descriptions	Unit of Meas.	Manhr / Unit	Labor Cost	Material Cost	Equip. Cost	Total Cost
2520	2-0 x 7-0	EA	1.000	80.00	170		250
2530	2-4 x 7-0	"	1.000	80.00	180		260
2540	2-6 x 7-0	"	1.000	80.00	180		260
2550	2-8 x 7-0	"	1.000	80.00	190		270
2560	3-0 x 7-0	"	1.000	80.00	190		270
2580	4-0 x 7-0	"	1.333	110	200		310
2590	5-0 x 7-0	"	1.333	110	210		320
2600	6-0 x 7-0	"	1.333	110	220		330
2610	Mullions, vertical						
2640	5-1/4" x 1-3/4"	LF	0.100	8.00	19.25		27.25
2650	5-1/4" x 2"	"	0.100	8.00	24.00		32.00
2700	Horizontal						
2730	5-1/4" x 1-3/4"	LF	0.100	8.00	19.25		27.25
2740	5-1/4" x 2"	"	0.100	8.00	24.00		32.00

08 - 11161 — ALUMINUM DOORS — 08 - 11161

ID Code	Component Descriptions	Unit of Meas.	Manhr / Unit	Labor Cost	Material Cost	Equip. Cost	Total Cost
1490	Aluminum doors, commercial						
1500	Narrow stile						
1520	2-6 x 7-0	EA	4.000	350	940		1,290
1540	3-0 x 7-0	"	4.000	350	990		1,340
1560	3-6 x 7-0	"	4.000	350	1,010		1,360
1570	Pair						
1580	5-0 x 7-0	EA	8.000	710	1,570		2,280
1600	6-0 x 7-0	"	8.000	710	1,590		2,300
1620	7-0 x 7-0	"	8.000	710	1,660		2,370
1700	Wide stile						
1720	2-6 x 7-0	EA	4.000	350	1,320		1,670
1740	3-0 x 7-0	"	4.000	350	1,360		1,710
1760	3-6 x 7-0	"	4.000	350	1,400		1,750
1770	Pair						
1780	5-0 x 7-0	EA	8.000	710	2,410		3,120
1800	6-0 x 7-0	"	8.000	710	2,520		3,230
1820	7-0 x 7-0	"	8.000	710	2,570		3,280

WOOD AND PLASTIC

	Descriptions	Output		Unit Costs			
ID Code	Component Descriptions	Unit of Meas.	Manhr / Unit	Labor Cost	Material Cost	Equip. Cost	Total Cost
08 - 14001		**WOOD DOORS**					**08 - 14001**
0980	Solid core, 1-3/8" thick						
1000	Birch faced						
1020	2-4 x 7-0	EA	1.000	80.00	180		260
1040	2-8 x 7-0	"	1.000	80.00	180		260
1060	3-0 x 7-0	"	1.000	80.00	180		260
1070	3-4 x 7-0	"	1.000	80.00	370		450
1080	2-4 x 6-8	"	1.000	80.00	180		260
1090	2-6 x 6-8	"	1.000	80.00	180		260
1095	2-8 x 6-8	"	1.000	80.00	180		260
1100	3-0 x 6-8	"	1.000	80.00	180		260
1120	Lauan faced						
1140	2-4 x 6-8	EA	1.000	80.00	160		240
1160	2-8 x 6-8	"	1.000	80.00	170		250
1180	3-0 x 6-8	"	1.000	80.00	180		260
1200	3-4 x 6-8	"	1.000	80.00	190		270
1300	Tempered hardboard faced						
1320	2-4 x 7-0	EA	1.000	80.00	200		280
1340	2-8 x 7-0	"	1.000	80.00	210		290
1360	3-0 x 7-0	"	1.000	80.00	240		320
1380	3-4 x 7-0	"	1.000	80.00	250		330
1420	Hollow core, 1-3/8" thick						
1440	Birch faced						
1460	2-4 x 7-0	EA	1.000	80.00	160		240
1480	2-8 x 7-0	"	1.000	80.00	160		240
1500	3-0 x 7-0	"	1.000	80.00	170		250
1520	3-4 x 7-0	"	1.000	80.00	180		260
1600	Lauan faced						
1620	2-4 x 6-8	EA	1.000	80.00	69.00		150
1630	2-6 x 6-8	"	1.000	80.00	74.00		150
1640	2-8 x 6-8	"	1.000	80.00	93.00		170
1660	3-0 x 6-8	"	1.000	80.00	97.00		180
1680	3-4 x 6-8	"	1.000	80.00	110		190
1740	Tempered hardboard faced						
1760	2-4 x 7-0	EA	1.000	80.00	84.00		160
1770	2-6 x 7-0	"	1.000	80.00	90.00		170
1780	2-8 x 7-0	"	1.000	80.00	100		180
1800	3-0 x 7-0	"	1.000	80.00	110		190
1820	3-4 x 7-0	"	1.000	80.00	120		200

WOOD AND PLASTIC

ID Code	Descriptions — Component Descriptions	Output — Unit of Meas.	Output — Manhr / Unit	Unit Costs — Labor Cost	Unit Costs — Material Cost	Unit Costs — Equip. Cost	Unit Costs — Total Cost
08 - 14001	**WOOD DOORS, Cont'd...**						**08 - 14001**
1900	Solid core, 1-3/4" thick						
1920	Birch faced						
1940	2-4 x 7-0	EA	1.000	80.00	280		360
1950	2-6 x 7-0	"	1.000	80.00	280		360
1960	2-8 x 7-0	"	1.000	80.00	290		370
1970	3-0 x 7-0	"	1.000	80.00	270		350
1980	3-4 x 7-0	"	1.000	80.00	280		360
2000	Lauan faced						
2020	2-4 x 7-0	EA	1.000	80.00	190		270
2030	2-6 x 7-0	"	1.000	80.00	220		300
2040	2-8 x 7-0	"	1.000	80.00	230		310
2060	3-4 x 7-0	"	1.000	80.00	240		320
2080	3-0 x 7-0	"	1.000	80.00	260		340
2140	Tempered hardboard faced						
2160	2-4 x 7-0	EA	1.000	80.00	250		330
2170	2-6 x 7-0	"	1.000	80.00	280		360
2180	2-8 x 7-0	"	1.000	80.00	300		380
2190	3-0 x 7-0	"	1.000	80.00	320		400
2200	3-4 x 7-0	"	1.000	80.00	340		420
2250	Hollow core, 1-3/4" thick						
2270	Birch faced						
2290	2-4 x 7-0	EA	1.000	80.00	190		270
2295	2-6 x 7-0	"	1.000	80.00	190		270
2300	2-8 x 7-0	"	1.000	80.00	200		280
2320	3-0 x 7-0	"	1.000	80.00	200		280
2340	3-4 x 7-0	"	1.000	80.00	220		300
2400	Lauan faced						
2420	2-4 x 6-8	EA	1.000	80.00	110		190
2430	2-6 x 6-8	"	1.000	80.00	130		210
2440	2-8 x 6-8	"	1.000	80.00	110		190
2460	3-0 x 6-8	"	1.000	80.00	120		200
2480	3-4 x 6-8	"	1.000	80.00	120		200
2520	Tempered hardboard						
2540	2-4 x 7-0	EA	1.000	80.00	100		180
2550	2-6 x 7-0	"	1.000	80.00	110		190
2560	2-8 x 7-0	"	1.000	80.00	110		190
2580	3-0 x 7-0	"	1.000	80.00	120		200
2600	3-4 x 7-0	"	1.000	80.00	130		210

WOOD AND PLASTIC

ID Code	Component Descriptions	Unit of Meas.	Manhr / Unit	Labor Cost	Material Cost	Equip. Cost	Total Cost
	Descriptions	**Output**		**Unit Costs**			

ID Code	Component Descriptions	Unit of Meas.	Manhr / Unit	Labor Cost	Material Cost	Equip. Cost	Total Cost
08 - 14001	**WOOD DOORS, Cont'd...**						**08 - 14001**
2620	Add-on, louver	EA	0.800	64.00	35.00		99.00
2640	Glass	"	0.800	64.00	110		170
2700	Exterior doors, 3-0 x 7-0 x 2-1/2", solid core						
2710	Carved						
2720	One face	EA	2.000	160	1,460		1,620
2740	Two faces	"	2.000	160	2,020		2,180
3000	Closet doors, 1-3/4" thick						
3001	Bi-fold or bi-passing, includes frame and trim						
3020	Paneled						
3040	4-0 x 6-8	EA	1.333	110	510		620
3060	6-0 x 6-8	"	1.333	110	580		690
3070	Louvered						
3080	4-0 x 6-8	EA	1.333	110	350		460
3100	6-0 x 6-8	"	1.333	110	420		530
3130	Flush						
3140	4-0 x 6-8	EA	1.333	110	260		370
3160	6-0 x 6-8	"	1.333	110	330		440
3170	Primed						
3180	4-0 x 6-8	EA	1.333	110	280		390
3200	6-0 x 6-8	"	1.333	110	310		420
08 - 14009	**WOOD FRAMES**						**08 - 14009**
0080	Frame, interior, pine						
0100	2-6 x 6-8	EA	1.143	91.00	100		190
0140	2-8 x 6-8	"	1.143	91.00	110		200
0160	3-0 x 6-8	"	1.143	91.00	120		210
0180	5-0 x 6-8	"	1.143	91.00	120		210
0200	6-0 x 6-8	"	1.143	91.00	130		220
0220	2-6 x 7-0	"	1.143	91.00	120		210
0240	2-8 x 7-0	"	1.143	91.00	140		230
0260	3-0 x 7-0	"	1.143	91.00	140		230
0280	5-0 x 7-0	"	1.600	130	150		280
0300	6-0 x 7-0	"	1.600	130	160		290
1000	Exterior, custom, with threshold, including trim						
1040	Walnut						
1060	3-0 x 7-0	EA	2.000	160	420		580
1080	6-0 x 7-0	"	2.000	160	480		640
1090	Oak						

WOOD AND PLASTIC

ID Code	Descriptions		Output		Unit Costs			
	Component Descriptions		Unit of Meas.	Manhr / Unit	Labor Cost	Material Cost	Equip. Cost	Total Cost
08 - 14009		**WOOD FRAMES, Cont'd...**						**08 - 14009**
1100	3-0 x 7-0		EA	2.000	160	380		540
1120	6-0 x 7-0		"	2.000	160	430		590
1200	Pine							
1220	2-4 x 7-0		EA	1.600	130	160		290
1240	2-6 x 7-0		"	1.600	130	160		290
1280	2-8 x 7-0		"	1.600	130	170		300
1300	3-0 x 7-0		"	1.600	130	180		310
1320	3-4 x 7-0		"	1.600	130	200		330
1340	6-0 x 7-0		"	2.667	210	210		420

SPECIALTY DOORS AND FRAMES

ID Code	Descriptions		Output		Unit Costs			
08 - 31131		**CONTROL**						**08 - 31131**
1020	Access control, 7' high, indoor or outdoor impenetrability							
1040	Remote or card control, type B		EA	10.667	870	1,850		2,720
1060	Free passage, type B		"	10.667	870	1,500		2,370
1080	Remote or card control, type AA		"	10.667	870	2,950		3,820
1100	Free passage, type AA		"	10.667	870	2,670		3,540

SPECIAL FUNCTION DOORS

ID Code	Descriptions		Output		Unit Costs			
08 - 34001		**SPECIAL DOORS**						**08 - 34001**
1000	Vault door and frame, class 5, steel		EA	8.000	640	7,940		8,580
1400	Overhead door, coiling insulated							
1500	Chain gear, no frame, 12' x 12'		EA	10.000	800	3,410		4,210
2000	Aluminum, bronze glass panels, 12-9 x 13-0		"	8.000	640	3,850		4,490
2200	Garage, flush, ins. metal, primed, 9-0 x 7-0		"	2.667	210	1,100		1,310
3020	Sliding fire doors, motorized, fusible link, 3 hr.							
3040	3-0 x 6-8		EA	16.000	1,280	5,620		6,900
3060	3-8 x 6-8		"	16.000	1,280	5,690		6,970
3080	4-0 x 8-0		"	16.000	1,280	5,790		7,070
3100	5-0 x 8-0		"	16.000	1,280	5,900		7,180
3180	Metal clad doors, including electric motor							
3200	Light duty							
3220	Minimum		SF	0.133	10.75	45.00		56.00
3240	Maximum		"	0.320	25.50	73.00		99.00
3250	Heavy duty							
3260	Minimum		SF	0.400	32.00	70.00		100

SPECIAL FUNCTION DOORS

	Descriptions	Output		Unit Costs			
ID Code	Component Descriptions	Unit of Meas.	Manhr / Unit	Labor Cost	Material Cost	Equip. Cost	Total Cost
08 - 34001	**SPECIAL DOORS, Cont'd...**						**08 - 34001**
3280	Maximum	SF	0.500	40.00	110		150
3300	Hangar doors, based on 150' openings						
3320	To 20' high	SF	0.096	6.01	61.00	4.20	71.00
3340	20' to 40' high	"	0.060	3.75	67.00	2.62	73.00
3360	40' to 60' high	"	0.040	2.50	70.00	1.75	74.00
3380	60' to 80' high	"	0.024	1.50	73.00	1.05	76.00
3400	Over 80' high	"	0.019	1.20	100	0.84	100
3480	Counter doors, (roll-up shutters), std, manual						
3500	Opening, 4' high						
3520	4' wide	EA	6.667	530	1,300		1,830
3540	6' wide	"	6.667	530	1,760		2,290
3560	8' wide	"	7.273	580	1,980		2,560
3580	10' wide	"	10.000	800	2,200		3,000
3590	14' wide	"	10.000	800	2,750		3,550
3600	6' high						
3610	4' wide	EA	6.667	530	1,540		2,070
3620	6' wide	"	7.273	580	2,010		2,590
3630	8' wide	"	8.000	640	2,200		2,840
3640	10' wide	"	10.000	800	2,480		3,280
3650	14' wide	"	11.429	910	2,810		3,720
3660	For stainless steel, add to material, 40%						
3670	For motor operator, add	EA					1,520
3700	Service doors, (roll up shutters), std, manual						
3800	Opening						
3820	8' high x 8' wide	EA	4.444	360	1,650		2,010
3830	10' high x 10' wide	"	6.667	530	2,060		2,590
3840	12' high x 12' wide	"	10.000	800	2,310		3,110
3850	14' high x 14' wide	"	13.333	1,070	3,030		4,100
3860	16' high x 14' wide	"	13.333	1,070	4,240		5,310
3870	20' high x 14' wide	"	20.000	1,600	4,790		6,390
3880	24' high x 16' wide	"	17.778	1,420	7,810		9,230
3890	For motor operator						
3900	Up to 12-0 x 12-0, add	EA					1,550
3920	Over 12-0 x 12-0, add	"					1,980
4000	Roll-up doors						
4050	13-0 high x 14-0 wide	EA	11.429	910	1,560		2,470
4060	12-0 high x 14-0 wide	"	11.429	910	1,980		2,890
4100	Top coiling grilles, manual, steel or aluminum						

SPECIAL FUNCTION DOORS

ID Code	Component Descriptions	Unit of Meas.	Manhr / Unit	Labor Cost	Material Cost	Equip. Cost	Total Cost
08 - 34001	**SPECIAL DOORS, Cont'd...**						**08 - 34001**
4120	Opening, 4' high x						
4140	4' wide	EA	3.200	260	1,830		2,090
4160	6' wide	"	3.200	260	1,890		2,150
4180	8' wide	"	4.444	360	2,190		2,550
4200	12' wide	"	4.444	360	2,530		2,890
4220	16' wide	"	6.667	530	2,900		3,430
4230	6' high x						
4240	4' wide	EA	6.667	530	1,920		2,450
4260	6' wide	"	7.273	580	2,140		2,720
4280	8' wide	"	8.000	640	2,220		2,860
4300	12' wide	"	8.889	710	2,690		3,400
4320	16' wide	"	11.429	910	3,420		4,330
4400	Side coiling grilles, manual, aluminum						
4430	Opening, 8' high x						
4440	18' wide	EA	60.000	3,760	4,370	2,630	10,750
4460	24' wide	"	68.571	4,300	5,640	3,000	12,940
4470	12' high x						
4480	12' wide	EA	60.000	3,760	4,430	2,630	10,810
4490	18' wide	"	68.571	4,300	5,640	3,000	12,940
4500	24' wide	"	80.000	5,010	8,060	3,500	16,570
5000	Accordion folding, tracks and fittings included						
5020	Vinyl covered, 2 layers	SF	0.320	25.50	14.50		40.00
5040	Woven mahogany and vinyl	"	0.320	25.50	18.25		43.75
5060	Economy vinyl	"	0.320	25.50	12.25		37.75
5080	Rigid polyvinyl chloride	"	0.320	25.50	20.00		45.50
5200	Sectional wood overhead, frames not incl.						
5220	Commercial grade, HD, 1-3/4" thick, manual						
5240	8' x 8'	EA	6.667	530	1,080		1,610
5260	10' x 10'	"	7.273	580	1,560		2,140
5280	12' x 12'	"	8.000	640	2,030		2,670
5290	Chain hoist						
5300	12' x 16' high	EA	13.333	1,070	3,000		4,070
5320	14' x 14' high	"	10.000	800	3,290		4,090
5340	20' x 8' high	"	16.000	1,280	2,830		4,110
5360	16' high	"	20.000	1,600	6,350		7,950
5800	Sectional metal overhead doors, complete						
5900	Residential grade, manual						
6020	9' x 7'	EA	3.200	260	740		1,000

SPECIAL FUNCTION DOORS

ID Code	Component Descriptions	Unit of Meas.	Manhr / Unit	Labor Cost	Material Cost	Equip. Cost	Total Cost
	Descriptions	**Output**		**Unit Costs**			

ID Code	Component Descriptions	Unit of Meas.	Manhr / Unit	Labor Cost	Material Cost	Equip. Cost	Total Cost
08 - 34001	**SPECIAL DOORS, Cont'd...**						**08 - 34001**
6040	16' x 7'	EA	4.000	320	1,330		1,650
6100	Commercial grade						
6120	8' x 8'	EA	6.667	530	860		1,390
6140	10' x 10'	"	7.273	580	1,150		1,730
6160	12' x 12'	"	8.000	640	1,910		2,550
6180	20' x 14', with chain hoist	"	16.000	1,280	4,560		5,840
6400	Sliding glass doors						
6410	Tempered plate glass, 1/4" thick						
6420	6' wide						
6440	Economy grade	EA	2.667	210	1,180		1,390
6450	Premium grade	"	2.667	210	1,350		1,560
6455	12' wide						
6460	Economy grade	EA	4.000	320	1,650		1,970
6465	Premium grade	"	4.000	320	2,480		2,800
6470	Insulating glass, 5/8" thick						
6475	6' wide						
6480	Economy grade	EA	2.667	210	1,450		1,660
6490	Premium grade	"	2.667	210	1,860		2,070
6500	12' wide						
6510	Economy grade	EA	4.000	320	1,800		2,120
6515	Premium grade	"	4.000	320	2,890		3,210
6520	1" thick						
6525	6' wide						
6530	Economy grade	EA	2.667	210	1,820		2,030
6535	Premium grade	"	2.667	210	2,100		2,310
6540	12' wide						
6550	Economy grade	EA	4.000	320	2,830		3,150
6560	Premium grade	"	4.000	320	4,140		4,460
6600	Added costs						
6610	Custom quality, add to material, 30%						
6630	Tempered glass, 6' wide, add	SF					5.08
6650	Vertical lift doors, channel frame construction						
6670	20' high x						
6720	10' wide	EA	9.600	600	41,820	530	42,950
6730	15' wide	"	9.600	600	52,280	530	53,410
6740	20' wide	"	17.143	1,070	57,500	950	59,520
6750	25' wide	"	17.143	1,070	62,730	950	64,750
6755	25' high x						

SPECIAL FUNCTION DOORS

ID Code	Component Descriptions	Unit of Meas.	Manhr / Unit	Labor Cost	Material Cost	Equip. Cost	Total Cost
	Descriptions	**Output**		**Unit Costs**			
08 - 34001	**SPECIAL DOORS, Cont'd...**						**08 - 34001**
6760	20' wide	EA	17.143	1,070	65,340	950	67,360
6770	25' wide	"	20.000	1,240	73,190	1,110	75,540
6775	30' high x						
6780	25' wide	EA	20.000	1,240	78,420	1,110	80,770
6790	30' wide	"	20.000	1,240	86,260	1,110	88,610
6800	35' wide	"	20.000	1,240	101,940	1,110	104,290
6850	Residential storm door						
6900	Minimum	EA	1.333	110	180		290
6920	Average	"	1.333	110	240		350
6940	Maximum	"	2.000	160	530		690

ENTRANCES AND STOREFRONTS

ID Code	Component Descriptions	Unit of Meas.	Manhr / Unit	Labor Cost	Material Cost	Equip. Cost	Total Cost
08 - 41001	**STOREFRONTS**						**08 - 41001**
0135	Storefront, aluminum and glass						
0140	Minimum	SF	0.100	8.83	29.25		38.00
0150	Average	"	0.114	10.00	43.75		54.00
0160	Maximum	"	0.133	11.75	87.00		99.00
1020	Entrance doors, premium, closers, panic dev.,etc.						
1030	1/2" thick glass						
1040	3' x 7'	EA	6.667	590	3,890		4,480
1060	6' x 7'	"	10.000	880	6,650		7,530
1065	3/4" thick glass						
1070	3' x 7'	EA	6.667	590	4,030		4,620
1080	6' x 7'	"	10.000	880	6,720		7,600
1085	1" thick glass						
1090	3' x 7'	EA	6.667	590	4,370		4,960
1100	6' x 7'	"	10.000	880	7,720		8,600
1150	Revolving doors						
1151	7' diameter, 7' high						
1160	Minimum	EA	60.000	3,730	27,660	3,330	34,710
1170	Average	"	96.000	5,970	34,800	5,320	46,090
1180	Maximum	"	120.000	7,460	44,910	6,650	59,020

GLAZED CURTAIN WALLS

ID Code	Component Descriptions	Unit of Meas.	Manhr / Unit	Labor Cost	Material Cost	Equip. Cost	Total Cost
	Descriptions	**Output**		**Unit Costs**			
08 - 44001	**GLAZED CURTAIN WALLS**						**08 - 44001**
1000	Curtain wall, aluminum system, framing sections						
1005	2" x 3"						
1010	Jamb	LF	0.067	5.88	19.50		25.50
1020	Horizontal	"	0.067	5.88	19.75		25.75
1030	Mullion	"	0.067	5.88	26.50		32.50
1035	2" x 4"						
1040	Jamb	LF	0.100	8.83	26.50		35.25
1060	Horizontal	"	0.100	8.83	27.25		36.00
1070	Mullion	"	0.100	8.83	26.50		35.25
1080	3" x 5-1/2"						
1090	Jamb	LF	0.100	8.83	35.00		43.75
1100	Horizontal	"	0.100	8.83	38.75		47.50
1110	Mullion	"	0.100	8.83	35.25		44.00
1115	4" corner mullion	"	0.133	11.75	46.75		59.00
1120	Coping sections						
1130	1/8" x 8"	LF	0.133	11.75	44.25		56.00
1140	1/8" x 9"	"	0.133	11.75	44.50		56.00
1150	1/8" x 12-1/2"	"	0.160	14.00	45.75		60.00
1160	Sill section						
1170	1/8" x 6"	LF	0.080	7.06	43.75		51.00
1180	1/8" x 7"	"	0.080	7.06	44.25		51.00
1190	1/8" x 8-1/2"	"	0.080	7.06	45.00		52.00
1200	Column covers, aluminum						
1210	1/8" x 26"	LF	0.200	17.75	43.75		62.00
1220	1/8" x 34"	"	0.211	18.50	48.50		67.00
1230	1/8" x 38"	"	0.211	18.50	49.00		68.00
1500	Doors						
1600	Aluminum framed, standard hardware						
1620	Narrow stile						
1630	2-6 x 7-0	EA	4.000	350	810		1,160
1640	3-0 x 7-0	"	4.000	350	810		1,160
1660	3-6 x 7-0	"	4.000	350	840		1,190
1700	Wide stile						
1720	2-6 x 7-0	EA	4.000	350	1,380		1,730
1730	3-0 x 7-0	"	4.000	350	1,490		1,840
1750	3-6 x 7-0	"	4.000	350	1,600		1,950
1800	Flush panel doors, to match adjacent wall panels						
1810	2-6 x 7-0	EA	5.000	440	1,170		1,610

GLAZED CURTAIN WALLS

ID Code	Component Descriptions	Unit of Meas.	Manhr / Unit	Labor Cost	Material Cost	Equip. Cost	Total Cost
	Descriptions	**Output**		**Unit Costs**			

08 - 44001 — GLAZED CURTAIN WALLS, Cont'd...   08 - 44001

ID Code	Component Descriptions	Unit of Meas.	Manhr / Unit	Labor Cost	Material Cost	Equip. Cost	Total Cost
1820	3-0 x 7-0	EA	5.000	440	1,230		1,670
1840	3-6 x 7-0	"	5.000	440	1,270		1,710
2100	Wall panel, insulated						
2120	"U"=.08	SF	0.067	5.88	14.75		20.75
2140	"U"=.10	"	0.067	5.88	14.00		20.00
2160	"U"=.15	"	0.067	5.88	12.50		18.50
3000	Window wall system, complete						
3010	Minimum	SF	0.080	7.06	42.75		49.75
3030	Average	"	0.089	7.84	68.00		76.00
3050	Maximum	"	0.114	10.00	160		170
4860	Added costs						
4870	For bronze, add 20% to material						
4880	For stainless steel, add 50% to material						

METAL WINDOWS

08 - 51131 — ALUMINUM WINDOWS   08 - 51131

ID Code	Component Descriptions	Unit of Meas.	Manhr / Unit	Labor Cost	Material Cost	Equip. Cost	Total Cost
0110	Jalousie						
0120	3-0 x 4-0	EA	1.000	88.00	390		480
0140	3-0 x 5-0	"	1.000	88.00	450		540
0220	Fixed window						
0240	6 sf to 8 sf	SF	0.114	10.00	19.25		29.25
0250	12 sf to 16 sf	"	0.089	7.84	17.00		24.75
0255	Projecting window						
0260	6 sf to 8 sf	SF	0.200	17.75	42.50		60.00
0270	12 sf to 16 sf	"	0.133	11.75	38.25		50.00
0275	Horizontal sliding						
0280	6 sf to 8 sf	SF	0.100	8.83	27.75		36.50
0290	12 sf to 16 sf	"	0.080	7.06	25.50		32.50
1140	Double hung						
1160	6 sf to 8 sf	SF	0.160	14.00	38.25		52.00
1180	10 sf to 12 sf	"	0.133	11.75	34.00		45.75
3010	Storm window, 0.5 cfm, up to						
3020	60 u.i. (united inches)	EA	0.400	35.25	89.00		120
3040	70 u.i.	"	0.400	35.25	92.00		130
3060	80 u.i.	"	0.400	35.25	100		140
3080	90 u.i.	"	0.444	39.25	100		140
3100	100 u.i.	"	0.444	39.25	110		150

METAL WINDOWS

ID Code	Component Descriptions	Unit of Meas.	Manhr / Unit	Labor Cost	Material Cost	Equip. Cost	Total Cost
	Descriptions	**Output**		**Unit Costs**			

ID Code	Component Descriptions	Unit of Meas.	Manhr / Unit	Labor Cost	Material Cost	Equip. Cost	Total Cost
08 - 51131	**ALUMINUM WINDOWS, Cont'd...**						**08 - 51131**
3110	2.0 cfm, up to						
3120	60 u.i.	EA	0.400	35.25	110		150
3140	70 u.i.	"	0.400	35.25	120		160
3160	80 u.i.	"	0.400	35.25	120		160
3180	90 u.i.	"	0.444	39.25	130		170
3200	100 u.i.	"	0.444	39.25	130		170
08 - 51231	**STEEL WINDOWS**						**08 - 51231**
0100	Steel windows, primed						
1000	Casements						
1010	Operable						
1020	Minimum	SF	0.047	4.15	52.00		56.00
1040	Maximum	"	0.053	4.70	78.00		83.00
1060	Fixed sash	"	0.040	3.53	41.25		44.75
1080	Double hung	"	0.044	3.92	78.00		82.00
1100	Industrial windows						
1120	Horizontally pivoted sash	SF	0.053	4.70	66.00		71.00
1130	Fixed sash	"	0.044	3.92	52.00		56.00
1135	Security sash						
1140	Operable	SF	0.053	4.70	82.00		87.00
1150	Fixed	"	0.044	3.92	73.00		77.00
1155	Picture window	"	0.044	3.92	35.25		39.25
1160	Projecting sash						
1170	Minimum	SF	0.050	4.41	61.00		65.00
1180	Maximum	"	0.050	4.41	75.00		79.00
1930	Mullions	LF	0.040	3.53	16.00		19.50

WOOD AND PLASTIC

ID Code	Component Descriptions	Unit of Meas.	Manhr / Unit	Labor Cost	Material Cost	Equip. Cost	Total Cost
08 - 52001	**WOOD WINDOWS**						**08 - 52001**
0980	Double hung						
0990	24" x 36"						
1000	Minimum	EA	0.800	64.00	240		300
1002	Average	"	1.000	80.00	350		430
1004	Maximum	"	1.333	110	470		580
1010	24" x 48"						
1020	Minimum	EA	0.800	64.00	280		340
1022	Average	"	1.000	80.00	410		490
1024	Maximum	"	1.333	110	570		680

WOOD AND PLASTIC

ID Code	Descriptions	Output		Unit Costs			
	Component Descriptions	Unit of Meas.	Manhr / Unit	Labor Cost	Material Cost	Equip. Cost	Total Cost
08 - 52001	**WOOD WINDOWS, Cont'd...**						**08 - 52001**
1030	30" x 48"						
1040	Minimum	EA	0.889	71.00	290		360
1042	Average	"	1.143	91.00	410		500
1044	Maximum	"	1.600	130	590		720
1050	30" x 60"						
1060	Minimum	EA	0.889	71.00	320		390
1062	Average	"	1.143	91.00	510		600
1064	Maximum	"	1.600	130	630		760
1160	Casement						
1180	1 leaf, 22" x 38" high						
1220	Minimum	EA	0.800	64.00	350		410
1222	Average	"	1.000	80.00	430		510
1224	Maximum	"	1.333	110	500		610
1230	2 leaf, 50" x 50" high						
1240	Minimum	EA	1.000	80.00	940		1,020
1242	Average	"	1.333	110	1,230		1,340
1244	Maximum	"	2.000	160	1,410		1,570
1250	3 leaf, 71" x 62" high						
1260	Minimum	EA	1.000	80.00	1,550		1,630
1262	Average	"	1.333	110	1,580		1,690
1264	Maximum	"	2.000	160	1,890		2,050
1270	4 leaf, 95" x 75" high						
1280	Minimum	EA	1.143	91.00	2,060		2,150
1282	Average	"	1.600	130	2,350		2,480
1284	Maximum	"	2.667	210	3,000		3,210
1290	5 leaf, 119" x 75" high						
1300	Minimum	EA	1.143	91.00	2,670		2,760
1302	Average	"	1.600	130	2,880		3,010
1304	Maximum	"	2.667	210	3,680		3,890
1360	Picture window, fixed glass, 54" x 54" high						
1400	Minimum	EA	1.000	80.00	550		630
1422	Average	"	1.143	91.00	620		710
1424	Maximum	"	1.333	110	1,100		1,210
1430	68" x 55" high						
1440	Minimum	EA	1.000	80.00	990		1,070
1442	Average	"	1.143	91.00	1,140		1,230
1444	Maximum	"	1.333	110	1,490		1,600
1480	Sliding, 40" x 31" high						

WOOD AND PLASTIC

ID Code	Descriptions — Component Descriptions	Output — Unit of Meas.	Output — Manhr / Unit	Unit Costs — Labor Cost	Unit Costs — Material Cost	Unit Costs — Equip. Cost	Unit Costs — Total Cost
08 - 52001	**WOOD WINDOWS, Cont'd...**						**08 - 52001**
1520	Minimum	EA	0.800	64.00	330		390
1522	Average	"	1.000	80.00	500		580
1524	Maximum	"	1.333	110	600		710
1530	52" x 39" high						
1540	Minimum	EA	1.000	80.00	410		490
1542	Average	"	1.143	91.00	610		700
1544	Maximum	"	1.333	110	650		760
1550	64" x 72" high						
1560	Minimum	EA	1.000	80.00	630		710
1562	Average	"	1.333	110	1,010		1,120
1564	Maximum	"	1.600	130	1,110		1,240
1760	Awning windows						
1780	34" x 21" high						
1800	Minimum	EA	0.800	64.00	330		390
1822	Average	"	1.000	80.00	380		460
1824	Maximum	"	1.333	110	440		550
1840	40" x 21" high						
1860	Minimum	EA	0.889	71.00	390		460
1862	Average	"	1.143	91.00	430		520
1864	Maximum	"	1.600	130	480		610
1880	48" x 27" high						
1900	Minimum	EA	0.889	71.00	410		480
1902	Average	"	1.143	91.00	490		580
1904	Maximum	"	1.600	130	570		700
1920	60" x 36" high						
1940	Minimum	EA	1.000	80.00	430		510
1942	Average	"	1.333	110	760		870
1944	Maximum	"	1.600	130	860		990
8000	Window frame, milled						
8010	Minimum	LF	0.160	12.75	6.09		18.75
8020	Average	"	0.200	16.00	6.80		22.75
8030	Maximum	"	0.267	21.25	10.25		31.50

SKYLIGHTS

ID Code	Component Descriptions	Unit of Meas.	Manhr / Unit	Labor Cost	Material Cost	Equip. Cost	Total Cost
		Descriptions	**Output**		**Unit Costs**		
08 - 62001	**PLASTIC SKYLIGHTS**					**08 - 62001**	
1020	Single thickness, not including mounting curb						
1040	2' x 4'	EA	1.000	76.00	410		490
1050	4' x 4'	"	1.333	100	550		650
1060	5' x 5'	"	2.000	150	730		880
1070	6' x 8'	"	2.667	200	1,560		1,760
1200	Double thickness, not including mounting curb						
1220	2' x 4'	EA	1.000	76.00	540		620
1240	4' x 4'	"	1.333	100	670		770
1260	5' x 5'	"	2.000	150	990		1,140
1270	6' x 8'	"	2.667	200	1,730		1,930
1290	Metal framed skylights						
1420	Translucent panels, 2-1/2" thick	SF	0.080	6.10	44.00		50.00
1490	Continuous vaults, 8' wide						
1500	Single glazed	SF	0.100	7.63	59.00		67.00
1560	Double glazed	"	0.114	8.72	95.00		100
08 - 62101	**SOLAR SKYLIGHTS**					**08 - 62101**	
0050	Tubular solar skylight, basic kit						
0100	Min.	EA	2.667	210	380		590
0200	Ave.	"	4.000	320	430		750
0300	Max.	"	8.000	640	480		1,120
0400	Tubular solar skylight dome, 10" Diameter						
0450	Min.	EA	0.800	64.00	79.00		140
0600	Ave.	"	1.000	80.00	85.00		160
0700	Max.	"	1.333	110	91.00		200
0800	14" Diameter						
0900	Min.	EA	0.800	64.00	91.00		160
1000	Ave.	"	1.000	80.00	97.00		180
1100	Max.	"	1.333	110	100		210
1200	Straight extension tube, 10" Diameter X 12" long						
1300	Min.	EA	0.667	53.00	52.00		110
1400	Ave.	"	0.800	64.00	61.00		130
1500	Max.	"	1.000	80.00	67.00		150
1700	24" long						
1800	Min.	EA	0.667	53.00	61.00		110
1900	Ave.	"	0.800	64.00	67.00		130
2000	Max.	"	1.000	80.00	73.00		150
2200	36" long						

SKYLIGHTS

ID Code	Component Descriptions	Unit of Meas.	Manhr / Unit	Labor Cost	Material Cost	Equip. Cost	Total Cost
	Descriptions	**Output**		**Unit Costs**			

08 - 62101   **SOLAR SKYLIGHTS, Cont'd...**   **08 - 62101**

ID Code	Component Descriptions	Unit of Meas.	Manhr / Unit	Labor Cost	Material Cost	Equip. Cost	Total Cost
2300	Min.	EA	0.667	53.00	90.00		140
2400	Ave.	"	0.800	64.00	97.00		160
2500	Max.	"	1.000	80.00	100		180
2700	48" long						
2800	Min.	EA	0.800	64.00	110		170
2900	Ave.	"	1.000	80.00	110		190
3000	Max.	"	1.333	110	120		230
3200	14" Diameter X 12" long						
3300	Min.	EA	0.667	53.00	67.00		120
3400	Ave.	"	0.800	64.00	73.00		140
3500	Max.	"	1.000	80.00	79.00		160
3700	24" long						
3800	Min.	EA	0.667	53.00	85.00		140
3900	Ave.	"	0.800	64.00	97.00		160
4000	Max.	"	1.000	80.00	110		190
4200	36" long						
4300	Min.	EA	0.667	53.00	110		160
4400	Ave.	"	0.800	64.00	120		180
4500	Max.	"	1.000	80.00	130		210
4700	90 Degree extension tubes, 10" Diameter						
4800	Min.	EA	0.444	35.50	61.00		97.00
4900	Ave.	"	0.500	40.00	70.00		110
5000	Max.	"	0.571	45.75	79.00		120
5100	14" Diameter						
5200	Min.	EA	0.444	35.50	75.00		110
5300	Ave.	"	0.500	40.00	83.00		120
5400	Max.	"	0.571	45.75	91.00		140
5500	Bottom tube adaptor, 10" Diameter						
5600	Min.	EA	0.444	35.50	64.00		100
5700	Ave.	"	0.500	40.00	70.00		110
5800	Max.	"	0.571	45.75	75.00		120
5900	14" Diameter						
6000	Min.	EA	0.444	35.50	79.00		110
6100	Ave.	"	0.500	40.00	85.00		130
6200	Max.	"	0.571	45.75	91.00		140
6300	Top tube adaptor, 10" Diameter						
6400	Min.	EA	0.444	35.50	64.00		100
6500	Ave.	"	0.500	40.00	70.00		110

SKYLIGHTS

ID Code	Component Descriptions	Unit of Meas.	Manhr / Unit	Labor Cost	Material Cost	Equip. Cost	Total Cost
	Descriptions	**Output**		**Unit Costs**			

08 - 62101 — SOLAR SKYLIGHTS, Cont'd... — 08 - 62101

ID Code	Component Descriptions	Unit of Meas.	Manhr / Unit	Labor Cost	Material Cost	Equip. Cost	Total Cost
6600	Max.	EA	0.571	45.75	75.00		120
6700	14" Diameter						
6800	Min.	EA	0.444	35.50	79.00		110
6900	Ave.	"	0.500	40.00	85.00		130
7000	Max.	"	0.571	45.75	91.00		140
7100	Tube flashing						
7200	Min.	EA	0.667	53.00	85.00		140
7300	Ave.	"	0.800	64.00	97.00		160
7400	Max.	"	1.000	80.00	110		190
7500	Daylight dimmer switch						
7600	Min.	EA	0.444	35.50	63.00		99.00
7700	Ave.	"	0.500	40.00	68.00		110
7800	Max.	"	0.571	45.75	73.00		120
7900	Dimmer						
8000	Min.	EA	0.444	35.50	250		290
8100	Ave.	"	0.500	40.00	280		320
8300	Max.	"	0.571	45.75	300		350

METAL-FRAMED SKYLIGHTS

08 - 63011 — METAL FRAMED SKYLIGHTS — 08 - 63011

ID Code	Component Descriptions	Unit of Meas.	Manhr / Unit	Labor Cost	Material Cost	Equip. Cost	Total Cost
1600	Metal Framed, 2-1/4" Thick, Translucent, <5,000 SF	SF	0.400	30.50	30.75		61.00
1700	> 5,000 SF	"	0.444	34.00	27.75		62.00
2000	Continous Vaulted - SemiCircular						
2020	Skylight, 2-1/4" Thick, to 8', Single Glazed	SF	0.400	30.50	36.25		67.00
2040	Double Glazed	"	0.400	30.50	44.25		75.00
2060	Skylight, 2-1/4" Thick, to 9', Single Glazed	"	0.444	34.00	62.00		96.00
2080	Double Glazed	"	0.444	34.00	70.00		100
2500	Pyramid Type, Self Supporting, Clear Opening						
2520	Minimum	SF	0.348	26.50	49.50		76.00
2540	Average	"	0.400	30.50	56.00		87.00
2560	Maximum	"	0.533	40.75	72.00		110
3000	Grid Type, 4' X 10' Modlule						
3020	Minimum	SF	0.320	24.50	30.25		55.00
3040	Maximum	"	0.533	40.75	56.00		97.00
3060	Preformed Acrylic Skylight						
3080	Minimum	SF	0.320	24.50	24.25		48.75
4000	Maximum	"	0.533	40.75	40.25		81.00

HARDWARE

ID Code	Component Descriptions	Unit of Meas.	Manhr / Unit	Labor Cost	Material Cost	Equip. Cost	Total Cost
		Output		**Unit Costs**			
08 - 71001	**HINGES**						**08 - 71001**
1200	Hinges, material only						
1250	3 x 3 butts, steel, interior, plain bearing	PAIR					20.75
1260	4 x 4 butts, steel, standard	"					30.50
1270	5 x 4-1/2 butts, bronze/s. steel, heavy duty	"					79.00
1290	Pivot hinges						
1300	Top pivot	EA					88.00
1310	Intermediate pivot	"					94.00
1320	Bottom pivot	"					180
1500	BHMA specifications						
1520	3-1/2 x 3-1/2, full mortise butts						
1540	Plain bearing	PAIR					24.75
1550	Ball bearing	"					29.75
1560	Half surface butts	"					42.25
1580	4 x 4						
1600	Full mortise butts, plain bearing, standard duty	PAIR					27.00
1640	Full mortise butts, ball bearing	"					32.50
1645	Half surface butts						
1650	Standard duty	PAIR					42.50
1660	Ball bearing	"					42.50
1670	4-1/2 x 4-1/2						
1680	Full mortise butts, plain bearing	PAIR					35.75
1690	Ball bearing, heavy duty	"					73.00
1695	Half mortise and half surface butts						
1700	Plain bearing	PAIR					42.25
1720	Full surface and half surface butts						
1740	Standard duty	PAIR					72.00
1780	Heavy duty	"					130
1785	Full mortise and full slide-in butts, ball bearing	"					33.00
1786	Half mortise butts, ball bearing						
1788	Standard duty	PAIR					150
1790	Heavy duty	"					170
1795	5 x 5, ball bearing						
1800	Full mortise butts	PAIR					69.00
1820	Half mortise, full & half surface butts	"					150
1830	Full mortise, full surface and half surface butts	"					200
1910	4 x 4						
1930	Full mortise butts, plain bearing, standard duty	PAIR					16.50
2020	5 x 4-1/2						

HARDWARE

ID Code	Component Descriptions	Unit of Meas.	Manhr / Unit	Labor Cost	Material Cost	Equip. Cost	Total Cost
08 - 71001	**HINGES, Cont'd...**						**08 - 71001**
2040	Full mortise butts, ball bearing, heavy duty	PAIR					77.00
08 - 71002	**LOCKSETS**						**08 - 71002**
1280	Latchset, heavy duty						
1300	Cylindrical	EA	0.500	40.00	190		230
1320	Mortise	"	0.800	64.00	200		260
1325	Lockset, heavy duty						
1330	Cylindrical	EA	0.500	40.00	310		350
1350	Mortise	"	0.800	64.00	350		410
2000	Mortise locks and latchsets, chrome						
2020	Latchset passage or closet latch	EA	0.667	53.00	240		290
2030	Privacy (bath or bedroom)	"	0.667	53.00	250		300
2040	Entry lockset	"	0.667	53.00	310		360
2050	Classroom lockset (outside key operated)	"	0.667	53.00	310		360
2060	Storeroom lock	"	0.667	53.00	310		360
2070	Front door lock	"	0.667	53.00	310		360
2080	Dormitory or exit lock	"	0.667	53.00	310		360
2200	Preassembled locks and latches, brass						
2220	Latchset, passage or closet latch	EA	0.667	53.00	280		330
2225	Lockset						
2230	Privacy (bath or bathroom)	EA	0.667	53.00	340		390
2240	Entry lock	"	0.667	53.00	490		540
2250	Classroom lock (outside key, operated)	"	0.667	53.00	490		540
2260	Storeroom lock	"	0.667	53.00	540		590
2270	Bored locks and latches, satin chrome plated						
2280	Latchset passage or closet latch	EA	0.667	53.00	160		210
2285	Lockset						
2290	Privacy (bath or bedroom)	EA	0.667	53.00	220		270
2300	Entry lock	"	0.667	53.00	240		290
2320	Classroom lock	"	0.667	53.00	240		290
2330	Corridor lock	"	0.667	53.00	240		290
4000	Miscellaneous locks						
4020	Exit lock with alarm, single door	EA	3.200	260	780		1,040
4040	Electric strike						
4050	Rim mounted wrought steel	EA	2.000	160	580		740
4060	Mortised, wrought steel with bronze plating	"	3.200	260	230		490
4065	Dead bolt						
4070	Bored, wrought brass, keyed both sides	EA	1.333	110	120		230

HARDWARE

ID Code	Component Descriptions	Unit of Meas.	Manhr / Unit	Labor Cost	Material Cost	Equip. Cost	Total Cost
	Descriptions	**Output**		**Unit Costs**			

08 - 71002 — LOCKSETS, Cont'd... 08 - 71002

ID Code	Component Descriptions	Unit of Meas.	Manhr / Unit	Labor Cost	Material Cost	Equip. Cost	Total Cost
4080	Mortised, cast brass	EA	1.333	110	330		440
4090	Lockset, cipher, mechanical	"	0.800	64.00	2,020		2,080

08 - 71003 — CLOSERS 08 - 71003

ID Code	Component Descriptions	Unit of Meas.	Manhr / Unit	Labor Cost	Material Cost	Equip. Cost	Total Cost
2600	Door closers						
2605	Surface mounted, traditional type, parallel arm						
2610	Standard	EA	1.000	80.00	240		320
2620	Heavy duty	"	1.000	80.00	280		360
2630	Modern type, parallel arm, standard duty	"	1.000	80.00	290		370
2640	Overhead, concealed, pivot hung, single acting						
2650	Interior	EA	1.000	80.00	450		530
2660	Exterior	"	1.000	80.00	670		750
2665	Floor concealed, single acting, offset, pivoted						
2670	Interior	EA	2.667	210	730		940
2680	Exterior	"	2.667	210	930		1,140

08 - 71004 — DOOR TRIM 08 - 71004

ID Code	Component Descriptions	Unit of Meas.	Manhr / Unit	Labor Cost	Material Cost	Equip. Cost	Total Cost
1100	Door bumper, bronze, wall type	EA	0.160	12.75	6.35		19.00
1105	Wall type, 4" dia. with convex rubber pad, aluminum	"	0.160	12.75	11.75		24.50
1108	Floor type						
1110	Aluminum	EA	0.160	12.75	5.37		18.00
1120	Brass	"	0.160	12.75	6.46		19.25
1130	Door holders						
1140	Wall type, bronze	EA	0.160	12.75	30.50		43.25
1160	Overhead	"	0.400	32.00	25.50		58.00
1180	Floor type	"	0.400	32.00	25.50		58.00
1200	Plunger type	"	0.400	32.00	24.75		57.00
1240	Wall type, aluminum	"	0.400	32.00	24.00		56.00
1520	Surface bolt	"	0.160	12.75	21.50		34.25
1600	Panic device						
1601	Rim type with thumb piece	EA	2.000	160	650		810
1610	Mortise	"	2.000	160	810		970
1620	Vertical rod	"	2.000	160	1,230		1,390
1630	Labeled, rim type	"	2.000	160	850		1,010
1640	Mortise	"	2.000	160	1,110		1,270
1650	Vertical rod	"	2.000	160	1,180		1,340
2070	Silencers, rubber type	"	0.016	1.28	3.06		4.34
2080	Dust proof strike with plate, brass	"	0.267	21.25	18.75		40.00
2090	Flush bolt, lever extension, brass, rated	"	0.160	12.75	34.25		47.00

HARDWARE

ID Code	Component Descriptions	Unit of Meas.	Manhr / Unit	Labor Cost	Material Cost	Equip. Cost	Total Cost
	Descriptions	**Output**		**Unit Costs**			
08 - 71004	**DOOR TRIM, Cont'd...**						**08 - 71004**
2100	Surface bolt with strike, brass, 6" long	EA	0.160	12.75	26.00		38.75
2250	Door coordinator, labeled, brass, satin chrome	"	0.571	45.75	120		170
2300	Door plates						
2305	Kick plate, aluminum, 3 beveled edges						
2310	10" x 28"	EA	0.400	32.00	30.50		63.00
2320	10" x 30"	"	0.400	32.00	33.50		66.00
2330	10" x 34"	"	0.400	32.00	36.50		69.00
2340	10" x 38"	"	0.400	32.00	39.75		72.00
2350	Push plate, 4" x 16"						
2360	Aluminum	EA	0.160	12.75	27.75		40.50
2371	Bronze	"	0.160	12.75	88.00		100
2380	Stainless steel	"	0.160	12.75	70.00		83.00
2385	Armor plate, 40" x 34"	"	0.320	25.50	81.00		110
2388	Pull handle, 4" x 16"						
2390	Aluminum	EA	0.160	12.75	98.00		110
2400	Bronze	"	0.160	12.75	190		200
2420	Stainless steel	"	0.160	12.75	140		150
2425	Hasp assembly						
2430	3"	EA	0.133	10.75	4.62		15.25
2440	4-1/2"	"	0.178	14.25	5.77		20.00
2450	6"	"	0.229	18.25	9.18		27.50
2720	Electro-magnetic door holder						
2730	Wall mounted	EA	2.667	210	200		410
2740	Floor mounted	"	2.667	210	350		560
2780	Smoke detector door holder						
2800	Photo electric type	EA	2.667	210	300		510
2810	Ionization type	"	2.667	210	300		510
5100	Pneumatic operators, activated by rubber mats						
5105	Swing						
5110	Single	EA	6.667	530	4,330		4,860
5120	Double	"	10.000	800	7,160		7,960
5125	Sliding						
5130	Single	EA	6.667	530	4,790		5,320
5140	Double	"	10.000	800	8,320		9,120

HARDWARE

ID Code	Component Descriptions	Unit of Meas.	Manhr / Unit	Labor Cost	Material Cost	Equip. Cost	Total Cost
		Descriptions (Output)			**Unit Costs**		

08 - 71006 — WEATHERSTRIPPING — 08 - 71006

ID Code	Component Descriptions	Unit of Meas.	Manhr / Unit	Labor Cost	Material Cost	Equip. Cost	Total Cost
0100	Weatherstrip, head and jamb, metal strip, neoprene bulb						
0140	Standard duty	LF	0.044	3.55	5.19		8.74
0160	Heavy duty	"	0.050	4.00	5.77		9.77
3980	Spring type						
4000	Metal doors	EA	2.000	160	55.00		210
4010	Wood doors	"	2.667	210	55.00		260
4020	Sponge type with adhesive backing	"	0.800	64.00	51.00		110
4025	Astragal						
4030	1-3/4" x 13 ga., aluminum	LF	0.067	5.33	6.76		12.00
4040	1-3/8" x 5/8", oak	"	0.053	4.26	5.50		9.76
4500	Thresholds						
4510	Bronze	LF	0.200	16.00	53.00		69.00
4515	Aluminum						
4520	Plain	LF	0.200	16.00	38.50		55.00
4525	Vinyl insert	"	0.200	16.00	39.25		55.00
4530	Aluminum with grit	"	0.200	16.00	37.50		54.00
4533	Steel						
4535	Plain	LF	0.200	16.00	29.75		45.75
4540	Interlocking	"	0.667	53.00	39.50		93.00

GLAZING

08 - 81001 — GLASS GLAZING — 08 - 81001

ID Code	Component Descriptions	Unit of Meas.	Manhr / Unit	Labor Cost	Material Cost	Equip. Cost	Total Cost
0800	Sheet glass, 1/8" thick	SF	0.044	3.92	8.91		12.75
1020	Plate glass, bronze or grey, 1/4" thick	"	0.073	6.42	13.00		19.50
1040	Clear	"	0.073	6.42	10.25		16.75
1060	Polished	"	0.073	6.42	12.00		18.50
1800	Plexiglass						
2000	1/8" thick	SF	0.073	6.42	5.73		12.25
2020	1/4" thick	"	0.044	3.92	10.25		14.25
3000	Float glass, clear						
3010	3/16" thick	SF	0.067	5.88	6.93		12.75
3020	1/4" thick	"	0.073	6.42	7.07		13.50
3030	5/16" thick	"	0.080	7.06	13.25		20.25
3040	3/8" thick	"	0.100	8.83	14.25		23.00
3050	1/2" thick	"	0.133	11.75	24.00		35.75
3060	5/8" thick	"	0.160	14.00	31.75		45.75
3070	3/4" thick	"	0.200	17.75	34.50		52.00

GLAZING

ID Code	Component Descriptions	Unit of Meas.	Manhr / Unit	Labor Cost	Material Cost	Equip. Cost	Total Cost
	Descriptions	**Output**		**Unit Costs**			

08 - 81001	**GLASS GLAZING, Cont'd...**						**08 - 81001**
3080	1" thick	SF	0.267	23.50	61.00		85.00
3100	Tinted glass, polished plate, twin ground						
3120	3/16" thick	SF	0.067	5.88	9.55		15.50
3130	1/4" thick	"	0.073	6.42	9.55		16.00
3140	3/8" thick	"	0.100	8.83	15.25		24.00
3150	1/2" thick	"	0.133	11.75	24.75		36.50
3190	Total, full vision, all glass window system						
3200	To 10' high						
3220	Minimum	SF	0.200	17.75	64.00		82.00
3222	Average	"	0.200	17.75	84.00		100
3224	Maximum	"	0.200	17.75	100		120
3225	10' to 20' high						
3230	Minimum	SF	0.200	17.75	77.00		95.00
3240	Average	"	0.200	17.75	94.00		110
3250	Maximum	"	0.200	17.75	120		140
5000	Insulated glass, bronze or gray						
5020	1/2" thick	SF	0.133	11.75	19.50		31.25
5040	1" thick	"	0.200	17.75	23.25		41.00
5100	Spandrel, polished, 1 side, 1/4" thick	"	0.073	6.42	15.50		22.00
5900	Tempered glass (safety)						
6000	Clear sheet glass						
6020	1/8" thick	SF	0.044	3.92	10.75		14.75
6030	3/16" thick	"	0.062	5.43	13.00		18.50
6040	Clear float glass						
6050	1/4" thick	SF	0.067	5.88	11.25		17.25
6060	5/16" thick	"	0.080	7.06	20.00		27.00
6070	3/8" thick	"	0.100	8.83	24.50		33.25
6080	1/2" thick	"	0.133	11.75	33.50		45.25
6090	5/8" thick	"	0.160	14.00	38.00		52.00
6100	3/4" thick	"	0.267	23.50	47.00		71.00
6160	Tinted float glass						
6180	3/16" thick	SF	0.062	5.43	13.50		19.00
6200	1/4" thick	"	0.067	5.88	14.75		20.75
6210	3/8" thick	"	0.100	8.83	26.75		35.50
6220	1/2" thick	"	0.133	11.75	35.75		47.50
6490	Laminated glass						
6500	Float safety glass with polyvinyl plastic layer						
6510	1/4", sheet or float						

GLAZING

ID Code	Component Descriptions	Unit of Meas.	Manhr / Unit	Labor Cost	Material Cost	Equip. Cost	Total Cost
08 - 81001	**GLASS GLAZING, Cont'd...**						**08 - 81001**
6530	Two lites, 1/8" thick, clear glass	SF	0.067	5.88	14.25		20.25
6540	1/2" thick, float glass						
6550	Two lites, 1/4" thick, clear glass	SF	0.133	11.75	21.75		33.50
6570	Tinted glass	"	0.133	11.75	25.50		37.25
6800	Insulating glass, two lites, clear float glass						
6840	1/2" thick	SF	0.133	11.75	13.75		25.50
6850	5/8" thick	"	0.160	14.00	16.00		30.00
6860	3/4" thick	"	0.200	17.75	17.50		35.25
6870	7/8" thick	"	0.229	20.25	18.50		38.75
6880	1" thick	"	0.267	23.50	24.75		48.25
6885	Glass seal edge						
6890	3/8" thick	SF	0.133	11.75	11.75		23.50
6895	Tinted glass						
6900	1/2" thick	SF	0.133	11.75	23.75		35.50
6910	1" thick	"	0.267	23.50	25.50		49.00
6920	Tempered, clear						
6930	1" thick	SF	0.267	23.50	46.50		70.00
6950	Wire reinforced	"	0.267	23.50	59.00		83.00
7100	Plate mirror glass						
7200	1/4" thick						
7210	15 sf	SF	0.080	7.06	11.75		18.75
7220	Over 15 sf	"	0.073	6.42	10.75		17.25
7230	Door type, 1/4" thick	"	0.080	7.06	12.00		19.00
7240	Transparent, one way vision, 1/4" thick	"	0.080	7.06	25.75		32.75
7250	Sheet mirror glass						
7260	3/16" thick	SF	0.080	7.06	10.75		17.75
7270	1/4" thick	"	0.067	5.88	11.25		17.25
7300	Wall tiles, 12" x 12"						
7310	Clear glass	SF	0.044	3.92	3.64		7.56
7320	Veined glass	"	0.044	3.92	4.62		8.54
8800	Wire glass, 1/4" thick						
8810	Clear	SF	0.267	23.50	21.75		45.25
8820	Hammered	"	0.267	23.50	21.75		45.25
8840	Obscure	"	0.267	23.50	25.25		48.75
8900	Bullet resistant, plate, with inter-leaved vinyl						
8910	1-3/16" thick						
8930	To 15 sf	SF	0.400	35.25	110		150
8940	Over 15 sf	"	0.400	35.25	120		160

GLAZING

ID Code	Descriptions — Component Descriptions	Output — Unit of Meas.	Output — Manhr / Unit	Unit Costs — Labor Cost	Unit Costs — Material Cost	Unit Costs — Equip. Cost	Unit Costs — Total Cost
08 - 81001	**GLASS GLAZING, Cont'd...**						**08 - 81001**
8945	2" thick						
8950	To 15 sf	SF	0.667	59.00	150		210
8960	Over 15 sf	"	0.667	59.00	160		220
9500	Glazing accessories						
9510	Neoprene glazing gaskets						
9530	1/4" glass	LF	0.032	2.82	2.28		5.10
9540	3/8" glass	"	0.033	2.94	2.54		5.48
9550	1/2" glass	"	0.035	3.07	2.67		5.74
9560	3/4" glass	"	0.036	3.21	3.81		7.02
9570	1" glass	"	0.040	3.53	4.44		7.97
9580	Mullion section						
9590	1/4" glass	LF	0.016	1.41	0.70		2.11
9600	3/8" glass	"	0.020	1.76	0.89		2.65
9610	1/2" glass	"	0.023	2.01	1.27		3.28
9620	3/4" glass	"	0.027	2.35	1.90		4.25
9630	1" glass	"	0.032	2.82	2.54		5.36
9640	Molded corners	EA	0.533	47.00	2.72		49.75

LOUVERS AND VENTS

ID Code	Descriptions — Component Descriptions	Output — Unit of Meas.	Output — Manhr / Unit	Unit Costs — Labor Cost	Unit Costs — Material Cost	Unit Costs — Equip. Cost	Unit Costs — Total Cost
08 - 91001	**VENTS AND WALL LOUVERS**						**08 - 91001**
0100	Block vent, 8"x16"x4" alum., w/screen, mill finish	EA	0.267	23.50	170		190
1200	Standard	"	0.250	22.00	96.00		120
1210	Vents w/screen, 4" deep, 8" wide, 5" high						
1220	Modular	EA	0.250	22.00	110		130
1230	Grilles and louvers						
2000	Aluminum gable louvers	SF	0.133	11.75	20.50		32.25
2020	Vent screen aluminum, 4" wide, continuous	LF	0.027	2.35	5.92		8.27
2040	Fixed type louvers						
2060	4 through 10 sf	SF	0.133	11.75	34.50		46.25
2080	Over 10 sf	"	0.100	8.83	40.75		49.50
2090	Movable type louvers						
2220	4 through 10 sf	SF	0.133	11.75	40.75		53.00
2240	Over 10 sf	"	0.100	8.83	45.00		54.00
2260	Aluminum louvers						
2980	Louvers, aluminum, anodized, fixed blade						
3000	Horizontal line	SF	0.200	17.75	60.00		78.00
3020	Vertical line	"	0.200	17.75	60.00		78.00

LOUVERS AND VENTS

ID Code	Component Descriptions	Unit of Meas.	Manhr / Unit	Labor Cost	Material Cost	Equip. Cost	Total Cost
	Descriptions	**Output**		**Unit Costs**			
08 - 91001	**VENTS AND WALL LOUVERS, Cont'd...**						**08 - 91001**
3040	Wall louver, aluminum mill finish						
3060	Under, 2 sf	SF	0.100	8.83	45.50		54.00
3080	2 to 4 sf	"	0.089	7.84	40.00		47.75
3090	5 to 10 sf	"	0.089	7.84	37.50		45.25
3110	Galvanized steel						
3120	Under 2 sf	SF	0.100	8.83	41.25		50.00
3140	2 to 4 sf	"	0.089	7.84	28.25		36.00
3160	5 to 10 sf	"	0.089	7.84	26.50		34.25
4000	Residential use, fixed type, with screen						
4050	8" x 8"	EA	0.400	35.25	20.75		56.00
4060	12" x 12"	"	0.400	35.25	23.00		58.00
4080	12" x 18"	"	0.400	35.25	27.50		63.00
4100	14" x 24"	"	0.400	35.25	39.50		75.00
4120	18" x 24"	"	0.400	35.25	44.50		80.00
4140	30" x 24"	"	0.444	39.25	61.00		100
08 - 91261	**DOOR LOUVERS**						**08 - 91261**
0110	Fixed, 1" thick, enameled steel						
0120	8"x8"	EA	0.100	8.00	62.00		70.00
0140	12"x8"	"	0.100	8.00	71.00		79.00
0160	12"x12"	"	0.114	9.14	80.00		89.00
0180	16"x12"	"	0.123	9.84	110		120
0200	18"x12"	"	0.200	16.00	110		130
0220	20"x8"	"	0.114	9.14	130		140
0240	20"x12"	"	0.229	18.25	150		170
0260	20"x16"	"	0.267	21.25	150		170
0270	20"x20"	"	0.320	25.50	160		190
0280	24"x12"	"	0.267	21.25	130		150
0290	24"x16"	"	0.286	22.75	140		160
0300	24"x18"	"	0.308	24.50	160		180
0320	24"x20"	"	0.333	26.75	170		200
0340	24"x24"	"	0.364	29.00	170		200
0390	26"x26"	"	0.500	40.00	200		240

DIVISION 09
FINISHES

SUPPORT SYSTEMS

ID Code	Component Descriptions	Unit of Meas.	Manhr / Unit	Labor Cost	Material Cost	Equip. Cost	Total Cost
		Descriptions	**Output**		**Unit Costs**		

09 - 21161　　　METAL STUDS　　　09 - 21161

ID Code	Component Descriptions	Unit of Meas.	Manhr / Unit	Labor Cost	Material Cost	Equip. Cost	Total Cost
0060	Studs, non load bearing, galvanized						
0080	2-1/2", 20 ga.						
0100	12" o.c.	SF	0.017	1.33	0.68		2.01
0102	16" o.c.	"	0.013	1.06	0.52		1.58
0110	25 ga.						
0120	12" o.c.	SF	0.017	1.33	0.46		1.79
0122	16" o.c.	"	0.013	1.06	0.36		1.42
0124	24" o.c.	"	0.011	0.88	0.28		1.16
0130	3-5/8", 20 ga.						
0140	12" o.c.	SF	0.020	1.60	0.81		2.41
0142	16" o.c.	"	0.016	1.28	0.62		1.90
0144	24" o.c.	"	0.013	1.06	0.47		1.53
0170	25 ga.						
0180	12" o.c.	SF	0.020	1.60	0.53		2.13
0182	16" o.c.	"	0.016	1.28	0.44		1.72
0184	24" o.c.	"	0.013	1.06	0.33		1.39
0188	4", 20 ga.						
0190	12" o.c.	SF	0.020	1.60	0.89		2.49
0192	16" o.c.	"	0.016	1.28	0.68		1.96
0194	24" o.c.	"	0.013	1.06	0.52		1.58
0198	25 ga.						
0200	12" o.c.	SF	0.020	1.60	0.60		2.20
0202	16" o.c.	"	0.016	1.28	0.47		1.75
0204	24" o.c.	"	0.013	1.06	0.35		1.41
0210	6", 20 ga.						
0220	12" o.c.	SF	0.025	2.00	1.14		3.14
0222	16" o.c.	"	0.020	1.60	0.83		2.43
0224	24" o.c.	"	0.017	1.33	0.68		2.01
0230	25 ga.						
0240	12" o.c.	SF	0.025	2.00	0.73		2.73
0242	16" o.c.	"	0.020	1.60	0.58		2.18
0244	24" o.c.	"	0.017	1.33	0.44		1.77
0980	Load bearing studs, galvanized						
0990	3-5/8", 16 ga.						
1000	12" o.c.	SF	0.020	1.60	1.47		3.07
1020	16" o.c.	"	0.016	1.28	1.36		2.64
1110	18 ga.						
1130	12" o.c.	SF	0.013	1.06	1.15		2.21

SUPPORT SYSTEMS

ID Code	Component Descriptions	Unit of Meas.	Manhr / Unit	Labor Cost	Material Cost	Equip. Cost	Total Cost
09 - 21161	**METAL STUDS, Cont'd...**						**09 - 21161**
1140	16" o.c.	SF	0.016	1.28	1.05		2.33
1145	4", 16 ga.						
1150	12" o.c.	SF	0.020	1.60	1.55		3.15
1160	16" o.c.	"	0.016	1.28	1.40		2.68
1980	6", 16 ga.						
2000	12" o.c.	SF	0.025	2.00	1.98		3.98
2001	16" o.c.	"	0.020	1.60	1.78		3.38
3000	Furring						
3160	On beams and columns						
3170	7/8" channel	LF	0.053	4.26	0.52		4.78
3180	1-1/2" channel	"	0.062	4.92	0.62		5.54
4460	On ceilings						
4470	3/4" furring channels						
4480	12" o.c.	SF	0.033	2.66	0.37		3.03
4490	16" o.c.	"	0.032	2.56	0.29		2.85
4495	24" o.c.	"	0.029	2.28	0.20		2.48
4500	1-1/2" furring channels						
4520	12" o.c.	SF	0.036	2.90	0.62		3.52
4540	16" o.c.	"	0.033	2.66	0.47		3.13
4560	24" o.c.	"	0.031	2.46	0.31		2.77
5000	On walls						
5020	3/4" furring channels						
5050	12" o.c.	SF	0.027	2.13	0.37		2.50
5100	16" o.c.	"	0.025	2.00	0.29		2.29
5150	24" o.c.	"	0.024	1.88	0.20		2.08
5200	1-1/2" furring channels						
5210	12" o.c.	SF	0.029	2.28	0.62		2.90
5220	16" o.c.	"	0.027	2.13	0.47		2.60
5230	24" o.c.	"	0.025	2.00	0.31		2.31

LATH AND PLASTER

ID Code	Descriptions — Component Descriptions	Output — Unit of Meas.	Output — Manhr / Unit	Unit Costs — Labor Cost	Unit Costs — Material Cost	Unit Costs — Equip. Cost	Unit Costs — Total Cost
09 - 22361	**GYPSUM LATH**						**09 - 22361**
1070	Gypsum lath, 1/2" thick						
1090	Clipped	SY	0.044	3.55	5.76		9.31
1110	Nailed	"	0.050	4.00	5.76		9.76
09 - 22362	**METAL LATH**						**09 - 22362**
0960	Diamond expanded, galvanized						
0980	2.5 lb., on walls						
1010	Nailed	SY	0.100	8.00	3.83		11.75
1030	Wired	"	0.114	9.14	3.83		13.00
1040	On ceilings						
1050	Nailed	SY	0.114	9.14	3.83		13.00
1070	Wired	"	0.133	10.75	3.83		14.50
1980	3.4 lb., on walls						
2000	Nailed	SY	0.100	8.00	5.21		13.25
2020	Wired	"	0.114	9.14	5.21		14.25
2030	On ceilings						
2040	Nailed	SY	0.114	9.14	5.21		14.25
2060	Wired	"	0.133	10.75	5.21		16.00
2064	Flat rib						
2068	2.75 lb., on walls						
2070	Nailed	SY	0.100	8.00	3.63		11.75
2100	Wired	"	0.114	9.14	3.63		12.75
2110	On ceilings						
2120	Nailed	SY	0.114	9.14	3.63		12.75
2140	Wired	"	0.133	10.75	3.63		14.50
2150	3.4 lb., on walls						
2160	Nailed	SY	0.100	8.00	4.36		12.25
2180	Wired	"	0.114	9.14	4.36		13.50
2190	On ceilings						
2200	Nailed	SY	0.114	9.14	4.36		13.50
2220	Wired	"	0.133	10.75	4.36		15.00
2230	Stucco lath						
2240	1.8 lb.	SY	0.100	8.00	4.51		12.50
2300	3.6 lb.	"	0.100	8.00	5.06		13.00
2310	Paper backed						
2320	Minimum	SY	0.080	6.40	3.50		9.90
2400	Maximum	"	0.114	9.14	5.65		14.75

LATH AND PLASTER

	Descriptions	Output		Unit Costs			
ID Code	Component Descriptions	Unit of Meas.	Manhr / Unit	Labor Cost	Material Cost	Equip. Cost	Total Cost
09 - 22366	**PLASTER ACCESSORIES**						**09 - 22366**
0120	Expansion joint, 3/4", 26 ga., galv.	LF	0.020	1.60	1.48		3.08
2000	Plaster corner beads, 3/4", galvanized	"	0.023	1.82	0.41		2.23
2020	Casing bead, expanded flange, galvanized	"	0.020	1.60	0.56		2.16
2100	Expanded wing, 1-1/4" wide, galvanized	"	0.020	1.60	0.66		2.26
2500	Joint clips for lath	EA	0.004	0.32	0.17		0.49
2580	Metal base, galvanized, 2-1/2" high	LF	0.027	2.13	0.75		2.88
2600	Stud clips for gypsum lath	EA	0.004	0.32	0.17		0.49
2700	Tie wire galvanized, 18 ga., 25 lb. hank	"					47.00
8000	Sound deadening board, 1/4"	SF	0.013	1.06	0.31		1.37

SUPPORTS FOR PLASTER GYPSUM BOARD

09 - 23001	**PLASTER**						**09 - 23001**
0980	Gypsum plaster, trowel finish, 2 coats						
1000	Ceilings	SY	0.250	18.50	4.30		22.75
1020	Walls	"	0.235	17.50	4.30		21.75
1030	3 coats						
1040	Ceilings	SY	0.348	26.00	5.96		32.00
1060	Walls	"	0.308	23.00	5.96		29.00
1960	Vermiculite plaster						
1980	2 coats						
2000	Ceilings	SY	0.381	28.50	4.89		33.50
2020	Walls	"	0.348	26.00	4.89		31.00
2030	3 coats						
2040	Ceilings	SY	0.471	35.00	7.68		42.75
2060	Walls	"	0.421	31.25	7.68		39.00
5960	Keenes cement plaster						
5980	2 coats						
6000	Ceilings	SY	0.308	23.00	2.09		25.00
6020	Walls	"	0.267	19.75	2.09		21.75
6030	3 coats						
6040	Ceilings	SY	0.348	26.00	2.14		28.25
6060	Walls	"	0.308	23.00	2.14		25.25
7000	On columns, add to installation, 50%	"					
7020	Chases, fascia, and soffits, add to installation, 50%	"					
7040	Beams, add to installation, 50%	"					

CEMENT PLASTERING

ID Code	Descriptions — Component Descriptions	Output — Unit of Meas.	Output — Manhr / Unit	Unit Costs — Labor Cost	Unit Costs — Material Cost	Unit Costs — Equip. Cost	Unit Costs — Total Cost
09 - 24001	**PORTLAND CEMENT PLASTER**						**09 - 24001**
2980	Stucco, portland, gray, 3 coat, 1" thick						
3000	Sand finish	SY	0.348	26.00	8.03		34.00
3020	Trowel finish	"	0.364	27.00	8.03		35.00
3030	White cement						
3040	Sand finish	SY	0.364	27.00	9.17		36.25
3060	Trowel finish	"	0.400	29.75	9.17		39.00
3980	Scratch coat						
4000	For ceramic tile	SY	0.080	5.96	2.91		8.87
4020	For quarry tile	"	0.080	5.96	2.91		8.87
5000	Portland cement plaster						
5020	2 coats, 1/2"	SY	0.160	12.00	5.78		17.75
5040	3 coats, 7/8"	"	0.200	15.00	6.90		22.00

GYPSUM BOARD

ID Code	GYPSUM BOARD	Unit of Meas.	Manhr / Unit	Labor Cost	Material Cost	Equip. Cost	Total Cost
09 - 29001	**GYPSUM BOARD**						**09 - 29001**
0080	Drywall, plasterboard, 3/8" clipped to						
0100	Metal furred ceiling	SF	0.009	0.71	0.41		1.12
0120	Columns and beams	"	0.020	1.60	0.41		2.01
0140	Walls	"	0.008	0.64	0.41		1.05
0150	Nailed or screwed to						
0160	Wood or metal framed ceiling	SF	0.008	0.64	0.41		1.05
0180	Columns and beams	"	0.018	1.42	0.41		1.83
0190	Walls	"	0.007	0.58	0.41		0.99
0220	1/2", clipped to						
0240	Metal furred ceiling	SF	0.009	0.71	0.42		1.13
0260	Columns and beams	"	0.020	1.60	0.38		1.98
0270	Walls	"	0.008	0.64	0.38		1.02
0280	Nailed or screwed to						
0290	Wood or metal framed ceiling	SF	0.008	0.64	0.38		1.02
0300	Columns and beams	"	0.018	1.42	0.38		1.80
0400	Walls	"	0.007	0.58	0.38		0.96
1000	5/8", clipped to						
1020	Metal furred ceiling	SF	0.010	0.80	0.42		1.22
1040	Columns and beams	"	0.022	1.77	0.42		2.19
1060	Walls	"	0.009	0.71	0.42		1.13
1070	Nailed or screwed to						
1080	Wood or metal framed ceiling	SF	0.010	0.80	0.42		1.22

GYPSUM BOARD

ID Code	Component Descriptions	Unit of Meas.	Manhr / Unit	Labor Cost	Material Cost	Equip. Cost	Total Cost
	Descriptions	**Output**		**Unit Costs**			
09 - 29001	**GYPSUM BOARD, Cont'd...**						**09 - 29001**
1100	Columns and beams	SF	0.022	1.77	0.42		2.19
1120	Walls	"	0.009	0.71	0.42		1.13
1122	Vinyl faced, clipped to metal studs						
1124	1/2"	SF	0.010	0.80	1.19		1.99
1126	5/8"	"	0.010	0.80	1.13		1.93
1130	Add for						
1140	Fire resistant	SF					0.12
1180	Water resistant	"					0.19
1200	Water and fire resistant	"					0.24
1220	Taping and finishing joints						
1222	Minimum	SF	0.005	0.42	0.04		0.46
1224	Average	"	0.007	0.53	0.07		0.60
1226	Maximum	"	0.008	0.64	0.10		0.74
5020	Casing bead						
5022	Minimum	LF	0.023	1.82	0.16		1.98
5024	Average	"	0.027	2.13	0.18		2.31
5026	Maximum	"	0.040	3.20	0.22		3.42
5040	Corner bead						
5042	Minimum	LF	0.023	1.82	0.18		2.00
5044	Average	"	0.027	2.13	0.22		2.35
5046	Maximum	"	0.040	3.20	0.27		3.47

TILE

ID Code	Component Descriptions	Unit of Meas.	Manhr / Unit	Labor Cost	Material Cost	Equip. Cost	Total Cost
09 - 30131	**CERAMIC TILE**						**09 - 30131**
0980	Glazed wall tile, 4-1/4" x 4-1/4"						
1000	Minimum	SF	0.057	4.35	2.32		6.67
1020	Average	"	0.067	5.08	3.68		8.76
1040	Maximum	"	0.080	6.10	13.25		19.25
1042	6" x 6"						
1044	Minimum	SF	0.050	3.81	1.65		5.46
1046	Average	"	0.057	4.35	2.22		6.57
1048	Maximum	"	0.067	5.08	2.77		7.85
2960	Base, 4-1/4" high						
2980	Minimum	LF	0.100	7.62	4.47		12.00
3000	Average	"	0.100	7.62	5.20		12.75
3040	Maximum	"	0.100	7.62	6.87		14.50
3042	Glazed moldings and trim, 12" x 12"						

TILE

ID Code	Descriptions	Output		Unit Costs			
	Component Descriptions	Unit of Meas.	Manhr / Unit	Labor Cost	Material Cost	Equip. Cost	Total Cost
09 - 30131	**CERAMIC TILE, Cont'd...**						**09 - 30131**
3044	Minimum	LF	0.080	6.10	2.46		8.56
3046	Average	"	0.080	6.10	3.75		9.85
3048	Maximum	"	0.080	6.10	5.04		11.25
6100	Unglazed floor tile						
6120	Portland cem., cushion edge, face mtd						
6140	1" x 1"	SF	0.073	5.54	8.87		14.50
6150	2" x 2"	"	0.067	5.08	9.38		14.50
6162	4" x 4"	"	0.067	5.08	8.73		13.75
6164	6" x 6"	"	0.057	4.35	3.12		7.47
6166	12" x 12"	"	0.050	3.81	2.75		6.56
6168	16" x 16"	"	0.044	3.38	2.38		5.76
6170	18" x 18"	"	0.040	3.05	2.31		5.36
6200	Adhesive bed, with white grout						
6220	1" x 1"	SF	0.073	5.54	7.38		13.00
6230	2" x 2"	"	0.067	5.08	7.81		13.00
6260	4" x 4"	"	0.067	5.08	7.81		13.00
6262	6" x 6"	"	0.057	4.35	2.60		6.95
6264	12" x 12"	"	0.050	3.81	2.28		6.09
6266	16" x 16"	"	0.044	3.38	1.98		5.36
6268	18" x 18"	"	0.040	3.05	1.92		4.97
6300	Organic adhesive bed, thin set, back mounted						
6320	1" x 1"	SF	0.073	5.54	7.38		13.00
6350	2" x 2"	"	0.067	5.08	8.59		13.75
6360	For group 2 colors, add to material, 10%						
6370	For group 3 colors, add to material, 20%						
6380	For abrasive surface, add to material, 25%						
6382	Porcelain floor tile						
6384	1" x 1"	SF	0.073	5.54	9.90		15.50
6386	2" x 2"	"	0.070	5.30	9.05		14.25
6388	4" x 4"	"	0.067	5.08	8.41		13.50
6390	6" x 6"	"	0.057	4.35	3.02		7.37
6392	12" x 12"	"	0.050	3.81	2.72		6.53
6394	16" x 16"	"	0.044	3.38	2.16		5.54
6396	18" x 18"	"	0.040	3.05	2.04		5.09
6400	Unglazed wall tile						
6420	Organic adhesive, face mounted cushion edge						
6425	1" x 1"						
6430	Minimum	SF	0.067	5.08	4.65		9.73

TILE

ID Code	Descriptions	Output		Unit Costs			
	Component Descriptions	Unit of Meas.	Manhr / Unit	Labor Cost	Material Cost	Equip. Cost	Total Cost
09 - 30131	**CERAMIC TILE, Cont'd...**						**09 - 30131**
6432	Average	SF	0.073	5.54	6.09		11.75
6434	Maximum	"	0.080	6.10	9.09		15.25
6448	2" x 2"						
6450	Minimum	SF	0.062	4.69	5.37		10.00
6452	Average	"	0.067	5.08	6.09		11.25
6454	Maximum	"	0.073	5.54	9.96		15.50
6500	Back mounted						
6510	1" x 1"						
6520	Minimum	SF	0.067	5.08	4.65		9.73
6522	Average	"	0.073	5.54	6.09		11.75
6524	Maximum	"	0.080	6.10	9.09		15.25
6538	2" x 2"						
6540	Minimum	SF	0.062	4.69	5.37		10.00
6542	Average	"	0.067	5.08	6.09		11.25
6544	Maximum	"	0.073	5.54	9.96		15.50
6600	For glazed finish, add to material, 25%						
6620	For glazed mosaic, add to material, 100%						
6630	For metallic colors, add to material, 125%						
6640	For exterior wall use, add to total, 25%						
6650	For exterior soffit, add to total, 25%						
6660	For portland cement bed, add to total, 25%						
6670	For dry set portland cement bed, add to total, 10%						
8020	Conductive floor tile, unglazed square edged						
8040	Portland cement bed						
8060	1 x 1	SF	0.100	7.62	6.93		14.50
8080	1-9/16 x 1-9/16	"	0.100	7.62	6.38		14.00
8100	Dry set						
8120	1 x 1	SF	0.100	7.62	6.93		14.50
8140	1-9/16 x 1-9/16	"	0.100	7.62	6.38		14.00
8160	Epoxy bed with epoxy joints						
8180	1 x 1	SF	0.100	7.62	6.93		14.50
8200	1-9/16 x 1-9/16	"	0.100	7.62	6.38		14.00
8400	For WWF in bed add to total, 15%						
8420	For abrasive surface, add to material, 40%						
8990	Ceramic accessories						
9000	Towel bar, 24" long						
9002	Minimum	EA	0.320	24.50	18.00		42.50
9004	Average	"	0.400	30.50	22.25		53.00

TILE

ID Code	Component Descriptions	Unit of Meas.	Manhr / Unit	Labor Cost	Material Cost	Equip. Cost	Total Cost
	Descriptions	**Output**		**Unit Costs**			

09 - 30131	**CERAMIC TILE, Cont'd...**						**09 - 30131**
9006	Maximum	EA	0.533	40.75	59.00		100
9020	Soap dish						
9022	Minimum	EA	0.533	40.75	8.47		49.25
9024	Average	"	0.667	51.00	11.50		63.00
9026	Maximum	"	0.800	61.00	30.25		91.00

09 - 30161	**QUARRY TILE**						**09 - 30161**
1060	Floor						
1080	4 x 4 x 1/2"	SF	0.107	8.13	6.57		14.75
1100	6 x 6 x 1/2"	"	0.100	7.62	6.44		14.00
1120	6 x 6 x 3/4"	"	0.100	7.62	7.99		15.50
1122	12 x 12x 3/4"	"	0.089	6.77	11.25		18.00
1124	16x1 6 x 3/4"	"	0.080	6.10	7.83		14.00
1126	18 x 18 x 3/4"	"	0.067	5.08	5.52		10.50
1150	Medallion						
1160	36" dia.	EA	2.000	150	350		500
1162	48" dia.	"	2.000	150	410		560
1200	Wall, applied to 3/4" portland cement bed						
1220	4 x 4 x 1/2"	SF	0.160	12.25	5.84		18.00
1240	6 x 6 x 3/4"	"	0.133	10.25	6.53		16.75
1320	Cove base						
1330	5 x 6 x 1/2" straight top	LF	0.133	10.25	6.66		17.00
1340	6 x 6 x 3/4" round top	"	0.133	10.25	6.18		16.50
1345	Moldings						
1350	2 x 12	LF	0.080	6.10	10.50		16.50
1352	4 x 12	"	0.080	6.10	16.50		22.50
1360	Stair treads 6 x 6 x 3/4"	"	0.200	15.25	9.13		24.50
1380	Window sill 6 x 8 x 3/4"	"	0.160	12.25	8.33		20.50
1400	For abrasive surface, add to material, 25%						

ACOUSTICAL TREATMENT

09 - 51001	**CEILINGS AND WALLS**						**09 - 51001**
1400	Acoustical panels, suspension system not included						
1420	Fiberglass panels						
1500	5/8" thick						
1560	2' x 2'	SF	0.011	0.91	1.61		2.52
1580	2' x 4'	"	0.009	0.71	1.34		2.05
1590	3/4" thick						

ACOUSTICAL TREATMENT

ID Code	Component Descriptions	Unit of Meas.	Manhr / Unit	Labor Cost	Material Cost	Equip. Cost	Total Cost
	Descriptions	**Output**		**Unit Costs**			
09 - 51001	**CEILINGS AND WALLS, Cont'd...**						**09 - 51001**
1600	2' x 2'	SF	0.011	0.91	2.14		3.05
1620	2' x 4'	"	0.009	0.71	2.07		2.78
1630	Glass cloth faced fiberglass panels						
1660	3/4" thick	SF	0.013	1.06	3.05		4.11
1680	1" thick	"	0.013	1.06	3.41		4.47
1690	Mineral fiber panels						
1700	5/8" thick						
1720	2' x 2'	SF	0.011	0.91	1.37		2.28
1740	2' x 4'	"	0.009	0.71	1.37		2.08
1750	3/4" thick						
1760	2' x 2'	SF	0.011	0.91	2.14		3.05
1780	2' x 4'	"	0.009	0.71	2.07		2.78
1790	For aluminum faced panels, add to material, 80%						
1800	For vinyl faced panels, add to total, 125%						
1810	For fire rated panels, add to material, 75%						
1820	Wood fiber panels						
1840	1/2" thick						
1850	2' x 2'	SF	0.011	0.91	1.77		2.68
1860	2' x 4'	"	0.009	0.71	1.77		2.48
1870	5/8" thick						
1880	2' x 2'	SF	0.011	0.91	2.03		2.94
1890	2' x 4'	"	0.009	0.71	2.03		2.74
1900	3/4" thick						
1910	2' x 2'	SF	0.011	0.91	2.49		3.40
1920	2' x 4'	"	0.009	0.71	2.49		3.20
1930	2" thick						
1940	2' x 2'	SF	0.013	1.06	2.91		3.97
1950	2' x 4'	"	0.010	0.80	2.91		3.71
2000	For flameproofing, add to material, 10%						
2010	For sculptured finish, add to material, 15%						
2020	Air distributing panels						
2060	3/4" thick	SF	0.020	1.60	2.64		4.24
2080	5/8" thick	"	0.016	1.28	2.26		3.54
2090	Acoustical tiles, suspension system not included						
2100	Fiberglass tile, 12" x 12"						
3040	5/8" thick	SF	0.015	1.16	2.00		3.16
3060	3/4" thick	"	0.018	1.42	2.32		3.74
3080	Glass cloth faced fiberglass tile						

ACOUSTICAL TREATMENT

ID Code	Component Descriptions	Unit of Meas.	Manhr / Unit	Labor Cost	Material Cost	Equip. Cost	Total Cost
		Descriptions	**Output**		**Unit Costs**		

09 - 51001   **CEILINGS AND WALLS, Cont'd...**   **09 - 51001**

ID Code	Component Descriptions	Unit of Meas.	Manhr / Unit	Labor Cost	Material Cost	Equip. Cost	Total Cost
3100	3/4" thick	SF	0.018	1.42	3.73		5.15
3120	3" thick	"	0.020	1.60	4.17		5.77
3130	Mineral fiber tile, 12" x 12"						
3140	5/8" thick						
3160	Standard	SF	0.016	1.28	1.05		2.33
3170	Vinyl faced	"	0.016	1.28	2.08		3.36
3180	3/4" thick						
3190	Standard	SF	0.016	1.28	1.53		2.81
3200	Vinyl faced	"	0.016	1.28	2.66		3.94
3240	Fire rated	"	0.016	1.28	3.39		4.67
3260	Aluminum or mylar faced	"	0.016	1.28	6.47		7.75
3280	Wood fiber tile, 12" x 12"						
3300	1/2" thick	SF	0.016	1.28	1.68		2.96
3320	3/4" thick	"	0.016	1.28	2.44		3.72
3340	For flameproofing, add to material, 10%						
3360	For sculptured 3 dimensional, add to material, 50%						
3380	Metal pan units, 24 ga. steel						
3700	12" x 12"	SF	0.032	2.56	6.00		8.56
3710	12" x 24"	"	0.027	2.13	6.83		8.96
3720	Aluminum, .025" thick						
3740	12" x 12"	SF	0.032	2.56	7.03		9.59
3750	12" x 24"	"	0.027	2.13	7.24		9.37
3760	Anodized aluminum, 0.25" thick						
3770	12" x 12"	SF	0.032	2.56	7.72		10.25
3775	12" x 24"	"	0.027	2.13	9.17		11.25
3780	Stainless steel, 24 ga.						
3790	12" x 12"	SF	0.032	2.56	17.75		20.25
3800	12" x 24"	"	0.027	2.13	15.25		17.50
3840	For flameproof sound absorbing pads, add to material	"					2.28
3860	Metal ceiling systems						
3880	.020" thick panels						
4030	10', 12', and 16' lengths	SF	0.023	1.82	5.49		7.31
4040	Custom lengths, 3' to 20'	"	0.023	1.82	5.55		7.37
4050	.025" thick panels						
4080	32 sf, 38 sf, and 52 sf pieces	SF	0.027	2.13	5.51		7.64
4100	Custom lengths, 10 sf to 65 sf	"	0.027	2.13	6.43		8.56
4140	Carriers, black, add	"					3.31
4160	Recess filler strip, add	"					1.11

ACOUSTICAL TREATMENT

	Descriptions	Output		Unit Costs			
ID Code	Component Descriptions	Unit of Meas.	Manhr / Unit	Labor Cost	Material Cost	Equip. Cost	Total Cost
09 - 51001	**CEILINGS AND WALLS, Cont'd...**						**09 - 51001**
4180	Custom lengths, add	SF					1.65
4190	Sound absorption walls, with fabric cover						
5000	2-6" x 9' x 3/4"	SF	0.027	2.13	10.25		12.50
5020	2' x 9' x 1"	"	0.027	2.13	11.25		13.50
5040	Starter spline	LF	0.020	1.60	1.65		3.25
5060	Internal spline	"	0.020	1.60	1.44		3.04
5080	Acoustical treatment						
5100	Barriers for plenums						
5120	Leaded vinyl						
5140	0.48 lb per sf	SF	0.038	3.04	4.23		7.27
5160	0.87 lb per sf	"	0.040	3.20	5.11		8.31
5170	Aluminum foil, fiberglass reinforcement						
5180	Minimum	SF	0.027	2.13	1.16		3.29
5200	Maximum	"	0.040	3.20	1.32		4.52
5220	Aluminum mesh, paper backed	"	0.027	2.13	1.09		3.22
5240	Fibered cement sheet, 3/16" thick	"	0.029	2.28	2.25		4.53
5260	Sheet lead, 1/64" thick	"	0.020	1.60	3.83		5.43
5300	Sound attenuation blanket						
5360	1" thick	SF	0.080	6.40	0.43		6.83
5380	1-1/2" thick	"	0.080	6.40	0.60		7.00
5390	2" thick	"	0.080	6.40	0.75		7.15
5400	3" thick	"	0.089	7.11	0.90		8.01
5420	Ceiling suspension systems						
5440	T bar system						
5510	2' x 4'	SF	0.008	0.64	1.15		1.79
5520	2' x 2'	"	0.009	0.71	1.25		1.96
5530	Concealed Z bar suspension system, 12" module	"	0.013	1.06	1.18		2.24
5550	For 1-1/2" carrier channels, 4' o.c., add	"					0.38
5560	Carrier channel for recessed light fixtures	"					0.69

FLOORING

		Descriptions	Output		Unit Costs			
ID Code		Component Descriptions	Unit of Meas.	Manhr / Unit	Labor Cost	Material Cost	Equip. Cost	Total Cost
09 - 62000		**FLOOR LEVELING**						**09 - 62000**
0980		Repair and level floors to receive new flooring						
1000		Minimum	SY	0.027	2.13	1.65		3.78
1020		Average	"	0.067	5.33	3.92		9.25
1030		Maximum	"	0.080	6.40	5.81		12.25
09 - 63161		**UNIT MASONRY FLOORING**						**09 - 63161**
1000		Clay brick						
1020		9 x 4-1/2 x 3" thick						
1040		Glazed	SF	0.067	5.33	8.03		13.25
1060		Unglazed	"	0.067	5.33	7.70		13.00
1070		8 x 4 x 3/4" thick						
1080		Glazed	SF	0.070	5.56	7.26		12.75
1100		Unglazed	"	0.070	5.56	6.93		12.50
1140		For herringbone pattern, add to labor, 15%						

WOOD FLOORING

		Descriptions	Output		Unit Costs			
09 - 64001		**WOOD FLOORING**						**09 - 64001**
0100		Wood strip flooring, unfinished						
1000		Fir floor						
1010		C and better						
1020		Vertical grain	SF	0.027	2.13	3.52		5.65
1040		Flat grain	"	0.027	2.13	4.40		6.53
1060		Oak floor						
1080		Minimum	SF	0.038	3.04	3.72		6.76
1100		Average	"	0.038	3.04	5.13		8.17
1120		Maximum	"	0.038	3.04	7.42		10.50
1200		Maple floor						
1220		25/32" x 2-1/4"						
1240		Minimum	SF	0.038	3.04	5.32		8.36
1260		Maximum	"	0.038	3.04	7.54		10.50
1280		33/32" x 3-1/4"						
1300		Minimum	SF	0.038	3.04	7.42		10.50
1320		Maximum	"	0.038	3.04	8.38		11.50
1340		Added costs						
1350		For factory finish, add to material, 10%						
1355		For random width floor, add to total, 20%						
1360		For simulated pegs, add to total, 10%						
1500		Wood block industrial flooring						

WOOD FLOORING

ID Code	Component Descriptions	Unit of Meas.	Manhr / Unit	Labor Cost	Material Cost	Equip. Cost	Total Cost
	Descriptions	**Output**		**Unit Costs**			

09 - 64001　　WOOD FLOORING, Cont'd...　　09 - 64001

ID Code	Component Descriptions	Unit of Meas.	Manhr / Unit	Labor Cost	Material Cost	Equip. Cost	Total Cost
1510	Creosoted						
1520	2" thick	SF	0.021	1.68	4.18		5.86
1540	2-1/2" thick	"	0.025	2.00	4.34		6.34
1560	3" thick	"	0.027	2.13	4.51		6.64
2500	Parquet, 5/16", white oak						
2520	Finished	SF	0.040	3.20	10.00		13.25
2540	Unfinished	"	0.040	3.20	4.84		8.04
3000	Gym floor, 2 ply felt, 25/32" maple, finished, in mastic	"	0.044	3.55	8.54		12.00
3020	Over wood sleepers	"	0.050	4.00	8.69		12.75
9020	Finishing, sand, fill, finish, and wax	"	0.020	1.60	0.66		2.26
9100	Refinish sand, seal, and 2 coats of polyurethane	"	0.027	2.13	1.16		3.29
9540	Clean and wax floors	"	0.004	0.32	0.24		0.56

RESILIENT FLOORING

09 - 65131　　RESILIENT BASE AND ACCESSORIES　　09 - 65131

ID Code	Component Descriptions	Unit of Meas.	Manhr / Unit	Labor Cost	Material Cost	Equip. Cost	Total Cost
1000	Wall base, vinyl						
1120	Group 1						
1130	4" high	LF	0.027	2.13	1.28		3.41
1140	6" high	"	0.027	2.13	1.74		3.87
1160	Group 2						
1180	4" high	LF	0.027	2.13	1.13		3.26
1200	6" high	"	0.027	2.13	1.79		3.92
1220	Group 3						
1230	4" high	LF	0.027	2.13	2.55		4.68
1240	6" high	"	0.027	2.13	2.87		5.00
6000	Stair accessories						
6010	Treads, 1/4" x 12", rubber diamond surface						
6020	Marbled	LF	0.067	5.33	15.50		20.75
6040	Plain	"	0.067	5.33	16.00		21.25
6080	Grit strip safety tread, 12" wide, colors						
6100	3/16" thick	LF	0.067	5.33	16.00		21.25
6120	5/16" thick	"	0.067	5.33	21.25		26.50
6140	Risers, 7" high, 1/8" thick, colors						
6160	Flat	LF	0.040	3.20	5.97		9.17
6180	Coved	"	0.040	3.20	4.12		7.32
6300	Nosing, rubber						
6310	3/16" thick, 3" wide						

RESILIENT FLOORING

ID Code	Component Descriptions	Unit of Meas.	Manhr / Unit	Labor Cost	Material Cost	Equip. Cost	Total Cost
	Descriptions	**Output**		**Unit Costs**			

09 - 65131 — RESILIENT BASE AND ACCESSORIES, Cont'd... — 09 - 65131

ID Code	Component Descriptions	Unit of Meas.	Manhr / Unit	Labor Cost	Material Cost	Equip. Cost	Total Cost
6320	Black	LF	0.040	3.20	5.18		8.38
6340	Colors	"	0.040	3.20	5.83		9.03
6350	6" wide						
6360	Black	LF	0.067	5.33	6.35		11.75
6380	Colors	"	0.067	5.33	6.63		12.00

09 - 65161 — RESILIENT SHEET FLOORING — 09 - 65161

ID Code	Component Descriptions	Unit of Meas.	Manhr / Unit	Labor Cost	Material Cost	Equip. Cost	Total Cost
0980	Vinyl sheet flooring						
1000	Minimum	SF	0.008	0.64	3.83		4.47
1002	Average	"	0.010	0.76	6.19		6.95
1004	Maximum	"	0.013	1.06	10.50		11.50
1020	Cove, to 6"	LF	0.016	1.28	2.28		3.56
2000	Fluid applied resilient flooring						
2020	Polyurethane, poured in place, 3/8" thick	SF	0.067	5.33	10.50		15.75
6200	Vinyl sheet goods, backed						
6220	0.070" thick	SF	0.010	0.80	3.90		4.70
6240	0.093" thick	"	0.010	0.80	6.05		6.85
6260	0.125" thick	"	0.010	0.80	6.98		7.78
6280	0.250" thick	"	0.010	0.80	8.03		8.83

09 - 65191 — RESILIENT TILE FLOORING — 09 - 65191

ID Code	Component Descriptions	Unit of Meas.	Manhr / Unit	Labor Cost	Material Cost	Equip. Cost	Total Cost
1020	Solid vinyl tile, 1/8" thick, 12" x 12"						
1040	Marble patterns	SF	0.020	1.60	4.66		6.26
1060	Solid colors	"	0.020	1.60	6.05		7.65
1080	Travertine patterns	"	0.020	1.60	6.79		8.39
2000	Conductive resilient flooring, vinyl tile						
2040	1/8" thick, 12" x 12"	SF	0.023	1.82	7.38		9.20

TERRAZZO FLOORING

09 - 66131 — TERRAZZO — 09 - 66131

ID Code	Component Descriptions	Unit of Meas.	Manhr / Unit	Labor Cost	Material Cost	Equip. Cost	Total Cost
1100	Floors on concrete, 1-3/4" thick, 5/8" topping						
1120	Gray cement	SF	0.114	8.51	5.67		14.25
1140	White cement	"	0.114	8.51	5.92		14.50
1200	Sand cushion, 3" thick, 5/8" top, 1/4"						
1220	Gray cement	SF	0.133	9.93	6.69		16.50
1240	White cement	"	0.133	9.93	6.96		17.00
1260	Monolithic terrazzo, 3-1/2" base slab, 5/8" topping	"	0.100	7.45	4.75		12.25
1280	Terrazzo wainscot, cast-in-place, 1/2" thick	"	0.200	15.00	5.77		20.75

TERRAZZO FLOORING

ID Code	Component Descriptions	Unit of Meas.	Manhr / Unit	Labor Cost	Material Cost	Equip. Cost	Total Cost
	Descriptions	**Output**		**Unit Costs**			
09 - 66131	**TERRAZZO, Cont'd...**						**09 - 66131**
1300	Base, cast in place, terrazzo cove type, 6" high	LF	0.114	8.51	7.26		15.75
1320	Curb, cast in place, 6" wide x 6" high, polished top	"	0.400	29.75	6.60		36.25
1340	For venetian type terrazzo, add to material, 10%						
1360	For abrasive heavy duty terrazzo, add to material, 15%						
1400	Divider strips						
1500	Zinc	LF					1.43
1510	Brass	"					2.66
1560	Stairs, cast-in-place, topping on concrete or metal						
1620	1-1/2" thick treads, 12" wide	LF	0.400	29.75	5.61		35.25
1640	Combined tread and riser	"	1.000	75.00	8.42		83.00
1680	Precast terrazzo, thin set						
1690	Terrazzo tiles, non-slip surface						
2120	9" x 9" x 1" thick	SF	0.114	8.51	16.00		24.50
2130	12" x 12"						
2140	1" thick	SF	0.107	7.94	17.25		25.25
2160	1-1/2" thick	"	0.114	8.51	18.00		26.50
2180	18" x 18" x 1-1/2" thick	"	0.114	8.51	23.50		32.00
2200	24" x 24" x 1-1/2" thick	"	0.094	7.01	30.25		37.25
2400	For white cement, add to material, 10%						
2800	For venetian type terrazzo, add to material, 25%						
3000	Terrazzo wainscot						
3020	12" x 12" x 1" thick	SF	0.200	15.00	8.83		23.75
3040	18" x 18" x 1-1/2" thick	"	0.229	17.00	14.50		31.50
3060	Base						
3080	6" high						
3220	Straight	LF	0.062	4.58	12.75		17.25
3240	Coved	"	0.062	4.58	15.00		19.50
3260	8" high						
3280	Straight	LF	0.067	4.96	14.25		19.25
3300	Coved	"	0.067	4.96	16.75		21.75
3310	Terrazzo curbs						
3320	8" wide x 8" high	LF	0.320	23.75	33.00		57.00
3340	6" wide x 6" high	"	0.267	19.75	29.75		49.50
3400	Precast terrazzo stair treads, 12" wide						
3410	1-1/2" thick						
3420	Diamond pattern	LF	0.145	10.75	39.75		51.00
3430	Non-slip surface	"	0.145	10.75	41.75		53.00
3440	2" thick						

TERRAZZO FLOORING

ID Code	Component Descriptions	Unit of Meas.	Manhr / Unit	Labor Cost	Material Cost	Equip. Cost	Total Cost
09 - 66131	**TERRAZZO, Cont'd...**						**09 - 66131**
3450	Diamond pattern	LF	0.145	10.75	41.75		53.00
3460	Non-slip surface	"	0.160	12.00	44.00		56.00
3480	Stair risers, 1" thick to 6" high						
3520	Straight sections	LF	0.080	5.96	13.25		19.25
3530	Cove sections	"	0.080	5.96	15.75		21.75
3600	Combined tread and riser						
3620	Straight sections						
3640	1-1/2" tread, 3/4" riser	LF	0.229	17.00	57.00		74.00
3660	3" tread, 1" riser	"	0.229	17.00	69.00		86.00
3680	Curved sections						
3700	2" tread, 1" riser	LF	0.267	19.75	73.00		93.00
3720	3" tread, 1" riser	"	0.267	19.75	76.00		96.00
3800	Stair stringers, notched for treads and risers						
3820	1" thick	LF	0.200	15.00	34.50		49.50
3840	2" thick	"	0.267	19.75	36.00		56.00
3860	Landings, structural, nonslip						
3870	1-1/2" thick	SF	0.133	9.93	32.75		42.75
3880	3" thick	"	0.160	12.00	45.75		58.00
4000	Conductive terrazzo, spark proof industrial floor						
4020	Epoxy terrazzo						
4040	Floor	SF	0.050	3.72	6.89		10.50
4060	Base	"	0.067	4.96	7.70		12.75
4070	Polyacrylate						
4080	Floor	SF	0.050	3.72	8.85		12.50
4100	Base	"	0.067	4.96	10.00		15.00
4110	Polyester						
4120	Floor	SF	0.032	2.38	4.12		6.50
4140	Base	"	0.040	2.98	4.40		7.38
4150	Synthetic latex mastic						
4170	Floor	SF	0.050	3.72	7.15		10.75
4180	Base	"	0.067	4.96	7.15		12.00

FLUID APPLIED FLOORING

ID Code	Component Descriptions	Unit of Meas.	Manhr / Unit	Labor Cost	Material Cost	Equip. Cost	Total Cost
	Descriptions	**Output**		**Unit Costs**			

09 - 67001 — SPECIAL FLOORING — 09 - 67001

ID Code	Component Descriptions	Unit of Meas.	Manhr / Unit	Labor Cost	Material Cost	Equip. Cost	Total Cost
1020	Epoxy flooring, marble chips						
1040	Epoxy with colored quartz chips in 1/4" base	SF	0.044	3.55	4.48		8.03
1060	Heavy duty epoxy topping, 3/16" thick	"	0.044	3.55	3.62		7.17
1080	Epoxy terrazzo						
1090	1/4" thick chemical resistant	SF	0.050	4.00	6.58		10.50

CARPET

09 - 68001 — CARPET PADDING — 09 - 68001

ID Code	Component Descriptions	Unit of Meas.	Manhr / Unit	Labor Cost	Material Cost	Equip. Cost	Total Cost
1000	Carpet padding						
1005	Foam rubber, waffle type, 0.3" thick	SY	0.040	3.20	6.74		9.94
1010	Jute padding						
1020	Minimum	SY	0.036	2.90	4.57		7.47
1022	Average	"	0.040	3.20	5.95		9.15
1024	Maximum	"	0.044	3.55	8.98		12.50
1030	Sponge rubber cushion						
1040	Minimum	SY	0.036	2.90	5.42		8.32
1042	Average	"	0.040	3.20	7.22		10.50
1044	Maximum	"	0.044	3.55	10.25		13.75
1050	Urethane cushion, 3/8" thick						
1060	Minimum	SY	0.036	2.90	5.42		8.32
1062	Average	"	0.040	3.20	6.32		9.52
1064	Maximum	"	0.044	3.55	8.24		11.75

09 - 68002 — CARPET — 09 - 68002

ID Code	Component Descriptions	Unit of Meas.	Manhr / Unit	Labor Cost	Material Cost	Equip. Cost	Total Cost
0990	Carpet, acrylic						
1000	24 oz., light traffic	SY	0.089	7.11	17.75		24.75
1020	28 oz., medium traffic	"	0.089	7.11	21.25		28.25
2000	Residential						
2010	Nylon						
2020	15 oz., light traffic	SY	0.089	7.11	24.50		31.50
2040	28 oz., medium traffic	"	0.089	7.11	32.00		39.00
2100	Commercial						
2110	Nylon						
2120	28 oz., medium traffic	SY	0.089	7.11	30.50		37.50
2140	35 oz., heavy traffic	"	0.089	7.11	37.25		44.25
2145	Wool						
2150	30 oz., medium traffic	SY	0.089	7.11	51.00		58.00
2160	36 oz., medium traffic	"	0.089	7.11	53.00		60.00

CARPET

	Descriptions	Output		Unit Costs			
ID Code	Component Descriptions	Unit of Meas.	Manhr / Unit	Labor Cost	Material Cost	Equip. Cost	Total Cost
09 - 68002	**CARPET, Cont'd...**						**09 - 68002**
2180	42 oz., heavy traffic	SY	0.089	7.11	71.00		78.00
3000	Carpet tile						
3020	Foam backed						
3022	Minimum	SF	0.016	1.28	4.07		5.35
3024	Average	"	0.018	1.42	4.71		6.13
3026	Maximum	"	0.020	1.60	7.47		9.07
3040	Tufted loop or shag						
3042	Minimum	SF	0.016	1.28	4.41		5.69
3044	Average	"	0.018	1.42	5.32		6.74
3046	Maximum	"	0.020	1.60	8.56		10.25
8980	Clean and vacuum carpet						
9000	Minimum	SY	0.004	0.25	0.36		0.61
9020	Average	"	0.005	0.42	0.56		0.98
9040	Maximum	"	0.008	0.64	0.77		1.41

ACCESS FLOORING

	ACCESS & PEDESTAL FLOOR						
09 - 69001							**09 - 69001**
0980	Panels, no covering, 2'x2'						
1000	Plain	SF	0.010	0.80	11.50		12.25
1040	Perforated	"	0.400	32.00	15.75		47.75
1100	Pedestals						
1120	For 6" to 12" clearance	EA	0.080	6.40	9.24		15.75
1200	Stringers						
1220	2'	LF	0.038	3.04	2.54		5.58
1240	6'	"	0.027	2.13	2.54		4.67
1300	Accessories						
1320	Ramp assembly	SF	0.032	2.56	54.00		57.00
1330	Elevated floor assembly	"	0.030	2.37	85.00		87.00
1340	Handrail	LF	0.400	32.00	66.00		98.00
1360	Fascia plate	"	0.200	16.00	32.25		48.25
1400	For carpet tiles, add	SF					8.92
1420	For vinyl flooring, add	"					10.25
1500	RF shielding components, floor liner						
1520	Hot rolled steel sheet						
1540	14 ga.	SF	0.020	1.60	15.25		16.75
1560	11 ga.	"	0.062	4.92	21.25		26.25

WALL COVERING

ID Code	Component Descriptions	Unit of Meas.	Manhr / Unit	Labor Cost	Material Cost	Equip. Cost	Total Cost
		Descriptions	**Output**		**Unit Costs**		

09 - 72001   **WALL COVERING**   **09 - 72001**

ID Code	Component Descriptions	Unit of Meas.	Manhr / Unit	Labor Cost	Material Cost	Equip. Cost	Total Cost
0900	Vinyl wall covering						
1000	Medium duty	SF	0.011	0.76	1.10		1.86
1010	Heavy duty	"	0.013	0.89	2.26		3.15
1020	Over pipes and irregular shapes						
1030	Lightweight, 13 oz.	SF	0.016	1.06	1.89		2.95
1040	Medium weight, 25 oz.	"	0.018	1.18	2.26		3.44
1060	Heavy weight, 34 oz.	"	0.020	1.33	2.77		4.10
1080	Cork wall covering						
1100	1' x 1' squares						
1140	1/4" thick	SF	0.020	1.33	5.66		6.99
1160	1/2" thick	"	0.020	1.33	7.19		8.52
1180	3/4" thick	"	0.020	1.33	8.10		9.43
1190	Wall fabrics						
1200	Natural fabrics, grass cloths						
1220	Minimum	SF	0.012	0.82	1.65		2.47
1240	Average	"	0.013	0.89	1.83		2.72
1260	Maximum	"	0.016	1.06	6.16		7.22
1280	Flexible gypsum coated wall fabric, fire resistant	"	0.008	0.53	1.85		2.38
2000	Vinyl corner guards						
2020	3/4" x 3/4" x 8'	EA	0.100	6.67	8.70		15.25
2040	2-3/4" x 2-3/4" x 4'	"	0.100	6.67	5.14		11.75

PAINT

09 - 91001   **PAINTING PREPARATION**   **09 - 91001**

ID Code	Component Descriptions	Unit of Meas.	Manhr / Unit	Labor Cost	Material Cost	Equip. Cost	Total Cost
1000	Dropcloths						
1050	Minimum	SF	0.001	0.03	0.16		0.19
1100	Average	"	0.001	0.04	0.18		0.22
1150	Maximum	"	0.001	0.05	0.37		0.42
1200	Masking						
1250	Paper and tape						
1300	Minimum	LF	0.008	0.53	0.04		0.57
1350	Average	"	0.010	0.66	0.06		0.72
1400	Maximum	"	0.013	0.89	0.07		0.96
1450	Doors						
1500	Minimum	EA	0.100	6.67	0.05		6.72
1550	Average	"	0.133	8.90	0.06		8.96
1600	Maximum	"	0.178	11.75	0.07		11.75

PAINT

ID Code	Component Descriptions	Unit of Meas.	Manhr / Unit	Labor Cost	Material Cost	Equip. Cost	Total Cost
	Descriptions	**Output**		**Unit Costs**			
09 - 91001	**PAINTING PREPARATION, Cont'd...**						**09 - 91001**
1650	Windows						
1700	Minimum	EA	0.100	6.67	0.05		6.72
1750	Average	"	0.133	8.90	0.06		8.96
1800	Maximum	"	0.178	11.75	0.07		11.75
2000	Sanding						
2050	Walls and flat surfaces						
2100	Minimum	SF	0.005	0.35			0.35
2150	Average	"	0.007	0.44			0.44
2200	Maximum	"	0.008	0.53			0.53
2250	Doors and windows						
2300	Minimum	EA	0.133	8.90			8.90
2350	Average	"	0.200	13.25			13.25
2400	Maximum	"	0.267	17.75			17.75
2450	Trim						
2500	Minimum	LF	0.010	0.66			0.66
2550	Average	"	0.013	0.89			0.89
2600	Maximum	"	0.018	1.18			1.18
2650	Puttying						
2700	Minimum	SF	0.012	0.82	0.01		0.83
2750	Average	"	0.016	1.06	0.02		1.08
2800	Maximum	"	0.020	1.33	0.03		1.36
09 - 91009	**PAINT**						**09 - 91009**
0830	Paint, enamel						
0850	600 sf per gal.	GAL					54.00
0900	550 sf per gal.	"					50.00
1000	500 sf per gal.	"					36.00
1020	450 sf per gal.	"					33.75
1060	350 sf per gal.	"					32.50
1100	Filler, 60 sf per gal.	"					38.50
1160	Latex, 400 sf per gal.	"					36.00
1170	Aluminum						
1180	400 sf per gal.	GAL					48.00
1190	500 sf per gal.	"					77.00
1200	Red lead, 350 sf per gal.	"					67.00
1220	Primer						
1240	400 sf per gal.	GAL					32.50
1250	300 sf per gal.	"					32.50

PAINT

ID Code	Component Descriptions	Unit of Meas.	Manhr / Unit	Labor Cost	Material Cost	Equip. Cost	Total Cost
	Descriptions	**Output**		**Unit Costs**			

09 - 91009 — PAINT, Cont'd... — 09 - 91009

ID Code	Component Descriptions	Unit of Meas.	Manhr / Unit	Labor Cost	Material Cost	Equip. Cost	Total Cost
1280	Latex base, interior, white	GAL					36.00
1480	Sealer and varnish						
1500	400 sf per gal.	GAL					33.75
1520	425 sf per gal.	"					48.00
1540	600 sf per gal.	"					62.00

09 - 91130 — EXT. PAINTING, SITEWORK — 09 - 91130

ID Code	Component Descriptions	Unit of Meas.	Manhr / Unit	Labor Cost	Material Cost	Equip. Cost	Total Cost
1020	Benches						
1040	Brush						
1060	First Coat						
1080	Minimum	SF	0.008	0.53	0.19		0.72
1100	Average	"	0.010	0.66	0.21		0.87
1120	Maximum	"	0.013	0.89	0.22		1.11
1140	Second Coat						
1160	Minimum	SF	0.005	0.33	0.18		0.51
1180	Average	"	0.006	0.38	0.19		0.57
1200	Maximum	"	0.007	0.44	0.21		0.65
1220	Roller						
1240	First Coat						
1260	Minimum	SF	0.004	0.26	0.19		0.45
1280	Average	"	0.004	0.29	0.21		0.50
1300	Maximum	"	0.005	0.33	0.22		0.55
1320	Second Coat						
1340	Minimum	SF	0.003	0.19	0.18		0.37
1360	Average	"	0.003	0.22	0.19		0.41
1380	Maximum	"	0.004	0.24	0.21		0.45
2000	Brickwork						
2020	Brush						
2040	First Coat						
2060	Minimum	SF	0.005	0.33	0.19		0.52
2080	Average	"	0.007	0.44	0.21		0.65
2100	Maximum	"	0.010	0.66	0.22		0.88
2120	Second Coat						
2140	Minimum	SF	0.004	0.29	0.19		0.48
2160	Average	"	0.005	0.35	0.21		0.56
2180	Maximum	"	0.007	0.44	0.22		0.66
2380	Spray						
2400	First Coat						

PAINT

ID Code	Component Descriptions	Unit of Meas.	Manhr / Unit	Labor Cost	Material Cost	Equip. Cost	Total Cost
		Descriptions	**Output**		**Unit Costs**		

09 - 91130   EXT. PAINTING, SITEWORK, Cont'd...   09 - 91130

ID Code	Component Descriptions	Unit of Meas.	Manhr / Unit	Labor Cost	Material Cost	Equip. Cost	Total Cost
2420	Minimum	SF	0.002	0.14	0.15		0.29
2440	Average	"	0.003	0.19	0.17		0.36
2460	Maximum	"	0.004	0.24	0.18		0.42
2480	Second Coat						
2500	Minimum	SF	0.002	0.14	0.15		0.29
2520	Average	"	0.003	0.17	0.17		0.34
2540	Maximum	"	0.003	0.22	0.18		0.40
3000	Concrete Block						
3020	Roller						
3040	First Coat						
3060	Minimum	SF	0.004	0.26	0.19		0.45
3080	Average	"	0.005	0.35	0.21		0.56
3100	Maximum	"	0.008	0.53	0.22		0.75
3120	Second Coat						
3140	Minimum	SF	0.003	0.22	0.19		0.41
3160	Average	"	0.004	0.29	0.21		0.50
3180	Maximum	"	0.007	0.44	0.22		0.66
3200	Spray						
3220	First Coat						
3240	Minimum	SF	0.002	0.14	0.15		0.29
3260	Average	"	0.003	0.17	0.17		0.34
3280	Maximum	"	0.003	0.20	0.18		0.38
3300	Second Coat						
3320	Minimum	SF	0.001	0.09	0.15		0.24
3340	Average	"	0.002	0.12	0.17		0.29
3360	Maximum	"	0.003	0.16	0.18		0.34
3500	Fences, Chain Link						
3520	Brush						
3540	First Coat						
3560	Minimum	SF	0.008	0.53	0.13		0.66
3580	Average	"	0.009	0.59	0.14		0.73
3600	Maximum	"	0.010	0.66	0.15		0.81
3620	Second Coat						
3640	Minimum	SF	0.005	0.35	0.13		0.48
3660	Average	"	0.006	0.41	0.14		0.55
3680	Maximum	"	0.007	0.48	0.15		0.63
3700	Roller						
3720	First Coat						

PAINT

ID Code	Descriptions Component Descriptions	Output Unit of Meas.	Output Manhr / Unit	Unit Costs Labor Cost	Unit Costs Material Cost	Unit Costs Equip. Cost	Unit Costs Total Cost
09 - 91130	**EXT. PAINTING, SITEWORK, Cont'd...**					**09 - 91130**	
3740	Minimum	SF	0.006	0.38	0.13		0.51
3760	Average	"	0.007	0.44	0.14		0.58
3780	Maximum	"	0.008	0.50	0.15		0.65
3800	Second Coat						
3820	Minimum	SF	0.003	0.22	0.13		0.35
3840	Average	"	0.004	0.26	0.14		0.40
3860	Maximum	"	0.005	0.33	0.15		0.48
3880	Spray						
3900	First Coat						
3920	Minimum	SF	0.003	0.16	0.10		0.26
3940	Average	"	0.003	0.19	0.11		0.30
3960	Maximum	"	0.003	0.22	0.13		0.35
3980	Second Coat						
4000	Minimum	SF	0.002	0.12	0.10		0.22
4060	Average	"	0.002	0.14	0.11		0.25
4080	Maximum	"	0.003	0.16	0.13		0.29
4200	Fences, Wood or Masonry						
4220	Brush						
4240	First Coat						
4260	Minimum	SF	0.008	0.56	0.19		0.75
4280	Average	"	0.010	0.66	0.21		0.87
4300	Maximum	"	0.013	0.89	0.22		1.11
4320	Second Coat						
4340	Minimum	SF	0.005	0.33	0.19		0.52
4360	Average	"	0.006	0.41	0.21		0.62
4380	Maximum	"	0.008	0.53	0.22		0.75
4400	Roller						
4420	First Coat						
4440	Minimum	SF	0.004	0.29	0.19		0.48
4460	Average	"	0.005	0.35	0.21		0.56
4480	Maximum	"	0.006	0.41	0.22		0.63
4500	Second Coat						
4520	Minimum	SF	0.003	0.20	0.19		0.39
4540	Average	"	0.004	0.25	0.21		0.46
4560	Maximum	"	0.005	0.33	0.22		0.55
4580	Spray						
4600	First Coat						
4620	Minimum	SF	0.003	0.19	0.15		0.34

PAINT

ID Code	Component Descriptions	Unit of Meas.	Manhr / Unit	Labor Cost	Material Cost	Equip. Cost	Total Cost
09 - 91130	**EXT. PAINTING, SITEWORK, Cont'd...**						**09 - 91130**
4640	Average	SF	0.004	0.24	0.17		0.41
4660	Maximum	"	0.005	0.33	0.18		0.51
4680	Second Coat						
4700	Minimum	SF	0.002	0.13	0.15		0.28
4760	Average	"	0.003	0.16	0.17		0.33
4780	Maximum	"	0.003	0.22	0.18		0.40
4800	Storage Tanks						
4820	Roller						
4840	First Coat						
4860	Minimum	SF	0.003	0.22	0.15		0.37
4880	Average	"	0.004	0.26	0.17		0.43
4900	Maximum	"	0.005	0.33	0.18		0.51
4920	Second Coat						
4940	Minimum	SF	0.003	0.17	0.15		0.32
4960	Average	"	0.003	0.21	0.17		0.38
4980	Maximum	"	0.004	0.26	0.18		0.44
5000	Spray						
5020	First Coat						
5040	Minimum	SF	0.002	0.13	0.13		0.26
5060	Average	"	0.002	0.15	0.14		0.29
5080	Maximum	"	0.003	0.19	0.15		0.34
5100	Second Coat						
5160	Minimum	SF	0.002	0.10	0.13		0.23
5180	Average	"	0.002	0.11	0.14		0.25
5200	Maximum	"	0.002	0.13	0.15		0.28
09 - 91131	**EXT. PAINTING, BUILDINGS**						**09 - 91131**
1000	Decks, Metal						
1020	Spray						
1040	First Coat						
1060	Minimum	SF	0.004	0.24	0.13		0.37
1080	Average	"	0.004	0.26	0.14		0.40
1100	Maximum	"	0.004	0.29	0.15		0.44
1120	Second Coat						
1140	Minimum	SF	0.003	0.16	0.11		0.27
1160	Average	"	0.003	0.19	0.13		0.32
1180	Maximum	"	0.003	0.22	0.14		0.36
1200	Decks, Wood, Stained						

PAINT

ID Code	Descriptions		Output		Unit Costs			
	Component Descriptions		Unit of Meas.	Manhr / Unit	Labor Cost	Material Cost	Equip. Cost	Total Cost
09 - 91131		**EXT. PAINTING, BUILDINGS, Cont'd...**						**09 - 91131**
1220	Brush							
1240	First Coat							
1260	Minimum		SF	0.004	0.26	0.15		0.41
1280	Average		"	0.004	0.29	0.17		0.46
1300	Maximum		"	0.005	0.33	0.18		0.51
1320	Second Coat							
1340	Minimum		SF	0.003	0.19	0.15		0.34
1360	Average		"	0.003	0.20	0.17		0.37
1380	Maximum		"	0.003	0.22	0.18		0.40
1400	Roller							
1420	First Coat							
1440	Minimum		SF	0.003	0.19	0.15		0.34
1460	Average		"	0.003	0.20	0.17		0.37
1480	Maximum		"	0.003	0.22	0.18		0.40
1500	Second Coat							
1520	Minimum		SF	0.003	0.16	0.15		0.31
1540	Average		"	0.003	0.17	0.17		0.34
1560	Maximum		"	0.003	0.20	0.18		0.38
1580	Spray							
1600	First Coat							
1620	Minimum		SF	0.003	0.16	0.13		0.29
1640	Average		"	0.003	0.17	0.14		0.31
1660	Maximum		"	0.003	0.20	0.15		0.35
1680	Second Coat							
1700	Minimum		SF	0.002	0.14	0.13		0.27
1720	Average		"	0.002	0.16	0.14		0.30
1740	Maximum		"	0.003	0.17	0.15		0.32
1760	Doors, Metal							
1780	Roller							
1800	First Coat							
1820	Minimum		SF	0.006	0.38	0.15		0.53
1840	Average		"	0.007	0.44	0.17		0.61
1860	Maximum		"	0.008	0.53	0.18		0.71
1880	Second Coat							
1900	Minimum		SF	0.004	0.26	0.15		0.41
1920	Average		"	0.004	0.29	0.17		0.46
1940	Maximum		"	0.005	0.33	0.18		0.51
1960	Spray							

PAINT

ID Code	Descriptions — Component Descriptions	Output — Unit of Meas.	Output — Manhr / Unit	Unit Costs — Labor Cost	Unit Costs — Material Cost	Unit Costs — Equip. Cost	Unit Costs — Total Cost
09 - 91131	**EXT. PAINTING, BUILDINGS, Cont'd...**						**09 - 91131**
1980	First Coat						
2000	Minimum	SF	0.005	0.33	0.13		0.46
2020	Average	"	0.006	0.38	0.14		0.52
2040	Maximum	"	0.007	0.44	0.15		0.59
2060	Second Coat						
2080	Minimum	SF	0.004	0.24	0.13		0.37
2100	Average	"	0.004	0.26	0.14		0.40
2120	Maximum	"	0.004	0.29	0.15		0.44
2140	Door Frames, Metal						
2160	Brush						
2180	First Coat						
2200	Minimum	LF	0.010	0.66	0.19		0.85
2220	Average	"	0.013	0.83	0.21		1.04
2240	Maximum	"	0.015	0.97	0.22		1.19
2260	Second Coat						
2280	Minimum	LF	0.006	0.38	0.19		0.57
2300	Average	"	0.007	0.44	0.21		0.65
2320	Maximum	"	0.008	0.53	0.22		0.75
2340	Spray						
2360	First Coat						
2380	Minimum	LF	0.004	0.29	0.13		0.42
2400	Average	"	0.006	0.38	0.14		0.52
2420	Maximum	"	0.008	0.53	0.15		0.68
2440	Second Coat						
2460	Minimum	LF	0.004	0.24	0.13		0.37
2480	Average	"	0.004	0.26	0.14		0.40
2500	Maximum	"	0.004	0.29	0.15		0.44
2520	Doors, Wood						
2540	Brush						
2560	First Coat						
2580	Minimum	SF	0.012	0.82	0.15		0.97
2600	Average	"	0.016	1.06	0.17		1.23
2620	Maximum	"	0.020	1.33	0.18		1.51
2640	Second Coat						
2660	Minimum	SF	0.010	0.66	0.15		0.81
2680	Average	"	0.011	0.76	0.17		0.93
2700	Maximum	"	0.013	0.89	0.18		1.07
2720	Roller						

PAINT

ID Code	Descriptions — Component Descriptions	Output — Unit of Meas.	Output — Manhr / Unit	Unit Costs — Labor Cost	Unit Costs — Material Cost	Unit Costs — Equip. Cost	Unit Costs — Total Cost
09 - 91131	**EXT. PAINTING, BUILDINGS, Cont'd...**						**09 - 91131**
2740	First Coat						
2760	Minimum	SF	0.005	0.35	0.15		0.50
2780	Average	"	0.007	0.44	0.17		0.61
2800	Maximum	"	0.010	0.66	0.18		0.84
2820	Second Coat						
2840	Minimum	SF	0.004	0.26	0.15		0.41
2860	Average	"	0.004	0.29	0.17		0.46
2880	Maximum	"	0.007	0.44	0.18		0.62
2900	Spray						
2920	First Coat						
2940	Minimum	SF	0.003	0.16	0.13		0.29
2960	Average	"	0.003	0.20	0.14		0.34
2980	Maximum	"	0.004	0.26	0.15		0.41
3000	Second Coat						
3020	Minimum	SF	0.002	0.13	0.13		0.26
3040	Average	"	0.002	0.15	0.14		0.29
3060	Maximum	"	0.003	0.17	0.15		0.32
3080	Gutters and Downspouts						
3100	Brush						
3120	First Coat						
3140	Minimum	LF	0.010	0.66	0.19		0.85
3160	Average	"	0.011	0.76	0.21		0.97
3180	Maximum	"	0.013	0.89	0.22		1.11
3200	Second Coat						
3220	Minimum	LF	0.007	0.44	0.19		0.63
3240	Average	"	0.008	0.53	0.21		0.74
3260	Maximum	"	0.010	0.66	0.22		0.88
3300	Siding, Metal						
3320	Roller						
3340	First Coat						
3360	Minimum	SF	0.003	0.22	0.15		0.37
3380	Average	"	0.004	0.24	0.17		0.41
3400	Maximum	"	0.004	0.26	0.18		0.44
3420	Second Coat						
3440	Minimum	SF	0.003	0.20	0.15		0.35
3460	Average	"	0.003	0.22	0.17		0.39
3480	Maximum	"	0.004	0.24	0.18		0.42
3500	Spray						

PAINT

ID Code	Descriptions — Component Descriptions	Output — Unit of Meas.	Output — Manhr / Unit	Unit Costs — Labor Cost	Unit Costs — Material Cost	Unit Costs — Equip. Cost	Unit Costs — Total Cost
09 - 91131	**EXT. PAINTING, BUILDINGS, Cont'd...**						**09 - 91131**
3520	First Coat						
3540	Minimum	SF	0.003	0.16	0.13		0.29
3560	Average	"	0.003	0.19	0.14		0.33
3580	Maximum	"	0.003	0.22	0.15		0.37
3600	Second Coat						
3620	Minimum	SF	0.002	0.10	0.13		0.23
3640	Average	"	0.002	0.13	0.14		0.27
3660	Maximum	"	0.003	0.17	0.15		0.32
3680	Siding, Wood						
3700	Roller						
3720	First Coat						
3740	Minimum	SF	0.003	0.19	0.13		0.32
3760	Average	"	0.003	0.22	0.14		0.36
3780	Maximum	"	0.004	0.24	0.15		0.39
3800	Second Coat						
3820	Minimum	SF	0.003	0.22	0.13		0.35
3840	Average	"	0.004	0.24	0.14		0.38
3860	Maximum	"	0.004	0.26	0.15		0.41
3880	Spray						
3900	First Coat						
3920	Minimum	SF	0.003	0.17	0.13		0.30
3940	Average	"	0.003	0.19	0.14		0.33
3960	Maximum	"	0.003	0.20	0.15		0.35
3980	Second Coat						
4000	Minimum	SF	0.002	0.13	0.13		0.26
4020	Average	"	0.003	0.17	0.14		0.31
4040	Maximum	"	0.004	0.26	0.15		0.41
4060	Stucco						
4080	Roller						
4100	First Coat						
4120	Minimum	SF	0.004	0.24	0.19		0.43
4140	Average	"	0.004	0.28	0.21		0.49
4160	Maximum	"	0.005	0.33	0.22		0.55
4180	Second Coat						
4200	Minimum	SF	0.003	0.19	0.19		0.38
4220	Average	"	0.003	0.22	0.21		0.43
4240	Maximum	"	0.004	0.26	0.22		0.48
4260	Spray						

PAINT

ID Code	Descriptions		Output		Unit Costs			
	Component Descriptions		Unit of Meas.	Manhr / Unit	Labor Cost	Material Cost	Equip. Cost	Total Cost
09 - 91131	**EXT. PAINTING, BUILDINGS, Cont'd...**							**09 - 91131**
4280	First Coat							
4300		Minimum	SF	0.003	0.16	0.15		0.31
4320		Average	"	0.003	0.19	0.17		0.36
4340		Maximum	"	0.003	0.22	0.18		0.40
4360	Second Coat							
4380		Minimum	SF	0.002	0.13	0.15		0.28
4400		Average	"	0.002	0.15	0.17		0.32
4420		Maximum	"	0.003	0.17	0.18		0.35
4440	Trim							
4460	Brush							
4480	First Coat							
4500		Minimum	LF	0.003	0.22	0.19		0.41
4520		Average	"	0.004	0.26	0.21		0.47
4540		Maximum	"	0.005	0.33	0.22		0.55
4560	Second Coat							
4580		Minimum	LF	0.003	0.16	0.19		0.35
4600		Average	"	0.003	0.22	0.21		0.43
4620		Maximum	"	0.005	0.33	0.22		0.55
4640	Walls							
4660	Roller							
4680	First Coat							
4700		Minimum	SF	0.003	0.19	0.15		0.34
4720		Average	"	0.003	0.19	0.17		0.36
4740		Maximum	"	0.003	0.21	0.18		0.39
4760	Second Coat							
4780		Minimum	SF	0.003	0.16	0.15		0.31
4800		Average	"	0.003	0.17	0.17		0.34
4820		Maximum	"	0.003	0.20	0.18		0.38
4840	Spray							
4860	First Coat							
4880		Minimum	SF	0.001	0.08	0.11		0.19
4900		Average	"	0.002	0.10	0.13		0.23
4920		Maximum	"	0.002	0.13	0.14		0.27
4940	Second Coat							
4960		Minimum	SF	0.001	0.07	0.11		0.18
4980		Average	"	0.001	0.08	0.13		0.21
5000		Maximum	"	0.002	0.11	0.14		0.25
5020	Windows							

PAINT

ID Code	Descriptions — Component Descriptions	Output — Unit of Meas.	Output — Manhr / Unit	Unit Costs — Labor Cost	Unit Costs — Material Cost	Unit Costs — Equip. Cost	Unit Costs — Total Cost
09 - 91131	**EXT. PAINTING, BUILDINGS, Cont'd...**						**09 - 91131**
5040	Brush						
5060	First Coat						
5080	Minimum	SF	0.013	0.89	0.13		1.02
5100	Average	"	0.016	1.06	0.14		1.20
5120	Maximum	"	0.020	1.33	0.15		1.48
5140	Second Coat						
5160	Minimum	SF	0.011	0.76	0.13		0.89
5180	Average	"	0.013	0.89	0.14		1.03
5200	Maximum	"	0.016	1.06	0.15		1.21
09 - 91132	**EXT. PAINTING, MISC.**						**09 - 91132**
1000	Gratings, Metal						
1020	Roller						
1040	First Coat						
1060	Minimum	SF	0.023	1.52	0.15		1.67
1080	Average	"	0.027	1.78	0.17		1.95
1100	Maximum	"	0.032	2.13	0.18		2.31
1120	Second Coat						
1140	Minimum	SF	0.016	1.06	0.15		1.21
1160	Average	"	0.020	1.33	0.17		1.50
1180	Maximum	"	0.027	1.78	0.18		1.96
1200	Spray						
1220	First Coat						
1240	Minimum	SF	0.011	0.76	0.13		0.89
1260	Average	"	0.013	0.89	0.14		1.03
1280	Maximum	"	0.016	1.06	0.15		1.21
1300	Second Coat						
1320	Minimum	SF	0.009	0.59	0.13		0.72
1340	Average	"	0.010	0.66	0.14		0.80
1360	Maximum	"	0.011	0.76	0.15		0.91
1500	Ladders						
1520	Brush						
1540	First Coat						
1560	Minimum	LF	0.020	1.33	0.19		1.52
1580	Average	"	0.023	1.52	0.21		1.73
1600	Maximum	"	0.027	1.78	0.22		2.00
1620	Second Coat						
1640	Minimum	LF	0.016	1.06	0.19		1.25

PAINT

ID Code	Descriptions — Component Descriptions	Output — Unit of Meas.	Output — Manhr / Unit	Unit Costs — Labor Cost	Unit Costs — Material Cost	Unit Costs — Equip. Cost	Unit Costs — Total Cost
09 - 91132	**EXT. PAINTING, MISC., Cont'd...**						**09 - 91132**
1660	Average	LF	0.018	1.18	0.21		1.39
1680	Maximum	"	0.020	1.33	0.22		1.55
1700	Spray						
1720	First Coat						
1740	Minimum	LF	0.013	0.89	0.13		1.02
1760	Average	"	0.015	0.97	0.14		1.11
1780	Maximum	"	0.016	1.06	0.15		1.21
1800	Second Coat						
1820	Minimum	LF	0.011	0.76	0.13		0.89
1840	Average	"	0.012	0.82	0.14		0.96
1860	Maximum	"	0.013	0.89	0.15		1.04
3000	Shakes						
3020	Spray						
3040	First Coat						
3060	Minimum	SF	0.003	0.22	0.14		0.36
3080	Average	"	0.004	0.24	0.15		0.39
3100	Maximum	"	0.004	0.26	0.17		0.43
3120	Second Coat						
3140	Minimum	SF	0.003	0.20	0.14		0.34
3160	Average	"	0.003	0.22	0.15		0.37
3180	Maximum	"	0.004	0.24	0.17		0.41
3200	Shingles, Wood						
3220	Roller						
3240	First Coat						
3260	Minimum	SF	0.004	0.29	0.15		0.44
3280	Average	"	0.005	0.33	0.17		0.50
3300	Maximum	"	0.006	0.38	0.18		0.56
3320	Second Coat						
3340	Minimum	SF	0.003	0.20	0.15		0.35
3360	Average	"	0.003	0.22	0.17		0.39
3380	Maximum	"	0.004	0.24	0.18		0.42
3400	Spray						
3420	First Coat						
3440	Minimum	LF	0.003	0.20	0.13		0.33
3460	Average	"	0.003	0.22	0.14		0.36
3480	Maximum	"	0.004	0.24	0.15		0.39
3500	Second Coat						
3520	Minimum	LF	0.002	0.15	0.13		0.28

PAINT

ID Code	Component Descriptions	Unit of Meas.	Manhr / Unit	Labor Cost	Material Cost	Equip. Cost	Total Cost
	Descriptions	**Output**		**Unit Costs**			

09 - 91132 — EXT. PAINTING, MISC., Cont'd... — 09 - 91132

ID Code	Component Descriptions	Unit of Meas.	Manhr / Unit	Labor Cost	Material Cost	Equip. Cost	Total Cost
3540	Average	LF	0.003	0.16	0.14		0.30
3560	Maximum	"	0.003	0.17	0.15		0.32
4000	Shutters and Louvres						
4020	Brush						
4040	First Coat						
4060	Minimum	EA	0.160	10.75	0.19		11.00
4080	Average	"	0.200	13.25	0.21		13.50
4100	Maximum	"	0.267	17.75	0.22		18.00
4120	Second Coat						
4140	Minimum	EA	0.100	6.67	0.19		6.86
4160	Average	"	0.123	8.21	0.21		8.42
4180	Maximum	"	0.160	10.75	0.22		11.00
4200	Spray						
4220	First Coat						
4240	Minimum	EA	0.053	3.56	0.14		3.70
4260	Average	"	0.064	4.27	0.15		4.42
4280	Maximum	"	0.080	5.34	0.17		5.51
4300	Second Coat						
4320	Minimum	EA	0.040	2.67	0.14		2.81
4340	Average	"	0.053	3.56	0.15		3.71
4360	Maximum	"	0.064	4.27	0.17		4.44
5000	Stairs, metal						
5020	Brush						
5040	First Coat						
5060	Minimum	SF	0.009	0.59	0.19		0.78
5080	Average	"	0.010	0.66	0.21		0.87
5100	Maximum	"	0.011	0.76	0.22		0.98
5120	Second Coat						
5140	Minimum	SF	0.005	0.33	0.19		0.52
5160	Average	"	0.006	0.38	0.21		0.59
5180	Maximum	"	0.007	0.44	0.22		0.66
5200	Spray						
5220	First Coat						
5240	Minimum	SF	0.004	0.29	0.14		0.43
5260	Average	"	0.006	0.38	0.15		0.53
5280	Maximum	"	0.006	0.41	0.17		0.58
5300	Second Coat						
5320	Minimum	SF	0.003	0.22	0.14		0.36

PAINT

ID Code	Descriptions	Output		Unit Costs			
	Component Descriptions	Unit of Meas.	Manhr / Unit	Labor Cost	Material Cost	Equip. Cost	Total Cost
09 - 91132	**EXT. PAINTING, MISC., Cont'd...**						**09 - 91132**
5340	Average	SF	0.004	0.26	0.15		0.41
5360	Maximum	"	0.005	0.33	0.17		0.50
7000	Steel, Structural, Light						
7020	Brush						
7040	First Coat						
7060	Minimum	SF	0.016	1.06	0.15		1.21
7080	Average	"	0.020	1.33	0.17		1.50
7100	Maximum	"	0.027	1.78	0.18		1.96
7120	Second Coat						
7140	Minimum	SF	0.011	0.76	0.14		0.90
7160	Average	"	0.013	0.89	0.15		1.04
7180	Maximum	"	0.016	1.06	0.17		1.23
7200	Roller						
7220	First Coat						
7240	Minimum	SF	0.011	0.76	0.15		0.91
7260	Average	"	0.013	0.89	0.17		1.06
7280	Maximum	"	0.016	1.06	0.18		1.24
7300	Second Coat						
7320	Minimum	SF	0.007	0.44	0.14		0.58
7340	Average	"	0.008	0.53	0.15		0.68
7360	Maximum	"	0.010	0.66	0.17		0.83
7380	Spray						
7400	First Coat						
7420	Minimum	SF	0.007	0.44	0.14		0.58
7440	Average	"	0.008	0.53	0.15		0.68
7460	Maximum	"	0.010	0.66	0.17		0.83
7480	Second Coat						
7500	Minimum	SF	0.006	0.38	0.10		0.48
7520	Average	"	0.007	0.44	0.11		0.55
7540	Maximum	"	0.008	0.53	0.13		0.66
7560	Steel, Medium to Heavy						
7580	Brush						
7600	First Coat						
7620	Minimum	SF	0.008	0.53	0.15		0.68
7640	Average	"	0.009	0.59	0.17		0.76
7660	Maximum	"	0.010	0.66	0.18		0.84
7680	Second Coat						
7700	Minimum	SF	0.007	0.44	0.14		0.58

PAINT

ID Code	Component Descriptions	Unit of Meas.	Manhr / Unit	Labor Cost	Material Cost	Equip. Cost	Total Cost
		Descriptions				**Unit Costs**	
			Output				

09 - 91132　　EXT. PAINTING, MISC., Cont'd...　　09 - 91132

ID Code	Component Descriptions	Unit of Meas.	Manhr / Unit	Labor Cost	Material Cost	Equip. Cost	Total Cost
7720	Average	SF	0.008	0.53	0.15		0.68
7740	Maximum	"	0.009	0.62	0.17		0.79
7760	Roller						
7780	First Coat						
7800	Minimum	SF	0.007	0.44	0.15		0.59
7820	Average	"	0.008	0.53	0.17		0.70
7840	Maximum	"	0.009	0.62	0.18		0.80
7860	Second Coat						
7880	Minimum	SF	0.005	0.33	0.14		0.47
7900	Average	"	0.006	0.38	0.15		0.53
7920	Maximum	"	0.007	0.44	0.17		0.61
7940	Spray						
7960	First Coat						
7980	Minimum	SF	0.004	0.29	0.14		0.43
8000	Average	"	0.005	0.33	0.15		0.48
8020	Maximum	"	0.006	0.38	0.17		0.55
8040	Second Coat						
8060	Minimum	SF	0.004	0.24	0.10		0.34
8080	Average	"	0.004	0.26	0.11		0.37
8100	Maximum	"	0.004	0.29	0.13		0.42

09 - 91233　　INT. PAINTING, BUILDINGS　　09 - 91233

ID Code	Component Descriptions	Unit of Meas.	Manhr / Unit	Labor Cost	Material Cost	Equip. Cost	Total Cost
1000	Acoustical Ceiling						
1020	Roller						
1040	First Coat						
1060	Minimum	SF	0.005	0.33	0.19		0.52
1080	Average	"	0.007	0.44	0.21		0.65
1100	Maximum	"	0.010	0.66	0.22		0.88
1120	Second Coat						
1140	Minimum	SF	0.004	0.26	0.19		0.45
1160	Average	"	0.005	0.33	0.21		0.54
1180	Maximum	"	0.007	0.44	0.22		0.66
1200	Spray						
1220	First Coat						
1240	Minimum	SF	0.002	0.14	0.15		0.29
1260	Average	"	0.003	0.17	0.17		0.34
1280	Maximum	"	0.003	0.22	0.18		0.40
1300	Second Coat						

PAINT

ID Code	Descriptions — Component Descriptions	Output — Unit of Meas.	Output — Manhr / Unit	Unit Costs — Labor Cost	Unit Costs — Material Cost	Unit Costs — Equip. Cost	Unit Costs — Total Cost
09 - 91233	**INT. PAINTING, BUILDINGS, Cont'd...**						**09 - 91233**
1320	Minimum	SF	0.002	0.11	0.15		0.26
1340	Average	"	0.002	0.13	0.17		0.30
1360	Maximum	"	0.002	0.15	0.18		0.33
1380	Cabinets and Casework						
1400	Brush						
1420	First Coat						
1440	Minimum	SF	0.008	0.53	0.19		0.72
1460	Average	"	0.009	0.59	0.21		0.80
1480	Maximum	"	0.010	0.66	0.22		0.88
1500	Second Coat						
1520	Minimum	SF	0.007	0.44	0.19		0.63
1540	Average	"	0.007	0.48	0.21		0.69
1560	Maximum	"	0.008	0.53	0.22		0.75
1580	Spray						
1600	First Coat						
1620	Minimum	SF	0.004	0.26	0.15		0.41
1640	Average	"	0.005	0.31	0.17		0.48
1660	Maximum	"	0.006	0.38	0.18		0.56
1680	Second Coat						
1700	Minimum	SF	0.003	0.21	0.15		0.36
1720	Average	"	0.003	0.23	0.17		0.40
1740	Maximum	"	0.004	0.29	0.18		0.47
1760	Ceilings						
1780	Roller						
1800	First Coat						
1820	Minimum	SF	0.003	0.22	0.15		0.37
1840	Average	"	0.004	0.24	0.17		0.41
1860	Maximum	"	0.004	0.26	0.18		0.44
1880	Second Coat						
1900	Minimum	SF	0.003	0.17	0.15		0.32
1920	Average	"	0.003	0.20	0.17		0.37
1940	Maximum	"	0.003	0.22	0.18		0.40
1960	Spray						
1980	First Coat						
2000	Minimum	SF	0.002	0.13	0.13		0.26
2020	Average	"	0.002	0.14	0.14		0.28
2040	Maximum	"	0.003	0.16	0.15		0.31
2060	Second Coat						

PAINT

ID Code	Descriptions — Component Descriptions	Output — Unit of Meas.	Output — Manhr / Unit	Unit Costs — Labor Cost	Unit Costs — Material Cost	Unit Costs — Equip. Cost	Unit Costs — Total Cost
09 - 91233	**INT. PAINTING, BUILDINGS, Cont'd...**						**09 - 91233**
2080	Minimum	SF	0.002	0.10	0.13		0.23
2100	Average	"	0.002	0.11	0.14		0.25
2120	Maximum	"	0.002	0.13	0.15		0.28
2140	Doors, Metal						
2160	Roller						
2180	First Coat						
2200	Minimum	LF	0.005	0.35	0.19		0.54
2220	Average	"	0.006	0.41	0.21		0.62
2240	Maximum	"	0.007	0.48	0.22		0.70
2260	Second Coat						
2280	Minimum	LF	0.004	0.25	0.19		0.44
2300	Average	"	0.004	0.28	0.21		0.49
2320	Maximum	"	0.005	0.31	0.22		0.53
2340	Spray						
2360	First Coat						
2380	Minimum	LF	0.004	0.29	0.13		0.42
2400	Average	"	0.005	0.33	0.14		0.47
2420	Maximum	"	0.006	0.38	0.15		0.53
2440	Second Coat						
2460	Minimum	LF	0.003	0.22	0.19		0.41
2480	Average	"	0.004	0.24	0.21		0.45
2500	Maximum	"	0.004	0.26	0.22		0.48
2520	Doors, Wood						
2540	Brush						
2560	First Coat						
2580	Minimum	SF	0.011	0.76	0.19		0.95
2600	Average	"	0.015	0.97	0.21		1.18
2620	Maximum	"	0.018	1.18	0.22		1.40
2640	Second Coat						
2660	Minimum	SF	0.009	0.59	0.14		0.73
2680	Average	"	0.010	0.66	0.15		0.81
2700	Maximum	"	0.011	0.76	0.17		0.93
2720	Spray						
2740	First Coat						
2760	Minimum	SF	0.002	0.15	0.14		0.29
2780	Average	"	0.003	0.19	0.15		0.34
2800	Maximum	"	0.004	0.24	0.17		0.41
2820	Second Coat						

PAINT

ID Code	Descriptions — Component Descriptions	Output — Unit of Meas.	Output — Manhr / Unit	Unit Costs — Labor Cost	Unit Costs — Material Cost	Unit Costs — Equip. Cost	Unit Costs — Total Cost
09 - 91233	**INT. PAINTING, BUILDINGS, Cont'd...**						**09 - 91233**
2840	Minimum	SF	0.002	0.12	0.14		0.26
2860	Average	"	0.002	0.14	0.15		0.29
2880	Maximum	"	0.003	0.16	0.17		0.33
2900	Ductwork						
2920	Brush						
2940	Minimum	LF	0.010	0.66	0.15		0.81
2960	Average	"	0.011	0.76	0.17		0.93
2980	Maximum	"	0.013	0.89	0.18		1.07
3000	Roller						
3020	Minimum	SF	0.007	0.44	0.15		0.59
3040	Average	"	0.007	0.48	0.17		0.65
3060	Maximum	"	0.008	0.53	0.18		0.71
3080	Spray						
3100	Minimum	SF	0.003	0.19	0.15		0.34
3120	Average	"	0.003	0.20	0.17		0.37
3140	Maximum	"	0.003	0.22	0.18		0.40
3160	Floors						
3180	Roller						
3200	First Coat						
3220	Minimum	SF	0.003	0.16	0.15		0.31
3240	Average	"	0.003	0.19	0.17		0.36
3260	Maximum	"	0.003	0.22	0.18		0.40
3280	Second Coat						
3300	Minimum	SF	0.002	0.13	0.15		0.28
3320	Average	"	0.002	0.14	0.17		0.31
3340	Maximum	"	0.002	0.15	0.18		0.33
3360	Spray						
3380	First Coat						
3400	Minimum	SF	0.002	0.11	0.14		0.25
3420	Average	"	0.002	0.12	0.15		0.27
3440	Maximum	"	0.002	0.14	0.17		0.31
3460	Second Coat						
3480	Minimum	SF	0.002	0.10	0.14		0.24
3500	Average	"	0.002	0.11	0.15		0.26
3520	Maximum	"	0.002	0.12	0.17		0.29
3540	Pipes to 6" diameter						
3560	Brush						
3580	Minimum	LF	0.010	0.66	0.19		0.85

PAINT

ID Code	Component Descriptions	Unit of Meas.	Manhr / Unit	Labor Cost	Material Cost	Equip. Cost	Total Cost
	Descriptions	**Output**		**Unit Costs**			
09 - 91233	**INT. PAINTING, BUILDINGS, Cont'd...**					**09 - 91233**	
3600	Average	LF	0.011	0.76	0.21		0.97
3620	Maximum	"	0.013	0.89	0.22		1.11
3640	Spray						
3660	Minimum	LF	0.003	0.22	0.15		0.37
3680	Average	"	0.004	0.26	0.17		0.43
3700	Maximum	"	0.005	0.35	0.18		0.53
3720	Pipes to 12" diameter						
3740	Brush						
3760	Minimum	LF	0.020	1.33	0.35		1.68
3780	Average	"	0.023	1.52	0.36		1.88
3800	Maximum	"	0.027	1.78	0.38		2.16
3820	Spray						
3840	Minimum	LF	0.007	0.44	0.31		0.75
3860	Average	"	0.008	0.53	0.33		0.86
3880	Maximum	"	0.010	0.66	0.34		1.00
3900	Trim						
3920	Brush						
3940	First Coat						
3960	Minimum	LF	0.003	0.21	0.19		0.40
3980	Average	"	0.004	0.24	0.21		0.45
4000	Maximum	"	0.004	0.29	0.22		0.51
4020	Second Coat						
4040	Minimum	LF	0.002	0.15	0.19		0.34
4060	Average	"	0.003	0.20	0.21		0.41
4080	Maximum	"	0.004	0.29	0.22		0.51
4100	Walls						
4120	Roller						
4140	First Coat						
4160	Minimum	SF	0.003	0.19	0.15		0.34
4180	Average	"	0.003	0.19	0.17		0.36
4200	Maximum	"	0.003	0.22	0.18		0.40
4220	Second Coat						
4240	Minimum	SF	0.003	0.16	0.15		0.31
4260	Average	"	0.003	0.17	0.17		0.34
4280	Maximum	"	0.003	0.20	0.18		0.38
4300	Spray						
4320	First Coat						
4340	Minimum	SF	0.001	0.08	0.13		0.21

PAINT

ID Code	Descriptions		Output		Unit Costs			
	Component Descriptions		Unit of Meas.	Manhr / Unit	Labor Cost	Material Cost	Equip. Cost	Total Cost
09 - 91233		**INT. PAINTING, BUILDINGS, Cont'd...**					**09 - 91233**	
4360	Average		SF	0.002	0.10	0.14		0.24
4380	Maximum		"	0.002	0.13	0.15		0.28
4400	Second Coat							
4420	Minimum		SF	0.001	0.07	0.13		0.20
4440	Average		"	0.001	0.09	0.14		0.23
4460	Maximum		"	0.002	0.12	0.15		0.27

DIVISION 10
SPECIALTIES

VISUAL DISPLAY UNITS

ID Code	Component Descriptions	Unit of Meas.	Manhr / Unit	Labor Cost	Material Cost	Equip. Cost	Total Cost
	Descriptions	**Output**		**Unit Costs**			

10 - 11130 — CHALKBOARDS — 10 - 11130

ID Code	Component Descriptions	Unit of Meas.	Manhr / Unit	Labor Cost	Material Cost	Equip. Cost	Total Cost
1020	Chalkboard, metal frame, 1/4" thick						
1040	48"x60"	EA	0.800	64.00	480		540
1060	48"x96"	"	0.889	71.00	660		730
1080	48"x144"	"	1.000	80.00	880		960
1100	48"x192"	"	1.143	91.00	1,190		1,280
1110	Liquid chalkboard						
1120	48"x60"	EA	0.800	64.00	640		700
1140	48"x96"	"	0.889	71.00	820		890
1160	48"x144"	"	1.000	80.00	1,220		1,300
1180	48"x192"	"	1.143	91.00	1,400		1,490
1200	Map rail, deluxe	LF	0.040	3.20	7.97		11.25

DIRECTORIES

10 - 13001 — IDENTIFYING DEVICES — 10 - 13001

ID Code	Component Descriptions	Unit of Meas.	Manhr / Unit	Labor Cost	Material Cost	Equip. Cost	Total Cost
1000	Directory and bulletin boards						
1020	Open face boards						
1040	Chrome plated steel frame	SF	0.400	32.00	37.75		70.00
1060	Aluminum framed	"	0.400	32.00	65.00		97.00
1080	Bronze framed	"	0.400	32.00	84.00		120
1100	Stainless steel framed	"	0.400	32.00	120		150
1140	Tack board, aluminum framed	"	0.400	32.00	26.50		59.00
1160	Visual aid board, aluminum framed	"	0.400	32.00	26.50		59.00
1200	Glass encased boards, hinged and keyed						
1210	Aluminum framed	SF	1.000	80.00	140		220
1220	Bronze framed	"	1.000	80.00	160		240
1230	Stainless steel framed	"	1.000	80.00	210		290
1240	Chrome plated steel framed	"	1.000	80.00	230		310

10 - 14004 — SIGNAGE — 10 - 14004

ID Code	Component Descriptions	Unit of Meas.	Manhr / Unit	Labor Cost	Material Cost	Equip. Cost	Total Cost
2020	Metal plaque						
2040	Cast bronze	SF	0.667	53.00	650		700
2060	Aluminum	"	0.667	53.00	370		420
2080	Metal engraved plaque						
2100	Porcelain steel	SF	0.667	53.00	780		830
2120	Stainless steel	"	0.667	53.00	620		670
2140	Brass	"	0.667	53.00	920		970
2160	Aluminum	"	0.667	53.00	570		620
2180	Metal built-up plaque						

DIRECTORIES

ID Code	Component Descriptions	Unit of Meas.	Manhr / Unit	Labor Cost	Material Cost	Equip. Cost	Total Cost
	Descriptions	**Output**		**Unit Costs**			

10 - 14004	**SIGNAGE, Cont'd...**						**10 - 14004**
2220	Bronze	SF	0.800	64.00	700		760
2240	Copper and bronze	"	0.800	64.00	620		680
2260	Copper and aluminum	"	0.800	64.00	680		740
2280	Metal nameplate plaques						
2300	Cast bronze	SF	0.500	40.00	690		730
2320	Cast aluminum	"	0.500	40.00	510		550
2330	Engraved, 1-1/2" x 6"						
2340	Bronze	EA	0.500	40.00	290		330
2360	Aluminum	"	0.500	40.00	220		260
2400	Letters, on masonry, aluminum, satin finish						
2440	1/2" thick						
2460	2" high	EA	0.320	25.50	27.00		53.00
2480	4" high	"	0.400	32.00	40.50		73.00
2500	6" high	"	0.444	35.50	54.00		90.00
2510	3/4" thick						
2520	8" high	EA	0.500	40.00	81.00		120
2540	10" high	"	0.571	45.75	94.00		140
2550	1" thick						
2560	12" high	EA	0.667	53.00	110		160
2580	14" high	"	0.800	64.00	120		180
2600	16" high	"	1.000	80.00	150		230
2610	For polished aluminum add, 15%						
2620	For clear anodized aluminum add, 15%						
2630	For colored anodic aluminum add, 30%						
2640	For profiled and color enameled letters add, 50%						
2650	Cast bronze, satin finish letters						
2680	3/8" thick						
2720	2" high	EA	0.320	25.50	32.75		58.00
2740	4" high	"	0.400	32.00	49.25		81.00
2760	1/2" thick, 6" high	"	0.444	35.50	67.00		100
2780	5/8" thick, 8" high	"	0.500	40.00	100		140
2790	1" thick						
2800	10" high	EA	0.571	45.75	120		170
2820	12" high	"	0.667	53.00	150		200
2840	14" high	"	0.800	64.00	190		250
2860	16" high	"	1.000	80.00	270		350
2880	Interior door signs, adhesive, flexible						
3060	2" x 8"	EA	0.200	12.50	25.25		37.75

DIRECTORIES

ID Code	Component Descriptions	Unit of Meas.	Manhr / Unit	Labor Cost	Material Cost	Equip. Cost	Total Cost
	Descriptions	**Output**		**Unit Costs**			

10 - 14004 — SIGNAGE, Cont'd... — 10 - 14004

ID Code	Component Descriptions	Unit of Meas.	Manhr / Unit	Labor Cost	Material Cost	Equip. Cost	Total Cost
3080	4" x 4"	EA	0.200	12.50	26.75		39.25
3100	6" x 7"	"	0.200	12.50	33.75		46.25
3120	6" x 9"	"	0.200	12.50	43.00		56.00
3140	10" x 9"	"	0.200	12.50	56.00		69.00
3160	10" x 12"	"	0.200	12.50	73.00		86.00
3180	Hard plastic type, no frame						
3220	3" x 8"	EA	0.200	12.50	56.00		69.00
3240	4" x 4"	"	0.200	12.50	56.00		69.00
3260	4" x 12"	"	0.200	12.50	60.00		73.00
3280	Hard plastic type, with frame						
3300	3" x 8"	EA	0.200	12.50	170		180
3320	4" x 4"	"	0.200	12.50	130		140
3340	4" x 12"	"	0.200	12.50	210		220

10 - 14530 — SIGNAGE — 10 - 14530

ID Code	Component Descriptions	Unit of Meas.	Manhr / Unit	Labor Cost	Material Cost	Equip. Cost	Total Cost
0100	Traffic signs						
1000	Reflectorized per OSHA stds., incl. post						
1030	Stop, 24"x24"	EA	0.533	33.50	89.00		120
1050	Yield, 30" triangle	"	0.533	33.50	48.50		82.00
1070	Speed limit, 12"x18"	"	0.533	33.50	55.00		89.00
1090	Directional, 12"x18"	"	0.533	33.50	67.00		100
1100	Exit, 12"x18"	"	0.533	33.50	67.00		100
1120	Entry, 12"x18"	"	0.533	33.50	67.00		100
1140	Warning, 24"x24"	"	0.533	33.50	88.00		120
1160	Informational, 12"x18"	"	0.533	33.50	44.75		78.00
1180	Handicap parking, 12"x18"	"	0.533	33.50	46.00		80.00

TELEPHONE SPECIALTIES

10 - 17001 — TELEPHONE ENCLOSURES — 10 - 17001

ID Code	Component Descriptions	Unit of Meas.	Manhr / Unit	Labor Cost	Material Cost	Equip. Cost	Total Cost
1000	Enclosure, wall mounted, shelf, 28" x 30" x 15"	EA	2.000	160	2,030		2,190
1800	Directory shelf, stainless steel, 3 binders	"	1.333	110	1,740		1,850

COMPARTMENTS AND CUBICLES

ID Code	Descriptions — Component Descriptions	Output — Unit of Meas.	Output — Manhr / Unit	Unit Costs — Labor Cost	Unit Costs — Material Cost	Unit Costs — Equip. Cost	Unit Costs — Total Cost
10 - 21130	**TOILET PARTITIONS**						**10 - 21130**
0100	Toilet partition, plastic laminate						
0120	Ceiling mounted	EA	2.667	210	1,180		1,390
0140	Floor mounted	"	2.000	160	780		940
0150	Metal						
0160	Ceiling mounted	EA	2.667	210	810		1,020
0180	Floor mounted	"	2.000	160	770		930
0190	Wheel chair partition, plastic laminate						
0200	Ceiling mounted	EA	2.667	210	1,770		1,980
0210	Floor mounted	"	2.000	160	1,550		1,710
0220	Painted metal						
0240	Ceiling mounted	EA	2.667	210	1,260		1,470
0260	Floor mounted	"	2.000	160	1,150		1,310
0280	Urinal screen, plastic laminate						
2000	Wall hung	EA	1.000	80.00	550		630
2100	Floor mounted	"	1.000	80.00	490		570
2120	Porcelain enameled steel, floor mounted	"	1.000	80.00	630		710
2140	Painted metal, floor mounted	"	1.000	80.00	420		500
2160	Stainless steel, floor mounted	"	1.000	80.00	800		880
2180	Metal toilet partitions						
2200	Front door and side divider, floor mounted						
5040	Porcelain enameled steel	EA	2.000	160	1,300		1,460
5060	Painted steel	"	2.000	160	760		920
5080	Stainless steel	"	2.000	160	1,890		2,050
10 - 21160	**SHOWER STALLS**						**10 - 21160**
1000	Shower receptors						
1010	Precast, terrazzo						
1020	32" x 32"	EA	0.667	58.00	690		750
1040	32" x 48"	"	0.800	70.00	720		790
1050	Concrete						
1060	32" x 32"	EA	0.667	58.00	280		340
1080	48" x 48"	"	0.889	78.00	310		390
1100	Shower door, trim and hardware						
1120	Economy, 24" wide, chrome, tempered glass	EA	0.800	70.00	310		380
1130	Porcelain enameled steel, flush	"	0.800	70.00	560		630
1140	Baked enameled steel, flush	"	0.800	70.00	330		400
1150	Aluminum, tempered glass, 48" wide, sliding	"	1.000	88.00	690		780
1161	Folding	"	1.000	88.00	670		760

COMPARTMENTS AND CUBICLES

ID Code	Component Descriptions	Unit of Meas.	Manhr / Unit	Labor Cost	Material Cost	Equip. Cost	Total Cost
	Descriptions	**Output**		**Unit Costs**			

10 - 21160 — SHOWER STALLS, Cont'd... — 10 - 21160

ID Code	Component Descriptions	Unit of Meas.	Manhr / Unit	Labor Cost	Material Cost	Equip. Cost	Total Cost
1190	Aluminum and tempered glass, molded plastic						
1200	Complete with receptor and door						
1220	32" x 32"	EA	2.000	180	840		1,020
1230	36" x 36"	"	2.000	180	950		1,130
1240	40" x 40"	"	2.286	200	990		1,190
5400	Shower compartment, precast concrete receptor						
5420	Single entry type						
5440	Porcelain enameled steel	EA	8.000	700	2,380		3,080
5460	Baked enameled steel	"	8.000	700	2,280		2,980
5480	Stainless steel	"	8.000	700	2,190		2,890
5500	Double entry type						
5520	Porcelain enameled steel	EA	10.000	880	4,250		5,130
5540	Baked enameled steel	"	10.000	880	2,900		3,780
5560	Stainless steel	"	10.000	880	4,690		5,570

10 - 21230 — CUBICLES — 10 - 21230

ID Code	Component Descriptions	Unit of Meas.	Manhr / Unit	Labor Cost	Material Cost	Equip. Cost	Total Cost
1020	Hospital track						
1040	Ceiling hung	LF	0.089	7.11	7.60		14.75
1060	Suspended	"	0.114	9.14	8.24		17.50
1080	Hospital metal dividers, galvanized steel						
1100	Baked enamel finish						
1110	54" high						
1120	10" glass light	LF	0.400	32.00	130		160
1140	14" glass light	"	0.400	32.00	130		160
1160	24" glass light	"	0.400	32.00	120		150
1170	60" high						
1180	10" glass light	LF	0.444	35.50	140		180
1190	14" glass light	"	0.444	35.50	140		180
1200	24" glass light	"	0.444	35.50	120		160
1300	Stainless steel						
1310	54" high						
1320	10" glass light	LF	0.444	35.50	220		260
1340	14" glass light	"	0.444	35.50	240		280
1360	24" glass light	"	0.444	35.50	280		320
1370	60" high						
1380	10" glass light	LF	0.500	40.00	250		290
1400	14" glass light	"	0.500	40.00	250		290
1420	24" glass light	"	0.500	40.00	310		350

PARTITIONS

ID Code	Component Descriptions	Unit of Meas.	Manhr / Unit	Labor Cost	Material Cost	Equip. Cost	Total Cost
	Descriptions	**Output**		**Unit Costs**			

10 - 22190　　　**MOVABLE PARTITIONS**　　　**10 - 22190**

ID Code	Component Descriptions	Unit of Meas.	Manhr / Unit	Labor Cost	Material Cost	Equip. Cost	Total Cost
0100	Partition, movable, 2-1/2" thick, vinyl-gypsum	SF	0.040	3.20	24.00		27.25
0120	Enameled steel frame, with 1/4" thick clear glass	"	0.040	3.20	29.50		32.75
0160	Door frame and hardware for movable partitions	EA	2.667	210	820		1,030
0200	Add for acoustic movable partition	SF					1.79
2900	Accordion partition, 12' high						
3000	Vinyl	SF	0.133	10.75	13.00		23.75
3020	Acoustical	"	0.133	10.75	15.50		26.25
3080	Standard office cubicles, 8' high, steel framed						
3200	Baked enamel finish						
3540	100% flush	LF	0.200	16.00	200		220
3550	75% flush and 25% glass	"	0.222	17.75	250		270
3560	50% flush and 50% glass	"	0.222	17.75	350		370
3570	100% glass	"	0.267	21.25	400		420
3600	Natural hardwood panels						
3620	100% flush	LF	0.267	21.25	220		240
3640	50% flush and 50% glass	"	0.286	22.75	280		300
3650	Plastic laminated panels						
3660	100% flush	LF	0.267	21.25	250		270
3670	75% flush and 25% glass	"	0.286	22.75	320		340
3680	50% flush and 50% glass	"	0.286	22.75	360		380
3700	Vinyl covered panels						
3710	100% flush	LF	0.276	22.00	220		240
3720	75% flush and 25% glass	"	0.296	23.75	280		300
3730	50% and 50% glass	"	0.296	23.75	350		370
3800	Aluminum framed						
3810	Enameled or anodized aluminum panels						
3830	100% flush	LF	0.200	16.00	170		190
3840	75% flush and 25% glass	"	0.222	17.75	160		180
3850	50% flush and 50% glass	"	0.222	17.75	150		170
3860	Vinyl covered panels						
3870	100% flush	LF	0.276	22.00	180		200
3880	75% flush and 25% glass	"	0.296	23.75	200		220
3890	50% flush and 50% glass	"	0.296	23.75	230		250
4000	60" high partitions, steel framed						
4040	Enameled panels	LF	0.178	14.25	87.00		100
4050	Natural hardwood panels, two sides	"	0.186	15.00	350		360
4060	Plastic laminated panels	"	0.186	15.00	190		200
4070	Vinyl covered panels	"	0.178	14.25	240		250

PARTITIONS

ID Code	Descriptions Component Descriptions	Output Unit of Meas.	Output Manhr / Unit	Unit Costs Labor Cost	Unit Costs Material Cost	Unit Costs Equip. Cost	Unit Costs Total Cost
10 - 22190	**MOVABLE PARTITIONS, Cont'd...**						**10 - 22190**
4100	Aluminum framed						
4120	Anodized or baked enamel panels	LF	0.178	14.25	130		140
4130	Natural hardwood panels	"	0.186	15.00	380		400
4140	Plastic laminated panels	"	0.186	15.00	190		200
4150	Vinyl covered panels	"	0.178	14.25	240		250
4200	Wire mesh partitions						
5000	Wall panels						
5030	4' x 7'	EA	0.500	40.00	180		220
5040	4' x 8'	"	0.533	42.75	190		230
5050	4' x 10'	"	0.615	49.25	220		270
5060	Wall filler panels						
5070	1' x 7'	EA	0.500	40.00	96.00		140
5080	1' x 8'	"	0.533	42.75	110		150
5090	1' x 10'	"	0.571	45.75	130		180
5100	2' x 7'	"	0.500	40.00	110		150
5120	2' x 8'	"	0.533	42.75	120		160
5130	2' x 10'	"	0.571	45.75	140		190
5140	3' x 7'	"	0.500	40.00	130		170
5150	3' x 8'	"	0.533	42.75	190		230
5160	3' x 10'	"	0.571	45.75	200		250
5200	Ceiling panels						
5210	10' x 2'	EA	1.143	91.00	140		230
5220	10' x 4'	"	1.600	130	210		340
5400	Wall panel with service window						
5410	5' wide						
5420	7' high	EA	0.500	40.00	560		600
5430	8' high	"	0.533	42.75	580		620
5440	10' high	"	0.571	45.75	560		610
5500	Doors						
5510	Sliding						
5520	3' x 7'	EA	2.000	160	380		540
5540	3' x 8'	"	2.286	180	500		680
5560	3' x 10'	"	3.200	260	530		790
5580	4' x 7'	"	2.286	180	470		650
5590	4' x 8'	"	3.200	260	530		790
5600	4' x 10'	"	4.000	320	560		880
5620	5' x 7'	"	3.200	260	520		780
5640	5' x 8'	"	4.000	320	560		880

PARTITIONS

ID Code	Descriptions	Output		Unit Costs			
	Component Descriptions	Unit of Meas.	Manhr / Unit	Labor Cost	Material Cost	Equip. Cost	Total Cost
10 - 22190	**MOVABLE PARTITIONS, Cont'd...**						**10 - 22190**
5660	5' x 10'	EA	4.000	320	630		950
5900	Swing door						
6000	3' x 7'	EA	2.000	160	310		470
6020	4' x 7'	"	2.286	180	350		530
6030	Swing door, with 1' transom						
6040	3' x 7'	EA	2.286	180	460		640
6050	4' x 7'	"	3.200	260	510		770
6060	Swing door, with 3' transom						
6070	3' x 7'	EA	3.200	260	560		820
6080	4' x 7'	"	4.000	320	600		920

TOILET, BATH AND LAUNDRY ACCESSORIES

ID Code	BATH ACCESSORIES	Output		Unit Costs			
10 - 28160							**10 - 28160**
1040	Ash receiver, wall mounted, aluminum	EA	0.400	32.00	170		200
1050	Grab bar, 1-1/2" dia., stainless steel, wall mounted						
1060	24" long	EA	0.400	32.00	57.00		89.00
1080	36" long	"	0.421	33.75	64.00		98.00
1090	42" long	"	0.444	35.50	71.00		110
1100	48" long	"	0.471	37.75	78.00		120
1120	52" long	"	0.500	40.00	85.00		130
1130	1" dia., stainless steel						
1140	12" long	EA	0.348	27.75	35.50		63.00
1160	18" long	"	0.364	29.00	42.50		72.00
1180	24" long	"	0.400	32.00	48.25		80.00
1200	30" long	"	0.421	33.75	57.00		91.00
1220	36" long	"	0.444	35.50	64.00		100
1240	48" long	"	0.471	37.75	71.00		110
1300	Hand dryer, surface mounted, 110 volt	"	1.000	80.00	810		890
1320	Medicine cabinet, 16 x 22, baked enamel, lighted	"	0.320	25.50	160		190
1340	With mirror, lighted	"	0.533	42.75	230		270
1420	Mirror, 1/4" plate glass, up to 10 sf	SF	0.080	6.40	12.50		19.00
1430	Mirror, stainless steel frame						
1440	18"x24"	EA	0.267	21.25	95.00		120
1460	18"x32"	"	0.320	25.50	110		140
1480	18"x36"	"	0.400	32.00	110		140
1500	24"x30"	"	0.400	32.00	120		150
1510	24"x36"	"	0.444	35.50	120		160

TOILET, BATH AND LAUNDRY ACCESSORIES

ID Code	Descriptions — Component Descriptions	Output — Unit of Meas.	Output — Manhr / Unit	Unit Costs — Labor Cost	Unit Costs — Material Cost	Unit Costs — Equip. Cost	Unit Costs — Total Cost
10 - 28160	**BATH ACCESSORIES, Cont'd...**						**10 - 28160**
1520	24"x48"	EA	0.667	53.00	170		220
1530	24"x60"	"	0.800	64.00	430		490
1560	30"x30"	"	0.800	64.00	380		440
1580	30"x72"	"	1.000	80.00	680		760
1600	48"x72"	"	1.333	110	740		850
1640	With shelf, 18"x24"	"	0.320	25.50	290		320
1820	Sanitary napkin dispenser, stainless steel	"	0.533	42.75	700		740
1830	Shower rod, 1" diameter						
1840	Chrome finish over brass	EA	0.400	32.00	250		280
1860	Stainless steel	"	0.400	32.00	180		210
1900	Soap dish, stainless steel, wall mounted	"	0.533	42.75	160		200
1910	Toilet tissue dispenser, stainless, wall mounted						
1920	Single roll	EA	0.200	16.00	79.00		95.00
1940	Double roll	"	0.229	18.25	150		170
1945	Towel dispenser, stainless steel						
1950	Flush mounted	EA	0.444	35.50	300		340
1960	Surface mounted	"	0.400	32.00	430		460
1970	Combination towel and waste receptacle	"	0.533	42.75	660		700
2000	Towel bar, stainless steel						
2020	18" long	EA	0.320	25.50	98.00		120
2040	24" long	"	0.364	29.00	130		160
2060	30" long	"	0.400	32.00	140		170
2070	36" long	"	0.444	35.50	150		190
2080	Toothbrush and tumbler holder	"	0.267	21.25	62.00		83.00
2100	Waste receptacle, stainless steel, wall mounted	"	0.667	53.00	500		550

FIRE PROTECTION SPECIALTIES

ID Code	Component Descriptions	Unit of Meas.	Manhr / Unit	Labor Cost	Material Cost	Equip. Cost	Total Cost
10 - 44001	**FIRE PROTECTION**						**10 - 44001**
1000	Portable fire extinguishers						
1020	Water pump tank type						
1030	2.5 gal.						
1040	Red enameled galvanized	EA	0.533	33.50	150		180
1060	Red enameled copper	"	0.533	33.50	220		250
1080	Polished copper	"	0.533	33.50	290		320
1200	Carbon dioxide type, red enamel steel						
1210	Squeeze grip with hose and horn						
1220	2.5 lb	EA	0.533	33.50	220		250

FIRE PROTECTION SPECIALTIES

ID Code	Component Descriptions	Unit of Meas.	Manhr / Unit	Labor Cost	Material Cost	Equip. Cost	Total Cost
	Descriptions	**Output**		**Unit Costs**			
10 - 44001	**FIRE PROTECTION, Cont'd...**						**10 - 44001**
1240	5 lb	EA	0.615	38.50	320		360
1260	10 lb	"	0.800	50.00	330		380
1280	15 lb	"	1.000	63.00	370		430
1300	20 lb	"	1.000	63.00	460		520
1310	Wheeled type						
1320	125 lb	EA	1.600	100	4,050		4,150
1340	250 lb	"	1.600	100	5,120		5,220
1360	500 lb	"	1.600	100	6,610		6,710
1400	Dry chemical, pressurized type						
1405	Red enameled steel						
1410	2.5 lb	EA	0.533	33.50	70.00		100
1430	5 lb	"	0.615	38.50	96.00		130
1440	10 lb	"	0.800	50.00	200		250
1450	20 lb	"	1.000	63.00	260		320
1460	30 lb	"	1.000	63.00	320		380
1480	Chrome plated steel, 2.5 lb	"	0.533	33.50	300		330
1500	Other type extinguishers						
1510	2.5 gal, stainless steel, pressurized water tanks	EA	0.533	33.50	230		260
1520	Soda and acid type	"	0.533	33.50	190		220
1530	Cartridge operated, water type	"	0.533	33.50	170		200
1540	Loaded stream, water type	"	0.533	33.50	200		230
1550	Foam type	"	0.533	33.50	270		300
1560	40 gal, wheeled foam type	"	1.600	100	6,050		6,150
1600	Fire extinguisher cabinets						
1605	Enameled steel						
1610	8" x 12" x 27"	EA	1.600	100	150		250
1620	8" x 16" x 38"	"	1.600	100	190		290
1625	Aluminum						
1630	8" x 12" x 27"	EA	1.600	100	240		340
1640	8" x 16" x 38"	"	1.600	100	280		380
1655	Stainless steel						
1660	8" x 16" x 38"	EA	1.600	100	270		370

LOCKERS

	Descriptions	Output		Unit Costs			
ID Code	Component Descriptions	Unit of Meas.	Manhr / Unit	Labor Cost	Material Cost	Equip. Cost	Total Cost
10 - 51001	**LOCKERS**						**10 - 51001**
0080	Locker bench, floor mounted, laminated maple						
0100	4'	EA	0.667	53.00	390		440
0120	6'	"	0.667	53.00	550		600
0130	Wardrobe locker, 12" x 60" x 15", baked on enamel						
0140	1-tier	EA	0.400	32.00	420		450
0160	2-tier	"	0.400	32.00	450		480
0180	3-tier	"	0.421	33.75	500		530
0200	4-tier	"	0.421	33.75	540		570
0240	12" x 72" x 15", baked on enamel						
0260	1-tier	EA	0.400	32.00	360		390
0280	2-tier	"	0.400	32.00	430		460
0300	4-tier	"	0.421	33.75	530		560
0320	5-tier	"	0.421	33.75	530		560
1200	15" x 60" x 15", baked on enamel						
1220	1-tier	EA	0.400	32.00	470		500
1240	4-tier	"	0.421	33.75	510		540
2040	Wardrobe locker, single tier type						
2060	12" x 15" x 72"	EA	0.800	64.00	320		380
2080	18" x 15" x 72"	"	0.842	67.00	390		460
2100	12" x 18" x 72"	"	0.889	71.00	350		420
2120	18" x 18" x 72"	"	0.941	75.00	450		530
2140	Double tier type						
2160	12" x 15" x 36"	EA	0.400	32.00	250		280
2180	18" x 15" x 36"	"	0.400	32.00	240		270
2200	12" x 18" x 36"	"	0.400	32.00	260		290
2220	18" x 18" x 36"	"	0.400	32.00	280		310
2240	Two person unit						
2260	18" x 15" x 72"	EA	1.333	110	670		780
2280	18" x 18" x 72"	"	1.600	130	750		880
2300	Duplex unit						
2320	15" x 15" x 72"	EA	0.800	64.00	680		740
2340	15" x 21" x 72"	"	0.800	64.00	720		780
2400	Basket lockers, basket sets with baskets						
2440	24 basket set	SET	4.000	320	1,680		2,000
2460	30 basket set	"	5.000	400	2,010		2,410
2480	36 basket set	"	6.667	530	2,280		2,810
2500	42 basket set	"	8.000	640	2,550		3,190

POSTAL SPECIALTIES

ID Code	Component Descriptions	Unit of Meas.	Manhr / Unit	Labor Cost	Material Cost	Equip. Cost	Total Cost
		Descriptions	**Output**		**Unit Costs**		
10 - 55001	**POSTAL SPECIALTIES**					**10 - 55001**	
1500	Mail chutes						
1520	Single mail chute						
1530	Finished aluminum	LF	2.000	160	860		1,020
1540	Bronze	"	2.000	160	1,200		1,360
1560	Single mail chute receiving box						
1580	Finished aluminum	EA	4.000	320	1,280		1,600
1600	Bronze	"	4.000	320	1,540		1,860
1620	Twin mail chute, double parallel						
1630	Finished aluminum	FLR	4.000	320	1,890		2,210
1640	Bronze	"	4.000	320	2,470		2,790
1660	Receiving box, 36" x 20" x 12"						
1680	Finished aluminum	EA	6.667	530	2,950		3,480
1690	Bronze	"	6.667	530	3,970		4,500
1700	Locked receiving mail box						
1720	Finished aluminum	EA	4.000	320	1,290		1,610
1730	Bronze	"	4.000	320	2,520		2,840
1750	Commercial postal accessories for mail chutes						
1760	Letter slot, brass	EA	1.333	110	120		230
1770	Bulk mail slot, brass	"	1.333	110	260		370
1780	Mail boxes						
1790	Residential postal accessories						
1800	Letter slot	EA	0.400	32.00	97.00		130
1810	Rural letter box	"	1.000	80.00	190		270
1820	Apartment house, keyed, 3.5" x 4.5" x 16"	"	0.267	21.25	170		190
1830	Ranch style	"	0.400	32.00	190		220
1840	Commercial postal accessories						
1860	Letter box, with combination lock	EA	0.286	22.75	140		160
1880	Key lock	"	0.286	22.75	150		170
1980	Mail box, aluminum w/glass front, 4x5						
2000	Horizontal rear load	EA	0.229	18.25	230		250
2020	Vertical front load	"	0.229	18.25	120		140

WARDROBE AND CLOSET SPECIALTIES

ID Code	Descriptions	Output		Unit Costs			
	Component Descriptions	Unit of Meas.	Manhr / Unit	Labor Cost	Material Cost	Equip. Cost	Total Cost
10 - 57001	**WARDROBE SPECIALTIES**						**10 - 57001**
1000	Hospital wardrobe units, 24" x 24" x 76", with door						
1020	Baked enameled steel	EA	4.444	360	3,250		3,610
1040	Hardwood	"	4.444	360	1,740		2,100
1060	Stainless steel	"	4.444	360	5,430		5,790
1080	Plastic laminated	"	4.444	360	1,960		2,320
2000	Dormitory wardrobe units, 24" x 76", with door						
2020	Hardwood	EA	4.444	360	1,810		2,170
2040	Plastic laminated	"	4.444	360	1,640		2,000
3000	Hat and coat rack						
3020	Single tier						
3040	Baked enameled steel	LF	0.200	16.00	210		230
3060	Stainless steel	"	0.200	16.00	230		250
3080	Aluminum	"	0.200	16.00	220		240
3100	Double tier						
3120	Baked enameled steel	LF	0.229	18.25	390		410
3140	Stainless steel	"	0.229	18.25	530		550
3160	Aluminum	"	0.229	18.25	450		470
10 - 57230	**SHELVING**						**10 - 57230**
0980	Shelving, enamel, closed side and back, 12" x 36"						
1000	5 shelves	EA	1.333	110	320		430
1020	8 shelves	"	1.778	140	350		490
1030	Open						
1040	5 shelves	EA	1.333	110	160		270
1060	8 shelves	"	1.778	140	180		320
2000	Metal storage shelving, baked enamel						
2030	7 shelf unit, 72" or 84" high						
2040	10" shelf	LF	0.800	64.00	46.00		110
2050	12" shelf	"	0.842	67.00	51.00		120
2060	15" shelf	"	0.889	71.00	88.00		160
2070	18" shelf	"	0.941	75.00	88.00		160
2080	24" shelf	"	1.000	80.00	110		190
2090	30" shelf	"	1.067	85.00	100		190
2100	36" shelf	"	1.143	91.00	120		210
2200	4 shelf unit, 40" high						
2230	10" shelf	LF	0.667	53.00	63.00		120
2240	12" shelf	"	0.727	58.00	68.00		130
2250	15" shelf	"	0.800	64.00	82.00		150

WARDROBE AND CLOSET SPECIALTIES

ID Code	Component Descriptions	Unit of Meas.	Manhr / Unit	Labor Cost	Material Cost	Equip. Cost	Total Cost
	Descriptions	**Output**		**Unit Costs**			
10 - 57230		**SHELVING, Cont'd...**					**10 - 57230**
2260	18" shelf	LF	0.842	67.00	93.00		160
2270	24" shelf	"	0.889	71.00	140		210
2300	3 shelf unit, 32" high						
2320	10" shelf	LF	0.400	32.00	54.00		86.00
2340	12" shelf	"	0.421	33.75	54.00		88.00
2350	15" shelf	"	0.444	35.50	59.00		95.00
2360	18" shelf	"	0.471	37.75	62.00		100
2370	24" shelf	"	0.500	40.00	68.00		110
2400	Single shelf unit, attached to masonry						
2410	10" shelf	LF	0.133	10.75	19.00		29.75
2420	12" shelf	"	0.145	11.75	21.00		32.75
2430	15" shelf	"	0.154	12.25	21.75		34.00
2440	18" shelf	"	0.163	13.00	24.50		37.50
2450	24" shelf	"	0.174	14.00	29.75		43.75
2460	For stainless steel, add to material, 120%						
2470	For attachment to gypsum board, add to labor, 50%						
2500	Built-in wood shelves						
2520	Posts and trimmed plywood	LF	0.114	9.14	4.94		14.00
2540	Solid clear pine	"	0.123	9.84	7.79		17.75
2560	Closet shelf, pine with rod	"	0.123	9.84	5.28		15.00
2580	For lumber edge band, add to material	"					2.70
2590	For prefinished shelves, add to material, 225%						

FLAGPOLES

ID Code	Component Descriptions	Unit of Meas.	Manhr / Unit	Labor Cost	Material Cost	Equip. Cost	Total Cost
10 - 75001		**FLAGPOLES**					**10 - 75001**
2020	Installed in concrete base						
2030	Fiberglass						
2040	25' high	EA	5.333	430	1,640		2,070
2080	50' high	"	13.333	1,070	4,330		5,400
2100	Aluminum						
2120	25' high	EA	5.333	430	1,590		2,020
2140	50' high	"	13.333	1,070	3,150		4,220
2160	Bonderized steel						
2180	25' high	EA	6.154	490	1,780		2,270
2200	50' high	"	16.000	1,280	3,560		4,840
2220	Freestanding tapered, fiberglass						
2240	30' high	EA	5.714	460	1,950		2,410

FLAGPOLES

ID Code	Component Descriptions	Unit of Meas.	Manhr / Unit	Labor Cost	Material Cost	Equip. Cost	Total Cost
10 - 75001	**FLAGPOLES, Cont'd...**						**10 - 75001**
2260	40' high	EA	7.273	580	2,540		3,120
2280	50' high	"	8.000	640	6,460		7,100
2300	60' high	"	9.412	750	6,910		7,660
2400	Wall mounted, with collar, brushed aluminum finish						
2420	15' long	EA	4.000	320	1,510		1,830
2440	18' long	"	4.000	320	1,710		2,030
2460	20' long	"	4.211	340	1,860		2,200
2480	24' long	"	4.706	380	2,000		2,380
2500	Outrigger, wall, including base						
2520	10' long	EA	5.333	430	1,530		1,960
2540	20' long	"	6.667	530	2,030		2,560

PEST CONTROL DEVICES

ID Code	Component Descriptions	Unit of Meas.	Manhr / Unit	Labor Cost	Material Cost	Equip. Cost	Total Cost
10 - 81001	**PEST CONTROL**						**10 - 81001**
1000	Termite control						
1010	Under slab spraying						
1020	Minimum	SF	0.002	0.12	1.21		1.33
1040	Average	"	0.004	0.25	1.21		1.46
1120	Maximum	"	0.008	0.50	1.73		2.23

DIVISION 11
EQUIPMENT

ARCHITECTURAL EQUIPMENT

ID Code	Component Descriptions	Unit of Meas.	Manhr / Unit	Labor Cost	Material Cost	Equip. Cost	Total Cost
	Descriptions	**Output**		**Unit Costs**			

ID Code	Component Descriptions	Unit of Meas.	Manhr / Unit	Labor Cost	Material Cost	Equip. Cost	Total Cost
11 - 11001	**SPECIAL SYSTEMS**						**11 - 11001**
1980	Air compressor, air cooled, two stage						
2000	5.0 cfm, 175 psi	EA	16.000	1,400	2,840		4,240
2020	10 cfm, 175 psi	"	17.778	1,560	3,470		5,030
2030	20 cfm, 175 psi	"	19.048	1,670	4,780		6,450
2040	50 cfm, 125 psi	"	21.053	1,850	6,970		8,820
2050	80 cfm, 125 psi	"	22.857	2,000	9,980		11,980
2055	Single stage, 125 psi						
2060	1.0 cfm	EA	11.429	1,000	2,740		3,740
2080	1.5 cfm	"	11.429	1,000	2,790		3,790
2090	2.0 cfm	"	11.429	1,000	2,860		3,860
8000	Automotive, hose reel, air and water, 50' hose	"	6.667	580	1,280		1,860
8010	Lube equipment, 3 reel, with pumps	"	32.000	2,810	6,680		9,490
8015	Tire changer						
8020	Truck	EA	11.429	1,000	15,150		16,150
8030	Passenger car	"	6.154	540	3,580		4,120
8040	Air hose reel, includes, 50' hose	"	6.154	540	950		1,490
8050	Hose reel, 5 reel, motor oil, gear oil, lube, air & water	"	32.000	2,810	8,840		11,650
8100	Water hose reel, 50' hose	"	6.154	540	950		1,490
8120	Pump, for motor or gear oil, fits 55 gal drum	"	0.800	70.00	1,240		1,310
8140	For chassis lube	"	0.800	70.00	2,020		2,090
8490	Fuel dispensing pump, lighted dial, one product						
8500	One hose	EA	6.667	580	4,410		4,990
8520	Two hose	"	6.667	580	7,780		8,360
8530	Two products, two hose	"	6.667	580	8,200		8,780

LOADING DOCK EQUIPMENT

ID Code	Component Descriptions	Unit of Meas.	Manhr / Unit	Labor Cost	Material Cost	Equip. Cost	Total Cost
11 - 13001	**LOADING DOCK EQUIPMENT**						**11 - 13001**
0080	Dock leveler, 10 ton capacity						
0100	6' x 8'	EA	8.000	640	5,760		6,400
0120	7' x 8'	"	8.000	640	6,610		7,250
0160	Bumpers, laminated rubber						
0165	4-1/2" thick						
0170	6" x 14"	EA	0.160	12.75	70.00		83.00
0175	6" x 36"	"	0.178	14.25	130		140
0180	10" x 14"	"	0.200	16.00	95.00		110
0200	10" x 24"	"	0.229	18.25	140		160
0220	10" x 36"	"	0.267	21.25	200		220

LOADING DOCK EQUIPMENT

ID Code	Component Descriptions	Unit of Meas.	Manhr / Unit	Labor Cost	Material Cost	Equip. Cost	Total Cost
	Descriptions	**Output**		**Unit Costs**			

11 - 13001   LOADING DOCK EQUIPMENT, Cont'd...   11 - 13001

ID Code	Component Descriptions	Unit of Meas.	Manhr / Unit	Labor Cost	Material Cost	Equip. Cost	Total Cost
0240	12" x 14"	EA	0.211	16.75	120		140
0260	12" x 24"	"	0.250	20.00	170		190
0280	12" x 36"	"	0.296	23.75	240		260
0290	6" thick						
0300	10" x 14"	EA	0.229	18.25	110		130
0320	10" x 24"	"	0.276	22.00	120		140
0340	10" x 36"	"	0.400	32.00	250		280
0350	Extruded rubber bumpers						
0351	T-section, 22" x 22" x 3"	EA	0.160	12.75	170		180
0355	Molded rubber bumpers						
0356	24" x 12" x 3" thick	EA	0.400	32.00	94.00		130
0360	Door seal, 12" x 12", vinyl covered	LF	0.200	16.00	57.00		73.00
1000	Dock boards, heavy duty, 5' x 5'						
1010	5000 lb						
1020	Minimum	EA	6.667	530	1,360		1,890
1040	Maximum	"	6.667	530	1,500		2,030
1050	9000 lb						
1060	Minimum	EA	6.667	530	1,560		2,090
1070	Maximum	"	7.273	580	1,870		2,450
1080	15,000 lb	"	7.273	580	2,130		2,710
1200	Truck shelters						
1220	Minimum	EA	6.154	490	1,200		1,690
1240	Maximum	"	11.429	910	2,000		2,910

SECURITY CONTROL EQUIPMENT

11 - 15001   SECURITY EQUIPMENT   11 - 15001

ID Code	Component Descriptions	Unit of Meas.	Manhr / Unit	Labor Cost	Material Cost	Equip. Cost	Total Cost
1000	Bulletproof teller window						
1020	4' x 4'	EA	13.333	1,070	2,610		3,680
1040	5' x 4'	"	16.000	1,280	3,370		4,650
1045	Bulletproof partitions						
1050	Up to 12' high, 2.5" thick	SF	0.053	4.26	220		220
1060	Counter for banks						
1080	Minimum	LF	1.600	130	920		1,050
1100	Maximum	"	2.667	210	4,130		4,340
1280	Drive-up window						
1300	Minimum	EA	11.429	910	5,740		6,650
1310	Maximum	"	26.667	2,130	6,220		8,350

SECURITY CONTROL EQUIPMENT

ID Code	Component Descriptions	Unit of Meas.	Manhr / Unit	Labor Cost	Material Cost	Equip. Cost	Total Cost
	Descriptions	**Output**		**Unit Costs**			
11 - 15001	**SECURITY EQUIPMENT, Cont'd...**						**11 - 15001**
1400	Night depository						
1420	Minimum	EA	11.429	910	10,770		11,680
1440	Maximum	"	26.667	2,130	15,310		17,440
1450	Office safes, 30" x 20" x 20", 1 hr rating	"	2.000	160	4,190		4,350
1460	30" x 16" x 15", 2 hr rating	"	1.600	130	2,140		2,270
1470	30" x 28" x 20", H&G rating	"	1.000	80.00	4,960		5,040
1600	Service windows, pass through painted steel						
1620	24" x 36"	EA	8.000	640	3,610		4,250
1640	48" x 40"	"	10.000	800	5,620		6,420
1660	72" x 40"	"	16.000	1,280	7,060		8,340
1670	Special doors and windows						
1680	3' x 7' bulletproof door with frame	EA	11.429	910	7,180		8,090
1690	12" x 12" vision panel	"	5.714	460	4,160		4,620
1700	Surveillance system						
1720	Minimum	EA	16.000	1,280	7,120		8,400
1740	Maximum	"	80.000	6,400	12,860		19,260
2040	Vault door, 3' wide, 6'6" high						
2060	3-1/2" thick	EA	100.000	8,000	4,630		12,630
2070	7" thick	"	133.333	10,670	7,420		18,090
2080	10" thick	"	160.000	12,800	9,270		22,070
2160	Insulated vault door						
2170	2 hr rating						
2180	32" wide	EA	8.000	640	4,630		5,270
2200	40" wide	"	8.421	670	5,150		5,820
2210	4 hr rating						
2220	32" wide	EA	8.889	710	5,120		5,830
2240	40" wide	"	10.000	800	5,970		6,770
2250	6 hr rating						
2260	32" wide	EA	8.889	710	5,900		6,610
2280	40" wide	"	10.000	800	6,890		7,690
3100	Insulated file room door						
3110	1 hr rating						
3120	32" wide	EA	8.000	640	4,560		5,200
3140	40" wide	"	8.889	710	5,070		5,780

VAULTS

| ID Code | Descriptions | Output | | Unit Costs | | | |
	Component Descriptions	Unit of Meas.	Manhr / Unit	Labor Cost	Material Cost	Equip. Cost	Total Cost
11 - 16001		**VAULTS**					**11 - 16001**
1000	Floor safes						
1005	Class C						
1010	1.0 cf	EA	0.667	53.00	930		980
1020	1.3 cf	"	1.000	80.00	1,030		1,110
1040	1.9 cf	"	1.333	110	1,350		1,460
1060	5.2 cf	"	1.333	110	2,760		2,870

RETAIL AND SERVICE EQUIPMENT

11 - 21330		**CHECKROOM EQUIPMENT**					**11 - 21330**
1000	Motorized checkroom equipment						
1020	No shelf system, 6'4" height						
1040	7'6" length	EA	8.000	640	5,420		6,060
1060	14'6" length	"	8.000	640	5,480		6,120
1080	28' length	"	8.000	640	6,600		7,240
1100	One shelf, 6'8" height						
1120	7'6" length	EA	8.000	640	6,640		7,280
1140	14'6" length	"	8.000	640	6,820		7,460
1160	28' length	"	8.000	640	8,200		8,840
1180	Two shelves, 7'5" height						
1200	7'6" length	EA	8.000	640	8,160		8,800
1220	14'6" length	"	8.000	640	10,300		10,940
1240	28' length	"	8.000	640	10,520		11,160
1300	Three shelves, 8' height						
1320	7'6" length	EA	16.000	1,280	8,340		9,620
1340	14'6" length	"	16.000	1,280	10,510		11,790
1360	28' length	"	16.000	1,280	10,600		11,880
1400	Four shelves, 8'7" height						
1420	7'6" length	EA	16.000	1,280	8,430		9,710
1440	14'6" length	"	16.000	1,280	10,760		12,040
1460	28' length	"	16.000	1,280	11,000		12,280

LAUNDRY EQUIPMENT

ID Code	Component Descriptions	Unit of Meas.	Manhr / Unit	Labor Cost	Material Cost	Equip. Cost	Total Cost
	Descriptions	**Output**		**Unit Costs**			

11 - 23001	LAUNDRY EQUIPMENT						11 - 23001
1000	High capacity, heavy duty						
1020	Washer extractors						
1030	135 lb						
1040	Standard	EA	6.667	530	37,190		37,720
1060	Pass through	"	6.667	530	42,730		43,260
1070	200 lb						
1080	Standard	EA	6.667	530	45,670		46,200
1100	Pass through	"	6.667	530	55,450		55,980
1120	110 lb dryer	"	6.667	530	13,990		14,520
1140	Hand operated presser	"	8.889	710	10,040		10,750
1160	Mushroom press	"	8.889	710	6,270		6,980
1200	Spreader feeders						
1220	2 station	EA	8.889	710	71,410		72,120
1240	4 station	"	16.000	1,280	84,390		85,670
1300	Delivery carts						
1320	12 bushel	EA	0.100	8.00	360		370
1340	16 bushel	"	0.107	8.53	450		460
1350	18 bushel	"	0.114	9.14	560		570
1360	30 bushel	"	0.133	10.75	820		830
1370	40 bushel	"	0.160	12.75	980		990
1500	Low capacity						
1520	Pressers						
1530	Air operated	EA	3.200	260	7,790		8,050
1540	Hand operated	"	3.200	260	6,170		6,430
1560	Extractor, low capacity	"	3.200	260	5,620		5,880
1570	Ironer, 48"	"	1.600	130	4,240		4,370
1600	Coin washers						
1610	10 lb capacity	EA	1.600	130	2,060		2,190
1620	20 lb capacity	"	1.600	130	4,870		5,000
1630	Coin dryer	"	1.000	80.00	980		1,060
1680	Coin dry cleaner, 20 lb	"	3.200	260	4,240		4,500

MAINTENANCE EQUIPMENT

ID Code	Component Descriptions	Unit of Meas.	Manhr / Unit	Labor Cost	Material Cost	Equip. Cost	Total Cost
	Descriptions	**Output**		**Unit Costs**			
11 - 24001	**MAINTENANCE EQUIPMENT**						**11 - 24001**
1000	Vacuum cleaning system						
1010	3 valves						
1020	1.5 hp	EA	8.889	710	1,000		1,710
1030	2.5 hp	"	11.429	910	1,200		2,110
1040	5 valves	"	16.000	1,280	1,870		3,150
1060	7 valves	"	20.000	1,600	2,490		4,090

FOOD SERVICE EQUIPMENT

ID Code	Component Descriptions	Unit of Meas.	Manhr / Unit	Labor Cost	Material Cost	Equip. Cost	Total Cost
11 - 26001	**FOOD SERVICE EQUIPMENT**						**11 - 26001**
1000	Unit kitchens						
1020	30" compact kitchen						
1040	Refrigerator, with range, sink	EA	4.000	330	1,620		1,950
1060	Sink only	"	2.667	220	2,070		2,290
1080	Range only	"	2.000	160	1,680		1,840
1100	Cabinet for upper wall section	"	1.143	93.00	420		510
1120	Stainless shield, for rear wall	"	0.320	26.00	170		200
1140	Side wall	"	0.320	26.00	120		150
1200	42" compact kitchen						
1220	Refrigerator with range, sink	EA	4.444	360	1,980		2,340
1240	Sink only	"	4.000	330	1,080		1,410
1260	Cabinet for upper wall section	"	1.333	110	840		950
1280	Stainless shield, for rear wall	"	0.333	27.25	670		700
1290	Side wall	"	0.333	27.25	190		220
1300	54" compact kitchen						
1310	Refrigerator, oven, range, sink	EA	5.714	470	2,650		3,120
1320	Cabinet for upper wall section	"	1.600	130	1,080		1,210
1330	Stainless shield, for						
1340	Rear wall	EA	0.364	29.50	670		700
1350	Side wall	"	0.364	29.50	190		220
1400	60" compact kitchen						
1420	Refrigerator, oven, range, sink	EA	5.714	470	3,600		4,070
1440	Cabinet for upper wall section	"	1.600	130	250		380
1450	Stainless shield, for						
1460	Rear wall	EA	0.364	29.50	800		830
1480	Side wall	"	0.364	29.50	200		230
1490	72" compact kitchen						
1500	Refrigerator, oven, range, sink	EA	6.667	540	3,810		4,350

FOOD SERVICE EQUIPMENT

ID Code	Component Descriptions	Unit of Meas.	Manhr / Unit	Labor Cost	Material Cost	Equip. Cost	Total Cost
	Descriptions	**Output**		**Unit Costs**			
11 - 26001	**FOOD SERVICE EQUIPMENT, Cont'd...**						**11 - 26001**
1510	Cabinet for upper wall section	EA	1.600	130	260		390
1520	Stainless shield for						
1540	Rear wall	EA	0.400	32.50	870		900
1550	Side wall	"	0.400	32.50	200		230
1560	Bake oven						
1580	Single deck						
1620	Minimum	EA	1.000	81.00	3,830		3,910
1640	Maximum	"	2.000	160	7,330		7,490
1650	Double deck						
1660	Minimum	EA	1.333	110	6,830		6,940
1670	Maximum	"	2.000	160	21,340		21,500
1680	Triple deck						
1690	Minimum	EA	1.333	110	24,220		24,330
1700	Maximum	"	2.667	220	43,210		43,430
1710	Convection type oven, electric, 40" x 45" x 57"						
1720	Minimum	EA	1.000	81.00	3,780		3,860
1740	Maximum	"	2.000	160	6,650		6,810
1800	Broiler, without oven, 69" x 26" x 39"						
1820	Minimum	EA	1.000	81.00	6,020		6,100
1840	Maximum	"	1.333	110	9,470		9,580
1900	Coffee urns, 10 gallons						
1920	Minimum	EA	2.667	220	4,580		4,800
1940	Maximum	"	4.000	330	5,180		5,510
2000	Fryer, with submerger						
2010	Single						
2020	Minimum	EA	1.600	130	1,880		2,010
2040	Maximum	"	2.667	220	5,160		5,380
2050	Double						
2060	Minimum	EA	2.000	160	3,110		3,270
2080	Maximum	"	2.667	220	16,700		16,920
2100	Griddle, counter						
2110	3' long						
2120	Minimum	EA	1.333	110	2,570		2,680
2140	Maximum	"	1.600	130	5,300		5,430
2150	5' long						
2160	Minimum	EA	2.000	160	5,580		5,740
2180	Maximum	"	2.667	220	12,850		13,070
2200	Kettles, steam, jacketed						

FOOD SERVICE EQUIPMENT

ID Code	Component Descriptions	Unit of Meas.	Manhr / Unit	Labor Cost	Material Cost	Equip. Cost	Total Cost
	Descriptions	**Output**		**Unit Costs**			
11 - 26001	**FOOD SERVICE EQUIPMENT, Cont'd...**						**11 - 26001**
2210	20 gallons						
2220	Minimum	EA	2.000	160	12,270		12,430
2240	Maximum	"	4.000	330	13,410		13,740
2250	40 gallons						
2260	Minimum	EA	2.000	160	18,820		18,980
2270	Maximum	"	4.000	330	27,180		27,510
2280	60 gallons						
2290	Minimum	EA	2.000	160	20,690		20,850
2300	Maximum	"	4.000	330	29,270		29,600
2310	Range						
2320	Heavy duty, single oven, open top						
2330	Minimum	EA	1.000	81.00	7,910		7,990
2340	Maximum	"	2.667	220	16,650		16,870
2350	Fry top						
2360	Minimum	EA	1.000	81.00	8,080		8,160
2380	Maximum	"	2.667	220	11,320		11,540
2390	Steamers, electric						
2400	27 kw						
2420	Minimum	EA	2.000	160	14,360		14,520
2440	Maximum	"	2.667	220	26,240		26,460
2450	18 kw						
2460	Minimum	EA	2.000	160	7,900		8,060
2480	Maximum	"	2.667	220	18,540		18,760
2500	Dishwasher, rack type						
2520	Single tank, 190 racks/hr	EA	4.000	330	21,050		21,380
2530	Double tank						
2540	234 racks/hr	EA	4.444	360	43,460		43,820
2560	265 racks/hr	"	5.333	430	51,950		52,380
2580	Dishwasher, automatic 100 meals/hr	"	2.667	220	16,900		17,120
2590	Disposals						
2620	100 gal/hr	EA	2.667	220	1,410		1,630
2640	120 gal/hr	"	2.759	220	1,640		1,860
2660	250 gal/hr	"	2.857	230	1,930		2,160
2670	Exhaust hood for dishwasher, gutter 4 sides						
2680	4'x4'x2'	EA	2.963	240	3,420		3,660
2690	4'x7'x2'	"	3.200	260	4,630		4,890
2700	Food preparation machines						
2710	Vertical cutter mixers						

FOOD SERVICE EQUIPMENT

ID Code	Component Descriptions	Unit of Meas.	Manhr / Unit	Labor Cost	Material Cost	Equip. Cost	Total Cost

11 - 26001 — FOOD SERVICE EQUIPMENT, Cont'd... — **11 - 26001**

ID Code	Component Descriptions	Unit of Meas.	Manhr / Unit	Labor Cost	Material Cost	Equip. Cost	Total Cost
2720	25 quart	EA	2.667	220	13,940		14,160
2730	40 quart	"	2.667	220	18,000		18,220
2740	80 quart	"	4.000	330	23,000		23,330
2750	130 quart	"	6.667	540	30,660		31,200
2760	Choppers						
2770	5 lb	EA	2.000	160	3,890		4,050
2780	16 lb	"	2.667	220	6,130		6,350
2790	40 lb	"	4.000	330	7,710		8,040
2800	Mixers, floor models						
2820	20 quart	EA	1.000	81.00	4,290		4,370
2840	60 quart	"	1.000	81.00	21,320		21,400
2860	80 quart	"	1.143	93.00	34,840		34,930
2870	140 quart	"	1.600	130	41,570		41,700
2890	Ice cube maker						
2900	50 lb per day						
2920	Minimum	EA	8.000	650	2,640		3,290
2940	Maximum	"	8.000	650	3,900		4,550
2950	500 lb per day						
2960	Minimum	EA	13.333	1,090	6,270		7,360
2970	Maximum	"	13.333	1,090	7,410		8,500
3000	Ice flakers						
3020	300 lb per day	EA	8.000	650	4,600		5,250
3040	600 lb per day	"	13.333	1,090	7,540		8,630
3050	1000 lb per day	"	17.778	1,450	8,600		10,050
3060	2000 lb per day	"	20.000	1,630	16,590		18,220
3100	Refrigerated cases						
3120	Dairy products						
3140	Multi deck type	LF	0.533	43.50	1,490		1,530
3160	For rear sliding doors, add	"					280
3180	Delicatessen case, service deli						
3190	Single deck	LF	4.000	330	1,060		1,390
3200	Multi deck	"	5.000	410	1,210		1,620
3210	Meat case						
3230	Single deck	LF	4.706	380	910		1,290
3240	Multi deck	"	5.000	410	1,070		1,480
3260	Produce case						
3270	Single deck	LF	4.706	380	1,060		1,440
3280	Multi deck	"	5.000	410	1,130		1,540

FOOD SERVICE EQUIPMENT

ID Code	Component Descriptions	Unit of Meas.	Manhr / Unit	Labor Cost	Material Cost	Equip. Cost	Total Cost

ID Code	Component Descriptions	Unit of Meas.	Manhr / Unit	Labor Cost	Material Cost	Equip. Cost	Total Cost
11 - 26001	**FOOD SERVICE EQUIPMENT, Cont'd...**						**11 - 26001**
3300	Bottle coolers						
3310	6' long						
3320	Minimum	EA	16.000	1,300	3,010		4,310
3330	Maximum	"	16.000	1,300	4,460		5,760
3340	10' long						
3350	Minimum	EA	26.667	2,170	3,900		6,070
3360	Maximum	"	26.667	2,170	7,670		9,840
3420	Frozen food cases						
3440	Chest type	LF	4.706	380	810		1,190
3460	Reach-in, glass door	"	5.000	410	1,120		1,530
3470	Island case, single	"	4.706	380	1,000		1,380
3480	Multi deck	"	5.000	410	1,590		2,000
3500	Ice storage bins						
3520	500 lb capacity	EA	11.429	930	1,680		2,610
3530	1000 lb capacity	"	22.857	1,860	2,510		4,370

DARKROOM EQUIPMENT

ID Code	Component Descriptions	Unit of Meas.	Manhr / Unit	Labor Cost	Material Cost	Equip. Cost	Total Cost
11 - 27001	**DARKROOM EQUIPMENT**						**11 - 27001**
0600	Dryers						
0620	36" x 25" x 68"	EA	4.000	350	11,480		11,830
0640	48" x 25" x 68"	"	4.000	350	11,860		12,210
0700	Processors, film						
0720	Black and white	EA	4.000	350	18,300		18,650
0740	Color negatives	"	4.000	350	20,720		21,070
0760	Prints	"	4.000	350	23,760		24,110
0780	Transparencies	"	4.000	350	26,070		26,420
1000	Sinks with cabinet and/or stand						
1020	5" sink with stand						
1040	24" x 48"	EA	2.000	180	1,020		1,200
1060	32" x 64"	"	2.667	230	1,570		1,800
1080	38" x 52"	"	2.667	230	2,210		2,440
1100	42" x 132"	"	4.000	350	3,300		3,650
1120	48" x 52"	"	4.000	350	2,530		2,880
1200	5" sink with cabinet						
1220	24" x 48"	EA	2.000	180	2,110		2,290
1240	32" x 64"	"	2.667	230	2,640		2,870
1260	38" x 52"	"	2.667	230	2,710		2,940

DARKROOM EQUIPMENT

ID Code	Component Descriptions	Unit of Meas.	Manhr / Unit	Labor Cost	Material Cost	Equip. Cost	Total Cost
	Descriptions	**Output**		**Unit Costs**			

11 - 27001   DARKROOM EQUIPMENT, Cont'd...   11 - 27001

ID Code	Component Descriptions	Unit of Meas.	Manhr / Unit	Labor Cost	Material Cost	Equip. Cost	Total Cost
1280	42" x 132"	EA	4.000	350	4,420		4,770
1290	48" x 52"	"	4.000	350	3,700		4,050
1300	10" sink with stand						
1320	24" x 48"	EA	2.000	180	1,750		1,930
1340	32" x 64"	"	2.667	230	1,850		2,080
1360	38" x 52"	"	2.667	230	2,510		2,740
1400	10" sink with cabinet						
1420	24" x 48"	EA	2.000	180	1,910		2,090
1460	38" x 52"	"	2.667	230	3,540		3,770

RESIDENTIAL EQUIPMENT

11 - 31001   RESIDENTIAL EQUIPMENT   11 - 31001

ID Code	Component Descriptions	Unit of Meas.	Manhr / Unit	Labor Cost	Material Cost	Equip. Cost	Total Cost
0300	Compactor, 4 to 1 compaction	EA	2.000	160	1,680		1,840
1300	Dishwasher, built-in						
1320	2 cycles	EA	4.000	330	830		1,160
1330	4 or more cycles	"	4.000	330	2,230		2,560
1340	Disposal						
1350	Garbage disposer	EA	2.667	220	230		450
1360	Heaters, electric, built-in						
1362	Ceiling type	EA	2.667	220	470		690
1363	Wall type						
1370	Minimum	EA	2.000	160	240		400
1380	Maximum	"	2.667	220	820		1,040
1390	Hood for range, 2-speed, vented						
1420	30" wide	EA	2.667	220	650		870
1440	42" wide	"	2.667	220	1,200		1,420
1460	Ice maker, automatic						
1480	30 lb per day	EA	1.143	93.00	2,200		2,290
1500	50 lb per day	"	4.000	330	2,790		3,120
1820	Folding access stairs, disappearing metal stair						
1840	8' long	EA	1.143	93.00	1,150		1,240
1850	11' long	"	1.143	93.00	1,200		1,290
1860	12' long	"	1.143	93.00	1,280		1,370
1940	Wood frame, wood stair						
1950	22" x 54" x 8'9" long	EA	0.800	65.00	220		290
1960	25" x 54" x 10' long	"	0.800	65.00	270		340
2020	Ranges electric						

RESIDENTIAL EQUIPMENT

ID Code	Component Descriptions	Unit of Meas.	Manhr / Unit	Labor Cost	Material Cost	Equip. Cost	Total Cost
		Output		**Unit Costs**			

11 - 31001 — RESIDENTIAL EQUIPMENT, Cont'd... — 11 - 31001

2040	Built-in, 30", 1 oven	EA	2.667	220	2,410		2,630
2050	2 oven	"	2.667	220	2,790		3,010
2060	Counter top, 4 burner, standard	"	2.000	160	1,390		1,550
2070	With grill	"	2.000	160	3,480		3,640
2198	Free standing, 21", 1 oven	"	2.667	220	1,250		1,470
2200	30", 1 oven	"	1.600	130	2,440		2,570
2220	2 oven	"	1.600	130	3,970		4,100
3600	Water softener						
3620	30 grains per gallon	EA	2.667	220	1,360		1,580
3640	70 grains per gallon	"	4.000	330	1,720		2,050

LABORATORY EQUIPMENT

11 - 53001 — LABORATORY EQUIPMENT — 11 - 53001

1000	Cabinets, base						
1020	Minimum	LF	0.667	53.00	510		560
1040	Maximum	"	0.667	53.00	930		980
1080	Full storage, 7' high						
1100	Minimum	LF	0.667	53.00	490		540
1140	Maximum	"	0.667	53.00	930		980
1150	Wall						
1160	Minimum	LF	0.800	64.00	180		240
1200	Maximum	"	0.800	64.00	310		370
1220	Counter tops						
1240	Minimum	SF	0.100	8.00	76.00		84.00
1260	Average	"	0.114	9.14	89.00		98.00
1280	Maximum	"	0.133	10.75	100		110
1300	Tables						
1320	Open underneath	SF	0.400	32.00	160		190
1330	Doors underneath	"	0.500	40.00	550		590
2000	Medical laboratory equipment						
2010	Analyzer						
2020	Chloride	EA	0.400	32.50	6,100		6,130
2060	Blood	"	0.667	54.00	33,540		33,590
2070	Bath, water, utility, countertop unit	"	0.800	65.00	1,260		1,330
2080	Hot plate, lab, countertop	"	0.727	59.00	480		540
2100	Stirrer	"	0.727	59.00	580		640
2120	Incubator, anaerobic, 23x23x36"	"	4.000	330	10,340		10,670

LABORATORY EQUIPMENT

ID Code	Component Descriptions	Unit of Meas.	Manhr / Unit	Labor Cost	Material Cost	Equip. Cost	Total Cost
		Descriptions		**Output**		**Unit Costs**	

11 - 53001 — LABORATORY EQUIPMENT, Cont'd... — 11 - 53001

ID Code	Component Descriptions	Unit of Meas.	Manhr / Unit	Labor Cost	Material Cost	Equip. Cost	Total Cost
2140	Dry heat bath	EA	1.333	110	1,120		1,230
2160	Incinerator, for sterilizing	"	0.080	6.51	770		780
2170	Meter, serum protein	"	0.100	8.14	1,190		1,200
2180	Ph analog, general purpose	"	0.114	9.30	1,280		1,290
2190	Refrigerator, blood bank	"	1.333	110	9,780		9,890
2200	5.4 cf, undercounter type	"	1.333	110	6,640		6,750
2210	Refrigerator/freezer, 4.4 cf, undercounter type	"	1.333	110	1,260		1,370
2220	Sealer, impulse, free standing, 20x12x4"	"	0.267	21.75	700		720
2240	Timer, electric, 1-60 minutes, bench or wall mounted	"	0.444	36.25	270		310
2260	Glassware washer - dryer, undercounter	"	10.000	810	11,580		12,390
2300	Balance, torsion suspension, tabletop, 4.5 lb capacity	"	0.444	36.25	1,520		1,560
2340	Binocular microscope, with in base illuminator	"	0.308	25.00	4,650		4,680
2400	Centrifuge, table model, 19x16x13"	"	0.320	26.00	1,780		1,810
2420	Clinical model, with four place head	"	0.178	14.50	1,930		1,940

VOCATIONAL SHOP EQUIPMENT

11 - 57001 — INDUSTRIAL EQUIPMENT — 11 - 57001

ID Code	Component Descriptions	Unit of Meas.	Manhr / Unit	Labor Cost	Material Cost	Equip. Cost	Total Cost
1000	Vehicular paint spray booth, solid back, 14'4" x 9'6"						
1020	24' deep	EA	8.000	640	9,610		10,250
1040	26'6" deep	"	8.000	640	10,980		11,620
1060	28'6" deep	"	8.000	640	12,680		13,320
1100	Drive through, 14'9" x 9'6"						
1120	24' deep	EA	8.000	640	10,230		10,870
1140	26'6" deep	"	8.000	640	12,330		12,970
1160	28'6" deep	"	8.000	640	14,070		14,710
1180	Water wash, paint spray booth						
1190	5' x 11'2" x 10'8"	EA	8.000	640	6,940		7,580
1200	6' x 11'2" x 10'8"	"	8.000	640	7,260		7,900
1220	8' x 11'2" x 10'8"	"	8.000	640	7,850		8,490
1240	10' x 11'2" x 11'2"	"	8.000	640	8,900		9,540
1260	12' x 12'2" x 11'2"	"	8.000	640	10,340		10,980
1280	14' x 12'2" x 11'2"	"	8.000	640	11,700		12,340
1290	16' x 12'2" x 11'2"	"	8.000	640	14,250		14,890
1300	20' x 12'2" x 11'2"	"	8.000	640	17,290		17,930
1320	Dry type spray booth, with paint arrestors						
1340	5'4" x 7'2" x 6'8"	EA	8.000	640	4,190		4,830
1360	6'4" x 7'2" x 6'8"	"	8.000	640	5,450		6,090

VOCATIONAL SHOP EQUIPMENT

ID Code	Descriptions	Output		Unit Costs			
	Component Descriptions	Unit of Meas.	Manhr / Unit	Labor Cost	Material Cost	Equip. Cost	Total Cost
11 - 57001	**INDUSTRIAL EQUIPMENT, Cont'd...**						**11 - 57001**
1380	8'4" x 7'2" x 9'2"	EA	8.000	640	6,180		6,820
1400	10'4" x 7'2" x 9'2"	"	8.000	640	7,270		7,910
1420	12'4" x 7'6" x 9'2"	"	8.000	640	7,230		7,870
1440	14'4" x 7'6" x 9'8"	"	8.000	640	9,780		10,420
1460	16'4" x 7'7" x 9'8"	"	8.000	640	11,180		11,820
1480	20'4" x 7'7" x 10'8"	"	8.000	640	12,720		13,360
1500	Air compressor, electric						
1510	1 hp						
1520	115 volt	EA	5.333	430	1,600		2,030
1535	7.5 hp						
1540	115 volt	EA	8.000	640	4,750		5,390
1550	230 volt	"	8.000	640	5,940		6,580
1600	Hydraulic lifts						
1620	8,000 lb capacity	EA	20.000	1,600	3,280		4,880
1640	11,000 lb capacity	"	32.000	2,560	5,870		8,430
1660	24,000 lb capacity	"	53.333	4,270	10,340		14,610
1680	Power tools						
1700	Band saws						
1720	10"	EA	0.667	53.00	1,400		1,450
1740	14"	"	0.800	64.00	2,100		2,160
1760	Motorized shaper	"	0.615	49.25	1,120		1,170
1780	Motorized lathe	"	0.667	53.00	1,330		1,380
1800	Bench saws						
1820	9" saw	EA	0.533	42.75	3,490		3,530
1830	10" saw	"	0.571	45.75	4,190		4,240
1840	12" saw	"	0.667	53.00	5,160		5,210
1900	Electric grinders						
1910	1/3 hp	EA	0.320	25.50	540		570
2000	1/2 hp	"	0.348	27.75	560		590
2020	3/4 hp	"	0.348	27.75	940		970

BROADCAST, THEATER, STAGE EQUIPMENT

ID Code	Descriptions — Component Descriptions	Output — Unit of Meas.	Output — Manhr / Unit	Unit Costs — Labor Cost	Unit Costs — Material Cost	Unit Costs — Equip. Cost	Unit Costs — Total Cost
11 - 61001	**THEATER EQUIPMENT**						**11 - 61001**
1000	Roll out stage, steel frame, wood floor						
1020	Manual	SF	0.050	4.00	58.00		62.00
1040	Electric	"	0.080	6.40	55.00		61.00
1100	Portable stages						
1120	8" high	SF	0.040	3.20	22.50		25.75
1140	18" high	"	0.044	3.55	26.25		29.75
1160	36" high	"	0.047	3.76	30.75		34.50
1180	48" high	"	0.050	4.00	34.25		38.25
1300	Band risers						
1320	Minimum	SF	0.040	3.20	59.00		62.00
1340	Maximum	"	0.040	3.20	120		120
1400	Chairs for risers						
1420	Minimum	EA	0.036	2.27	770		770
1440	Maximum	"	0.036	2.27	1,230		1,230

ATHLETIC EQUIPMENT

ID Code	Descriptions — Component Descriptions	Output — Unit of Meas.	Output — Manhr / Unit	Unit Costs — Labor Cost	Unit Costs — Material Cost	Unit Costs — Equip. Cost	Unit Costs — Total Cost
11 - 66001	**ATHLETIC EQUIPMENT**						**11 - 66001**
1000	Basketball backboard						
1020	Fixed	EA	10.000	800	2,520		3,320
1040	Swing-up	"	16.000	1,280	4,030		5,310
1060	Portable, hydraulic	"	4.000	320	19,800		20,120
1080	Suspended type, standard	"	16.000	1,280	5,740		7,020
1200	For glass backboard, add	"					1,670
1220	For electrically operated, add	"					1,940
2000	Bleacher, telescoping, manual						
2020	15 tier, minimum	SEAT	0.160	12.75	150		160
2040	Maximum	"	0.160	12.75	380		390
2060	20 tier, minimum	"	0.178	14.25	110		120
2080	Maximum	"	0.178	14.25	320		330
2100	30 tier, minimum	"	0.267	21.25	86.00		110
2120	Maximum	"	0.267	21.25	250		270
2220	Boxing ring elevated, complete, 22' x 22'	EA	114.286	9,140	10,560		19,700
2400	Gym divider curtain						
2420	Minimum	SF	0.011	0.85	3.43		4.28
2440	Maximum	"	0.011	0.85	5.15		6.00
2460	Scoreboards, single face						
2480	Minimum	EA	8.000	640	7,290		7,930

ATHLETIC EQUIPMENT

ID Code	Component Descriptions	Unit of Meas.	Manhr / Unit	Labor Cost	Material Cost	Equip. Cost	Total Cost
11 - 66001	**ATHLETIC EQUIPMENT, Cont'd...**						**11 - 66001**
2500	Maximum	EA	40.000	3,200	39,600		42,800
2540	Parallel bars						
2620	Minimum	EA	8.000	640	1,520		2,160
2630	Maximum	"	13.333	1,070	8,090		9,160
11 - 66002	**POLICE EQUIPMENT**						**11 - 66002**
9000	Firing range equipment, rifle						
9040	3 position	EA	26.667	2,130	19,600		21,730
9060	4 position	"	40.000	3,200	25,120		28,320
9080	5 position	"	44.444	3,560	30,630		34,190
9100	6 position	"	47.059	3,760	36,760		40,520

PLAY FIELD EQUIPMENT AND STRUCTURES

ID Code	Component Descriptions	Unit of Meas.	Manhr / Unit	Labor Cost	Material Cost	Equip. Cost	Total Cost
11 - 68230	**RECREATIONAL COURTS**						**11 - 68230**
1000	Walls, galvanized steel						
1020	8' high	LF	0.160	10.00	16.00		26.00
1040	10' high	"	0.178	11.25	18.75		30.00
1060	12' high	"	0.211	13.25	21.75		35.00
1200	Vinyl coated						
1220	8' high	LF	0.160	10.00	15.25		25.25
1240	10' high	"	0.178	11.25	18.75		30.00
1260	12' high	"	0.211	13.25	20.75		34.00
2010	Gates, galvanized steel						
2200	Single, 3' transom						
2210	3'x7'	EA	4.000	250	370		620
2220	4'x7'	"	4.571	290	390		680
2230	5'x7'	"	5.333	330	540		870
2240	6'x7'	"	6.400	400	580		980
2245	Double, 3' transom						
2250	10'x7'	EA	16.000	1,000	900		1,900
2260	12'x7'	"	17.778	1,110	1,160		2,270
2270	14'x7'	"	20.000	1,250	1,390		2,640
2275	Double, no transom						
2280	10'x10'	EA	13.333	840	980		1,820
2290	12'x10'	"	16.000	1,000	1,170		2,170
2300	14'x10'	"	17.778	1,110	1,340		2,450
2400	Vinyl coated						
2405	Single, 3' transom						

PLAY FIELD EQUIPMENT AND STRUCTURES

ID Code	Component Descriptions	Unit of Meas.	Manhr / Unit	Labor Cost	Material Cost	Equip. Cost	Total Cost
		Output		**Unit Costs**			
11 - 68230	**RECREATIONAL COURTS, Cont'd...**					**11 - 68230**	
2410	3'x7'	EA	4.000	250	730		980
2420	4'x7'	"	4.571	290	790		1,080
2430	5'x7'	"	5.333	330	790		1,120
2440	6'x7'	"	6.400	400	820		1,220
2445	Double, 3'						
2450	10'x7'	EA	16.000	1,000	2,150		3,150
2460	12'x7'	"	17.778	1,110	2,210		3,320
2470	14'x7'	"	20.000	1,250	2,390		3,640
2475	Double, no transom						
2480	10'x10'	EA	13.333	840	2,140		2,980
2490	12'x10'	"	16.000	1,000	2,180		3,180
2500	14'x10'	"	17.778	1,110	2,390		3,500
3000	Baseball backstop, regulation, including material						
3020	Galvanized	EA					8,210
3040	Vinyl coated	"					11,430
3100	Softball backstop, regulation, including material						
3110	14' high						
3130	Galvanized	EA					9,350
3140	Vinyl coated	"					14,850
3160	18' high						
3180	Galvanized	EA					10,340
3200	Vinyl coated	"					14,950
3300	20' high						
3320	Galvanized	EA					12,250
3330	Vinyl coated	"					17,640
3340	22' high						
3350	Galvanized	EA					14,160
3360	Vinyl coated	"					20,680
3380	24' high						
3400	Galvanized	EA					14,970
3420	Vinyl coated	"					24,620
4000	Wire and miscellaneous metal fences						
4020	Chicken wire, post 4' o.c.						
4030	2" mesh						
4040	4' high	LF	0.040	2.50	1.95		4.45
4060	6' high	"	0.053	3.34	2.20		5.54
4100	Galvanized steel						
4120	12 gauge, 2" by 4" mesh, posts 5' o.c.						

PLAY FIELD EQUIPMENT AND STRUCTURES

ID Code	Component Descriptions	Unit of Meas.	Manhr / Unit	Labor Cost	Material Cost	Equip. Cost	Total Cost
		Descriptions		**Output**		**Unit Costs**	
11 - 68230	**RECREATIONAL COURTS, Cont'd...**						**11 - 68230**
4140	3' high	LF	0.040	2.50	3.12		5.62
4160	5' high	"	0.050	3.13	4.45		7.58
4200	14 gauge, 1" by 2" mesh, posts 5' o.c.						
4210	3' high	LF	0.040	2.50	2.61		5.11
4220	5' high	"	0.050	3.13	4.25		7.38
11 - 68330	**RECREATIONAL FACILITIES**						**11 - 68330**
1000	Bleachers, outdoor, portable, per seat						
1020	10 tiers						
1040	Minimum	EA	0.150	9.32	87.00	8.31	100
1060	Maximum	"	0.200	12.50	110	11.00	130
1100	20 tiers						
1120	Minimum	EA	0.141	8.77	92.00	7.82	110
1140	Maximum	"	0.185	11.50	120	10.25	140
1500	Grandstands, fixed, wood seat, steel frame						
1520	Per seat, 15 tiers						
1540	Minimum	EA	0.240	15.00	75.00	13.25	100
1560	Maximum	"	0.400	24.75	130	22.25	180
1600	30 tiers						
1620	Minimum	EA	0.218	13.50	78.00	12.00	100
1660	Maximum	"	0.343	21.25	170	19.00	210
1700	Seats						
1720	Seat backs only						
1740	Fiberglass	EA	0.080	5.01	43.00		48.00
1760	Steel and wood seat	"	0.080	5.01	62.00		67.00
1800	Seat restoration, fiberglass on wood						
1820	Seats	EA	0.160	10.00	31.00		41.00
1840	Plain bench, no backs	"	0.067	4.17	19.00		23.25
2000	Benches						
2020	Park, precast concrete with backs						
2040	4' long	EA	2.667	170	1,190		1,360
2060	8' long	"	4.000	250	2,620		2,870
2100	Fiberglass, with backs						
2120	4' long	EA	2.000	130	950		1,080
2140	8' long	"	2.667	170	1,820		1,990
2200	Wood, with backs and fiberglass supports						
2220	4' long	EA	2.000	130	530		660
2240	8' long	"	2.667	170	550		720

PLAY FIELD EQUIPMENT AND STRUCTURES

ID Code	Component Descriptions	Unit of Meas.	Manhr / Unit	Labor Cost	Material Cost	Equip. Cost	Total Cost
	Descriptions	**Output**		**Unit Costs**			

ID Code	Component Descriptions	Unit of Meas.	Manhr / Unit	Labor Cost	Material Cost	Equip. Cost	Total Cost
11 - 68330	**RECREATIONAL FACILITIES, Cont'd...**						**11 - 68330**
2300	Steel frame, 6' long						
2320	All steel	EA	2.000	130	450		580
2340	Hardwood boards	"	2.000	130	310		440
2360	Players bench, steel frame, fir seat, 10' long	"	2.667	170	340		510
3000	Backstops						
3200	Handball or squash court, outdoor						
3220	Wood	EA					52,860
3240	Masonry	"					39,450
3260	Soccer goal posts	PAIR					3,530
4000	Running track						
4020	Gravel and cinders over stone base	SY	0.060	3.72	10.75	3.32	17.75
4040	Rubber-cork base resilient pavement	"	0.480	29.75	15.25	26.50	71.00
4060	For colored surfaces, add	"	0.048	2.98	9.62	2.66	15.25
4080	Colored rubberized asphalt	"	0.600	37.25	20.50	33.25	92.00
4100	Artificial resilient mat over asphalt	"	1.200	75.00	48.25	67.00	190
4200	Tennis courts						
4240	Bituminous pavement, 2-1/2" thick	SY	0.150	9.32	33.25	8.31	51.00
4300	Colored sealer, acrylic emulsion						
4320	3 coats	SY	0.053	3.34	8.10		11.50
4340	For 2 color seal coating, add	"	0.008	0.50	1.48		1.98
4360	For preparing old courts, add	"	0.005	0.33	3.42		3.75
4400	Net, nylon, 42' long	EA	1.000	63.00	470		530
4520	Paint markings on asphalt, 2 coats	"	8.000	500	180		680
4580	Complete court with fence, etc., bituminous						
4600	Minimum	EA					33,530
4620	Average	"					57,710
4640	Maximum	"					81,900
4680	Clay court						
4700	Minimum	EA					34,900
4720	Average	"					47,570
4740	Maximum	"					72,140
5000	Playground equipment						
5010	Basketball backboard						
5012	Minimum	EA	2.000	130	1,020		1,150
5014	Maximum	"	2.286	140	1,930		2,070
5016	Bike rack, 10' long	"	1.600	100	650		750
5018	Golf shelter, fiberglass	"	2.000	130	3,240		3,370
5020	Ground socket for movable posts						

PLAY FIELD EQUIPMENT AND STRUCTURES

ID Code	Component Descriptions	Unit of Meas.	Manhr / Unit	Labor Cost	Material Cost	Equip. Cost	Total Cost
	Descriptions	**Output**		**Unit Costs**			
11 - 68330	**RECREATIONAL FACILITIES, Cont'd...**						**11 - 68330**
5040	Minimum	EA	0.500	31.25	150		180
5060	Maximum	"	0.500	31.25	300		330
5070	Horizontal monkey ladder, 14' long	"	1.333	84.00	990		1,070
5072	Posts, tether ball	"	0.400	25.00	480		500
5074	Multiple purpose, 10' long	"	0.800	50.00	490		540
5080	See-saw, steel						
5100	Minimum	EA	3.200	200	1,170		1,370
5120	Average	"	4.000	250	2,260		2,510
5140	Maximum	"	5.333	330	3,320		3,650
5150	Slide						
5160	Minimum	EA	6.400	400	2,260		2,660
5180	Maximum	"	7.273	460	5,980		6,440
5800	Swings, plain seats						
5810	8' high						
5820	Minimum	EA	5.333	330	1,080		1,410
5840	Maximum	"	6.154	390	2,050		2,440
5850	12' high						
5860	Minimum	EA	6.154	390	1,650		2,040
5880	Maximum	"	8.889	560	2,980		3,540

EXAMINATION AND TREATMENT EQUIPMENT

ID Code	Component Descriptions	Unit of Meas.	Manhr / Unit	Labor Cost	Material Cost	Equip. Cost	Total Cost
11 - 72001	**MEDICAL EQUIPMENT**						**11 - 72001**
1000	Hospital equipment, lights						
1020	Examination, portable	EA	0.667	54.00	2,130		2,180
1200	Meters						
1220	Air flow meter	EA	0.444	36.25	110		150
1240	Oxygen flow meters	"	0.333	27.25	140		170
1300	Racks						
1320	40 chart, revolving open frame; mobile caddy	EA	0.667	54.00	1,470		1,520
1400	Scales						
1420	Clinical, metric with measure rod, 350 lb	EA	0.727	59.00	780		840
1900	Physical therapy						
1930	Chair, hydrotherapy	EA	0.133	10.75	820		830
1940	Diathermy, shortwave, portable, on casters	"	0.320	25.50	3,540		3,570
1950	Exercise bicycle, floor standing, 35" x 15"	"	0.267	21.25	3,440		3,460
1960	Hydrocollator, 4 pack, portable, 129 x 90 x 160"	"	0.114	9.14	620		630
1970	Lamp, infrared, mobile with variable heat control	"	0.615	49.25	830		880

EXAMINATION AND TREATMENT EQUIPMENT

ID Code	Component Descriptions	Unit of Meas.	Manhr / Unit	Labor Cost	Material Cost	Equip. Cost	Total Cost
	Descriptions	**Output**		**Unit Costs**			
11 - 72001	**MEDICAL EQUIPMENT, Cont'd...**						**11 - 72001**
1980	Ultra violet, base mounted	EA	0.615	49.25	770		820
1990	Mirror, posture training, 27" wide and 72" high	"	0.200	16.00	850		870
2000	Parallel bars, adjustable	"	1.000	80.00	3,670		3,750
2020	Platform mat 10'x6', 1" thick	"	0.200	16.00	1,180		1,200
2030	Pulley, duplex, wall mounted	"	2.667	210	2,010		2,220
2040	Rack, crutch, wall mounted, 66 x 16 x 13"	"	0.800	64.00	490		550
2070	Stimulator, galvanic-faradic, hand held	"	0.053	4.26	430		430
2080	Ultrasound, stimulator, portable, 13x13x8"	"	0.067	5.33	3,680		3,690
2100	Sandbag set, velcro straps, saddle bag type	"	0.114	9.14	190		200
2120	Whirlpool, 85 gallon	"	4.000	320	7,070		7,390
2141	65 gallon capacity	"	4.000	320	6,380		6,700
2260	Radiology						
2280	Radiographic table, motor driven tilting table	EA	80.000	6,400	62,350		68,750
2290	Fluoroscope image/tv system	"	160.000	12,800	103,440		116,240
2300	Processor for washing and drying radiographs						
2310	Water filter unit, 30" x 48-1/2" x 37-1/2"	EA	13.333	1,090	140		1,230
2320	Cassette transfer cabinet	"	0.667	54.00	2,980		3,030
2340	Base storage cabinets, sectional design						
2350	With back splash, 24" deep and 35" high	LF	0.667	54.00	710		760
2360	Wall storage cabinets	"	1.000	81.00	280		360
2400	Steam sterilizers						
2410	For heat and moisture stable materials	EA	0.800	65.00	6,020		6,090
2420	For fast drying after sterilization	"	1.000	81.00	7,790		7,870
2430	Compact unit	"	1.000	81.00	2,520		2,600
2440	Semi-automatic	"	4.000	330	2,980		3,310
2450	Floor loading						
2460	Single door	EA	6.667	540	88,280		88,820
2480	Double door	"	8.000	650	96,710		97,360
2490	Utensil washer, sanitizer	"	6.154	500	19,410		19,910
2500	Automatic washer/sterilizer	"	16.000	1,300	21,250		22,550
2510	16 x 16 x 26", including accessories	"	26.667	2,170	24,430		26,600
2520	Steam generator, elec., 10 kw to 180 kw	"	16.000	1,300	40,380		41,680
2550	Surgical scrub						
2560	Minimum	EA	2.667	220	2,130		2,350
2580	Maximum	"	2.667	220	12,330		12,550
2610	Gas sterilizers						
2620	Automatic, free standing, 21x19x29"	EA	8.000	650	7,580		8,230
2640	Surgical tables						

EXAMINATION AND TREATMENT EQUIPMENT

ID Code	Component Descriptions	Unit of Meas.	Manhr / Unit	Labor Cost	Material Cost	Equip. Cost	Total Cost
	Descriptions	**Output**		**Unit Costs**			

11 - 72001 — MEDICAL EQUIPMENT, Cont'd... — 11 - 72001

ID Code	Component Descriptions	Unit of Meas.	Manhr / Unit	Labor Cost	Material Cost	Equip. Cost	Total Cost
2660	Minimum	EA	11.429	930	26,260		27,190
2680	Maximum	"	16.000	1,300	31,950		33,250
2720	Surgical lights, ceiling mounted						
2740	Minimum	EA	13.333	1,090	10,490		11,580
2760	Maximum	"	16.000	1,300	21,400		22,700
2880	Water stills						
2900	4 liters/hr	EA	2.667	220	4,750		4,970
2920	8 liters/hr	"	2.667	220	7,580		7,800
2940	19 liters/hr	"	6.667	540	15,590		16,130
3040	X-ray equipment						
3060	Mobile unit						
3080	Minimum	EA	4.000	330	13,880		14,210
3100	Maximum	"	8.000	650	26,880		27,530
3110	Film viewers						
3120	Minimum	EA	1.333	110	350		460
3140	Maximum	"	2.667	220	1,200		1,420
3200	Autopsy table						
3220	Minimum	EA	8.000	650	19,370		20,020
3240	Maximum	"	8.000	650	27,370		28,020
3300	Incubators						
3320	15 cf	EA	4.000	330	9,670		10,000
3330	29 cf	"	6.667	540	13,110		13,650
3340	Infant transport, portable	"	4.211	340	7,280		7,620
3400	Beds						
3420	Stretcher, with pad, 30" x 78"	EA	2.000	160	5,410		5,570
3440	Transfer, for patient transport	"	2.000	160	6,370		6,530
3450	Headwall						
3460	Aluminum, with back frame and console	EA	4.000	330	5,460		5,790
6000	Hospital ground detection system						
6010	Power ground module	EA	2.286	190	1,710		1,900
6020	Ground slave module	"	1.739	140	720		860
6030	Master ground module	"	1.509	120	640		760
6040	Remote indicator	"	1.600	130	670		800
6050	X-ray indicator	"	1.739	140	1,910		2,050
6060	Micro ammeter	"	2.000	160	2,270		2,430
6070	Supervisory module	"	1.739	140	1,910		2,050
6080	Ground cords	"	0.296	24.00	180		200
6100	Hospital isolation monitors, 5 ma						

EXAMINATION AND TREATMENT EQUIPMENT

ID Code	Component Descriptions	Unit of Meas.	Manhr / Unit	Labor Cost	Material Cost	Equip. Cost	Total Cost
	Descriptions	**Output**		**Unit Costs**			

11 - 72001   MEDICAL EQUIPMENT, Cont'd...   11 - 72001

ID Code	Component Descriptions	Unit of Meas.	Manhr / Unit	Labor Cost	Material Cost	Equip. Cost	Total Cost
6110	120v	EA	3.478	280	3,620		3,900
6120	208v	"	3.478	280	3,620		3,900
6130	240v	"	3.478	280	3,920		4,200
6210	Digital clock-timers separate display	"	1.600	130	1,590		1,720
6220	One display	"	1.600	130	1,020		1,150
6230	Remote control	"	1.250	100	500		600
6240	Battery pack	"	1.250	100	120		220
6310	Surgical chronometer clock and 3 timers	"	2.500	200	2,980		3,180
6320	Auxiliary control	"	1.159	94.00	810		900

DENTAL EQUIPMENT

11 - 74001   DENTAL EQUIPMENT   11 - 74001

ID Code	Component Descriptions	Unit of Meas.	Manhr / Unit	Labor Cost	Material Cost	Equip. Cost	Total Cost
3500	Dental care equipment						
3520	Drill console with accessories	EA	13.333	1,090	5,710		6,800
3540	Amalgamator	"	0.400	32.50	610		640
3560	Lathe	"	0.267	21.75	1,410		1,430
3580	Finish polisher	"	0.533	43.50	1,850		1,890
3590	Model trimmer	"	0.364	29.50	1,140		1,170
3600	Motor, wall mounted	"	0.364	29.50	1,280		1,310
3640	Cleaner, ultrasonic	"	0.800	65.00	3,430		3,500
3660	Curing unit, bench mounted	"	1.333	110	5,270		5,380
3680	Oral evacuation system, dual pump	"	1.000	81.00	6,420		6,500
3700	Sterilizer, table top, self contained	"	0.444	36.25	2,710		2,750
3720	Dental lights						
3740	Light, floor or ceiling mounted	EA	4.000	330	2,300		2,630
3780	X-ray unit						
3790	Portable	EA	2.000	160	5,710		5,870
3820	Wall mounted with remote control	"	6.667	540	7,990		8,530
3830	Illuminator, single panel	"	11.429	930	820		1,750
3840	X-ray film processor	"	6.667	540	9,970		10,510
3850	Shield, portable x-ray, lead lined	"	0.533	43.50	1,850		1,890

RECYCLING SYSTEMS

ID Code	Descriptions — Component Descriptions	Output — Unit of Meas.	Output — Manhr / Unit	Unit Costs — Labor Cost	Unit Costs — Material Cost	Unit Costs — Equip. Cost	Unit Costs — Total Cost
11 - 82001	**WASTE HANDLING**						**11 - 82001**
1000	Incinerator, electric						
1010	100 lb/hr						
1020	Minimum	EA	8.000	650	16,310		16,960
1040	Maximum	"	8.000	650	28,020		28,670
1050	400 lb/hr						
1060	Minimum	EA	16.000	1,300	41,070		42,370
1070	Maximum	"	16.000	1,300	51,340		52,640
1075	1000 lb/hr						
1080	Minimum	EA	24.242	1,970	96,630		98,600
1090	Maximum	"	24.242	1,970	144,950		146,920
1200	Incinerator, medical-waste						
1220	25 lb/hr, 2-7 x 4-0	EA	16.000	1,300	13,890		15,190
1230	50 lb/hr, 2-11 x 4-11	"	16.000	1,300	26,940		28,240
1240	75 lb/hr, 3-8 x 5-0	"	32.000	2,600	36,240		38,840
1250	100 lb/hr, 3-8 x 6-0	"	32.000	2,600	54,360		56,960
1500	Industrial compactor						
1520	1 cy	EA	8.889	720	14,250		14,970
1540	3 cy	"	11.429	930	22,230		23,160
1560	5 cy	"	16.000	1,300	42,280		43,580
2000	Trash chutes steel, including sprinklers						
2020	18" dia.	LF	4.000	320	110		430
2030	24" dia.	"	4.211	340	130		470
2040	30" dia.	"	4.444	360	170		530
2050	36" dia.	"	4.706	380	200		580
2060	Refuse bottom hopper	EA	4.444	360	1,810		2,170
11 - 82230	**GRAY WATER RECYCLING SYSTEM**						**11 - 82230**
1000	Residential, small commercial, 150 Gallons						
1010	Min.	EA					4,040
1020	Ave.	"					4,580
1030	Max.	"					5,110
1040	250 Gallons						
1050	Min.	EA					4,710
1060	Ave.	"					5,250
1070	Max.	"					5,790
1080	350 Gallons						
1090	Min.	EA					5,110
1100	Ave.	"					5,520

RECYCLING SYSTEMS

ID Code	Component Descriptions	Unit of Meas.	Manhr / Unit	Labor Cost	Material Cost	Equip. Cost	Total Cost
	Descriptions	**Output**		**Unit Costs**			
11 - 82230	**GRAY WATER RECYCLING SYSTEM, Cont'd...**						**11 - 82230**
1110	Max.	EA					5,920
1120	450 Gallons						
1130	Min.	EA					5,380
1140	Ave.	"					5,790
1150	Max.	"					6,190
1160	550 Gallons						
1170	Min.	EA					6,600
1180	Ave.	"					5,450
1190	Max.	"					7,000

DIVISION 12
FURNISHINGS

WINDOW BLINDS

ID Code	Component Descriptions	Unit of Meas.	Manhr / Unit	Labor Cost	Material Cost	Equip. Cost	Total Cost
	Descriptions	**Output**		**Unit Costs**			

12 - 21001	**BLINDS**						**12 - 21001**
0990	Venetian blinds						
1000	2" slats	SF	0.020	1.60	39.50		41.00
1020	1" slats	"	0.020	1.60	42.25		43.75

CURTAINS AND DRAPES

12 - 22001	**WINDOW TREATMENT**						**12 - 22001**
1000	Drapery tracks, wall or ceiling mounted						
1040	Basic traverse rod						
1080	50 to 90"	EA	0.400	32.00	57.00		89.00
1100	84 to 156"	"	0.444	35.50	76.00		110
1120	136 to 250"	"	0.444	35.50	110		150
1140	165 to 312"	"	0.500	40.00	170		210
1160	Traverse rod with stationary curtain rod						
1180	30 to 50"	EA	0.400	32.00	86.00		120
1200	50 to 90"	"	0.400	32.00	98.00		130
1220	84 to 156"	"	0.444	35.50	140		180
1240	136 to 250"	"	0.500	40.00	170		210
1260	Double traverse rod						
1280	30 to 50"	EA	0.400	32.00	100		130
1300	50 to 84"	"	0.400	32.00	130		160
1320	84 to 156"	"	0.444	35.50	140		180
1340	136 to 250"	"	0.500	40.00	170		210

MANUFACTURED WOOD CASEWORK

12 - 32001	**WOOD CASEWORK**						**12 - 32001**
0080	Kitchen base cabinet, standard, 24" deep, 35" high						
0100	12"wide	EA	0.800	64.00	220		280
0120	18" wide	"	0.800	64.00	260		320
0140	24" wide	"	0.889	71.00	330		400
0160	27" wide	"	0.889	71.00	370		440
0180	36" wide	"	1.000	80.00	450		530
0200	48" wide	"	1.000	80.00	540		620
0210	Drawer base, 24" deep, 35" high						
0220	15"wide	EA	0.800	64.00	280		340
0230	18" wide	"	0.800	64.00	300		360
0240	24" wide	"	0.889	71.00	480		550

MANUFACTURED WOOD CASEWORK

ID Code	Component Descriptions	Unit of Meas.	Manhr / Unit	Labor Cost	Material Cost	Equip. Cost	Total Cost
						Unit Costs	
12 - 32001	**WOOD CASEWORK, Cont'd...**						**12 - 32001**
0250	27" wide	EA	0.889	71.00	550		620
0260	30" wide	"	0.889	71.00	640		710
0270	Sink-ready, base cabinet						
0280	30" wide	EA	0.889	71.00	300		370
0290	36" wide	"	0.889	71.00	310		380
0300	42" wide	"	0.889	71.00	340		410
0310	60" wide	"	1.000	80.00	410		490
0320	Corner cabinet, 36" wide	"	1.000	80.00	560		640
4000	Wall cabinet, 12" deep, 12" high						
4020	30" wide	EA	0.800	64.00	280		340
4060	36" wide	"	0.800	64.00	300		360
4070	15" high						
4080	30" wide	EA	0.889	71.00	330		400
4100	36" wide	"	0.889	71.00	500		570
4110	24" high						
4120	30" wide	EA	0.889	71.00	370		440
4140	36" wide	"	0.889	71.00	380		450
4150	30" high						
4160	12" wide	EA	1.000	80.00	210		290
4180	18" wide	"	1.000	80.00	250		330
4200	24" wide	"	1.000	80.00	260		340
4300	27" wide	"	1.000	80.00	310		390
4320	30" wide	"	1.143	91.00	350		440
4340	36" wide	"	1.143	91.00	360		450
4350	Corner cabinet, 30" high						
4360	24" wide	EA	1.333	110	390		500
4380	30" wide	"	1.333	110	470		580
4390	36" wide	"	1.333	110	510		620
5020	Wardrobe	"	2.000	160	1,040		1,200
6980	Vanity with top, laminated plastic						
7000	24" wide	EA	2.000	160	860		1,020
7020	30" wide	"	2.000	160	960		1,120
7040	36" wide	"	2.667	210	1,110		1,320
7060	48" wide	"	3.200	260	1,240		1,500

COUNTERTOPS

ID Code	Component Descriptions	Unit of Meas.	Manhr / Unit	Labor Cost	Material Cost	Equip. Cost	Total Cost
12 - 36001	**COUNTERTOPS**						**12 - 36001**
1020	Stainless steel, counter top, with backsplash	SF	0.200	16.00	260		280
2000	Acid-proof, kemrock surface	"	0.133	10.75	100		110

RUGS AND MATS

ID Code	Component Descriptions	Unit of Meas.	Manhr / Unit	Labor Cost	Material Cost	Equip. Cost	Total Cost
12 - 48001	**FLOOR MATS**						**12 - 48001**
1020	Recessed entrance mat, 3/8" thick, aluminum link	SF	0.400	32.00	58.00		90.00
1040	Steel, flexible	"	0.400	32.00	20.75		53.00

DIVISION 13
SPECIAL CONSTRUCTION

SWIMMING POOLS

ID Code	Descriptions	Output		Unit Costs			
	Component Descriptions	Unit of Meas.	Manhr / Unit	Labor Cost	Material Cost	Equip. Cost	Total Cost
13 - 11001	**SWIMMING POOL EQUIPMENT**						**13 - 11001**
1100	Diving boards						
1110	14' long						
1120	Aluminum	EA	4.444	280	4,970		5,250
1140	Fiberglass	"	4.444	280	3,760		4,040
1500	Ladders, heavy duty						
1510	2 steps						
1520	Minimum	EA	1.600	100	1,180		1,280
1540	Maximum	"	1.600	100	1,840		1,940
1550	4 steps						
1560	Minimum	EA	2.000	130	1,260		1,390
1580	Maximum	"	2.000	130	2,020		2,150
1600	Lifeguard chair						
1620	Minimum	EA	8.000	500	3,340		3,840
1640	Maximum	"	8.000	500	5,180		5,680
1700	Lights, underwater						
1705	12 volt, with transformer, 100 watt						
1710	Incandescent	EA	2.000	130	250		380
1715	Halogen	"	2.000	130	210		340
1720	LED	"	2.000	130	670		800
1730	110 volt						
1740	Minimum	EA	2.000	130	1,130		1,260
1760	Maximum	"	2.000	130	2,720		2,850
1780	Ground fault interrupter for 110 volt, each light	"	0.667	41.75	240		280
2000	Pool cover						
2020	Reinforced polyethylene	SF	0.062	3.85	2.41		6.26
2030	Vinyl water tube						
2040	Minimum	SF	0.062	3.85	1.48		5.33
2060	Maximum	"	0.062	3.85	2.20		6.05
2100	Slides with water tube						
2120	Minimum	EA	6.667	420	1,180		1,600
2140	Maximum	"	6.667	420	25,210		25,630

SPECIAL ACTIVITY ROOMS

ID Code	Descriptions — Component Descriptions	Output — Unit of Meas.	Output — Manhr / Unit	Unit Costs — Labor Cost	Unit Costs — Material Cost	Unit Costs — Equip. Cost	Unit Costs — Total Cost
13 - 24160	**SAUNAS**						**13 - 24160**
0010	Prefabricated, cedar siding, insulated panels, prehung door,						
0020	4'x8"x4'-8"x6'-6"	EA					6,500
0030	5'-8"x6'-8"x6'-6"	"					7,870
0040	6'-8"x6'-8"x6'-6"	"					9,160
0050	7'-8"x7'-8"x6'-6"	"					11,060
0060	7'-8"x9'-8"x6'-6"	"					14,570

FABRICATED ENGINEERED STRUCTURES

ID Code	Component Descriptions	Unit of Meas.	Manhr / Unit	Labor Cost	Material Cost	Equip. Cost	Total Cost
13 - 34190	**PRE-ENGINEERED BUILDINGS**						**13 - 34190**
1080	Pre-engineered metal building, 40'x100'						
1100	14' eave height	SF	0.032	2.56	9.33	3.06	15.00
1120	16' eave height	"	0.037	2.95	10.50	3.53	17.00
1140	20' eave height	"	0.048	3.84	12.00	4.60	20.50
1150	60'x100'						
1160	14' eave height	SF	0.032	2.56	11.75	3.06	17.25
1180	16' eave height	"	0.037	2.95	13.00	3.53	19.50
1190	20' eave height	"	0.048	3.84	14.50	4.60	23.00
1195	80'x100'						
1200	14' eave height	SF	0.032	2.56	9.03	3.06	14.75
1210	16' eave height	"	0.037	2.95	9.33	3.53	15.75
1220	20' eave height	"	0.048	3.84	10.50	4.60	19.00
1280	100'x100'						
1300	14' eave height	SF	0.032	2.56	8.81	3.06	14.50
1320	16' eave height	"	0.037	2.95	9.18	3.53	15.75
1340	20' eave height	"	0.048	3.84	10.00	4.60	18.50
1350	100'x150'						
1360	14' eave height	SF	0.032	2.56	7.85	3.06	13.50
1380	16' eave height	"	0.037	2.95	8.15	3.53	14.75
1400	20' eave height	"	0.048	3.84	8.74	4.60	17.25
1410	120'x150'						
1420	14' eave height	SF	0.032	2.56	8.30	3.06	14.00
1440	16' eave height	"	0.037	2.95	8.44	3.53	15.00
1460	20' eave height	"	0.048	3.84	8.81	4.60	17.25
1480	140'x150'						
1500	14' eave height	SF	0.032	2.56	7.85	3.06	13.50
1520	16' eave height	"	0.037	2.95	8.05	3.53	14.50
1540	20' eave height	"	0.048	3.84	8.74	4.60	17.25

FABRICATED ENGINEERED STRUCTURES

ID Code	Component Descriptions	Unit of Meas.	Manhr / Unit	Labor Cost	Material Cost	Equip. Cost	Total Cost
	Descriptions	**Output**		**Unit Costs**			
13 - 34190	**PRE-ENGINEERED BUILDINGS, Cont'd...**						**13 - 34190**
1600	160'x200'						
1620	14' eave height	SF	0.032	2.56	6.05	3.06	11.75
1640	16' eave height	"	0.037	2.95	6.24	3.53	12.75
1680	20' eave height	"	0.048	3.84	6.60	4.60	15.00
1690	200'x200'						
1700	14' eave height	SF	0.032	2.56	5.21	3.06	10.75
1720	16' eave height	"	0.037	2.95	5.73	3.53	12.25
1740	20' eave height	"	0.048	3.84	6.10	4.60	14.50
5020	Hollow metal door and frame, 6' x 7'	EA					1,390
5030	Sectional steel overhead door, manually operated						
5040	8' x 8'	EA					2,280
5080	12' x 12'	"					3,040
5100	Roll-up steel door, manually operated						
5120	10' x 10'	EA					1,770
5140	12' x 12'	"					3,180
5160	For gravity ridge ventilator with birdscreen	"					760
5161	9" throat x 10'	"					830
5181	12" throat x 10'	"					1,010
5200	For 20" rotary vent with damper	"					380
5220	For 4' x 3' fixed louver	"					270
5240	For 4' x 3' aluminum sliding window	"					240
5260	For 3' x 9' fiberglass panels	"					180
8020	Liner panel, 26 ga, painted steel	SF	0.020	1.76	3.34		5.10
8040	Wall panel insulated, 26 ga. steel, foam core	"	0.020	1.76	10.50		12.25
8060	Roof panel, 26 ga. painted steel	"	0.011	1.00	3.16		4.16
8080	Plastic (sky light)	"	0.011	1.00	7.12		8.12
9000	Insulation, 3-1/2" thick blanket, R11	"	0.005	0.47	2.13		2.60

DIVISION 14
CONVEYING

CONVEYING EQUIPMENT

ID Code	Descriptions	Output		Unit Costs			
	Component Descriptions	Unit of Meas.	Manhr / Unit	Labor Cost	Material Cost	Equip. Cost	Total Cost

14 - 11001   DUMBWAITERS   14 - 11001

ID Code	Component Descriptions	Unit of Meas.	Manhr / Unit	Labor Cost	Material Cost	Equip. Cost	Total Cost
0100	28' travel, extruded alum., 4 stops, 100 lbs. capacity	EA					6,760
0120	150 lbs. capacity	"					9,510
0140	200 lbs. capacity	"					13,650

CONVEYING EQUIPMENT

14 - 21001   ELEVATORS   14 - 21001

ID Code	Component Descriptions	Unit of Meas.	Manhr / Unit	Labor Cost	Material Cost	Equip. Cost	Total Cost
0420	Passenger elevators, electric, geared						
0440	Based on a shaft of 6 stops and 6 openings						
0450	50 fpm, 2000 lb	EA	24.000	1,490	145,640	1,330	148,460
0510	100 fpm, 2000 lb	"	26.667	1,660	151,020	1,480	154,160
0520	150 fpm						
0530	2000 lb	EA	30.000	1,860	166,620	1,660	170,150
0540	3000 lb	"	34.286	2,130	209,870	1,900	213,900
0550	4000 lb	"	40.000	2,490	218,380	2,220	223,080
0560	200 fpm						
0570	2500 lb	EA	34.286	2,130	201,370	1,900	205,400
0580	3000 lb	"	36.923	2,290	207,040	2,050	211,380
0590	4000 lb	"	40.000	2,490	218,380	2,220	223,080
0600	250 fpm						
0610	2500 lb	EA	34.286	2,130	208,460	1,900	212,490
0620	3000 lb	"	36.923	2,290	220,010	2,050	224,350
0630	4000 lb	"	40.000	2,490	225,120	2,220	229,820
0640	300 fpm						
0650	2500 lb	EA	34.286	2,130	206,470	1,900	210,500
0660	3000 lb	"	36.923	2,290	218,380	2,050	222,720
0670	4000 lb	"	24.000	1,490	222,210	1,330	225,030
0680	For each additional; 50 fpm, add per stop, $3000						
0690	500 lb, add per stop, $4000						
0700	Opening, add per stop, $4500						
0710	Stop, add per stop, $4000						
0720	Bonderized steel door, add per opening, $150						
0730	Colored aluminum door, add per opening, $850						
0740	Stainless steel door, add per opening, $600						
0750	Cast bronze door, add per opening, $1100						
0760	Two speed door, add per opening, $360						
0770	Bi-parting door, add per opening, $850						
0780	Custom cab interior add, $4800						

CONVEYING EQUIPMENT

ID Code	Component Descriptions	Unit of Meas.	Manhr / Unit	Labor Cost	Material Cost	Equip. Cost	Total Cost
		Output		**Unit Costs**			
14 - 21001	**ELEVATORS, Cont'd...**						**14 - 21001**
0790	Based on a shaft of 8 stops and 8 openings						
1010	300 fpm						
1020	3000 lb	EA	48.000	2,980	270,190	2,660	275,830
1040	3500 lb	"	48.000	2,980	274,450	2,660	280,090
1060	4000 lb	"	53.333	3,310	287,960	2,960	294,230
1070	5000 lb	"	57.143	3,550	319,960	3,170	326,680
1080	400 fpm						
1090	3000 lb	EA	48.000	2,980	283,060	2,660	288,700
1100	3500 lb	"	48.000	2,980	287,960	2,660	293,600
1120	4000 lb	"	53.333	3,310	307,870	2,960	314,140
1140	5000 lb	"	57.143	3,550	350,530	3,170	357,250
1150	600 fpm						
1160	3000 lb	EA	53.333	3,310	398,670	2,960	404,940
1180	3500 lb	"	57.143	3,550	408,130	3,170	414,850
1190	4000 lb	"	58.537	3,640	412,390	3,240	419,270
1200	5000 lb	"	60.000	3,730	423,770	3,330	430,820
1210	800 fpm						
1220	3000 lb	EA	53.333	3,310	472,830	2,960	479,100
1240	3500 lb	"	57.143	3,550	477,810	3,170	484,530
1260	4000 lb	"	58.537	3,640	483,490	3,240	490,370
1280	5000 lb	"	60.000	3,730	486,690	3,330	493,740
1300	For each additional; 100 fpm add per stop, $13,000						
1310	500 lb, add per stop, $6500						
1320	Opening add per stop, $12,000						
1330	Stop add per stop, $4800						
1340	Bypass floor, add per each, $2000						
1350	Bonderized steel door, add per opening, $150						
1360	Colored aluminum door, add per opening, $900						
1370	Stainless steel door, add per opening, $600						
1380	Cast bronze door, add per opening, $600						
1390	Two speed bi-parting door, add per opening, $1000						
1400	Custom cab interior, add $5000						
1410	Hydraulic, based on a shaft of 3 stops, 3 openings						
1420	50 fpm						
1500	2000 lb	EA	20.000	1,240	101,250	1,110	103,600
1510	2500 lb	"	20.000	1,240	108,270	1,110	110,620
1520	3000 lb	"	20.870	1,300	114,260	1,160	116,710
1530	100 fpm						

CONVEYING EQUIPMENT

ID Code	Component Descriptions	Unit of Meas.	Manhr / Unit	Labor Cost	Material Cost	Equip. Cost	Total Cost
	Descriptions	**Output**		**Unit Costs**			
14 - 21001	**ELEVATORS, Cont'd...**						**14 - 21001**
1540	2000 lb	EA	20.000	1,240	110,920	1,110	113,270
1550	2500 lb	"	20.870	1,300	116,960	1,160	119,410
1560	3000 lb	"	21.818	1,360	125,140	1,210	127,710
1570	150 fpm						
1580	2000 lb	EA	20.000	1,240	120,160	1,110	122,510
1590	2500 lb	"	20.870	1,300	131,540	1,160	133,990
1600	3000 lb	"	22.857	1,420	140,780	1,270	143,470
1610	For each additional; 50 fpm add per stop, $3500						
1620	500 lb, add per stop, $3500						
1630	Opening, add, $4200						
1640	Stop, add per stop, $5300						
1650	Bonderized steel door, add per opening, $400						
1660	Colored aluminum door, add per opening, $1500						
1670	Stainless steel door, add per opening, $650						
1680	Cast bronze door, add per opening, $1200						
1690	Two speed door, add per opening, $400						
1700	Bi-parting door, add per opening, $900						
1710	Custom cab interior, add per cab, $5000						
1720	Small elevators, 4 to 6 passenger capacity						
1730	Electric, push						
2010	2 stops	EA	20.000	1,240	34,510	1,110	36,860
2020	3 stops	"	21.818	1,360	43,140	1,210	45,710
2030	4 stops	"	24.000	1,490	49,110	1,330	51,930
2080	Freight elevators, electric						
2090	Based on a shaft of 6 stops and 6 openings						
2100	50 fpm						
2110	3500 lb	EA	26.667	1,660	260,160	1,480	263,300
2120	4000 lb	"	26.667	1,660	260,820	1,480	263,960
2130	5000 lb	"	30.000	1,860	265,470	1,660	269,000
2140	100 fpm						
2150	3500 lb	EA	30.000	1,860	272,100	1,660	275,630
2160	4000 lb	"	30.000	1,860	276,080	1,660	279,610
2170	5000 lb	"	34.286	2,130	280,930	1,900	284,960
2180	200 fpm						
2190	3500 lb	EA	34.286	2,130	270,770	1,900	274,800
2200	4000 lb	"	34.286	2,130	272,100	1,900	276,130
2210	5000 lb	"	40.000	2,490	274,760	2,220	279,460
2220	For elevator with manual door, deduct 15%						

CONVEYING EQUIPMENT

ID Code	Component Descriptions	Unit of Meas.	Manhr / Unit	Labor Cost	Material Cost	Equip. Cost	Total Cost
14 - 21001	**ELEVATORS, Cont'd...**						**14 - 21001**
2230	For variable voltage control, add 20%						
2300	Based on shaft of 8 stops and 8 openings						
2310	100 fpm						
2320	4000 lb	EA	30.000	1,860	261,950	1,660	265,480
2330	6000 lb	"	30.769	1,910	264,140	1,710	267,760
2340	8000 lb	"	32.432	2,020	268,780	1,800	272,590
2350	150 fpm						
2360	4000 lb	EA	34.286	2,130	265,470	1,900	269,500
2370	6000 lb	"	35.294	2,190	265,470	1,960	269,620
2380	8000 lb	"	37.500	2,330	273,430	2,080	277,840
2390	200 fpm						
2400	4000 lb	EA	40.000	2,490	266,790	2,220	271,490
2410	6000 lb	"	41.379	2,570	273,430	2,290	278,290
2420	8000 lb	"	43.636	2,710	285,370	2,420	290,500
2430	For each additional; 50 fpm, add per stop, $2000						
2440	500 lb, add per stop, $600						
2450	Opening, add per stop, $7000						
2460	Stop, add per stop, $5500						
2470	For variable voltage, add 20%						
2480	Hydraulic, based on 3 stops and 3 openings						
2490	50 fpm						
2510	3000 lb	EA	17.143	1,070	111,500	950	113,520
2520	4000 lb	"	17.778	1,100	122,110	990	124,200
2530	6000 lb	"	18.462	1,150	142,020	1,020	144,190
2540	100 fpm						
2550	3000 lb	EA	17.143	1,070	126,100	950	128,120
2560	4000 lb	"	17.778	1,100	132,730	990	134,820
2570	6000 lb	"	18.462	1,150	156,620	1,020	158,790
2580	150 fpm						
2590	3000 lb	EA	17.143	1,070	138,040	950	140,060
2600	4000 lb	"	17.778	1,100	148,660	990	150,750
2610	6000 lb	"	18.462	1,150	169,900	1,020	172,070
2620	For each additional; 50 fpm, add per stop, $2000						
2630	500 lb, add per stop, $600						
2640	Opening, add per stop, $5500						
2650	Stop, add per stop, $5500						
2660	For elevator with manual door deduct from total, 15%						

ESCALATORS

ID Code	Component Descriptions	Unit of Meas.	Manhr / Unit	Labor Cost	Material Cost	Equip. Cost	Total Cost
	Descriptions	**Output**		**Unit Costs**			
14 - 31001	**ESCALATORS**						**14 - 31001**
1000	Escalators						
1020	32" wide, floor to floor						
1040	12' high	EA	40.000	2,490	180,150	2,220	184,850
1050	15' high	"	48.000	2,980	196,830	2,660	202,470
1060	18' high	"	60.000	3,730	211,990	3,330	219,040
1070	22' high	"	80.000	4,970	209,770	4,430	219,180
1080	25' high	"	96.000	5,970	238,380	5,320	249,670
1085	48" wide						
1090	12' high	EA	41.379	2,570	200,710	2,290	205,570
1100	15' high	"	50.000	3,110	219,050	2,770	224,930
1120	18' high	"	63.158	3,930	235,310	3,500	242,740
1130	22' high	"	85.714	5,330	263,410	4,750	273,490
1140	25' high	"	96.000	5,970	281,260	5,320	292,550

LIFTS

ID Code	Component Descriptions	Unit of Meas.	Manhr / Unit	Labor Cost	Material Cost	Equip. Cost	Total Cost
14 - 41001	**PERSONNEL LIFTS**						**14 - 41001**
1000	Electrically operated, 1 or 2 person lift						
1001	With attached foot platforms						
1020	3 stops	EA					12,390
1040	5 stops	"					19,320
1060	7 stops	"					22,520
2000	For each additional stop, add $1250						
3020	Residential stair climber, per story	EA	6.667	540	5,750		6,290
3030	curved	"	8.000	650	12,150		12,800

WHEELCHAIR LIFTS

ID Code	Component Descriptions	Unit of Meas.	Manhr / Unit	Labor Cost	Material Cost	Equip. Cost	Total Cost
14 - 42001	**WHEELCHAIR LIFTS**						**14 - 42001**
1000	600 lb, Residential	EA	8.000	650	6,830		7,480
1001	Commercial	"	8.000	650	16,150		16,800

VEHICLE LIFTS

ID Code	Component Descriptions	Unit of Meas.	Manhr / Unit	Labor Cost	Material Cost	Equip. Cost	Total Cost
	Descriptions	**Output**		**Unit Costs**			

14 - 45001 — VEHICLE LIFTS — 14 - 45001

ID Code	Component Descriptions	Unit of Meas.	Manhr / Unit	Labor Cost	Material Cost	Equip. Cost	Total Cost
1020	Automotive hoist, one post, semi-hydraulic, 8,000 lb	EA	24.000	1,490	4,140	1,330	6,960
1040	Full hydraulic, 8,000 lb	"	24.000	1,490	4,270	1,330	7,090
1060	2 post, semi-hydraulic, 10,000 lb	"	34.286	2,130	4,460	1,900	8,490
1070	Full hydraulic						
1080	10,000 lb	EA	34.286	2,130	5,250	1,900	9,280
1100	13,000 lb	"	60.000	3,730	6,570	3,330	13,620
1120	18,500 lb	"	60.000	3,730	10,500	3,330	17,550
1140	24,000 lb	"	60.000	3,730	14,770	3,330	21,820
1160	26,000 lb	"	60.000	3,730	14,380	3,330	21,430
1170	Pneumatic hoist, fully hydraulic						
1180	11,000 lb	EA	80.000	4,970	7,090	4,430	16,500
1200	24,000 lb	"	80.000	4,970	12,800	4,430	22,210

MATERIAL HANDLING

14 - 91001 — CHUTES — 14 - 91001

ID Code	Component Descriptions	Unit of Meas.	Manhr / Unit	Labor Cost	Material Cost	Equip. Cost	Total Cost
1020	Linen chutes, stainless steel, with supports						
1030	18" dia.	LF	0.057	5.04	170		180
1040	24" dia.	"	0.062	5.43	210		220
1050	30" dia.	"	0.067	5.88	220		230
1060	Hopper	EA	0.533	47.00	2,680		2,730
1070	Skylight	"	0.800	71.00	1,630		1,700
1080	Sprinkler unit at top	"	0.889	78.00	610		690
1100	For galvanized metal, deduct from material cost, 35%						
1120	For aluminum, deduct from material cost, 25%						

PNEUMATIC TUBE SYSTEMS

14 - 92001 — PNEUMATIC SYSTEMS — 14 - 92001

ID Code	Component Descriptions	Unit of Meas.	Manhr / Unit	Labor Cost	Material Cost	Equip. Cost	Total Cost
1000	Pneumatic message tube system						
1010	Average, 20 station job						
1020	3" round system	EA	72.727	5,920	44,630		50,550
1040	4" round system	"	80.000	6,510	56,380		62,890
1060	6" round system	"	88.889	7,240	96,740		103,980
1080	4" x 7" oval system	"	160.000	13,020	101,900		114,920
5000	Trash and linen tube system						
5020	10 stations	EA	120.000	7,460	30,070	6,650	44,180
5030	15 stations	"	160.000	9,940	37,690	8,870	56,500

PNEUMATIC TUBE SYSTEMS

ID Code	Component Descriptions	Unit of Meas.	Manhr / Unit	Labor Cost	Material Cost	Equip. Cost	Total Cost
	Descriptions	**Output**		**Unit Costs**			
14 - 92001	**PNEUMATIC SYSTEMS, Cont'd...**					**14 - 92001**	
5040	20 stations	EA	184.615	11,470	50,230	10,230	71,930
5060	30 stations	"	218.182	13,560	65,330	12,090	90,980

DIVISION 21
FIRE SUPPRESSION

COMPONENTS

ID Code	Descriptions		Output		Unit Costs			
	Component Descriptions		Unit of Meas.	Manhr / Unit	Labor Cost	Material Cost	Equip. Cost	Total Cost
21 - 11000	**HYDRANTS**							**21 - 11000**
0980	Wall hydrant							
1000	8" thick		EA	1.333	120	400		520
1020	12" thick		"	1.600	140	470		610
1040	18" thick		"	1.778	160	510		670
1060	24" thick		"	2.000	180	560		740
1070	Ground hydrant							
1080	2' deep		EA	1.000	88.00	740		830
1100	4' deep		"	1.143	100	860		960
1120	6' deep		"	1.333	120	970		1,090
1140	8' deep		"	2.000	180	1,090		1,270

FIRE PROTECTION

ID Code	Descriptions		Output		Unit Costs			
21 - 13001	**WET SPRINKLER SYSTEM**							**21 - 13001**
0120	Sprinkler head, 212 deg, brass, exposed piping		EA	0.320	28.00	16.00		44.00
0140	Chrome, concealed piping		"	0.444	39.00	19.50		59.00
0160	Water motor alarm		"	1.333	120	370		490
0180	Fire department inlet connection		"	1.600	140	270		410
0190	Wall plate for fire dept connection		"	0.667	58.00	130		190
0220	Swing check valve flanged iron body, 4"		"	2.667	230	350		580
0240	Check valve, 6"		"	4.000	350	1,150		1,500
0280	Wet pipe valve, flange to groove, 4"		"	0.889	78.00	990		1,070
0290	Flange to flange							
0300	6"		EA	1.333	120	1,340		1,460
0320	8"		"	2.667	230	2,360		2,590
0380	Alarm valve, flange to flange, (wet valve)							
0400	4"		EA	0.889	78.00	1,530		1,610
0420	8"		"	6.667	580	2,420		3,000
0800	Inspector's test connection		"	0.667	58.00	70.00		130
1000	Wall hydrant, polished brass, 2-1/2" x 2-1/2", single		"	0.571	50.00	470		520
1020	2-way		"	0.571	50.00	1,060		1,110
1040	3-way		"	0.571	50.00	2,170		2,220
2080	Wet valve trim, includes retard chamber & gauges, 4"-6"		"	0.667	58.00	740		800
2100	Retard pressure switch for wet systems		"	1.600	140	1,300		1,440
2500	Air maintenance device		"	0.667	58.00	390		450
8000	Wall hydrant non-freeze, 8" thick wall, vacuum breaker		"	0.400	35.00	51.00		86.00
8020	12" thick wall		"	0.400	35.00	56.00		91.00

CARBON-DIOXIDE FIRE EXTINGUISHING SYSTEMS

ID Code	Component Descriptions	Unit of Meas.	Manhr / Unit	Labor Cost	Material Cost	Equip. Cost	Total Cost
		Descriptions	**Output**		**Unit Costs**		
21 - 21001	**CO$_2$ SYSTEM**						**21 - 21001**
0980	CO$_2$ system, high pressure, 75# cylinder with						
1000	Valve assemblies	EA	1.600	140	2,660		2,800
1020	Storage rack	"	1.143	100	1,420		1,520
1040	Manifold	"	5.714	500	1,030		1,530
1060	Flexible loops	"	0.100	8.77	84.00		93.00
1080	Beam scale for cylinders	"	1.333	120	700		820
1090	Mechanically controlled head	"	0.533	46.75	590		640
1100	Electrically controlled head	"	0.533	46.75	590		640
1120	Stop valves	"	0.800	70.00	1,500		1,570
1140	Check valves	"	1.000	88.00	680		770
1160	Activation station	"	0.800	70.00	790		860
1180	Nozzles	"	0.667	58.00	130		190
1200	Hose reel with 75' of 3/4" hose	"	4.000	350	4,750		5,100
1220	Main/reserve transfer switch	"	1.333	120	5,530		5,650
1240	Pressure switch	"	0.800	70.00	490		560
1260	Heat responsive device	"	1.333	120	780		900
1280	Battery and charger	"	4.000	350	4,430		4,780
2000	Low pressure						
2020	Battery and charger	EA	4.000	350	4,430		4,780
2040	Pressure switch	"	0.889	78.00	440		520
2060	Nozzles	"	0.727	64.00	130		190
2080	Master selector valve	"	1.333	120	380		500
2100	Selector valve	"	1.333	120	5,530		5,650
2120	Low pressure hose reel with 75' of 3/4" hose	"	4.000	350	6,860		7,210
2140	Tank fill lines	"	1.000	88.00	1,550		1,640
2160	Activation stations	"	0.667	58.00	780		840
2180	Electro manual pilot panels	"	1.000	88.00	1,550		1,640

DRY CHEMICAL FIRE EXTINGUISHING SYSTEMS

ID Code	Component Descriptions	Unit of Meas.	Manhr / Unit	Labor Cost	Material Cost	Equip. Cost	Total Cost
21 - 24001	**DRY SPRINKLER SYSTEM**						**21 - 24001**
0080	Dry pipe valve, flange to flange						
0100	4"	EA	1.600	140	2,250		2,390
0120	6"	"	2.000	180	2,820		3,000
0140	Trim, 4" and 6", includes gauges	"	0.667	58.00	870		930
0160	Field testing and flushing	"	6.667	580			580
0180	Disinfection	"	6.667	580			580
0200	Pressure switch double circuit, open/close contacts	"	2.000	180	420		600

DRY CHEMICAL FIRE EXTINGUISHING SYSTEMS

ID Code	Component Descriptions	Unit of Meas.	Manhr / Unit	Labor Cost	Material Cost	Equip. Cost	Total Cost
21 - 24001	**DRY SPRINKLER SYSTEM, Cont'd...**						**21 - 24001**
0210	Low air						
0220	Supervisory unit	EA	1.333	120	1,360		1,480
0240	Pressure switch	"	0.667	58.00	430		490

DIVISION 22
PLUMBING

BASIC MATERIALS

ID Code	Component Descriptions	Unit of Meas.	Manhr / Unit	Labor Cost	Material Cost	Equip. Cost	Total Cost
	Descriptions	**Output**		**Unit Costs**			

22 - 05236 — **VALVES** — **22 - 05236**

ID Code	Component Descriptions	Unit of Meas.	Manhr / Unit	Labor Cost	Material Cost	Equip. Cost	Total Cost
0600	Gate valve, 125 lb, bronze, soldered						
0800	1/2"	EA	0.200	17.50	34.50		52.00
1000	3/4"	"	0.200	17.50	41.25		59.00
1010	1"	"	0.267	23.50	51.00		75.00
1030	1-1/2"	"	0.320	28.00	89.00		120
1040	2"	"	0.400	35.00	120		160
1050	2-1/2"	"	0.500	43.75	290		330
1055	Threaded						
1058	1/4", 125 lb	EA	0.320	28.00	32.25		60.00
1059	1/2"						
1060	125 lb	EA	0.320	28.00	31.00		59.00
1075	300 lb	"	0.320	28.00	78.00		110
1078	3/4"						
1083	125 lb	EA	0.320	28.00	36.25		64.00
1088	300 lb	"	0.320	28.00	94.00		120
1089	1"						
1091	125 lb	EA	0.320	28.00	47.00		75.00
1098	300 lb	"	0.400	35.00	130		160
1099	1-1/2"						
1100	125 lb	EA	0.400	35.00	82.00		120
1115	300 lb	"	0.444	39.00	240		280
1117	2"						
1118	125 lb	EA	0.571	50.00	110		160
1122	300 lb	"	0.667	58.00	300		360
1123	Cast iron, flanged						
1124	2", 150 lb	EA	0.667	58.00	450		510
1125	2-1/2"						
1126	125 lb	EA	0.667	58.00	430		490
1128	250 lb	"	0.667	58.00	1,190		1,250
1130	3"						
1132	125 lb	EA	0.800	70.00	520		590
1134	250 lb	"	0.800	70.00	1,090		1,160
1136	4"						
1138	125 lb	EA	1.143	100	680		780
1140	250 lb	"	1.143	100	1,470		1,570
1144	6"						
1148	125 lb	EA	1.600	140	1,260		1,400
1150	250 lb	"	1.600	140	2,930		3,070

BASIC MATERIALS

ID Code	Component Descriptions	Unit of Meas.	Manhr / Unit	Labor Cost	Material Cost	Equip. Cost	Total Cost
	Descriptions	**Output**		**Unit Costs**			

ID Code	Component Descriptions	Unit of Meas.	Manhr / Unit	Labor Cost	Material Cost	Equip. Cost	Total Cost
22 - 05236	**VALVES, Cont'd...**						**22 - 05236**
1151	8"						
1152	125 lb	EA	2.000	180	2,000		2,180
1154	250 lb	"	2.000	180	5,690		5,870
1160	OS&Y, flanged						
1165	2"						
1170	125 lb	EA	0.667	58.00	410		470
1180	250 lb	"	0.667	58.00	1,080		1,140
1185	2-1/2"						
1190	125 lb	EA	0.667	58.00	420		480
1200	250 lb	"	0.800	70.00	1,340		1,410
1205	3"						
1210	125 lb	EA	0.800	70.00	480		550
1215	250 lb	"	0.800	70.00	1,390		1,460
1218	4"						
1220	125 lb	EA	1.333	120	630		750
1225	250 lb	"	1.333	120	2,120		2,240
1227	6"						
1228	125 lb	EA	1.600	140	1,050		1,190
1230	250 lb	"	1.600	140	3,370		3,510
3980	Ball valve, bronze, 250 lb, threaded						
4000	1/2"	EA	0.320	28.00	20.50		48.50
4010	3/4"	"	0.320	28.00	30.50		59.00
4020	1"	"	0.400	35.00	38.75		74.00
4030	1-1/4"	"	0.444	39.00	57.00		96.00
4040	1-1/2"	"	0.500	43.75	90.00		130
4050	2"	"	0.571	50.00	100		150
4980	Angle valve, bronze, 150 lb, threaded						
5000	1/2"	EA	0.286	25.00	100		130
5010	3/4"	"	0.320	28.00	140		170
5020	1"	"	0.320	28.00	210		240
5030	1-1/4"	"	0.400	35.00	270		300
5040	1-1/2"	"	0.444	39.00	350		390
5980	Balancing valve, meter connections, circuit setter						
6000	1/2"	EA	0.320	28.00	90.00		120
6010	3/4"	"	0.364	32.00	95.00		130
6020	1"	"	0.400	35.00	120		160
6030	1-1/4"	"	0.444	39.00	170		210
6040	1-1/2"	"	0.533	46.75	210		260

BASIC MATERIALS

	Descriptions	Output		Unit Costs			
ID Code	Component Descriptions	Unit of Meas.	Manhr / Unit	Labor Cost	Material Cost	Equip. Cost	Total Cost
22 - 05236	**VALVES, Cont'd...**						**22 - 05236**
6050	2"	EA	0.667	58.00	290		350
6060	2-1/2"	"	0.800	70.00	570		640
6070	3"	"	1.000	88.00	830		920
6080	4"	"	1.333	120	1,170		1,290
8100	Pressure reducing valve, bronze, threaded, 250 lb						
8120	1/2"	EA	0.500	43.75	180		220
8140	3/4"	"	0.500	43.75	180		220
8200	1"	"	0.500	43.75	280		320
8210	1-1/4"	"	0.571	50.00	410		460
8220	1-1/2"	"	0.667	58.00	470		530
8225	Pressure regulating valve, bronze, class 300						
8230	1"	EA	0.500	43.75	680		720
8240	1-1/2"	"	0.615	54.00	910		960
8250	2"	"	0.800	70.00	1,030		1,100
8260	3"	"	1.143	100	1,160		1,260
8270	4"	"	1.600	140	1,450		1,590
8280	5"	"	2.000	180	2,200		2,380
8290	6"	"	2.667	230	2,240		2,470
8480	Solar water temperature regulating valve						
8500	3/4"	EA	0.667	58.00	700		760
8510	1"	"	0.800	70.00	710		780
8520	1-1/4"	"	0.889	78.00	770		850
8530	1-1/2"	"	1.000	88.00	860		950
8540	2"	"	1.143	100	1,060		1,160
8550	2-1/2"	"	2.000	180	2,010		2,190
8980	Tempering valve, threaded						
9000	3/4"	EA	0.267	23.50	380		400
9010	1"	"	0.320	28.00	480		510
9020	1-1/4"	"	0.400	35.00	710		750
9030	1-1/2"	"	0.400	35.00	820		860
9040	2"	"	0.500	43.75	1,120		1,160
9050	2-1/2"	"	0.667	58.00	1,890		1,950
9060	3"	"	0.800	70.00	2,500		2,570
9070	4"	"	1.143	100	5,000		5,100
9180	Thermostatic mixing valve, threaded						
9200	1/2"	EA	0.286	25.00	130		160
9210	3/4"	"	0.320	28.00	130		160
9220	1"	"	0.348	30.50	480		510

BASIC MATERIALS

ID Code	Component Descriptions	Unit of Meas.	Manhr / Unit	Labor Cost	Material Cost	Equip. Cost	Total Cost
	Descriptions	**Output**		**Unit Costs**			

22 - 05236	**VALVES, Cont'd...**						**22 - 05236**
9230	1-1/2"	EA	0.400	35.00	540		580
9240	2"	"	0.500	43.75	680		720
9245	Sweat connection						
9250	1/2"	EA	0.286	25.00	150		180
9260	3/4"	"	0.320	28.00	180		210
9265	Mixing valve, sweat connection						
9270	1/2"	EA	0.286	25.00	79.00		100
9280	3/4"	"	0.320	28.00	79.00		110
9480	Liquid level gauge, aluminum body						
9500	3/4"	EA	0.320	28.00	400		430
9505	125 psi, pvc body						
9510	3/4"	EA	0.320	28.00	470		500
9520	150 psi, crs body						
9530	3/4"	EA	0.320	28.00	380		410
9540	1"	"	0.320	28.00	410		440
9560	175 psi, bronze body, 1/2"	"	0.286	25.00	760		780

22 - 05291	**PIPE HANGERS, HEAVY**						**22 - 05291**
0160	Hangers						
0180	1/2" pipe, clevis pipe hanger						
0200	Black steel	EA	0.267	23.50	1.87		25.25
0210	Galvanized	"	0.267	23.50	2.81		26.25
0230	U bolt	"	0.080	7.01	1.74		8.75
0290	3/4" pipe, clevis pipe hanger						
0300	Black steel	EA	0.267	23.50	1.91		25.50
0310	Galvanized	"	0.267	23.50	2.88		26.50
0390	1" pipe, clevis pipe hanger						
0400	Black steel	EA	0.267	23.50	1.96		25.50
0410	Galvanized	"	0.267	23.50	3.09		26.50
0690	2" pipe, clevis pipe hanger						
0700	Black steel	EA	0.267	23.50	2.66		26.25
0705	Galvanized	"	0.267	23.50	4.36		27.75
0880	3" pipe, clevis pipe hanger						
0900	Black steel	EA	0.267	23.50	5.22		28.75
0910	Galvanized	"	0.267	23.50	9.10		32.50
1080	4" pipe, clevis pipe hanger						
1100	Black steel	EA	0.267	23.50	6.39		30.00
1110	Galvanized	"	0.267	23.50	11.50		35.00

BASIC MATERIALS

ID Code	Component Descriptions	Unit of Meas.	Manhr / Unit	Labor Cost	Material Cost	Equip. Cost	Total Cost
	Descriptions	**Output**		**Unit Costs**			
22 - 05291	**PIPE HANGERS, HEAVY, Cont'd...**						**22 - 05291**
1300	6" pipe, clevis pipe hanger						
1320	Black steel	EA	0.320	28.00	10.25		38.25
1330	Galvanized	"	0.320	28.00	20.50		48.50
1560	12" pipe, clevis pipe hanger						
1580	Black steel	EA	0.320	28.00	36.00		64.00
1590	Galvanized	"	0.320	28.00	53.00		81.00
8000	Threaded rod, galvanized, material only						
8010	3/8"	LF					0.68
8020	1/2"	"					1.36
8065	Hex nuts, galvanized						
8070	3/8"	EA					0.23
8080	1/2"	"					0.48
8210	1"	"					3.04
8220	C-clamp, steel, with lock nut						
8230	3/8"	EA	0.100	8.77	2.71		11.50
8240	1/2"	"	0.100	8.77	3.04		11.75
22 - 06291	**PIPE HANGERS, LIGHT**						**22 - 06291**
0010	A band, black iron						
0020	1/2"	EA	0.057	5.01	1.03		6.04
0030	1"	"	0.059	5.19	1.11		6.30
0040	1-1/4"	"	0.062	5.39	1.23		6.62
0050	1-1/2"	"	0.067	5.84	1.28		7.12
0060	2"	"	0.073	6.37	1.36		7.73
0070	2-1/2"	"	0.080	7.01	2.03		9.04
0080	3"	"	0.089	7.79	2.48		10.25
0090	4"	"	0.100	8.77	3.26		12.00
0100	5"	"	0.107	9.35	4.13		13.50
0110	6"	"	0.114	10.00	7.14		17.25
0120	8"	"	0.133	11.75	11.50		23.25
0130	Copper						
0140	1/2"	EA	0.057	5.01	1.67		6.68
0150	3/4"	"	0.059	5.19	1.94		7.13
0160	1"	"	0.059	5.19	1.94		7.13
0170	1-1/4"	"	0.062	5.39	2.09		7.48
0180	1-1/2"	"	0.067	5.84	2.24		8.08
0190	2"	"	0.073	6.37	2.37		8.74
0200	2-1/2"	"	0.080	7.01	4.79		11.75

BASIC MATERIALS

ID Code	Descriptions	Output		Unit Costs			
	Component Descriptions	Unit of Meas.	Manhr / Unit	Labor Cost	Material Cost	Equip. Cost	Total Cost
22 - 06291	**PIPE HANGERS, LIGHT, Cont'd...**						**22 - 06291**
0210	3"	EA	0.089	7.79	4.99		12.75
0220	4"	"	0.100	8.77	5.51		14.25
0230	Black riser friction hangers						
0240	3/4"	EA	0.067	5.84	4.22		10.00
0250	1"	"	0.070	6.10	4.27		10.25
0260	1-1/4"	"	0.073	6.37	5.34		11.75
0270	1-1/2"	"	0.076	6.68	5.80		12.50
0280	2"	"	0.080	7.01	5.91		13.00
0290	2-1/2"	"	0.089	7.79	6.38		14.25
0300	3"	"	0.100	8.77	6.56		15.25
0310	4"	"	0.114	10.00	8.37		18.25
0360	Short pattern black riser clamps						
0370	1-1/2"	EA	0.073	6.37	5.55		12.00
0380	2"	"	0.076	6.68	5.81		12.50
0390	3"	"	0.080	7.01	6.38		13.50
0400	4"	"	0.089	7.79	7.32		15.00
0410	Copper riser friction hanger						
0420	1/2"	EA	0.062	5.39	7.19		12.50
0430	3/4"	"	0.064	5.61	7.40		13.00
0440	1"	"	0.067	5.84	7.54		13.50
0450	1-1/4"	"	0.070	6.10	9.39		15.50
0460	1-1/2"	"	0.073	6.37	10.25		16.50
0470	2"	"	0.076	6.68	10.50		17.25
0480	2-1/2"	"	0.080	7.01	11.25		18.25
0490	3"	"	0.080	7.01	11.50		18.50
0501	4"	"	0.089	7.79	14.75		22.50
0510	Auto grip hangers, galvanized						
0520	1/2"	EA	0.057	5.01	1.03		6.04
0540	1"	"	0.064	5.61	1.22		6.83
0570	2"	"	0.073	6.37	2.03		8.40
0590	3"	"	0.080	7.01	4.02		11.00
0600	4"	"	0.089	7.79	4.98		12.75
0610	Copper						
0620	1/2"	EA	0.057	5.01	1.70		6.71
0640	1"	"	0.064	5.61	1.98		7.59
0670	2"	"	0.073	6.37	3.28		9.65
0690	3"	"	0.080	7.01	6.45		13.50
0700	4"	"	0.089	7.79	7.98		15.75

BASIC MATERIALS

ID Code	Component Descriptions	Unit of Meas.	Manhr / Unit	Labor Cost	Material Cost	Equip. Cost	Total Cost
	Descriptions	**Output**		**Unit Costs**			
22 - 06291	**PIPE HANGERS, LIGHT, Cont'd...**						**22 - 06291**
0710	Split rings (F&M), galvanized						
0730	1/2"	EA	0.062	5.39	3.38		8.77
0750	1"	"	0.067	5.84	4.67		10.50
0780	2"	"	0.076	6.68	6.69		13.25
0800	3"	"	0.084	7.38	16.25		23.75
0810	4"	"	0.089	7.79	17.00		24.75
0820	Copper						
0850	1/2"	EA	0.062	5.39	5.11		10.50
0870	1"	"	0.067	5.84	7.06		13.00
0900	2"	"	0.076	6.68	10.00		16.75
0920	3"	"	0.084	7.38	24.50		32.00
0930	4"	"	0.089	7.79	25.50		33.25
1000	2 hole clips, galvanized						
1030	3/4"	EA	0.053	4.67	0.27		4.94
1040	1"	"	0.055	4.83	0.30		5.13
1050	1-1/4"	"	0.057	5.01	0.39		5.40
1060	1-1/2"	"	0.059	5.19	0.48		5.67
1070	2"	"	0.062	5.39	0.63		6.02
1080	2-1/2"	"	0.064	5.61	1.14		6.75
1090	3"	"	0.067	5.84	1.66		7.50
1110	4"	"	0.073	6.37	3.56		9.93
1120	Perforated strap						
1130	3/4"						
1140	Galvanized, 20 ga.	LF	0.040	3.50	0.44		3.94
1150	Copper, 22 ga.	"	0.040	3.50	0.69		4.19
1160	Threaded rod-couplings						
1170	1/4"	EA	0.050	4.38	1.57		5.95
1180	3/4"	"	0.053	4.67	1.65		6.32
1190	1/2"	"	0.057	5.01	1.87		6.88
1200	5/8"	"	0.062	5.39	2.88		8.27
1220	Reducing rod coupling, 1/2" x 3/8"	"	0.057	5.01	2.59		7.60
1230	C-clamps						
1240	3/4"	EA	0.080	7.01	2.24		9.25
1250	Top beam clamp						
1260	3/8"	EA	0.067	5.84	3.45		9.29
1270	1/2"	"	0.073	6.37	4.27		10.75
1280	Side beam connector						
1290	3/8"	EA	0.067	5.84	1.49		7.33

BASIC MATERIALS

ID Code	Component Descriptions	Unit of Meas.	Manhr / Unit	Labor Cost	Material Cost	Equip. Cost	Total Cost
	Descriptions	**Output**		**Unit Costs**			

22 - 06291	**PIPE HANGERS, LIGHT, Cont'd...**						**22 - 06291**
1300	1/2"	EA	0.073	6.37	3.31		9.68
1310	Hex nuts, heavy, material only						
1320	1"	EA					3.80
1330	Heavy washers						
1340	3/8"	EA					0.11
1350	1/2"	"					0.26
1360	5/8"	"					0.53
1370	3/4"	"					1.06
1380	Lag rod, 3/8" x						
1390	4"	EA					0.49
1400	4-1/2"	"					0.49
1410	6"	"					0.51
1420	8"	"					0.92
1430	10"	"					1.08
1440	12"	"					1.34
1450	18"	"					1.81
1740	J-Hooks						
1750	1/2"	EA	0.036	3.18	0.79		3.97
1760	3/4"	"	0.036	3.18	0.84		4.02
1770	1"	"	0.038	3.34	0.86		4.20
1780	1-1/4"	"	0.039	3.42	0.91		4.33
1790	1-1/2"	"	0.040	3.50	0.93		4.43
1800	2"	"	0.040	3.50	0.97		4.47
1810	3"	"	0.042	3.69	1.12		4.81
1820	4"	"	0.042	3.69	1.21		4.90
1830	PVC coated hangers, galvanized, 28 ga.						
1840	1-1/2" x 12"	EA	0.053	4.67	1.29		5.96
1850	2" x 12"	"	0.057	5.01	1.41		6.42
1860	3" x 12"	"	0.062	5.39	1.58		6.97
1870	4" x 12"	"	0.067	5.84	1.76		7.60
1880	Copper, 30 ga.						
1890	1-1/2" x 12"	EA	0.053	4.67	1.99		6.66
1900	2" x 12"	"	0.057	5.01	2.36		7.37
1910	3" x 12"	"	0.062	5.39	2.61		8.00
1920	4" x 12"	"	0.067	5.84	2.87		8.71
2090	Wire hook hangers						
2095	Black wire, 1/2" x						
2100	4"	EA	0.040	3.50	0.44		3.94

BASIC MATERIALS

ID Code	Descriptions — Component Descriptions	Output — Unit of Meas.	Output — Manhr / Unit	Unit Costs — Labor Cost	Unit Costs — Material Cost	Unit Costs — Equip. Cost	Unit Costs — Total Cost
22 - 06291	**PIPE HANGERS, LIGHT, Cont'd...**						**22 - 06291**
2110	6"	EA	0.042	3.69	0.50		4.19
2120	8"	"	0.044	3.89	0.55		4.44
2130	10"	"	0.044	3.89	0.70		4.59
2140	12"	"	0.047	4.12	0.83		4.95
2150	3/4" x						
2160	4"	EA	0.042	3.69	0.53		4.22
2170	6"	"	0.044	3.89	0.58		4.47
2180	8"	"	0.047	4.12	0.59		4.71
2190	10"	"	0.050	4.38	0.81		5.19
2200	12"	"	0.053	4.67	0.82		5.49
2210	1" x						
2220	4"	EA	0.044	3.89	0.53		4.42
2230	6"	"	0.047	4.12	0.55		4.67
2240	8"	"	0.050	4.38	0.59		4.97
2250	10"	"	0.053	4.67	0.80		5.47
2260	12"	"	0.057	5.01	0.86		5.87
4000	Copper wire hooks						
4010	1/2" x						
4020	4"	EA	0.040	3.50	0.58		4.08
4030	6"	"	0.042	3.69	0.66		4.35
4040	8"	"	0.044	3.89	0.74		4.63
4050	10"	"	0.047	4.12	0.93		5.05
4060	12"	"	0.050	4.38	1.06		5.44
4070	3/4" x						
4080	4"	EA	0.042	3.69	0.58		4.27
4090	6"	"	0.044	3.89	0.72		4.61
4100	8"	"	0.047	4.12	0.83		4.95
4110	10"	"	0.050	4.38	0.95		5.33
4120	12"	"	0.053	4.67	1.13		5.80
22 - 06481	**VIBRATION CONTROL**						**22 - 06481**
0120	Vibration isolator, in-line, stainless connector						
0140	1/2"	EA	0.444	39.00	100		140
0180	1"	"	0.500	43.75	120		160
0280	2"	"	0.615	54.00	230		280
0300	3"	"	0.727	64.00	400		460
0340	6"	"	0.889	78.00	860		940

BASIC MATERIALS

ID Code	Component Descriptions	Unit of Meas.	Manhr / Unit	Labor Cost	Material Cost	Equip. Cost	Total Cost
		Descriptions	**Output**		**Unit Costs**		
22 - 06931	**SPECIALTIES**					**22 - 06931**	
1000	Wall penetration						
1010	Concrete wall, 6" thick						
1020	2" dia.	EA	0.267	16.75			16.75
1040	4" dia.	"	0.400	25.00			25.00
1060	8" dia.	"	0.571	35.75			35.75
1090	12" thick						
1100	2" dia.	EA	0.364	22.75			22.75
1120	4" dia.	"	0.571	35.75			35.75
1140	8" dia.	"	0.889	56.00			56.00
3010	Non-destructive testing, piping systems						
3020	X-ray of welds						
3030	3" dia. pipe	EA	0.800	70.00	20.50		91.00
3040	4" dia. pipe	"	0.800	70.00	27.50		98.00
3050	6" dia. pipe	"	0.800	70.00	27.50		98.00
3060	8" dia. pipe	"	1.000	88.00	27.50		120
3070	10" dia. pipe	"	1.000	88.00	36.00		120
3130	Liquid penetration of welds						
3140	2" dia. pipe	EA	0.500	43.75	5.15		49.00
3160	3" dia. pipe	"	0.500	43.75	5.15		49.00
3180	4" dia. pipe	"	0.500	43.75	5.15		49.00
3200	6" dia. pipe	"	0.500	43.75	5.15		49.00
3220	8" dia. pipe	"	0.500	43.75	7.73		51.00
3240	10" dia. pipe	"	0.500	43.75	7.73		51.00

INSULATION

ID Code	Component Descriptions	Unit of Meas.	Manhr / Unit	Labor Cost	Material Cost	Equip. Cost	Total Cost
22 - 07161	**EQUIPMENT INSULATION**					**22 - 07161**	
0100	Equipment insulation, 2" thick, cellular glass	SF	0.050	4.38	3.56		7.94
0120	Urethane, rigid, jacket, plastered finish	"	0.100	8.77	3.81		12.50
0140	Fiberglass, rigid, with vapor barrier	"	0.044	3.89	3.56		7.45
22 - 07191	**FIBERGLASS PIPE INSULATION**					**22 - 07191**	
1030	Fiberglass insulation on 1/2" pipe						
1040	1" thick	LF	0.027	2.33	1.25		3.58
1060	1-1/2" thick	"	0.033	2.92	2.64		5.56
1070	3/4" pipe						
1080	1" thick	LF	0.027	2.33	1.52		3.85
1100	1-1/2" thick	"	0.033	2.92	2.78		5.70
1110	1" pipe						

INSULATION

ID Code	Component Descriptions	Unit of Meas.	Manhr / Unit	Labor Cost	Material Cost	Equip. Cost	Total Cost
	Descriptions	**Output**		**Unit Costs**			
22 - 07191	**FIBERGLASS PIPE INSULATION, Cont'd...**						**22 - 07191**
1120	1" thick	LF	0.027	2.33	1.52		3.85
1140	1-1/2" thick	"	0.033	2.92	2.91		5.83
1310	2" pipe						
1340	1" thick	LF	0.033	2.92	2.07		4.99
1360	1-1/2" thick	"	0.036	3.18	3.60		6.78
1380	2" thick	"	0.040	3.50	5.28		8.78
1430	2-1/2" pipe						
1440	1" thick	LF	0.033	2.92	2.21		5.13
1460	1-1/2" thick	"	0.036	3.18	3.88		7.06
1470	2" thick	"	0.040	3.50	5.63		9.13
1530	3" pipe						
1540	1" thick	LF	0.038	3.34	2.49		5.83
1560	1-1/2" thick	"	0.040	3.50	4.02		7.52
1580	2" thick	"	0.044	3.89	6.09		9.98
1640	4" pipe						
1660	1" thick	LF	0.038	3.34	3.19		6.53
1680	1-1/2" thick	"	0.040	3.50	4.57		8.07
1700	2" thick	"	0.044	3.89	7.01		11.00
1770	5" pipe						
1780	1" thick	LF	0.038	3.34	3.67		7.01
1800	2" thick	"	0.040	3.50	7.90		11.50
1850	6" pipe						
1870	1" thick	LF	0.042	3.69	4.15		7.84
1880	2" thick	"	0.044	3.89	8.61		12.50
1980	8" pipe						
2000	2" thick	LF	0.042	3.69	10.75		14.50
2020	3" thick	"	0.044	3.89	17.00		21.00
2070	10" pipe						
2080	2" thick	LF	0.042	3.69	13.25		17.00
2100	3" thick	"	0.044	3.89	19.75		23.75
2150	12" pipe						
2160	2" thick	LF	0.042	3.69	14.75		18.50
2180	3" thick	"	0.044	3.89	22.25		26.25

INSULATION

ID Code	Descriptions Component Descriptions	Output Unit of Meas.	Output Manhr / Unit	Unit Costs Labor Cost	Unit Costs Material Cost	Unit Costs Equip. Cost	Unit Costs Total Cost
22 - 07193	**EXTERIOR PIPE INSULATION**						**22 - 07193**
0090	Fiberglass insulation, aluminum jacket						
0110	1/2" pipe						
0120	1" thick	LF	0.062	5.39	1.96		7.35
0140	1-1/2" thick	"	0.067	5.84	3.71		9.55
0150	3/4" pipe						
0160	1" thick	LF	0.062	5.39	2.32		7.71
0180	1-1/2" thick	"	0.067	5.84	3.93		9.77
0190	1" pipe						
0200	1" thick	LF	0.062	5.39	2.40		7.79
0220	1-1/2" thick	"	0.067	5.84	4.14		9.98
0250	1-1/4" pipe						
0260	1" thick	LF	0.073	6.37	2.68		9.05
0280	1-1/2" thick	"	0.076	6.68	4.49		11.25
0310	1-1/2" pipe						
0320	1" thick	LF	0.073	6.37	2.90		9.27
0340	1-1/2" thick	"	0.076	6.68	4.66		11.25
0420	2" pipe						
0440	1" thick	LF	0.073	6.37	3.27		9.64
0460	1-1/2" thick	"	0.076	6.68	4.87		11.50
1030	3" pipe						
1040	1" thick	LF	0.080	7.01	3.93		11.00
1060	1-1/2" thick	"	0.084	7.38	5.81		13.25
1750	6" pipe						
1790	1" thick	LF	0.089	7.79	6.54		14.25
1800	2" thick	"	0.094	8.25	11.50		19.75
2250	10" pipe						
2260	2" thick	LF	0.089	7.79	16.50		24.25
2280	3" thick	"	0.094	8.25	23.75		32.00
22 - 07194	**PIPE INSULATION FITTINGS**						**22 - 07194**
0100	Insulation protection saddle						
0200	1" thick covering						
1000	1/2" pipe	EA	0.320	28.00	7.05		35.00
1020	3/4" pipe	"	0.320	28.00	7.24		35.25
1040	1" pipe	"	0.320	28.00	7.42		35.50
1100	2" pipe	"	0.320	28.00	8.19		36.25
1140	3" pipe	"	0.364	32.00	9.34		41.25
1180	6" pipe	"	0.500	43.75	9.22		53.00

INSULATION

ID Code	Descriptions — Component Descriptions	Output — Unit of Meas.	Output — Manhr / Unit	Unit Costs — Labor Cost	Unit Costs — Material Cost	Unit Costs — Equip. Cost	Unit Costs — Total Cost
22 - 07194	**PIPE INSULATION FITTINGS, Cont'd...**						**22 - 07194**
1190	1-1/2" thick covering						
1200	3/4" pipe	EA	0.320	28.00	11.75		39.75
1220	1" pipe	"	0.320	28.00	12.25		40.25
1280	2" pipe	"	0.320	28.00	10.50		38.50
1300	3" pipe	"	0.320	28.00	11.75		39.75
1360	6" pipe	"	0.500	43.75	14.00		58.00
1400	10" pipe	"	0.667	58.00	14.50		73.00

FACILITY WATER DISTRIBUTION

ID Code	Component Descriptions	Unit of Meas.	Manhr / Unit	Labor Cost	Material Cost	Equip. Cost	Total Cost
22 - 11161	**COPPER PIPE**						**22 - 11161**
0600	Type "K" copper						
0900	1/2"	LF	0.025	2.19	3.77		5.96
1000	3/4"	"	0.027	2.33	7.03		9.36
1020	1"	"	0.029	2.50	9.20		11.75
1100	1-1/4"	"	0.031	2.69	11.50		14.25
1180	1-1/2"	"	0.033	2.92	15.00		18.00
1240	2"	"	0.036	3.18	23.00		26.25
1280	2-1/2"	"	0.040	3.50	33.75		37.25
1300	3"	"	0.042	3.69	47.00		51.00
1340	4"	"	0.044	3.89	78.00		82.00
3000	DWV, copper						
3020	1-1/4"	LF	0.033	2.92	10.25		13.25
3030	1-1/2"	"	0.036	3.18	13.00		16.25
3040	2"	"	0.040	3.50	17.00		20.50
3070	3"	"	0.044	3.89	29.00		33.00
3080	4"	"	0.050	4.38	50.00		54.00
3090	6"	"	0.057	5.01	200		210
4000	Refrigeration tubing, copper, sealed						
4010	1/8"	LF	0.032	2.80	0.73		3.53
4020	3/16"	"	0.033	2.92	0.85		3.77
4030	1/4"	"	0.035	3.05	1.02		4.07
4040	5/16"	"	0.036	3.18	1.31		4.49
4050	3/8"	"	0.038	3.34	1.51		4.85
4060	1/2"	"	0.040	3.50	1.98		5.48
4090	7/8"	"	0.046	4.00	4.81		8.81
4100	1-1/8"	"	0.053	4.67	6.90		11.50
4110	1-3/8"	"	0.062	5.39	10.50		16.00

FACILITY WATER DISTRIBUTION

ID Code	Component Descriptions	Unit of Meas.	Manhr / Unit	Labor Cost	Material Cost	Equip. Cost	Total Cost
22 - 11161	**COPPER PIPE, Cont'd...**						**22 - 11161**
6000	Type "L" copper						
6090	1/4"	LF	0.024	2.06	1.52		3.58
6095	3/8"	"	0.024	2.06	2.33		4.39
6100	1/2"	"	0.025	2.19	2.71		4.90
6190	3/4"	"	0.027	2.33	4.33		6.66
6240	1"	"	0.029	2.50	6.50		9.00
6300	1-1/4"	"	0.031	2.69	9.31		12.00
6360	1-1/2"	"	0.033	2.92	12.00		15.00
6400	2"	"	0.036	3.18	18.75		22.00
6460	2-1/2"	"	0.040	3.50	27.75		31.25
6480	3"	"	0.042	3.69	37.25		41.00
6500	3-1/2"	"	0.043	3.79	48.75		53.00
6520	4"	"	0.044	3.89	62.00		66.00
6580	Type "M" copper						
6600	1/2"	LF	0.025	2.19	1.91		4.10
6620	3/4"	"	0.027	2.33	3.12		5.45
6630	1"	"	0.029	2.50	5.06		7.56
6650	1-1/4"	"	0.031	2.69	7.46		10.25
6660	2"	"	0.036	3.18	16.25		19.50
6670	2-1/2"	"	0.040	3.50	23.75		27.25
6680	3"	"	0.042	3.69	31.50		35.25
6690	4"	"	0.044	3.89	55.00		59.00
22 - 11162	**COPPER FITTINGS**						**22 - 11162**
0460	Coupling, with stop						
0470	1/4"	EA	0.267	23.50	0.95		24.50
0480	3/8"	"	0.320	28.00	1.24		29.25
0485	1/2"	"	0.348	30.50	0.99		31.50
0490	5/8"	"	0.400	35.00	2.87		37.75
0495	3/4"	"	0.444	39.00	1.97		41.00
0498	1"	"	0.471	41.25	4.06		45.25
0499	3"	"	0.800	70.00	49.25		120
0510	4"	"	1.000	88.00	110		200
0520	Reducing coupling						
0530	1/4" x 1/8"	EA	0.320	28.00	2.54		30.50
0540	3/8" x 1/4"	"	0.348	30.50	2.79		33.25
0545	1/2" x						
0550	3/8"	EA	0.400	35.00	2.10		37.00

FACILITY WATER DISTRIBUTION

ID Code	Component Descriptions	Unit of Meas.	Manhr / Unit	Labor Cost	Material Cost	Equip. Cost	Total Cost
		Descriptions	**Output**		**Unit Costs**		
22 - 11162			**COPPER FITTINGS, Cont'd...**				**22 - 11162**
0560	1/4"	EA	0.400	35.00	2.54		37.50
0570	1/8"	"	0.400	35.00	2.80		37.75
0575	3/4" x						
0580	3/8"	EA	0.444	39.00	4.50		43.50
0590	1/2"	"	0.444	39.00	3.56		42.50
0595	1" x						
0600	3/8"	EA	0.500	43.75	8.08		52.00
0610	1" x 1/2"	"	0.500	43.75	7.82		52.00
0620	1" x 3/4"	"	0.500	43.75	6.59		50.00
0625	1-1/4" x						
0630	1/2"	EA	0.533	46.75	9.82		57.00
0640	3/4"	"	0.533	46.75	9.29		56.00
0650	1"	"	0.533	46.75	9.29		56.00
0655	1-1/2" x						
0660	1/2"	EA	0.571	50.00	16.25		66.00
0670	3/4"	"	0.571	50.00	15.50		66.00
0680	1"	"	0.571	50.00	15.50		66.00
0690	1-1/4"	"	0.571	50.00	15.50		66.00
0695	2" x						
0700	1/2"	EA	0.667	58.00	26.75		85.00
0710	3/4"	"	0.667	58.00	25.50		84.00
0720	1"	"	0.667	58.00	25.00		83.00
0730	1-1/4"	"	0.667	58.00	23.75		82.00
0740	1-1/2"	"	0.667	58.00	23.75		82.00
0745	2-1/2" x						
0750	1"	EA	0.800	70.00	61.00		130
0760	1-1/4"	"	0.800	70.00	61.00		130
0770	1-1/2"	"	0.800	70.00	54.00		120
0780	2"	"	0.800	70.00	53.00		120
0785	3" x						
0790	1-1/2"	EA	1.000	88.00	74.00		160
0800	2"	"	1.000	88.00	66.00		150
0810	2-1/2"	"	1.000	88.00	67.00		160
0815	4" x						
0820	2"	EA	1.143	100	150		250
0830	2-1/2"	"	1.143	100	150		250
0840	3"	"	1.143	100	130		230
0850	Slip coupling						

FACILITY WATER DISTRIBUTION

	Descriptions	Output		Unit Costs			
ID Code	Component Descriptions	Unit of Meas.	Manhr / Unit	Labor Cost	Material Cost	Equip. Cost	Total Cost
22 - 11162	**COPPER FITTINGS, Cont'd...**						**22 - 11162**
0860	1/4"	EA	0.267	23.50	0.78		24.25
0870	1/2"	"	0.320	28.00	1.31		29.25
0880	3/4"	"	0.400	35.00	2.74		37.75
0890	1"	"	0.444	39.00	5.82		44.75
0900	1-1/4"	"	0.500	43.75	8.76		53.00
1000	1-1/2"	"	0.533	46.75	11.75		59.00
1020	2"	"	0.667	58.00	20.00		78.00
1030	2-1/2"	"	0.667	58.00	26.25		84.00
1040	3"	"	0.800	70.00	50.00		120
1050	4"	"	1.000	88.00	93.00		180
1060	Coupling with drain						
1070	1/2"	EA	0.400	35.00	10.00		45.00
1080	3/4"	"	0.444	39.00	14.75		54.00
1090	1"	"	0.500	43.75	18.25		62.00
1110	Reducer						
1120	3/8" x 1/4"	EA	0.320	28.00	2.85		30.75
1130	1/2" x 3/8"	"	0.320	28.00	2.29		30.25
1135	3/4" x						
1140	1/4"	EA	0.364	32.00	4.65		36.75
1150	3/8"	"	0.364	32.00	4.86		36.75
1160	1/2"	"	0.364	32.00	5.06		37.00
1165	1" x						
1170	1/2"	EA	0.400	35.00	6.99		42.00
1180	3/4"	"	0.400	35.00	5.36		40.25
1185	1-1/4" x						
1190	1/2"	EA	0.444	39.00	9.87		48.75
1200	3/4"	"	0.444	39.00	9.87		48.75
1210	1"	"	0.444	39.00	9.87		48.75
1215	1-1/2" x						
1220	1/2"	EA	0.500	43.75	12.75		57.00
1230	3/4"	"	0.500	43.75	12.75		57.00
1240	1"	"	0.500	43.75	12.75		57.00
1250	1-1/4"	"	0.500	43.75	12.75		57.00
1255	2" x						
1260	1/2"	EA	0.571	50.00	25.50		76.00
1270	3/4"	"	0.571	50.00	25.50		76.00
1280	1"	"	0.571	50.00	25.50		76.00
1290	1-1/4"	"	0.571	50.00	24.25		74.00

FACILITY WATER DISTRIBUTION

ID Code	Component Descriptions	Unit of Meas.	Manhr / Unit	Labor Cost	Material Cost	Equip. Cost	Total Cost
	Descriptions	**Output**		**Unit Costs**			
22 - 11162	**COPPER FITTINGS, Cont'd...**						**22 - 11162**
1300	1-1/2"	EA	0.571	50.00	24.25		74.00
1310	2-1/2" x						
1320	1"	EA	0.667	58.00	56.00		110
1330	1-1/4"	"	0.667	58.00	50.00		110
1340	1-1/2"	"	0.667	58.00	49.25		110
1350	2"	"	0.667	58.00	48.25		110
1355	3" x						
1360	1-1/4"	EA	0.800	70.00	66.00		140
1370	1-1/2"	"	0.800	70.00	68.00		140
1380	2"	"	0.800	70.00	61.00		130
1390	2-1/2"	"	0.800	70.00	62.00		130
1395	4" x						
1400	2"	EA	1.000	88.00	140		230
1410	3"	"	1.000	88.00	130		220
1415	Female adapters						
1430	1/4"	EA	0.320	28.00	7.40		35.50
1440	3/8"	"	0.364	32.00	7.58		39.50
1450	1/2"	"	0.400	35.00	3.60		38.50
1460	3/4"	"	0.444	39.00	4.94		44.00
1470	1"	"	0.444	39.00	11.50		51.00
1480	1-1/4"	"	0.500	43.75	16.75		61.00
1490	1-1/2"	"	0.500	43.75	26.00		70.00
1500	2"	"	0.533	46.75	35.75		83.00
1510	2-1/2"	"	0.571	50.00	130		180
1520	3"	"	0.667	58.00	200		260
1530	4"	"	0.800	70.00	240		310
1540	Increasing female adapters						
1545	1/8" x						
1550	3/8"	EA	0.320	28.00	7.27		35.25
1560	1/2"	"	0.320	28.00	6.78		34.75
1570	1/4" x 1/2"	"	0.348	30.50	7.10		37.50
1580	3/8" x 1/2"	"	0.364	32.00	7.62		39.50
1585	1/2" X						
1590	3/4"	EA	0.400	35.00	8.08		43.00
1600	1"	"	0.400	35.00	16.25		51.00
1605	3/4" X						
1610	1"	EA	0.444	39.00	17.25		56.00
1620	1-1/4"	"	0.444	39.00	29.25		68.00

FACILITY WATER DISTRIBUTION

ID Code	Component Descriptions	Unit of Meas.	Manhr / Unit	Labor Cost	Material Cost	Equip. Cost	Total Cost
	Descriptions	**Output**		**Unit Costs**			
22 - 11162	**COPPER FITTINGS, Cont'd...**						**22 - 11162**
1625	1" x						
1630	1-1/4"	EA	0.444	39.00	31.00		70.00
1640	1-1/2"	"	0.444	39.00	34.00		73.00
1645	1-1/4" x						
1650	1-1/2"	EA	0.500	43.75	37.00		81.00
1660	2"	"	0.500	43.75	47.25		91.00
1670	1-1/2" x 2"	"	0.533	46.75	69.00		120
1675	Reducing female adapters						
1690	3/8" x 1/4"	EA	0.364	32.00	6.55		38.50
1695	1/2" x						
1700	1/4"	EA	0.400	35.00	5.63		40.75
1710	3/8"	"	0.400	35.00	5.63		40.75
1720	3/4" x 1/2"	"	0.444	39.00	7.86		46.75
1725	1" x						
1730	1/2"	EA	0.444	39.00	21.00		60.00
1740	3/4"	"	0.444	39.00	16.75		56.00
1745	1-1/4" x						
1750	1/2"	EA	0.500	43.75	28.50		72.00
1760	3/4"	"	0.500	43.75	35.50		79.00
1770	1"	"	0.500	43.75	35.50		79.00
1780	1-1/2" x						
1790	1"	EA	0.533	46.75	33.25		80.00
1800	1-1/4"	"	0.533	46.75	36.00		83.00
1805	2" x						
1810	1"	EA	0.571	50.00	45.00		95.00
1820	1-1/4"	"	0.571	50.00	67.00		120
1830	1-1/2"	"	0.571	50.00	58.00		110
1840	Female fitting adapters						
1850	1/2"	EA	0.400	35.00	10.00		45.00
1860	3/4"	"	0.400	35.00	13.00		48.00
1870	3/4" x 1/2"	"	0.421	37.00	15.50		53.00
1880	1"	"	0.444	39.00	17.25		56.00
1890	1-1/4"	"	0.471	41.25	27.75		69.00
1900	1-1/2"	"	0.500	43.75	36.50		80.00
1910	2"	"	0.533	46.75	48.50		95.00
1920	Male adapters						
1930	1/4"	EA	0.364	32.00	11.25		43.25
1940	3/8"	"	0.364	32.00	5.63		37.75

FACILITY WATER DISTRIBUTION

ID Code	Component Descriptions	Unit of Meas.	Manhr / Unit	Labor Cost	Material Cost	Equip. Cost	Total Cost
22 - 11162	**COPPER FITTINGS, Cont'd...**						**22 - 11162**
1950	3"	EA	0.667	58.00	140		200
1960	4"	"	0.800	70.00	200		270
1970	Increasing male adapters						
1980	3/8" x 1/2"	EA	0.364	32.00	7.68		39.75
1985	1/2" x						
1990	3/4"	EA	0.400	35.00	6.66		41.75
2000	1"	"	0.400	35.00	15.00		50.00
2005	3/4" x						
2010	1"	EA	0.421	37.00	14.75		52.00
2020	1-1/4"	"	0.421	37.00	18.75		56.00
2030	1" x 1-1/4"	"	0.444	39.00	18.75		58.00
2035	1-1/2" x						
2040	3/4"	EA	0.471	41.25	22.50		64.00
2050	1"	"	0.471	41.25	33.25		75.00
2060	1-1/4"	"	0.471	41.25	36.00		77.00
2065	2" x						
2070	1"	EA	0.500	43.75	85.00		130
2080	1-1/4"	"	0.500	43.75	87.00		130
2090	1-1/2"	"	0.500	43.75	83.00		130
2100	2" x 2-1/2"	"	0.533	46.75	140		190
8000	Copper pipe fittings						
8010	1/2"						
8020	90 deg ell	EA	0.178	15.50	1.47		17.00
8040	45 deg ell	"	0.178	15.50	1.86		17.25
8060	Tee	"	0.229	20.00	2.46		22.50
8100	Cap	"	0.089	7.79	1.00		8.79
8120	Coupling	"	0.178	15.50	1.07		16.50
8160	Union	"	0.200	17.50	7.46		25.00
8200	3/4"						
8220	90 deg ell	EA	0.200	17.50	3.21		20.75
8240	45 deg ell	"	0.200	17.50	3.76		21.25
8260	Tee	"	0.267	23.50	5.38		29.00
8290	Cap	"	0.094	8.25	1.96		10.25
8300	Coupling	"	0.200	17.50	2.19		19.75
8320	Union	"	0.229	20.00	11.00		31.00
8360	1"						
8380	90 deg ell	EA	0.267	23.50	7.46		31.00
8390	45 deg ell	"	0.267	23.50	9.72		33.25

FACILITY WATER DISTRIBUTION

ID Code	Descriptions Component Descriptions	Output Unit of Meas.	Manhr / Unit	Unit Costs Labor Cost	Material Cost	Equip. Cost	Total Cost
22 - 11162	**COPPER FITTINGS, Cont'd...**						**22 - 11162**
8400	Tee	EA	0.320	28.00	12.25		40.25
8420	Cap	"	0.133	11.75	3.64		15.50
8430	Coupling	"	0.267	23.50	5.38		29.00
8450	Union	"	0.267	23.50	14.50		38.00
8480	1-1/4"						
8500	90 deg ell	EA	0.229	20.00	10.25		30.25
8510	45 deg ell	"	0.229	20.00	12.50		32.50
8520	Tee	"	0.400	35.00	16.50		52.00
8540	Cap	"	0.133	11.75	2.90		14.75
8560	Union	"	0.286	25.00	23.75		48.75
8580	1-1/2"						
8600	90 deg ell	EA	0.286	25.00	13.25		38.25
8610	45 deg ell	"	0.286	25.00	15.75		40.75
8620	Tee	"	0.444	39.00	21.75		61.00
8640	Cap	"	0.133	11.75	2.90		14.75
8660	Coupling	"	0.267	23.50	9.72		33.25
8680	Union	"	0.364	32.00	36.25		68.00
8905	2"						
8910	90 deg ell	EA	0.320	28.00	25.75		54.00
8920	45 deg ell	"	0.500	43.75	23.75		68.00
8930	Tee	"	0.500	43.75	37.25		81.00
8950	Cap	"	0.160	14.00	6.01		20.00
8960	Coupling	"	0.320	28.00	15.75		43.75
8980	Union	"	0.400	35.00	39.25		74.00
9000	2-1/2"						
9020	90 deg ell	EA	0.400	35.00	49.75		85.00
9030	45 deg ell	"	0.400	35.00	43.50		79.00
9040	Tee	"	0.571	50.00	49.75		100
9070	Cap	"	0.200	17.50	12.25		29.75
9080	Coupling	"	0.400	35.00	23.75		59.00
9100	Union	"	0.444	39.00	72.00		110
22 - 11165	**BRASS FITTINGS**						**22 - 11165**
1000	Compression fittings, union						
1020	3/8"	EA	0.133	11.75	1.81		13.50
1030	1/2"	"	0.133	11.75	3.91		15.75
1040	5/8"	"	0.133	11.75	4.98		16.75
1050	Union elbow						

FACILITY WATER DISTRIBUTION

ID Code	Component Descriptions	Unit of Meas.	Manhr / Unit	Labor Cost	Material Cost	Equip. Cost	Total Cost
	Descriptions	**Output**		**Unit Costs**			
22 - 11165	**BRASS FITTINGS, Cont'd...**						**22 - 11165**
1060	3/8"	EA	0.133	11.75	5.80		17.50
1070	1/2"	"	0.133	11.75	9.66		21.50
1080	5/8"	"	0.133	11.75	13.00		24.75
1090	Union tee						
1100	3/8"	EA	0.133	11.75	5.44		17.25
1120	1/2"	"	0.133	11.75	7.87		19.50
1130	5/8"	"	0.133	11.75	11.00		22.75
2000	Brass flare fittings, union						
2020	3/8"	EA	0.129	11.25	2.35		13.50
2030	1/2"	"	0.129	11.25	3.24		14.50
2040	5/8"	"	0.129	11.25	4.18		15.50
2050	90 deg elbow union						
2060	3/8"	EA	0.129	11.25	5.04		16.25
2070	1/2"	"	0.129	11.25	7.39		18.75
2080	5/8"	"	0.129	11.25	13.00		24.25
22 - 11167	**CHROME PLATED FITTINGS**						**22 - 11167**
0005	Fittings						
0010	90 ell						
0020	3/8"	EA	0.200	17.50	27.50		45.00
0030	1/2"	"	0.200	17.50	35.50		53.00
0035	45 ell						
0040	3/8"	EA	0.200	17.50	35.50		53.00
0050	1/2"	"	0.200	17.50	46.75		64.00
0055	Tee						
0060	3/8"	EA	0.267	23.50	34.00		58.00
0070	1/2"	"	0.267	23.50	40.50		64.00
0075	Coupling						
0080	3/8"	EA	0.200	17.50	21.50		39.00
0090	1/2"	"	0.200	17.50	21.50		39.00
0095	Union						
0100	3/8"	EA	0.200	17.50	35.50		53.00
0110	1/2"	"	0.200	17.50	36.75		54.00
0115	Tee						
0130	1/2" x 3/8" x 3/8"	EA	0.267	23.50	40.50		64.00
0140	1/2" x 3/8" x 1/2"	"	0.267	23.50	41.25		65.00

FACILITY WATER DISTRIBUTION

ID Code	Component Descriptions	Unit of Meas.	Manhr / Unit	Labor Cost	Material Cost	Equip. Cost	Total Cost

22 - 11168 — **PVC/CPVC PIPE** — **22 - 11168**

ID Code	Component Descriptions	Unit of Meas.	Manhr / Unit	Labor Cost	Material Cost	Equip. Cost	Total Cost
0900	PVC schedule 40						
1000	1/2" pipe	LF	0.033	2.92	0.50		3.42
1020	3/4" pipe	"	0.036	3.18	0.69		3.87
1040	1" pipe	"	0.040	3.50	0.88		4.38
1060	1-1/4" pipe	"	0.044	3.89	1.13		5.02
1080	1-1/2" pipe	"	0.050	4.38	1.69		6.07
1100	2" pipe	"	0.057	5.01	2.14		7.15
1110	2-1/2" pipe	"	0.067	5.84	3.46		9.30
1120	3" pipe	"	0.080	7.01	4.41		11.50
1130	4" pipe	"	0.100	8.77	6.30		15.00
1140	6" pipe	"	0.200	17.50	11.25		28.75
1150	8" pipe	"	0.267	23.50	16.50		40.00
2965	PVC schedule 80 pipe						
3070	1-1/2" pipe	LF	0.050	4.38	2.15		6.53
3071	2" pipe	"	0.057	5.01	2.91		7.92
3100	3" pipe	"	0.080	7.01	6.00		13.00
3110	4" pipe	"	0.100	8.77	7.84		16.50
7000	Polypropylene, acid resistant, DWV pipe						
7010	Schedule 40						
7030	1-1/2" pipe	LF	0.057	5.01	9.18		14.25
7040	2" pipe	"	0.067	5.84	12.50		18.25
7050	3" pipe	"	0.080	7.01	25.25		32.25
7060	4" pipe	"	0.100	8.77	32.25		41.00
7070	6" pipe	"	0.200	17.50	64.00		82.00
7800	Polyethylene pipe and fittings						
7900	SDR-21						
8020	3" pipe	LF	0.100	8.77	4.12		13.00
8030	4" pipe	"	0.133	11.75	6.51		18.25
8040	6" pipe	"	0.200	17.50	11.25		28.75
8050	8" pipe	"	0.229	20.00	16.50		36.50
8060	10" pipe	"	0.267	23.50	18.50		42.00

22 - 11169 — **STEEL PIPE** — **22 - 11169**

ID Code	Component Descriptions	Unit of Meas.	Manhr / Unit	Labor Cost	Material Cost	Equip. Cost	Total Cost
1000	Black steel, extra heavy pipe, threaded						
1030	1/2" pipe	LF	0.032	2.80	2.81		5.61
1100	3/4" pipe	"	0.032	2.80	3.64		6.44
1200	1" pipe	"	0.040	3.50	4.68		8.18
1400	1-1/2" pipe	"	0.044	3.89	7.03		11.00

FACILITY WATER DISTRIBUTION

ID Code	Component Descriptions	Unit of Meas.	Manhr / Unit	Labor Cost	Material Cost	Equip. Cost	Total Cost
	Descriptions	**Output**		**Unit Costs**			
22 - 11169	**STEEL PIPE, Cont'd...**						**22 - 11169**
1500	2-1/2" pipe	LF	0.100	8.77	14.00		22.75
1610	3" pipe	"	0.133	11.75	18.75		30.50
1700	4" pipe	"	0.160	14.00	28.25		42.25
1800	5" pipe	"	0.200	17.50	38.25		56.00
1900	6" pipe	"	0.200	17.50	47.75		65.00
2000	8" pipe	"	0.267	23.50	70.00		94.00
2100	10" pipe	"	0.320	28.00	110		140
2200	12" pipe	"	0.400	35.00	140		180
4000	Fittings, malleable iron, threaded, 1/2" pipe						
4010	90 deg ell	EA	0.267	23.50	3.37		26.75
4020	45 deg ell	"	0.267	23.50	4.56		28.00
4030	Tee	"	0.400	35.00	3.66		38.75
4085	3/4" pipe						
4090	90 deg ell	EA	0.267	23.50	3.95		27.50
4100	45 deg ell	"	0.400	35.00	6.26		41.25
4120	Tee	"	0.400	35.00	5.31		40.25
4178	1" pipe						
4180	90 deg ell	EA	0.320	28.00	6.12		34.00
4200	45 deg ell	"	0.320	28.00	8.09		36.00
4210	Tee	"	0.444	39.00	9.18		48.25
4265	1-1/2" pipe						
4270	90 deg ell	EA	0.400	35.00	12.50		47.50
4280	45 deg ell	"	0.400	35.00	15.50		51.00
4300	Tee	"	0.571	50.00	18.25		68.00
4365	2-1/2" pipe						
4370	90 deg ell	EA	1.000	88.00	48.25		140
4380	45 deg ell	"	1.000	88.00	68.00		160
4400	Tee	"	1.333	120	67.00		190
4448	3" pipe						
4450	90 deg ell	EA	1.333	120	71.00		190
4470	45 deg ell	"	1.333	120	88.00		210
4480	Tee	"	2.000	180	99.00		280
4535	4" pipe						
4540	90 deg ell	EA	1.600	140	150		290
4550	45 deg ell	"	1.600	140	170		310
4560	Tee	"	2.667	230	240		470
4710	90 deg ell	"	1.600	140	420		560
4715	6" pipe						

FACILITY WATER DISTRIBUTION

ID Code	Component Descriptions	Unit of Meas.	Manhr / Unit	Labor Cost	Material Cost	Equip. Cost	Total Cost
22 - 11169	**STEEL PIPE, Cont'd...**						**22 - 11169**
4720	45 deg ell	EA	1.600	140	490		630
4730	Tee	"	2.667	230	750		980
4880	8" pipe						
4900	90 deg ell	EA	3.200	280	840		1,120
4905	45 deg ell	"	3.200	280	950		1,230
4910	Tee	"	5.000	440	590		1,030
4980	10" pipe						
4985	90 deg ell	EA	4.000	350	930		1,280
4990	45 deg ell	"	4.000	350	1,050		1,400
5030	Tee	"	5.000	440	670		1,110
5100	12" pipe						
5110	90 deg ell	EA	5.000	440	1,020		1,460
5120	45 deg ell	"	5.000	440	1,160		1,600
5130	Tee	"	6.667	580	780		1,360
22 - 11170	**GALVANIZED STEEL PIPE**						**22 - 11170**
1000	Galvanized pipe						
1020	1/2" pipe	LF	0.080	7.01	3.01		10.00
1040	3/4" pipe	"	0.100	8.77	3.92		12.75
1050	1" pipe	"	0.114	10.00	6.01		16.00
1060	1-1/4" pipe	"	0.133	11.75	7.45		19.25
1070	1-1/2" pipe	"	0.160	14.00	8.18		22.25
1080	2" pipe	"	0.200	17.50	11.75		29.25
1090	2-1/2" pipe	"	0.267	23.50	17.00		40.50
1100	3" pipe	"	0.286	25.00	23.50		48.50
1110	4" pipe	"	0.333	29.25	32.00		61.00
1120	6" pipe	"	0.667	58.00	58.00		120
22 - 11171	**STAINLESS STEEL PIPE**						**22 - 11171**
3900	Stainless steel, schedule 40, threaded						
4000	1/2" pipe	LF	0.114	10.00	10.50		20.50
4005	3/4" pipe	"	0.118	10.25	14.75		25.00
4090	1" pipe	"	0.123	10.75	17.25		28.00
4100	1-1/2" pipe	"	0.133	11.75	23.50		35.25
4200	2" pipe	"	0.145	12.75	35.25		48.00
4220	2-1/2" pipe	"	0.160	14.00	49.50		64.00
4240	3" pipe	"	0.178	15.50	69.00		85.00
4260	4" pipe	"	0.200	17.50	89.00		110

FACILITY WATER DISTRIBUTION

ID Code	Component Descriptions	Unit of Meas.	Manhr / Unit	Labor Cost	Material Cost	Equip. Cost	Total Cost
	Descriptions	**Output**		**Unit Costs**			
22 - 11191	**BACKFLOW PREVENTERS**						**22 - 11191**
0080	Backflow preventer, flanged, cast iron, with valves						
0100	3" pipe	EA	4.000	350	4,030		4,380
0120	4" pipe	"	4.444	390	4,700		5,090
0130	6" pipe	"	6.667	580	8,030		8,610
0140	8" pipe	"	8.000	700	12,240		12,940
1900	Threaded						
2000	3/4" pipe	EA	0.500	43.75	750		790
2020	2" pipe	"	0.800	70.00	1,320		1,390
3000	Reduced pressure assembly, bronze, threaded						
3100	3/4"	EA	0.500	43.75	640		680
3120	1"	"	0.571	50.00	660		710
3140	1-1/4"	"	0.667	58.00	960		1,020
3160	1-1/2"	"	0.800	70.00	1,080		1,150
22 - 11196	**VACUUM BREAKERS**						**22 - 11196**
1000	Vacuum breaker, atmospheric, threaded connection						
1010	3/4"	EA	0.320	28.00	55.00		83.00
1015	1"	"	0.320	28.00	81.00		110
1018	Anti-siphon, brass						
1020	3/4"	EA	0.320	28.00	60.00		88.00
1030	1"	"	0.320	28.00	93.00		120
1040	1-1/4"	"	0.400	35.00	160		200
1050	1-1/2"	"	0.444	39.00	190		230
1060	2"	"	0.500	43.75	300		340
22 - 11230	**PUMPS**						**22 - 11230**
0900	In-line pump, bronze, centrifugal						
1000	5 gpm, 20' head	EA	0.500	43.75	680		720
1010	20 gpm, 40' head	"	0.500	43.75	1,220		1,260
1015	50 gpm						
1020	50' head	EA	1.000	88.00	1,390		1,480
1065	Cast iron, centrifugal						
1070	50 gpm, 200' head	EA	1.000	88.00	1,320		1,410
1075	100 gpm						
1080	100' head	EA	1.333	120	2,250		2,370
1500	Centrifugal, close coupled, c.i., single stage						
1520	50 gpm, 100' head	EA	1.000	88.00	1,580		1,670
1530	100 gpm, 100' head	"	1.333	120	1,920		2,040
1535	Base mounted						

FACILITY WATER DISTRIBUTION

ID Code	Descriptions		Output		Unit Costs			
	Component Descriptions		Unit of Meas.	Manhr / Unit	Labor Cost	Material Cost	Equip. Cost	Total Cost
22 - 11230		**PUMPS, Cont'd...**						**22 - 11230**
1540	50 gpm, 100' head		EA	1.000	88.00	3,220		3,310
1550	100 gpm, 50' head		"	1.333	120	3,660		3,780
1560	200 gpm, 100' head		"	2.000	180	4,690		4,870
1570	300 gpm, 175' head		"	2.000	180	6,080		6,260
5980	Condensate pump, simplex							
6000	1000 sf EDR, 2 gpm		EA	6.667	580	1,650		2,230
6010	2000 sf EDR, 3 gpm		"	6.667	580	1,680		2,260
6020	4000 sf EDR, 6 gpm		"	7.273	640	1,690		2,330
6030	6000 sf EDR, 9 gpm		"	7.273	640	1,720		2,360
6035	Duplex, bronze							
6040	8000 sf EDR, 12 gpm		EA	7.273	640	2,360		3,000
6050	10,000 sf EDR, 15 gpm		"	10.000	880	2,450		3,330
6060	15,000 sf EDR, 23 gpm		"	11.429	1,000	2,940		3,940
6070	20,000 sf EDR, 30 gpm		"	16.000	1,400	3,420		4,820
6080	25,000 sf EDR, 38 gpm		"	16.000	1,400	3,540		4,940

FACILITY POTABLE-WATER STORAGE TANKS

ID Code	Descriptions		Output		Unit Costs			
22 - 12004		**STORAGE TANKS**						**22 - 12004**
0980	Hot water storage tank, cement lined							
1000	10 gallon		EA	2.667	230	510		740
1020	70 gallon		"	4.000	350	1,620		1,970
1040	200 gallon		"	5.714	500	3,070		3,570
1060	900 gallon		"	10.000	880	12,730		13,610
1080	1100 gallon		"	10.000	880	17,020		17,900
1100	2000 gallon		"	10.000	880	24,300		25,180

FACILITY SANITARY SEWERAGE

ID Code	Descriptions		Output		Unit Costs			
22 - 13140		**EXTRA HEAVY SOIL PIPE**						**22 - 13140**
0005	Extra heavy soil pipe, single hub							
0010	2" x 5'		EA	0.160	14.00	61.00		75.00
0020	3" x 5'		"	0.170	15.00	68.00		83.00
0030	4" x 5'		"	0.186	16.25	79.00		95.00
0040	6" x 5'		"	0.200	17.50	150		170
0045	Double hub							
0050	2" x 5'		EA	0.200	17.50	68.00		86.00
0060	4" x 5'		"	0.211	18.50	86.00		100

FACILITY SANITARY SEWERAGE

ID Code	Component Descriptions	Unit of Meas.	Manhr / Unit	Labor Cost	Material Cost	Equip. Cost	Total Cost
		Descriptions	**Output**		**Unit Costs**		
22 - 13140	**EXTRA HEAVY SOIL PIPE, Cont'd...**						**22 - 13140**
0070	5" x 5'	EA	0.222	19.50	130		150
0080	6" x 5'	"	0.229	20.00	160		180
0085	Single hub						
0090	3" x 10'	EA	0.133	11.75	140		150
0100	4" x 10'	"	0.138	12.00	180		190
0110	6" x 10'	"	0.145	12.75	270		280
22 - 13150	**SERVICE WEIGHT PIPE**						**22 - 13150**
0005	Service weight pipe, single hub						
0020	3" x 5'	EA	0.170	15.00	52.00		67.00
0030	4" x 5'	"	0.178	15.50	60.00		76.00
0050	6" x 5'	"	0.200	17.50	110		130
0085	Double hub						
0100	3" x 5'	EA	0.216	19.00	58.00		77.00
0110	4" x 5'	"	0.229	20.00	66.00		86.00
0130	6" x 5'	"	0.267	23.50	120		140
0155	Single hub						
0170	3" x 10'	EA	0.216	19.00	68.00		87.00
0180	4" x 10'	"	0.229	20.00	89.00		110
0200	6" x 10'	"	0.267	23.50	150		170
0395	1/8 bend						
0410	3"	EA	0.320	28.00	11.00		39.00
0420	4"	"	0.364	32.00	16.00		48.00
0440	6"	"	0.400	35.00	27.00		62.00
0525	1/4 bend						
0540	3"	EA	0.320	28.00	13.00		41.00
0550	4"	"	0.364	32.00	20.25		52.00
0570	6"	"	0.400	35.00	35.50		71.00
0635	Sweep						
0650	3"	EA	0.320	28.00	21.00		49.00
0660	4"	"	0.364	32.00	31.00		63.00
0680	6"	"	0.400	35.00	62.00		97.00
0765	Sanitary T						
0790	3"	EA	0.571	50.00	22.00		72.00
0820	4"	"	0.667	58.00	27.00		85.00
0840	6"	"	0.727	64.00	61.00		130
0845	Wye						
0870	3"	EA	0.444	39.00	23.00		62.00

FACILITY SANITARY SEWERAGE

ID Code	Descriptions		Output		Unit Costs			
	Component Descriptions		Unit of Meas.	Manhr / Unit	Labor Cost	Material Cost	Equip. Cost	Total Cost
22 - 13150	**SERVICE WEIGHT PIPE, Cont'd...**							**22 - 13150**
0900	4"		EA	0.471	41.25	30.75		72.00
0990	6"		"	0.571	50.00	71.00		120
22 - 13160	**C.I. PIPE, ABOVE GROUND**							**22 - 13160**
0980	No hub pipe							
1000	1-1/2" pipe		LF	0.057	5.01	10.75		15.75
1010	2" pipe		"	0.067	5.84	9.45		15.25
1100	3" pipe		"	0.080	7.01	13.00		20.00
1200	4" pipe		"	0.133	11.75	17.00		28.75
1300	6" pipe		"	0.160	14.00	30.00		44.00
1400	8" pipe		"	0.267	23.50	48.25		72.00
1500	10" pipe		"	0.320	28.00	76.00		100
4980	No hub fittings, 1-1/2" pipe							
5000	1/4 bend		EA	0.267	23.50	9.85		33.25
5060	1/8 bend		"	0.267	23.50	8.25		31.75
5100	Sanitary tee		"	0.400	35.00	13.75		48.75
5180	Coupling		"					19.50
5200	Wye		"	0.400	35.00	17.00		52.00
5370	2" pipe							
5380	1/4 bend		EA	0.320	28.00	11.50		39.50
5440	1/8 bend		"	0.320	28.00	9.18		37.25
5480	Sanitary tee		"	0.533	46.75	15.50		62.00
5560	Coupling		"					17.25
5600	Wye		"	0.667	58.00	14.50		73.00
5980	3" pipe							
6000	1/4 bend		EA	0.400	35.00	15.50		51.00
6080	1/8 bend		"	0.400	35.00	13.00		48.00
6120	Sanitary tee		"	0.500	43.75	19.00		63.00
6260	Coupling		"					19.75
6280	Wye		"	0.667	58.00	20.75		79.00
6810	4" pipe							
6820	1/4 bend		EA	0.400	35.00	22.50		58.00
6900	1/8 bend		"	0.400	35.00	16.50		52.00
6940	Sanitary tee		"	0.667	58.00	29.50		88.00
7100	Coupling		"					19.25
7120	Wye		"	0.667	58.00	33.75		92.00
7595	6" pipe							
7600	1/4 bend		EA	0.667	58.00	57.00		110

FACILITY SANITARY SEWERAGE

ID Code	Component Descriptions	Unit of Meas.	Manhr / Unit	Labor Cost	Material Cost	Equip. Cost	Total Cost
	Descriptions	**Output**		**Unit Costs**			
22 - 13160	**C.I. PIPE, ABOVE GROUND, Cont'd...**						**22 - 13160**
7640	1/8 bend	EA	0.667	58.00	38.25		96.00
7660	Sanitary tee	"	0.800	70.00	86.00		160
7700	Coupling	"					48.50
7710	Wye	"	0.800	70.00	90.00		160
7980	8" pipe						
7990	1/4 bend	EA	0.667	58.00	99.00		160
8030	1/8 bend	"	0.667	58.00	69.00		130
8050	Sanitary tee	"	1.000	88.00	220		310
8090	Coupling	"					92.00
8100	Wye	"	0.800	70.00	130		200
8355	10" pipe						
8360	1/4 bend	EA	0.667	58.00	200		260
8380	1/8 bend	"	0.667	58.00	130		190
8420	Coupling	"					120
8450	Wye	"	1.333	120	290		410
8490	10x6" wye	"	1.333	120	210		330
22 - 13161	**C.I. PIPE, BELOW GROUND**						**22 - 13161**
1010	No hub pipe						
1020	1-1/2" pipe	LF	0.040	3.50	8.66		12.25
1030	2" pipe	"	0.044	3.89	8.89		12.75
1120	3" pipe	"	0.050	4.38	12.25		16.75
1220	4" pipe	"	0.067	5.84	16.00		21.75
1320	6" pipe	"	0.073	6.37	27.50		33.75
1420	8" pipe	"	0.089	7.79	42.75		51.00
1520	10" pipe	"	0.100	8.77	71.00		80.00
5000	Fittings, 1-1/2"						
5010	1/4 bend	EA	0.229	20.00	10.25		30.25
5080	1/8 bend	"	0.229	20.00	8.63		28.75
5220	Wye	"	0.320	28.00	14.50		42.50
5370	2"						
5390	1/4 bend	EA	0.267	23.50	11.25		34.75
5460	1/8 bend	"	0.267	23.50	9.67		33.25
6000	3"						
6020	1/4 bend	EA	0.320	28.00	15.50		43.50
6100	1/8 bend	"	0.320	28.00	13.00		41.00
6300	Wye	"	0.500	43.75	20.75		65.00
6820	4"						

FACILITY SANITARY SEWERAGE

ID Code	Component Descriptions	Unit of Meas.	Manhr / Unit	Labor Cost	Material Cost	Equip. Cost	Total Cost
	Descriptions	**Output**		**Unit Costs**			
22 - 13161	**C.I. PIPE, BELOW GROUND, Cont'd...**						**22 - 13161**
6840	1/4 bend	EA	0.320	28.00	22.50		51.00
6920	1/8 bend	"	0.320	28.00	16.50		44.50
7140	Wye	"	0.500	43.75	33.75		78.00
7780	6"						
7800	1/4 bend	EA	0.500	43.75	35.75		80.00
7820	1/8 bend	"	0.500	43.75	24.00		68.00
7990	8"						
8000	1/4 bend	EA	0.500	43.75	99.00		140
8040	1/8 bend	"	0.500	43.75	69.00		110
8120	Wye	"	0.667	58.00	130		190
8350	10"						
8370	1/4 bend	EA	0.500	43.75	200		240
8390	1/8 bend	"	0.500	43.75	130		170
8410	Plug	"					61.00
8460	Wye	"	1.000	88.00	290		380
22 - 13163	**ABS DWV PIPE**						**22 - 13163**
1480	Schedule 40 ABS						
1500	1-1/2" pipe	LF	0.040	3.50	1.58		5.08
1520	2" pipe	"	0.044	3.89	2.11		6.00
1530	3" pipe	"	0.057	5.01	4.32		9.33
1540	4" pipe	"	0.080	7.01	6.12		13.25
1550	6" pipe	"	0.100	8.77	12.50		21.25
22 - 13165	**PLASTIC PIPE**						**22 - 13165**
1000	Fiberglass reinforced pipe						
1010	2" pipe	LF	0.062	5.39	4.38		9.77
1020	3" pipe	"	0.067	5.84	6.23		12.00
1030	4" pipe	"	0.073	6.37	8.14		14.50
1040	6" pipe	"	0.080	7.01	15.50		22.50
1050	8" pipe	"	0.133	11.75	22.75		34.50
1060	10" pipe	"	0.160	14.00	34.00		48.00
1070	12" pipe	"	0.200	17.50	44.25		62.00

FACILITY SANITARY SEWERAGE

ID Code	Component Descriptions	Unit of Meas.	Manhr / Unit	Labor Cost	Material Cost	Equip. Cost	Total Cost
	Descriptions	**Output**		**Unit Costs**			

ID Code	Component Descriptions	Unit of Meas.	Manhr / Unit	Labor Cost	Material Cost	Equip. Cost	Total Cost
22 - 13167	**DRAINS, ROOF & FLOOR**						**22 - 13167**
1020	Floor drain, cast iron, with cast iron top						
1030	2"	EA	0.667	58.00	180		240
1040	3"	"	0.667	58.00	180		240
1050	4"	"	0.667	58.00	390		450
1060	6"	"	0.800	70.00	500		570
1090	Roof drain, cast iron						
1100	2"	EA	0.667	58.00	280		340
1110	3"	"	0.667	58.00	290		350
1120	4"	"	0.667	58.00	370		430
1130	5"	"	0.800	70.00	540		610
1140	6"	"	0.800	70.00	550		620
22 - 13168	**TRAPS**						**22 - 13168**
0980	Bucket trap, threaded						
1000	3/4"	EA	0.500	43.75	230		270
1010	1"	"	0.533	46.75	650		700
1020	1-1/4"	"	0.615	54.00	770		820
1030	1-1/2"	"	0.727	64.00	1,160		1,220
1080	Inverted bucket steam trap, threaded						
1100	3/4"	EA	0.500	43.75	280		320
1110	1"	"	0.500	43.75	550		590
1120	1-1/4"	"	0.444	39.00	830		870
1140	1-1/2"	"	0.667	58.00	880		940
1480	Float trap, 15 psi						
1500	3/4"	EA	0.500	43.75	200		240
1510	1"	"	0.533	46.75	310		360
1520	1-1/4"	"	0.571	50.00	400		450
1530	1-1/2"	"	0.667	58.00	510		570
1540	2"	"	0.800	70.00	880		950
1980	Float and thermostatic trap, 15 psi						
2000	3/4"	EA	0.500	43.75	210		250
2010	1"	"	0.533	46.75	240		290
2020	1-1/4"	"	0.571	50.00	370		420
2030	1-1/2"	"	0.667	58.00	480		540
2040	2"	"	0.800	70.00	880		950
2135	Steam trap, cast iron body, threaded, 125 psi						
2140	3/4"	EA	0.500	43.75	250		290
2150	1"	"	0.533	46.75	290		340

FACILITY SANITARY SEWERAGE

ID Code	Component Descriptions	Unit of Meas.	Manhr / Unit	Labor Cost	Material Cost	Equip. Cost	Total Cost
22 - 13168	**TRAPS, Cont'd...**						**22 - 13168**
2160	1-1/4"	EA	0.571	50.00	430		480
2170	1-1/2"	"	0.667	58.00	690		750
22 - 13192	**CLEANOUTS**						**22 - 13192**
0980	Cleanout, wall						
1000	2"	EA	0.533	46.75	240		290
1020	3"	"	0.533	46.75	340		390
1040	4"	"	0.667	58.00	340		400
1042	6"	"	0.800	70.00	560		630
1046	8"	"	1.000	88.00	780		870
1050	Floor						
1060	2"	EA	0.667	58.00	220		280
1080	3"	"	0.667	58.00	290		350
1100	4"	"	0.800	70.00	300		370
1120	6"	"	1.000	88.00	410		500
1140	8"	"	1.143	100	770		870
22 - 13193	**GREASE TRAPS**						**22 - 13193**
1000	Grease traps, cast iron, 3" pipe						
1020	35 gpm, 70 lb capacity	EA	8.000	700	4,840		5,540
1040	50 gpm, 100 lb capacity	"	10.000	880	6,160		7,040

DOMESTIC WATER HEATERS

ID Code	Component Descriptions	Unit of Meas.	Manhr / Unit	Labor Cost	Material Cost	Equip. Cost	Total Cost
22 - 33001	**DOMESTIC WATER HEATERS**						**22 - 33001**
0900	Water heater, electric						
1000	6 gal	EA	1.333	120	450		570
1020	10 gal	"	1.333	120	460		580
1030	15 gal	"	1.333	120	450		570
1040	20 gal	"	1.600	140	630		770
1050	30 gal	"	1.600	140	650		790
1060	40 gal	"	1.600	140	710		850
1070	52 gal	"	2.000	180	800		980
1080	66 gal	"	2.000	180	970		1,150
1090	80 gal	"	2.000	180	1,050		1,230
1100	100 gal	"	2.667	230	1,300		1,530
1120	120 gal	"	2.667	230	1,670		1,900
2980	Oil fired						
3000	20 gal	EA	4.000	350	1,430		1,780

DOMESTIC WATER HEATERS

ID Code	Descriptions — Component Descriptions	Output — Unit of Meas.	Output — Manhr / Unit	Unit Costs — Labor Cost	Unit Costs — Material Cost	Unit Costs — Equip. Cost	Unit Costs — Total Cost
22 - 33001	**DOMESTIC WATER HEATERS, Cont'd...**						**22 - 33001**
3020	50 gal	EA	5.714	500	2,230		2,730
5000	Tankless water heater, natural gas						
5010	Min.	EA	5.333	470	770		1,240
5020	Ave.	"	8.000	700	880		1,580
5030	Max.	"	16.000	1,400	990		2,390
5040	Propane						
5050	Min.	EA	5.333	470	660		1,130
5060	Ave.	"	8.000	700	770		1,470
5070	Max.	"	16.000	1,400	880		2,280
22 - 33002	**SOLAR WATER HEATERS**						**22 - 33002**
1000	Hydronic system, 100-120 Gallons including material						
1010	Min.	EA					13,670
1020	Ave.	"					14,400
1030	Max.	"					15,130
1040	Direct-Solar, 100-120 Gallons						
1050	Min.	EA					9,080
1060	Ave.	"					9,500
1070	Max.	"					9,920
1080	Indirect-Solar tank, 50-80 Gallons						
1090	Min.	EA					1,810
1100	Ave.	"					2,240
1110	Max.	"					2,660
1120	100-120 Gallons						
1130	Min.	EA					3,030
1140	Ave.	"					3,450
1150	Max.	"					3,870
1160	Solar water collector panel, 3 x 8						
1170	Min.	EA	1.000	88.00	970		1,060
1180	Ave.	"	1.143	100	1,000		1,100
1190	Max.	"	1.333	120	1,030		1,150
1200	4 x 7						
1210	Min.	EA	1.000	88.00	1,090		1,180
1220	Ave.	"	1.143	100	1,120		1,220
1230	Max.	"	1.333	120	1,150		1,270
1240	4 x 8						
1250	Min.	EA	1.000	88.00	1,150		1,240
1260	Ave.	"	1.143	100	1,180		1,280

DOMESTIC WATER HEATERS

ID Code	Component Descriptions	Unit of Meas.	Manhr / Unit	Labor Cost	Material Cost	Equip. Cost	Total Cost
	Descriptions	**Output**		**Unit Costs**			

22 - 33002	SOLAR WATER HEATERS, Cont'd...						22 - 33002
1270	Max.	EA	1.333	120	1,210		1,330
1280	4 x 10						
1290	Min.	EA	1.143	100	1,330		1,430
1300	Ave.	"	1.333	120	1,450		1,570
1310	Max.	"	1.600	140	1,570		1,710
1320	Passive tube tank system, 12 Tube						
1330	Min.	EA	1.000	88.00	730		820
1340	Ave.	"	1.143	100	910		1,010
1350	Max.	"	1.333	120	1,090		1,210
1360	24 Tube						
1370	Min.	EA	1.000	88.00	1,090		1,180
1380	Ave.	"	1.143	100	1,270		1,370
1390	Max.	"	1.333	120	1,450		1,570
1400	27 Tube						
1410	Min.	EA	1.000	88.00	1,210		1,300
1420	Ave.	"	1.143	100	1,510		1,610
1430	Max.	"	1.333	120	1,810		1,930

COMMERCIAL PLUMBING FIXTURES

22 - 42009	FIXTURE CARRIERS						22 - 42009
0980	Water fountain, wall carrier						
1000	Minimum	EA	0.800	70.00	70.00		140
1020	Average	"	1.000	88.00	94.00		180
1040	Maximum	"	1.333	120	120		240
1110	Lavatory, wall carrier						
1120	Minimum	EA	0.800	70.00	160		230
1140	Average	"	1.000	88.00	230		320
1160	Maximum	"	1.333	120	290		410
1380	Sink, industrial, wall carrier						
1400	Minimum	EA	0.800	70.00	210		280
1420	Average	"	1.000	88.00	240		330
1440	Maximum	"	1.333	120	300		420
1510	Toilets, water closets, wall carrier						
1520	Minimum	EA	0.800	70.00	310		380
1540	Average	"	1.000	88.00	360		450
1560	Maximum	"	1.333	120	470		590
1570	Floor support						

COMMERCIAL PLUMBING FIXTURES

ID Code	Component Descriptions	Unit of Meas.	Manhr / Unit	Labor Cost	Material Cost	Equip. Cost	Total Cost
	Descriptions	**Output**		**Unit Costs**			

22 - 42009 — FIXTURE CARRIERS, Cont'd... — 22 - 42009

ID Code	Component Descriptions	Unit of Meas.	Manhr / Unit	Labor Cost	Material Cost	Equip. Cost	Total Cost
1580	Minimum	EA	0.667	58.00	150		210
1600	Average	"	0.800	70.00	180		250
1620	Maximum	"	1.000	88.00	200		290
1630	Urinals, wall carrier						
1640	Minimum	EA	0.800	70.00	160		230
1660	Average	"	1.000	88.00	210		300
1680	Maximum	"	1.333	120	250		370
1690	Floor support						
1700	Minimum	EA	0.667	58.00	130		190
1720	Average	"	0.800	70.00	190		260
1740	Maximum	"	1.000	88.00	220		310

22 - 42135 — URINALS — 22 - 42135

ID Code	Component Descriptions	Unit of Meas.	Manhr / Unit	Labor Cost	Material Cost	Equip. Cost	Total Cost
0980	Urinal, flush valve, floor mounted						
1000	Minimum	EA	2.000	180	540		720
1010	Average	"	2.667	230	640		870
1020	Maximum	"	4.000	350	750		1,100
1040	Wall mounted						
1060	Minimum	EA	2.000	180	450		630
1080	Average	"	2.667	230	620		850
1100	Maximum	"	4.000	350	800		1,150
8980	For trim and rough-in						
9000	Minimum	EA	2.000	180	200		380
9020	Average	"	4.000	350	290		640
9040	Maximum	"	5.333	470	390		860

22 - 42136 — WATER CLOSETS — 22 - 42136

ID Code	Component Descriptions	Unit of Meas.	Manhr / Unit	Labor Cost	Material Cost	Equip. Cost	Total Cost
0980	Water closet flush tank, floor mounted						
1000	Minimum	EA	2.000	180	360		540
1010	Average	"	2.667	230	710		940
1020	Maximum	"	4.000	350	1,130		1,480
1030	Handicapped						
1040	Minimum	EA	2.667	230	490		720
1050	Average	"	4.000	350	890		1,240
1060	Maximum	"	8.000	700	1,680		2,380
1180	Bowl, with flush valve, floor mounted						
1200	Minimum	EA	2.000	180	510		690
1220	Average	"	2.667	230	560		790
1240	Maximum	"	4.000	350	1,090		1,440

COMMERCIAL PLUMBING FIXTURES

ID Code	Component Descriptions	Unit of Meas.	Manhr / Unit	Labor Cost	Material Cost	Equip. Cost	Total Cost
		Descriptions	**Output**		**Unit Costs**		
22 - 42136	**WATER CLOSETS, Cont'd...**						**22 - 42136**
1250	Wall mounted						
1260	Minimum	EA	2.000	180	510		690
1280	Average	"	2.667	230	590		820
1300	Maximum	"	4.000	350	1,140		1,490
8980	For trim and rough-in						
9000	Minimum	EA	2.000	180	230		410
9020	Average	"	2.667	230	270		500
9040	Maximum	"	4.000	350	360		710
22 - 42162	**LAVATORIES**						**22 - 42162**
1980	Lavatory, counter top, porcelain enamel on cast iron						
2000	Minimum	EA	1.600	140	210		350
2010	Average	"	2.000	180	320		500
2020	Maximum	"	2.667	230	570		800
2080	Wall hung, china						
2100	Minimum	EA	1.600	140	290		430
2110	Average	"	2.000	180	340		520
2120	Maximum	"	2.667	230	850		1,080
2280	Handicapped						
2300	Minimum	EA	2.000	180	470		650
2310	Average	"	2.667	230	540		770
2320	Maximum	"	4.000	350	910		1,260
8980	For trim and rough-in						
9000	Minimum	EA	2.000	180	240		420
9020	Average	"	2.667	230	410		640
9040	Maximum	"	4.000	350	510		860
22 - 42164	**SINKS**						**22 - 42164**
0980	Service sink, 24"x29"						
1000	Minimum	EA	2.000	180	700		880
1020	Average	"	2.667	230	870		1,100
1040	Maximum	"	4.000	350	1,280		1,630
2000	Kitchen sink, single, stainless steel, single bowl						
2020	Minimum	EA	1.600	140	310		450
2040	Average	"	2.000	180	350		530
2060	Maximum	"	2.667	230	640		870
2070	Double bowl						
2080	Minimum	EA	2.000	180	350		530
2100	Average	"	2.667	230	390		620

COMMERCIAL PLUMBING FIXTURES

ID Code	Component Descriptions	Unit of Meas.	Manhr / Unit	Labor Cost	Material Cost	Equip. Cost	Total Cost
	Descriptions	**Output**		**Unit Costs**			

22 - 42164	**SINKS, Cont'd...**						**22 - 42164**
2120	Maximum	EA	4.000	350	680		1,030
2190	Porcelain enamel, cast iron, single bowl						
2200	Minimum	EA	1.600	140	220		360
2220	Average	"	2.000	180	290		470
2240	Maximum	"	2.667	230	450		680
2250	Double bowl						
2260	Minimum	EA	2.000	180	300		480
2280	Average	"	2.667	230	420		650
2300	Maximum	"	4.000	350	600		950
2980	Mop sink, 24"x36"x10"						
3000	Minimum	EA	1.600	140	530		670
3020	Average	"	2.000	180	640		820
3040	Maximum	"	2.667	230	860		1,090
5980	Washing machine box						
6000	Minimum	EA	2.000	180	190		370
6040	Average	"	2.667	230	280		510
6060	Maximum	"	4.000	350	340		690
8980	For trim and rough-in						
9000	Minimum	EA	2.667	230	310		540
9020	Average	"	4.000	350	480		830
9040	Maximum	"	5.333	470	620		1,090

22 - 42190	**BATHS**						**22 - 42190**
0980	Bath tub, 5' long						
1000	Minimum	EA	2.667	230	580		810
1020	Average	"	4.000	350	1,270		1,620
1040	Maximum	"	8.000	700	2,900		3,600
1050	6' long						
1060	Minimum	EA	2.667	230	650		880
1080	Average	"	4.000	350	1,330		1,680
1100	Maximum	"	8.000	700	3,760		4,460
1110	Square tub, whirlpool, 4'x4'						
1120	Minimum	EA	4.000	350	2,000		2,350
1140	Average	"	8.000	700	2,830		3,530
1160	Maximum	"	10.000	880	8,640		9,520
1170	5'x5'						
1180	Minimum	EA	4.000	350	2,000		2,350
1200	Average	"	8.000	700	2,830		3,530

COMMERCIAL PLUMBING FIXTURES

ID Code	Component Descriptions	Unit of Meas.	Manhr / Unit	Labor Cost	Material Cost	Equip. Cost	Total Cost
22 - 42190	**BATHS, Cont'd...**						**22 - 42190**
1220	Maximum	EA	10.000	880	8,800		9,680
1230	6'x6'						
1240	Minimum	EA	4.000	350	2,430		2,780
1260	Average	"	8.000	700	3,560		4,260
1280	Maximum	"	10.000	880	10,200		11,080
8980	For trim and rough-in						
9000	Minimum	EA	2.667	230	210		440
9020	Average	"	4.000	350	300		650
9040	Maximum	"	8.000	700	860		1,560
22 - 42230	**SHOWERS**						**22 - 42230**
0980	Shower, fiberglass, 36"x34"x84"						
1000	Minimum	EA	5.714	500	630		1,130
1020	Average	"	8.000	700	880		1,580
1040	Maximum	"	8.000	700	1,270		1,970
2980	Steel, 1 piece, 36"x36"						
3000	Minimum	EA	5.714	500	580		1,080
3020	Average	"	8.000	700	880		1,580
3040	Maximum	"	8.000	700	1,040		1,740
3980	Receptor, molded stone, 36"x36"						
4000	Minimum	EA	2.667	230	240		470
4020	Average	"	4.000	350	410		760
4040	Maximum	"	6.667	580	630		1,210
8980	For trim and rough-in						
9000	Minimum	EA	3.636	320	240		560
9020	Average	"	4.444	390	410		800
9040	Maximum	"	8.000	700	510		1,210
22 - 42260	**DISPOSALS & ACCESSORIES**						**22 - 42260**
0040	Disposal, continuous feed						
0050	Minimum	EA	1.600	140	79.00		220
0070	Maximum	"	2.667	230	420		650
0200	Batch feed, 1/2 hp						
0220	Minimum	EA	1.600	140	300		440
0240	Maximum	"	2.667	230	1,040		1,270
1100	Hot water dispenser						
1110	Minimum	EA	1.600	140	220		360
1130	Maximum	"	2.667	230	560		790

COMMERCIAL PLUMBING FIXTURES

ID Code	Component Descriptions	Unit of Meas.	Manhr / Unit	Labor Cost	Material Cost	Equip. Cost	Total Cost
	Descriptions	**Output**		**Unit Costs**			
22 - 42390		**FAUCETS**					**22 - 42390**
0980	Kitchen						
1000	Minimum	EA	1.333	120	91.00		210
1020	Average	"	1.600	140	250		390
1040	Maximum	"	2.000	180	310		490
1050	Bath						
1060	Minimum	EA	1.333	120	91.00		210
1080	Average	"	1.600	140	270		410
1100	Maximum	"	2.000	180	410		590
1110	Lavatory, domestic						
1120	Minimum	EA	1.333	120	97.00		220
1140	Average	"	1.600	140	310		450
1160	Maximum	"	2.000	180	510		690
1170	Hospital, patient rooms						
1180	Minimum	EA	2.000	180	130		310
1200	Average	"	2.667	230	420		650
1220	Maximum	"	4.000	350	740		1,090
1230	Operating room						
1240	Minimum	EA	2.000	180	280		460
1260	Average	"	2.667	230	600		830
1280	Maximum	"	4.000	350	880		1,230
1290	Washroom						
1300	Minimum	EA	1.333	120	120		240
1320	Average	"	1.600	140	300		440
1340	Maximum	"	2.000	180	560		740
1350	Handicapped						
1360	Minimum	EA	1.600	140	130		270
1380	Average	"	2.000	180	400		580
1400	Maximum	"	2.667	230	620		850
1410	Shower						
1420	Minimum	EA	1.333	120	120		240
1440	Average	"	1.600	140	350		490
1460	Maximum	"	2.000	180	560		740
1480	For trim and rough-in						
1500	Minimum	EA	1.600	140	85.00		230
1520	Average	"	2.000	180	130		310
1540	Maximum	"	4.000	350	220		570

COMMERCIAL PLUMBING FIXTURES

ID Code	Component Descriptions	Unit of Meas.	Manhr / Unit	Labor Cost	Material Cost	Equip. Cost	Total Cost
	Descriptions	**Output**		**Unit Costs**			

22 - 42398 — **HOSE BIBBS** — **22 - 42398**

ID Code	Component Descriptions	Unit of Meas.	Manhr / Unit	Labor Cost	Material Cost	Equip. Cost	Total Cost
0005	Hose bibb						
0010	1/2"	EA	0.267	23.50	10.50		34.00
0200	3/4"	"	0.267	23.50	11.00		34.50

DRINKING FOUNTAINS AND WATER COOLERS

22 - 47001 — **MISCELLANEOUS FIXTURES** — **22 - 47001**

ID Code	Component Descriptions	Unit of Meas.	Manhr / Unit	Labor Cost	Material Cost	Equip. Cost	Total Cost
0900	Electric water cooler						
1000	Floor mounted	EA	2.667	230	1,110		1,340
1020	Wall mounted	"	2.667	230	1,040		1,270
1980	Wash fountain						
2000	Wall mounted	EA	4.000	350	2,660		3,010
2020	Circular, floor supported	"	8.000	700	4,660		5,360
4000	Deluge shower and eye wash	"	4.000	350	1,110		1,460

POOLS AND FOUNTAIN PLUMBING SYSTEMS

22 - 51007 — **SOLAR WATER HEATERS, POOLS** — **22 - 51007**

ID Code	Component Descriptions	Unit of Meas.	Manhr / Unit	Labor Cost	Material Cost	Equip. Cost	Total Cost
1000	Solar Water Heater, 1000 BTU/SF panel, 4x8	EA	1.000	88.00	130		220
1100	4X10	"	1.143	100	150		250
1200	4X12	"	1.333	120	170		290
2200	Panel Mounting Kit, 4x8	"	0.400	35.00	36.25		71.00
2300	4X10	"	0.444	39.00	54.00		93.00
2400	4X12	"	0.500	43.75	67.00		110

GAS AND VACUUM SYSTEMS

22 - 66001 — **GLASS PIPE** — **22 - 66001**

ID Code	Component Descriptions	Unit of Meas.	Manhr / Unit	Labor Cost	Material Cost	Equip. Cost	Total Cost
0980	Glass pipe						
1000	1-1/2" dia.	LF	0.160	14.00	13.00		27.00
1020	2" dia.	"	0.178	15.50	17.50		33.00
1040	3" dia.	"	0.200	17.50	23.50		41.00
1060	4" dia.	"	0.229	20.00	42.75		63.00
1080	6" dia.	"	0.267	23.50	78.00		100

DIVISION 23
HVAC

INSULATION

ID Code	Descriptions	Output		Unit Costs			
	Component Descriptions	Unit of Meas.	Manhr / Unit	Labor Cost	Material Cost	Equip. Cost	Total Cost

23 - 07131   DUCTWORK INSULATION   23 - 07131

ID Code	Component Descriptions	Unit of Meas.	Manhr / Unit	Labor Cost	Material Cost	Equip. Cost	Total Cost
0980	Fiberglass duct insulation, plain blanket						
1000	1-1/2" thick	SF	0.010	0.87	0.22		1.09
1060	2" thick	"	0.013	1.16	0.30		1.46
1500	With vapor barrier						
1520	1-1/2" thick	SF	0.010	0.87	0.26		1.13
1540	2" thick	"	0.013	1.16	0.33		1.49
2000	Rigid with vapor barrier						
2020	2" thick	SF	0.027	2.33	1.45		3.78
2040	3" thick	"	0.032	2.80	1.99		4.79
2060	4" thick	"	0.040	3.50	2.54		6.04
2080	6" thick	"	0.053	4.67	3.99		8.66
3180	Weatherproof, poly, 3" thick, w/vapor barrier	"	0.080	7.01	3.08		10.00
3200	Urethane board with vapor barrier	"	0.100	8.77	4.35		13.00

CONTROLS

23 - 09131   HVAC CONTROLS   23 - 09131

ID Code	Component Descriptions	Unit of Meas.	Manhr / Unit	Labor Cost	Material Cost	Equip. Cost	Total Cost
1000	Pressure gauge, direct reading gage cock and siphon	EA	0.500	43.75	130		170
1210	Control valve, 1", modulating						
1220	2-way	EA	0.667	58.00	960		1,020
1240	3-way	"	1.000	88.00	1,090		1,180
1260	Self contained control valve w/ sensing elmnt, 3/4"	"	0.500	43.75	180		220
1920	Inst air syst 2-1/2 hp comp, rcvr refrg dryer	"					8,080
2020	Thermostat primary control device	"					180
2040	Humidistat primary control device	"					140
2060	Timers primary control device, indoor/outdoor, 24 hour	"					280
2080	Thermometer, dir. reading, 3 dial	"					140
4380	Control dampers, round						
4400	6" dia.	EA	0.320	28.00	120		150
4401	8" dia	"	0.320	28.00	170		200
4402	10" dia	"	0.320	28.00	230		260
4403	12" dia	"	0.320	28.00	300		330
4404	16" dia	"	0.400	35.00	450		480
4405	18" dia	"	0.400	35.00	480		520
4406	20" dia	"	0.400	35.00	640		680
4407	Rectangular, parallel blade standard leakage						
4480	12" x 12"	EA	0.400	35.00	91.00		130
4525	16" x 16"	"	0.400	35.00	130		160

CONTROLS

ID Code	Descriptions — Component Descriptions	Output — Unit of Meas.	Output — Manhr / Unit	Unit Costs — Labor Cost	Unit Costs — Material Cost	Unit Costs — Equip. Cost	Unit Costs — Total Cost
23 - 09131	**HVAC CONTROLS, Cont'd...**						**23 - 09131**
4530	20" x 20"	EA	0.400	35.00	160		200
4600	48" x 48"	"	1.143	100	480		580
4680	48" x 60"	"	1.333	120	610		730
4700	48" x 72"	"	1.333	120	740		860
4980	Low leakage						
5000	12" x 12"	EA	0.400	35.00	170		200
5040	16" x 16"	"	0.400	35.00	220		250
5140	36" x 36"	"	0.667	58.00	570		630
5220	48" x 48"	"	1.143	100	1,020		1,120
5320	48" x 72"	"	1.333	120	1,580		1,700
5980	Rectangular, opposed horizontal blade						
6000	12" x 12"	EA	0.400	35.00	120		160
6040	16" x 16"	"	0.400	35.00	160		200
6080	24" x 24"	"	0.400	35.00	220		250
6140	36" x 36"	"	0.667	58.00	360		420
6320	48" x 72"	"	1.333	120	1,020		1,140

HYDRONIC PIPING AND PUMPS

ID Code	Component Descriptions	Unit of Meas.	Manhr / Unit	Labor Cost	Material Cost	Equip. Cost	Total Cost
23 - 21136	**EXPANSION TANKS**						**23 - 21136**
0980	Expansion tank, 125 psi, steel						
1000	20 gallon	EA	1.000	88.00	750		840
1060	80 gallon	"	2.286	200	1,130		1,330
23 - 21137	**STRAINERS**						**23 - 21137**
0980	Strainer, Y pattern, 125 psi, cast iron body, threaded						
1000	3/4"	EA	0.286	25.00	13.75		38.75
1010	1"	"	0.320	28.00	17.75		45.75
1020	1-1/4"	"	0.400	35.00	22.25		57.00
1030	1-1/2"	"	0.400	35.00	28.25		63.00
1040	2"	"	0.500	43.75	42.00		86.00
1980	250 psi, brass body, threaded						
2000	3/4"	EA	0.320	28.00	36.00		64.00
2010	1"	"	0.320	28.00	50.00		78.00
2040	1-1/4"	"	0.400	35.00	63.00		98.00
2100	1-1/2"	"	0.400	35.00	88.00		120
2120	2"	"	0.500	43.75	150		190
2130	Cast iron body, threaded						
2140	3/4"	EA	0.320	28.00	21.00		49.00

HYDRONIC PIPING AND PUMPS

ID Code	Descriptions — Component Descriptions	Output — Unit of Meas.	Output — Manhr / Unit	Unit Costs — Labor Cost	Unit Costs — Material Cost	Unit Costs — Equip. Cost	Unit Costs — Total Cost
23 - 21137	**STRAINERS, Cont'd...**						**23 - 21137**
2160	1"	EA	0.320	28.00	26.75		55.00
2180	1-1/4"	"	0.400	35.00	35.50		71.00
2200	1-1/2"	"	0.400	35.00	47.00		82.00
2220	2"	"	0.500	43.75	60.00		100

AIR DISTRIBUTION

23 - 31130	**METAL DUCTWORK**						**23 - 31130**
0090	Rectangular duct						
0100	Galvanized steel						
1000	Minimum	LB	0.073	6.37	0.88		7.25
1010	Average	"	0.089	7.79	1.10		8.89
1020	Maximum	"	0.133	11.75	1.68		13.50
1080	Aluminum						
1100	Minimum	LB	0.160	14.00	2.29		16.25
1120	Average	"	0.200	17.50	3.05		20.50
1140	Maximum	"	0.267	23.50	3.79		27.25
1160	Fittings						
1180	Minimum	EA	0.267	23.50	7.26		30.75
1200	Average	"	0.400	35.00	11.00		46.00
1220	Maximum	"	0.800	70.00	16.00		86.00
1230	For work						
1240	10-20' high, add per pound, $.30						
1260	30-50', add per pound, $.50						

AIR DUCT ACCESSORIES

23 - 33130	**DAMPERS**						**23 - 33130**
0980	Horizontal parallel aluminum backdraft damper						
1000	12" x 12"	EA	0.200	17.50	58.00		76.00
1010	16" x 16"	"	0.229	20.00	60.00		80.00
1030	24" x 24"	"	0.400	35.00	92.00		130
1060	36" x 36"	"	0.571	50.00	210		260
1100	48" x 48"	"	0.800	70.00	380		450
2000	"Up", parallel dampers						
2010	12" x 12"	EA	0.200	17.50	94.00		110
2020	16" x 16"	"	0.229	20.00	130		150
2040	24" x 24"	"	0.400	35.00	160		200

AIR DUCT ACCESSORIES

	Descriptions	Output		Unit Costs			
ID Code	Component Descriptions	Unit of Meas.	Manhr / Unit	Labor Cost	Material Cost	Equip. Cost	Total Cost

23 - 33130 — DAMPERS, Cont'd... — 23 - 33130

2070	36" x 36"	EA	0.571	50.00	280		330
2100	48" x 48"	"	0.800	70.00	540		610
3000	"Down", parallel dampers						
3010	12" x 12"	EA	0.200	17.50	94.00		110
3020	16" x 16"	"	0.229	20.00	130		150
3040	24" x 24"	"	0.400	35.00	160		200
3070	36" x 36"	"	0.571	50.00	280		330
3100	48" x 48"	"	0.800	70.00	540		610
3980	Fire damper, 1.5 hr rating						
4000	12" x 12"	EA	0.400	35.00	38.25		73.00
4010	16" x 16"	"	0.400	35.00	61.00		96.00
4030	24" x 24"	"	0.400	35.00	77.00		110
4060	36" x 36"	"	0.800	70.00	130		200
4090	48" x 48"	"	1.143	100	250		350

23 - 33460 — FLEXIBLE DUCTWORK — 23 - 33460

1010	Flexible duct, 1.25" fiberglass						
1020	5" dia.	LF	0.040	3.50	3.31		6.81
1040	6" dia.	"	0.044	3.89	3.68		7.57
1060	7" dia.	"	0.047	4.12	4.54		8.66
1080	8" dia.	"	0.050	4.38	4.76		9.14
1100	10" dia.	"	0.057	5.01	6.34		11.25
1120	12" dia.	"	0.062	5.39	6.93		12.25
1140	14" dia.	"	0.067	5.84	8.69		14.50
1160	16" dia.	"	0.073	6.37	13.00		19.25
9000	Flexible duct connector, 3" wide fabric	"	0.133	11.75	2.31		14.00

HVAC FANS

23 - 34001 — EXHAUST FANS — 23 - 34001

0160	Belt drive roof exhaust fans						
1020	640 cfm, 2618 fpm	EA	1.000	88.00	1,140		1,230
1030	940 cfm, 2604 fpm	"	1.000	88.00	1,480		1,570
1040	1050 cfm, 3325 fpm	"	1.000	88.00	1,320		1,410
1050	1170 cfm, 2373 fpm	"	1.000	88.00	1,920		2,010
1110	2440 cfm, 4501 fpm	"	1.000	88.00	1,500		1,590
1120	2760 cfm, 4950 fpm	"	1.000	88.00	1,660		1,750
1140	3890 cfm, 6769 fpm	"	1.000	88.00	1,890		1,980
1160	2380 cfm, 3382 fpm	"	1.000	88.00	2,100		2,190

HVAC FANS

ID Code	Descriptions	Output		Unit Costs			
	Component Descriptions	Unit of Meas.	Manhr / Unit	Labor Cost	Material Cost	Equip. Cost	Total Cost
23 - 34001	**EXHAUST FANS, Cont'd...**						**23 - 34001**
1180	2880 cfm, 3859 fpm	EA	1.000	88.00	2,200		2,290
1200	3200 cfm, 4173 fpm	"	1.333	120	2,220		2,340
1260	3660 cfm, 3437 fpm	"	1.333	120	2,260		2,380
3020	Direct drive fans						
3040	60 to 390 cfm	EA	1.000	88.00	930		1,020
3060	145 to 590 cfm	"	1.000	88.00	1,130		1,220
3080	295 to 860 cfm	"	1.000	88.00	1,370		1,460
3100	235 to 1300 cfm	"	1.000	88.00	1,470		1,560
3120	415 to 1630 cfm	"	1.000	88.00	1,660		1,750
3160	590 to 2045 cfm	"	1.000	88.00	1,920		2,010

AIR OUTLETS AND INLETS

ID Code	Descriptions	Output		Unit Costs			
23 - 37131	**DIFFUSERS**						**23 - 37131**
1980	Ceiling diffusers, round, baked enamel finish						
2000	6" dia.	EA	0.267	23.50	40.25		64.00
2060	12" dia.	"	0.333	29.25	69.00		98.00
2100	16" dia.	"	0.364	32.00	100		130
2140	20" dia.	"	0.400	35.00	140		180
2480	Rectangular						
2500	6x6"	EA	0.267	23.50	43.00		67.00
2540	12x12"	"	0.400	35.00	76.00		110
2580	18x18"	"	0.400	35.00	120		160
2620	24x24"	"	0.500	43.75	170		210
3000	Lay in, flush mounted, perforated face, with grid						
3010	6x6/24x24	EA	0.320	28.00	62.00		90.00
3080	12x12/24x24	"	0.320	28.00	72.00		100
3140	18x18/24x24	"	0.320	28.00	110		140
5000	Two-way slot diffuser with balancing damper, 4'	"	0.800	70.00	69.00		140
23 - 37134	**REGISTERS AND GRILLES**						**23 - 37134**
0980	Lay in flush mounted, perforated face, return						
1000	6x6/24x24	EA	0.320	28.00	51.00		79.00
1020	8x8/24x24	"	0.320	28.00	51.00		79.00
1040	9x9/24x24	"	0.320	28.00	55.00		83.00
1060	10x10/24x24	"	0.320	28.00	60.00		88.00
1080	12x12/24x24	"	0.320	28.00	60.00		88.00
3040	Rectangular, ceiling return, single deflection						
3060	10x10	EA	0.400	35.00	30.75		66.00

AIR OUTLETS AND INLETS

ID Code	Component Descriptions	Unit of Meas.	Manhr / Unit	Labor Cost	Material Cost	Equip. Cost	Total Cost
	Descriptions	**Output**		**Unit Costs**			
23 - 37134	**REGISTERS AND GRILLES, Cont'd...**						**23 - 37134**
3080	12x12	EA	0.400	35.00	35.75		71.00
3100	14x14	"	0.400	35.00	43.50		79.00
3120	16x8	"	0.400	35.00	35.75		71.00
3140	16x16	"	0.400	35.00	35.75		71.00
3220	24x12	"	0.400	35.00	97.00		130
3240	24x18	"	0.400	35.00	130		160
3260	36x24	"	0.444	39.00	240		280
3280	36x30	"	0.444	39.00	350		390
4980	Wall, return air register						
5000	12x12	EA	0.200	17.50	51.00		69.00
5020	16x16	"	0.200	17.50	75.00		93.00
5040	18x18	"	0.200	17.50	89.00		110
5060	20x20	"	0.200	17.50	110		130
5080	24x24	"	0.200	17.50	150		170
5980	Ceiling, return air grille						
6000	6x6	EA	0.267	23.50	29.50		53.00
6020	8x8	"	0.320	28.00	36.75		65.00
6040	10x10	"	0.320	28.00	45.50		74.00
6980	Ceiling, exhaust grille, aluminum egg crate						
7000	6x6	EA	0.267	23.50	20.25		43.75
7020	8x8	"	0.320	28.00	20.25		48.25
7040	10x10	"	0.320	28.00	22.50		51.00
7060	12x12	"	0.400	35.00	27.75		63.00
7080	14x14	"	0.400	35.00	36.25		71.00
7100	16x16	"	0.400	35.00	42.50		78.00
7120	18x18	"	0.400	35.00	51.00		86.00
23 - 37232	**RELIEF VENTILATORS**						**23 - 37232**
0980	Intake ventilator, aluminum, with screen, no curbs						
1000	12" x 12"	EA	0.667	58.00	230		290
1020	16" x 16"	"	0.800	70.00	310		380
1100	36" x 36"	"	1.333	120	1,210		1,330
1140	48" x 48"	"	1.600	140	1,990		2,130

AIR OUTLETS AND INLETS

ID Code	Descriptions — Component Descriptions	Output — Unit of Meas.	Output — Manhr / Unit	Unit Costs — Labor Cost	Unit Costs — Material Cost	Unit Costs — Equip. Cost	Unit Costs — Total Cost
23 - 37238	**PENTHOUSE LOUVERS**						**23 - 37238**
0100	Penthouse louvers						
1000	12" high, extruded aluminum, 4" louver						
1020	6' perimeter	EA	2.000	180	500		680
1080	12' perimeter	"	2.000	180	1,210		1,390
1160	20' perimeter	"	5.333	470	2,490		2,960
2000	16" high x 4' perimeter	"	2.000	180	410		590
2020	6' perimeter	"	2.000	180	580		760
2080	12' perimeter	"	2.000	180	1,360		1,540
2160	20' perimeter	"	5.333	470	2,920		3,390
3000	20" high x 4' perimeter	"	2.000	180	580		760
3020	6' perimeter	"	2.000	180	620		800
3080	12' perimeter	"	2.000	180	1,520		1,700
3160	20' perimeter	"	5.333	470	3,120		3,590
4000	24" high x 4' perimeter	"	2.000	180	580		760
4020	6' perimeter	"	2.000	180	700		880
4080	12' perimeter	"	2.000	180	1,690		1,870
4160	20' perimeter	"	5.333	470	3,520		3,990

CENTRAL HEATING EQUIPMENT

ID Code	Component Descriptions	Unit of Meas.	Manhr / Unit	Labor Cost	Material Cost	Equip. Cost	Total Cost
23 - 52230	**BOILERS**						**23 - 52230**
0900	Cast iron, gas fired, hot water						
1000	115 mbh	EA	20.000	1,240	3,150	1,110	5,500
1020	175 mbh	"	21.818	1,360	3,750	1,210	6,320
1040	235 mbh	"	24.000	1,490	4,800	1,330	7,620
1060	940 mbh	"	48.000	2,980	16,530	2,660	22,170
1080	1600 mbh	"	60.000	3,730	22,860	3,330	29,910
1100	3000 mbh	"	80.000	4,970	36,980	4,430	46,390
1120	6000 mbh	"	120.000	7,460	74,000	6,650	88,110
1130	Steam						
1140	115 mbh	EA	20.000	1,240	3,470	1,110	5,820
1160	175 mbh	"	21.818	1,360	4,180	1,210	6,750
1180	235 mbh	"	24.000	1,490	4,950	1,330	7,770
1200	940 mbh	"	48.000	2,980	17,280	2,660	22,920
1220	1600 mbh	"	60.000	3,730	22,360	3,330	29,410
1240	3000 mbh	"	80.000	4,970	33,300	4,430	42,710
1260	6000 mbh	"	120.000	7,460	70,280	6,650	84,390
1980	Electric, hot water						

CENTRAL HEATING EQUIPMENT

ID Code	Descriptions — Component Descriptions	Output — Unit of Meas.	Output — Manhr / Unit	Unit Costs — Labor Cost	Unit Costs — Material Cost	Unit Costs — Equip. Cost	Unit Costs — Total Cost
23 - 52230	**BOILERS, Cont'd...**						**23 - 52230**
2000	115 mbh	EA	12.000	750	5,630	670	7,040
2020	175 mbh	"	12.000	750	6,230	670	7,640
2040	235 mbh	"	12.000	750	7,110	670	8,520
2060	940 mbh	"	24.000	1,490	17,290	1,330	20,110
2080	1600 mbh	"	48.000	2,980	24,490	2,660	30,130
2100	3000 mbh	"	60.000	3,730	36,580	3,330	43,630
2120	6000 mbh	"	80.000	4,970	42,430	4,430	51,840
2130	Steam						
2140	115 mbh	EA	12.000	750	7,110	670	8,520
2160	175 mbh	"	12.000	750	8,700	670	10,110
2180	235 mbh	"	12.000	750	9,500	670	10,910
2190	940 mbh	"	24.000	1,490	18,910	1,330	21,730
2200	1600 mbh	"	48.000	2,980	31,700	2,660	37,340
2220	3000 mbh	"	60.000	3,730	45,040	3,330	52,090
2240	6000 mbh	"	80.000	4,970	46,800	4,430	56,210
3980	Oil fired, hot water						
4000	115 mbh	EA	16.000	990	4,150	890	6,030
4010	175 mbh	"	18.462	1,150	5,270	1,020	7,440
4020	235 mbh	"	21.818	1,360	7,280	1,210	9,850
4030	940 mbh	"	40.000	2,490	13,820	2,220	18,520
4040	1600 mbh	"	48.000	2,980	21,900	2,660	27,540
4060	3000 mbh	"	60.000	3,730	31,750	3,330	38,800
4080	6000 mbh	"	120.000	7,460	73,440	6,650	87,550
4190	Steam						
4200	115 mbh	EA	16.000	990	4,150	890	6,030
4220	175 mbh	"	18.462	1,150	5,270	1,020	7,440
4240	235 mbh	"	21.818	1,360	6,720	1,210	9,290
4260	940 mbh	"	40.000	2,490	13,420	2,220	18,120
4280	1600 mbh	"	48.000	2,980	21,900	2,660	27,540
4300	3000 mbh	"	60.000	3,730	29,550	3,330	36,600
4320	6000 mbh	"	120.000	7,460	73,440	6,650	87,550

FURNACES

ID Code	Descriptions — Component Descriptions	Output — Unit of Meas.	Output — Manhr / Unit	Unit Costs — Labor Cost	Unit Costs — Material Cost	Unit Costs — Equip. Cost	Unit Costs — Total Cost
23 - 54130	**FURNACES**						**23 - 54130**
0980	Electric, hot air						
1000	40 mbh	EA	4.000	350	850		1,200
1020	60 mbh	"	4.211	370	920		1,290
1040	80 mbh	"	4.444	390	1,000		1,390
1060	100 mbh	"	4.706	410	1,130		1,540
1080	125 mbh	"	4.848	430	1,380		1,810
1100	160 mbh	"	5.000	440	1,900		2,340
1120	200 mbh	"	5.161	450	2,760		3,210
1140	400 mbh	"	5.333	470	4,890		5,360
1980	Gas fired hot air						
2000	40 mbh	EA	4.000	350	850		1,200
2020	60 mbh	"	4.211	370	910		1,280
2040	80 mbh	"	4.444	390	1,050		1,440
2060	100 mbh	"	4.706	410	1,090		1,500
2080	125 mbh	"	4.848	430	1,200		1,630
2100	160 mbh	"	5.000	440	1,430		1,870
2120	200 mbh	"	5.161	450	2,540		2,990
2140	400 mbh	"	5.333	470	4,540		5,010
2980	Oil fired hot air						
3000	40 mbh	EA	4.000	350	1,140		1,490
3020	60 mbh	"	4.211	370	1,890		2,260
3040	80 mbh	"	4.444	390	1,900		2,290
3060	100 mbh	"	4.706	410	1,930		2,340
3080	125 mbh	"	4.848	430	2,000		2,430
3100	160 mbh	"	5.000	440	2,300		2,740
3120	200 mbh	"	5.161	450	2,700		3,150
3140	400 mbh	"	5.333	470	4,480		4,950

CENTRAL COOLING EQUIPMENT

ID Code	CONDENSING UNITS	Unit of Meas.	Manhr / Unit	Labor Cost	Material Cost	Equip. Cost	Total Cost
23 - 63001	**CONDENSING UNITS**						**23 - 63001**
0980	Air cooled condenser, single circuit						
1000	3 ton	EA	1.333	120	1,730		1,850
1030	5 ton	"	1.333	120	2,590		2,710
1040	7.5 ton	"	3.810	330	4,240		4,570
1050	20 ton	"	4.000	350	12,590		12,940
1060	25 ton	"	4.000	350	18,980		19,330
1070	30 ton	"	4.000	350	21,630		21,980

CENTRAL COOLING EQUIPMENT

ID Code	Component Descriptions	Unit of Meas.	Manhr / Unit	Labor Cost	Material Cost	Equip. Cost	Total Cost
			Output		**Unit Costs**		

23 - 63001   **CONDENSING UNITS, Cont'd...**   **23 - 63001**

ID Code	Component Descriptions	Unit of Meas.	Manhr / Unit	Labor Cost	Material Cost	Equip. Cost	Total Cost
1080	40 ton	EA	5.714	500	27,970		28,470
1090	50 ton	"	5.714	500	34,020		34,520
1100	60 ton	"	5.000	440	39,160		39,600
1480	With low ambient dampers						
1500	3 ton	EA	2.000	180	1,880		2,060
1530	5 ton	"	2.000	180	2,970		3,150
1550	7.5 ton	"	4.000	350	4,570		4,920
1570	20 ton	"	5.333	470	12,630		13,100
1590	25 ton	"	5.333	470	19,230		19,700
1610	30 ton	"	5.333	470	22,090		22,560
1630	40 ton	"	6.667	580	29,310		29,890
1650	50 ton	"	7.273	640	35,360		36,000
1670	60 ton	"	7.273	640	40,550		41,190
2980	Dual circuit						
3000	10 ton	EA	4.000	350	4,040		4,390
3010	15 ton	"	5.714	500	5,910		6,410
3030	20 ton	"	5.714	500	12,080		12,580
3040	25 ton	"	5.714	500	19,240		19,740
3050	30 ton	"	5.714	500	22,380		22,880
3060	40 ton	"	6.667	580	32,000		32,580
3070	50 ton	"	6.667	580	35,360		35,940
3080	60 ton	"	6.667	580	36,700		37,280
3100	80 ton	"	8.889	780	45,880		46,660
3120	100 ton	"	8.889	780	53,710		54,490
3130	120 ton	"	8.889	780	63,780		64,560
4030	With low ambient dampers						
4050	15 ton	EA	5.714	500	6,580		7,080
4080	20 ton	"	5.714	500	12,840		13,340
4100	25 ton	"	5.714	500	20,370		20,870
4120	30 ton	"	5.714	500	22,960		23,460
4140	40 ton	"	6.667	580	33,120		33,700
4160	50 ton	"	6.667	580	36,480		37,060
4180	60 ton	"	6.667	580	37,820		38,400
4190	80 ton	"	8.889	780	48,110		48,890
4200	100 ton	"	8.889	780	55,950		56,730
4210	120 ton	"	8.889	780	66,690		67,470

PACKAGED WATER CHILLERS

ID Code	Descriptions — Component Descriptions	Output — Unit of Meas.	Output — Manhr / Unit	Unit Costs — Labor Cost	Unit Costs — Material Cost	Unit Costs — Equip. Cost	Unit Costs — Total Cost
23 - 64001	**CHILLERS**						**23 - 64001**
0980	Chiller, reciprocal						
1000	Air cooled, remote condenser, starter						
1020	20 ton	EA	8.000	500	29,960	440	30,900
1030	25 ton	"	8.000	500	33,810	440	34,750
1040	30 ton	"	8.000	500	35,750	440	36,690
1050	40 ton	"	12.000	750	52,870	670	54,280
1060	50 ton	"	13.333	830	58,690	740	60,260
1120	100 ton	"	24.000	1,490	96,330	1,330	99,150
1160	200 ton	"	40.000	2,490	175,530	2,220	180,230
2000	Water cooled, with starter						
2020	20 ton	EA	8.000	500	25,690	440	26,630
2030	25 ton	"	8.000	500	28,470	440	29,410
2040	30 ton	"	12.000	750	34,240	670	35,650
2050	40 ton	"	12.000	750	47,090	670	48,500
2060	50 ton	"	13.333	830	51,370	740	52,940
2120	100 ton	"	24.000	1,490	74,920	1,330	77,740
2160	200 ton	"	40.000	2,490	119,870	2,220	124,570
2980	Packaged, air cooled, with starter						
3000	20 ton	EA	6.000	370	28,690	330	29,400
3010	25 ton	"	6.000	370	31,040	330	31,750
3020	30 ton	"	6.000	370	36,180	330	36,890
3030	40 ton	"	6.000	370	41,530	330	42,240
3980	Heat recovery, air cooled, with starter						
4010	50 ton	EA	12.000	750	55,650	670	57,060
4040	100 ton	"	24.000	1,490	79,630	1,330	82,450
4045	Water cooled, with starter						
4050	40 ton	EA	12.000	750	47,520	670	48,930
4090	100 ton	"	26.667	1,660	85,830	1,480	88,970
4980	Centrifugal, single bundle condenser, with starter						
5000	80 ton	EA	34.286	2,130	112,380	1,900	116,410
5040	230 ton	"	53.333	3,310	129,460	2,960	135,730
5070	460 ton	"	80.000	4,970	196,150	4,430	205,560
5090	670 ton	"	96.000	5,970	261,580	5,320	272,870

COOLING TOWERS

ID Code	Component Descriptions	Unit of Meas.	Manhr / Unit	Labor Cost	Material Cost	Equip. Cost	Total Cost
	Descriptions	**Output**		**Unit Costs**			
23 - 65001	**COOLING TOWERS**					**23 - 65001**	
5980	Cooling tower, propeller type						
6000	100 ton	EA	8.000	500	14,750	440	15,690
6030	400 ton	"	24.000	1,490	49,260	1,330	52,080
6060	1000 ton	"	60.000	3,730	118,280	3,330	125,330
6065	Centrifugal						
6070	100 ton	EA	8.000	500	20,460	440	21,400
6110	400 ton	"	24.000	1,490	59,000	1,330	61,820
6140	1000 ton	"	60.000	3,730	138,040	3,330	145,090

AIR HANDLING

ID Code	Component Descriptions	Unit of Meas.	Manhr / Unit	Labor Cost	Material Cost	Equip. Cost	Total Cost
23 - 74001	**AIR HANDLING UNITS**					**23 - 74001**	
0980	Air handling unit, medium pressure, single zone						
1000	1500 cfm	EA	5.000	440	4,840		5,280
1060	3000 cfm	"	8.889	780	6,360		7,140
1180	4000 cfm	"	10.000	880	8,150		9,030
2000	5000 cfm	"	10.667	940	10,270		11,210
2120	6000 cfm	"	11.429	1,000	13,200		14,200
2240	7000 cfm	"	12.308	1,080	15,150		16,230
3000	8500 cfm	"	13.333	1,170	18,630		19,800
3120	10,500 cfm	"	16.000	1,400	20,460		21,860
3240	12,500 cfm	"	17.778	1,560	23,550		25,110
8980	Rooftop air handling units						
9000	4950 cfm	EA	8.889	780	13,910		14,690
9060	7370 cfm	"	11.429	1,000	17,640		18,640
9080	9790 cfm	"	13.333	1,170	18,770		19,940
9100	14,300 cfm	"	11.429	1,000	26,510		27,510
9120	21,725 cfm	"	11.429	1,000	37,550		38,550
9140	33,000 cfm	"	13.333	1,170	53,020		54,190
23 - 74009	**ROOF CURBS**					**23 - 74009**	
0980	8" high, insulated, with liner and raised can						
1000	15" x 15"	EA	0.400	35.00	120		160
1060	21" x 21"	"	0.400	35.00	150		190
1160	36" x 36"	"	0.571	50.00	210		260
1200	48" x 48"	"	0.615	54.00	600		650
1260	60" x 60"	"	0.800	70.00	1,100		1,170
1320	72" x 72"	"	1.000	88.00	1,760		1,850

HVAC EQUIPMENT

ID Code	Descriptions	Output		Unit Costs			
	Component Descriptions	Unit of Meas.	Manhr / Unit	Labor Cost	Material Cost	Equip. Cost	Total Cost
23 - 81132	**ROOFTOP UNITS**						**23 - 81132**
0980	Packaged, single zone rooftop unit, with roof curb						
1000	2 ton	EA	8.000	700	4,130		4,830
1020	3 ton	"	8.000	700	4,340		5,040
1040	4 ton	"	10.000	880	4,740		5,620
1060	5 ton	"	13.333	1,170	5,140		6,310
1070	7.5 ton	"	16.000	1,400	7,470		8,870
23 - 81230	**COMPUTER ROOM A/C**						**23 - 81230**
1010	Air cooled, alarm, high efficiency filter, elec. heat						
1020	3 ton	EA	6.154	540	16,940		17,480
1040	5 ton	"	6.667	580	18,090		18,670
1060	7.5 ton	"	8.000	700	32,780		33,480
1070	10 ton	"	10.000	880	34,260		35,140
1080	15 ton	"	11.429	1,000	37,650		38,650
1090	Steam heat						
1100	3 ton	EA	6.154	540	18,130		18,670
1120	5 ton	"	6.667	580	19,290		19,870
1140	7.5 ton	"	8.000	700	30,720		31,420
1160	10 ton	"	10.000	880	31,650		32,530
1180	15 ton	"	11.429	1,000	35,000		36,000
1190	Hot water heat						
1200	3 ton	EA	6.154	540	18,130		18,670
1220	5 ton	"	6.667	580	19,290		19,870
1240	7.5 ton	"	8.000	700	30,720		31,420
1260	10 ton	"	10.000	880	31,650		32,530
1300	15 ton	"	11.429	1,000	35,110		36,110
1310	Air cooled condenser, low ambient damper						
1320	3 ton	EA	1.600	140	1,810		1,950
1340	5 ton	"	2.000	180	2,850		3,030
1360	7.5 ton	"	4.000	350	4,380		4,730
1400	10 ton	"	5.714	500	6,400		6,900
1420	15 ton	"	4.706	410	7,070		7,480
3010	Water cooled, high efficiency filter, alarm, elec. heat						
3020	3 ton	EA	5.714	500	18,800		19,300
3040	5 ton	"	6.667	580	20,250		20,830
3060	7.5 ton	"	10.000	880	32,260		33,140
3080	10 ton	"	11.429	1,000	33,470		34,470
3100	15 ton	"	13.333	1,170	39,170		40,340

HVAC EQUIPMENT

	Descriptions	Output		Unit Costs			
ID Code	Component Descriptions	Unit of Meas.	Manhr / Unit	Labor Cost	Material Cost	Equip. Cost	Total Cost

23 - 81230   COMPUTER ROOM A/C, Cont'd...   23 - 81230

ID Code	Component Descriptions	Unit of Meas.	Manhr / Unit	Labor Cost	Material Cost	Equip. Cost	Total Cost
3110	Steam heat						
3120	3 ton	EA	5.714	500	21,470		21,970
3140	5 ton	"	6.667	580	24,500		25,080
3160	7.5 ton	"	10.000	880	34,560		35,440
3180	10 ton	"	11.429	1,000	35,780		36,780
3200	15 ton	"	13.333	1,170	41,600		42,770
3210	Hot water heat						
3220	3 ton	EA	5.714	500	21,470		21,970
3240	5 ton	"	6.667	580	22,920		23,500
3260	7.5 ton	"	10.000	880	34,560		35,440
3280	10 ton	"	11.429	1,000	35,780		36,780
3300	15 ton	"	13.333	1,170	41,600		42,770

CONVECTION HEATING AND COOLING UNITS

23 - 82190   FAN COIL UNITS   23 - 82190

ID Code	Component Descriptions	Unit of Meas.	Manhr / Unit	Labor Cost	Material Cost	Equip. Cost	Total Cost
0980	Fan coil unit, 2 pipe, complete						
1000	200 cfm ceiling hung	EA	2.667	230	1,220		1,450
1020	Floor mounted	"	2.000	180	1,150		1,330
1100	300 cfm, ceiling hung	"	3.200	280	1,290		1,570
1130	Floor mounted	"	2.667	230	1,230		1,460
1200	400 cfm, ceiling hung	"	3.810	330	1,360		1,690
1220	Floor mounted	"	2.667	230	1,310		1,540
1300	500 cfm, ceiling hung	"	4.000	350	1,580		1,930
1310	Floor mounted	"	3.077	270	1,520		1,790
1400	600 cfm, ceiling hung	"	4.420	390	2,000		2,390
1420	Floor mounted	"	3.636	320	1,860		2,180

23 - 82390   UNIT HEATERS   23 - 82390

ID Code	Component Descriptions	Unit of Meas.	Manhr / Unit	Labor Cost	Material Cost	Equip. Cost	Total Cost
0980	Steam unit heater, horizontal						
1000	12,500 btuh, 200 cfm	EA	1.333	120	560		680
1010	17,000 btuh, 300 cfm	"	1.333	120	740		860
1020	40,000 btuh, 500 cfm	"	1.333	120	900		1,020
1030	60,000 btuh, 700 cfm	"	1.333	120	940		1,060
1040	70,000 btuh, 1000 cfm	"	2.000	180	980		1,160
1045	Vertical						
1050	12,500 btuh, 200 cfm	EA	1.333	120	560		680
1060	17,000 btuh, 300 cfm	"	1.333	120	930		1,050
1070	40,000 btuh, 500 cfm	"	1.333	120	900		1,020

CONVECTION HEATING AND COOLING UNITS

ID Code	Component Descriptions	Unit of Meas.	Manhr / Unit	Labor Cost	Material Cost	Equip. Cost	Total Cost
		Descriptions		**Output**	**Unit Costs**		

ID Code	Component Descriptions	Unit of Meas.	Manhr / Unit	Labor Cost	Material Cost	Equip. Cost	Total Cost
23 - 82390	**UNIT HEATERS, Cont'd...**						**23 - 82390**
1080	60,000 btuh, 700 cfm	EA	1.333	120	940		1,060
1090	70,000 btuh, 1000 cfm	"	1.333	120	980		1,100
1980	Gas unit heater, horizontal						
2000	27,400 btuh	EA	3.200	280	860		1,140
2010	38,000 btuh	"	3.200	280	900		1,180
2020	56,000 btuh	"	3.200	280	940		1,220
2030	82,200 btuh	"	3.200	280	980		1,260
2040	103,900 btuh	"	5.000	440	1,090		1,530
2060	125,700 btuh	"	5.000	440	1,280		1,720
2080	133,200 btuh	"	5.000	440	1,380		1,820
2090	149,000 btuh	"	5.000	440	1,630		2,070
2100	172,000 btuh	"	5.000	440	1,760		2,200
2120	190,000 btuh	"	5.000	440	1,850		2,290
2130	225,000 btuh	"	5.000	440	2,030		2,470
3980	Hot water unit heater, horizontal						
4000	12,500 btuh, 200 cfm	EA	1.333	120	450		570
4010	17,000 btuh, 300 cfm	"	1.333	120	500		620
4020	25,000 btuh, 500 cfm	"	1.333	120	580		700
4030	30,000 btuh, 700 cfm	"	1.333	120	680		800
4040	50,000 btuh, 1000 cfm	"	2.000	180	740		920
4050	60,000 btuh, 1300 cfm	"	2.000	180	780		960
4055	Vertical						
4060	12,500 btuh, 200 cfm	EA	1.333	120	660		780
4070	17,000 btuh, 300 cfm	"	1.333	120	660		780
4080	25,000 btuh, 500 cfm	"	1.333	120	660		780
4090	30,000 btuh, 700 cfm	"	1.333	120	660		780
4100	50,000 btuh, 1000 cfm	"	1.333	120	690		810
4120	60,000 btuh, 1300 cfm	"	1.333	120	850		970
5000	Cabinet unit heaters, ceiling, exposed, hot water						
5010	200 cfm	EA	2.667	230	1,290		1,520
5030	300 cfm	"	3.200	280	1,380		1,660
5050	400 cfm	"	3.810	330	1,440		1,770
5070	600 cfm	"	4.211	370	1,480		1,850
5090	800 cfm	"	5.000	440	1,850		2,290
5120	1000 cfm	"	5.714	500	2,410		2,910
5140	1200 cfm	"	6.667	580	2,590		3,170
5160	2000 cfm	"	8.889	780	4,040		4,820

RESISTANCE HEATING

ID Code	Component Descriptions	Unit of Meas.	Manhr / Unit	Labor Cost	Material Cost	Equip. Cost	Total Cost
23 - 83330	**ELECTRIC HEATING**						**23 - 83330**
1000	Baseboard heater						
1020	2', 375w	EA	1.000	81.00	41.75		120
1040	3', 500w	"	1.000	81.00	49.50		130
1060	4', 750w	"	1.143	93.00	55.00		150
1100	5', 935w	"	1.333	110	78.00		190
1120	6', 1125w	"	1.600	130	92.00		220
1140	7', 1310w	"	1.818	150	100		250
1160	8', 1500w	"	2.000	160	120		280
1180	9', 1680w	"	2.222	180	130		310
1200	10', 1875w	"	2.286	190	180		370
1210	Unit heater, wall mounted						
1220	1500w	EA	1.667	140	220		360
1240	2500w	"	1.818	150	240		390
1260	4000w	"	2.286	190	320		510
1270	Thermostat						
1280	Integral	EA	0.500	40.75	37.50		78.00
1300	Line voltage	"	0.500	40.75	38.50		79.00
1320	Electric heater connection	"	0.250	20.25	1.65		22.00

HUMIDITY CONTROL EQUIPMENT

ID Code	Component Descriptions	Unit of Meas.	Manhr / Unit	Labor Cost	Material Cost	Equip. Cost	Total Cost
23 - 84160	**DEHUMIDIFIERS**						**23 - 84160**
1000	Desiccant dehumidifier, 1125 cfm	EA					35,230

DIVISION 26
ELECTRICAL

CONDUCTORS, CONDUIT AND RACEWAYS

	Descriptions	Output		Unit Costs			
ID Code	Component Descriptions	Unit of Meas.	Manhr / Unit	Labor Cost	Material Cost	Equip. Cost	Total Cost
26 - 05134	**COPPER CONDUCTORS**						**26 - 05134**
0980	Copper conductors, type THW, solid						
1000	#14	LF	0.004	0.32	0.12		0.44
1040	#12	"	0.005	0.40	0.18		0.58
1060	#10	"	0.006	0.49	0.28		0.77
1070	Stranded						
1080	#14	LF	0.004	0.32	0.13		0.45
1100	#12	"	0.005	0.40	0.16		0.56
1120	#10	"	0.006	0.49	0.25		0.74
1140	#8	"	0.008	0.65	0.41		1.06
1160	#6	"	0.009	0.73	0.67		1.40
1180	#4	"	0.010	0.81	1.04		1.85
1200	#3	"	0.010	0.81	1.32		2.13
1220	#2	"	0.012	0.97	1.66		2.63
1240	#1	"	0.014	1.14	2.10		3.24
1260	1/0	"	0.016	1.30	2.50		3.80
1280	2/0	"	0.020	1.62	3.14		4.76
1300	3/0	"	0.025	2.03	3.96		5.99
1520	4/0	"	0.028	2.28	4.95		7.23
1540	250 MCM	"	0.030	2.45	6.10		8.55
1560	300 MCM	"	0.033	2.71	7.18		9.89
1580	350 MCM	"	0.040	3.25	8.40		11.75
1600	400 MCM	"	0.044	3.61	9.57		13.25
1620	500 MCM	"	0.052	4.20	11.75		16.00
1640	600 MCM	"	0.059	4.82	15.75		20.50
1660	750 MCM	"	0.067	5.42	19.75		25.25
1680	1000 MCM	"	0.076	6.20	24.75		31.00
2010	THHN-THWN, solid						
2020	#14	LF	0.004	0.32	0.12		0.44
2040	#12	"	0.005	0.40	0.18		0.58
2060	#10	"	0.006	0.49	0.28		0.77
2070	Stranded						
2080	#14	LF	0.004	0.32	0.12		0.44
2100	#12	"	0.005	0.40	0.18		0.58
2120	#10	"	0.006	0.49	0.28		0.77
2140	#8	"	0.008	0.65	0.49		1.14
2160	#6	"	0.009	0.73	0.77		1.50
2180	#4	"	0.010	0.81	1.22		2.03
2200	#2	"	0.012	0.97	1.70		2.67

CONDUCTORS, CONDUIT AND RACEWAYS

	Descriptions	Output		Unit Costs			
ID Code	Component Descriptions	Unit of Meas.	Manhr / Unit	Labor Cost	Material Cost	Equip. Cost	Total Cost
26 - 05134	**COPPER CONDUCTORS, Cont'd...**					**26 - 05134**	
2220	#1	LF	0.014	1.14	2.15		3.29
2240	1/0	"	0.016	1.30	2.65		3.95
2260	2/0	"	0.020	1.62	3.27		4.89
2280	3/0	"	0.025	2.03	4.11		6.14
2300	4/0	"	0.028	2.28	5.14		7.42
2320	250 MCM	"	0.030	2.45	6.29		8.74
2340	350 MCM	"	0.040	3.25	7.50		10.75
26 - 05135	**SHEATHED CABLE**					**26 - 05135**	
6700	Non-metallic sheathed cable						
6705	Type NM cable with ground						
6710	#14/2	LF	0.015	1.21	0.28		1.49
6720	#12/2	"	0.016	1.30	0.44		1.74
6730	#10/2	"	0.018	1.44	0.69		2.13
6740	#8/2	"	0.020	1.62	1.13		2.75
6750	#6/2	"	0.025	2.03	1.78		3.81
6760	#14/3	"	0.026	2.10	0.39		2.49
6770	#12/3	"	0.027	2.17	0.62		2.79
6780	#10/3	"	0.027	2.20	0.99		3.19
6790	#8/3	"	0.028	2.24	1.66		3.90
6800	#6/3	"	0.028	2.28	2.68		4.96
6810	#4/3	"	0.032	2.60	5.55		8.15
6820	#2/3	"	0.035	2.83	8.34		11.25
6825	Type U.F. cable with ground						
6830	#14/2	LF	0.016	1.30	0.33		1.63
6840	#12/2	"	0.019	1.55	0.49		2.04
6850	#10/2	"	0.020	1.62	0.79		2.41
6860	#8/2	"	0.023	1.86	1.36		3.22
6870	#6/2	"	0.027	2.20	2.12		4.32
6880	#14/3	"	0.020	1.62	0.46		2.08
6890	#12/3	"	0.022	1.78	0.70		2.48
6900	#10/3	"	0.025	2.03	1.08		3.11
6910	#8/3	"	0.028	2.28	2.05		4.33
6920	#6/3	"	0.032	2.60	3.33		5.93

CONDUCTORS, CONDUIT AND RACEWAYS

ID Code	Component Descriptions	Unit of Meas.	Manhr / Unit	Labor Cost	Material Cost	Equip. Cost	Total Cost
	Descriptions	**Output**		**Unit Costs**			
26 - 05261	**GROUNDING**					**26 - 05261**	
0400	Ground rods, copper clad, 1/2" x						
0510	6'	EA	0.667	54.00	17.00		71.00
0520	8'	"	0.727	59.00	23.50		83.00
0530	10'	"	1.000	81.00	29.25		110
0535	5/8" x						
0540	5'	EA	0.615	50.00	21.00		71.00
0550	6'	"	0.727	59.00	22.75		82.00
0560	8'	"	1.000	81.00	29.25		110
0570	10'	"	1.250	100	36.25		140
0580	3/4" x						
0590	8'	EA	0.727	59.00	52.00		110
0600	10'	"	0.800	65.00	57.00		120
1060	Ground rod clamp						
1080	5/8"	EA	0.123	10.00	6.94		17.00
1100	3/4"	"	0.123	10.00	9.82		19.75
26 - 05292	**CONDUIT SPECIALTIES**					**26 - 05292**	
8005	Rod beam clamp, 1/2"	EA	0.050	4.07	6.94		11.00
8007	Hanger rod						
8010	3/8"	LF	0.040	3.25	1.46		4.71
8020	1/2"	"	0.050	4.07	3.65		7.72
8030	All thread rod						
8040	1/4"	LF	0.030	2.45	0.47		2.92
8060	3/8"	"	0.040	3.25	0.53		3.78
8080	1/2"	"	0.050	4.07	1.00		5.07
8100	5/8"	"	0.080	6.51	1.76		8.27
8120	Hanger channel, 1-1/2"						
8140	No holes	EA	0.030	2.45	4.62		7.07
8160	Holes	"	0.030	2.45	5.70		8.15
8170	Channel strap						
8180	1/2"	EA	0.050	4.07	1.44		5.51
8200	3/4"	"	0.050	4.07	1.93		6.00
8220	1"	"	0.050	4.07	2.47		6.54
8240	1-1/4"	"	0.080	6.51	1.99		8.50
8260	1-1/2"	"	0.080	6.51	2.39		8.90
8280	2"	"	0.080	6.51	2.59		9.10
8290	2-1/2"	"	0.123	10.00	4.97		15.00
8300	3"	"	0.123	10.00	5.41		15.50

CONDUCTORS, CONDUIT AND RACEWAYS

ID Code	Component Descriptions	Unit of Meas.	Manhr / Unit	Labor Cost	Material Cost	Equip. Cost	Total Cost
	Descriptions	**Output**		**Unit Costs**			

26 - 05292 — CONDUIT SPECIALTIES, Cont'd... — 26 - 05292

ID Code	Component Descriptions	Unit of Meas.	Manhr / Unit	Labor Cost	Material Cost	Equip. Cost	Total Cost
8310	3-1/2"	EA	0.123	10.00	6.74		16.75
8320	4"	"	0.145	11.75	7.62		19.25
8340	5"	"	0.145	11.75	12.25		24.00
8360	6"	"	0.145	11.75	14.00		25.75
8410	Conduit penetrations, roof and wall, 8" thick						
8420	1/2"	EA	0.615	50.00			50.00
8460	3/4"	"	0.615	50.00			50.00
8480	1"	"	0.800	65.00			65.00
8500	1-1/4"	"	0.800	65.00			65.00
8520	1-1/2"	"	0.800	65.00			65.00
8540	2"	"	1.600	130			130
8560	2-1/2"	"	1.600	130			130
8580	3"	"	1.600	130			130
8590	3-1/2"	"	2.000	160			160
8600	4"	"	2.000	160			160
9505	Fireproofing, for conduit penetrations						
9510	1/2"	EA	0.500	40.75	3.57		44.25
9520	3/4"	"	0.500	40.75	3.70		44.50
9530	1"	"	0.500	40.75	3.78		44.50
9540	1-1/4"	"	0.727	64.00	8.89		73.00
9550	1-1/2"	"	0.727	59.00	5.25		64.00
9560	2"	"	0.727	59.00	5.39		64.00
9570	2-1/2"	"	0.899	73.00	10.25		83.00
9580	3"	"	0.899	79.00	10.75		90.00
9590	3-1/2"	"	1.250	100	12.50		110
9600	4"	"	1.509	120	15.00		140

26 - 05334 — SURFACE MOUNTED RACEWAY — 26 - 05334

ID Code	Component Descriptions	Unit of Meas.	Manhr / Unit	Labor Cost	Material Cost	Equip. Cost	Total Cost
0980	Single Raceway						
1000	3/4" x 17/32" Conduit	LF	0.040	3.25	1.83		5.08
1020	Mounting Strap	EA	0.053	4.34	0.49		4.83
1040	Connector	"	0.053	4.34	0.66		5.00
1060	Elbow						
2000	45 degree	EA	0.050	4.07	8.38		12.50
2020	90 degree	"	0.050	4.07	2.67		6.74
2040	internal	"	0.050	4.07	3.36		7.43
2050	external	"	0.050	4.07	3.10		7.17
2060	Switch	"	0.400	32.50	21.75		54.00

CONDUCTORS, CONDUIT AND RACEWAYS

ID Code	Component Descriptions	Unit of Meas.	Manhr / Unit	Labor Cost	Material Cost	Equip. Cost	Total Cost
	Descriptions	**Output**		**Unit Costs**			
26 - 05334	**SURFACE MOUNTED RACEWAY, Cont'd...**						**26 - 05334**
2100	Utility Box	EA	0.400	32.50	14.50		47.00
2110	Receptacle	"	0.400	32.50	25.75		58.00
2140	3/4" x 21/32" Conduit	LF	0.040	3.25	2.09		5.34
2160	Mounting Strap	EA	0.053	4.34	0.77		5.11
2180	Connector	"	0.053	4.34	0.79		5.13
2200	Elbow						
2210	45 degree	EA	0.050	4.07	10.25		14.25
2220	90 degree	"	0.050	4.07	2.85		6.92
2240	internal	"	0.050	4.07	3.87		7.94
2260	external	"	0.050	4.07	3.87		7.94
3000	Switch	"	0.400	32.50	21.75		54.00
3010	Utility Box	"	0.400	32.50	14.50		47.00
3020	Receptacle	"	0.400	32.50	25.75		58.00
26 - 05335	**PULL BOXES AND CABINETS**						**26 - 05335**
2500	Galvanized pull boxes, screw cover						
2520	4x4x4	EA	0.190	15.50	7.83		23.25
2540	4x6x4	"	0.190	15.50	9.33		24.75
2560	6x6x4	"	0.190	15.50	11.75		27.25
2580	6x8x4	"	0.190	15.50	14.00		29.50
2620	8x8x4	"	0.250	20.25	17.50		37.75
3020	8x10x4	"	0.242	19.75	20.25		40.00
3040	8x12x4	"	0.250	20.25	22.25		42.50
3050	Screw cover						
3060	10x10x4	EA	0.308	25.00	22.25		47.25
3200	12x12x6	"	0.444	36.25	32.75		69.00
3220	12x15x6	"	0.444	36.25	39.00		75.00
3240	12x18x6	"	0.500	40.75	43.25		84.00
3250	15x18x6	"	0.571	46.50	48.25		95.00
3260	18x24x6	"	0.615	50.00	90.00		140
3270	18x30x6	"	0.727	59.00	100		160
3280	24x36x6	"	0.727	59.00	150		210
26 - 05337	**WIREWAYS**						**26 - 05337**
0960	Wireway, hinge cover type						
0980	2-1/2" x 2-1/2"						
1000	1' section	EA	0.154	12.50	17.50		30.00
1040	2'	"	0.190	15.50	25.00		40.50
1060	3'	"	0.250	20.25	33.75		54.00

CONDUCTORS, CONDUIT AND RACEWAYS

ID Code	Component Descriptions	Unit of Meas.	Manhr / Unit	Labor Cost	Material Cost	Equip. Cost	Total Cost
	Descriptions	**Output**		**Unit Costs**			

ID Code	Component Descriptions	Unit of Meas.	Manhr / Unit	Labor Cost	Material Cost	Equip. Cost	Total Cost
26 - 05337	**WIREWAYS, Cont'd...**						**26 - 05337**
1080	5'	EA	0.381	31.00	57.00		88.00
1100	10'	"	0.667	54.00	120		170
1110	4" x 4"						
1120	1'	EA	0.250	20.25	19.25		39.50
1140	2'	"	0.250	20.25	28.00		48.25
1160	3'	"	0.308	25.00	41.50		67.00
1180	4'	"	0.308	25.00	57.00		82.00
1200	10'	"	0.800	65.00	170		240
26 - 05339	**PULL AND JUNCTION BOXES**						**26 - 05339**
1050	4"						
1060	Octagon box	EA	0.114	9.30	3.96		13.25
1070	Box extension	"	0.059	4.82	6.67		11.50
1080	Plaster ring	"	0.059	4.82	3.66		8.48
1100	Cover blank	"	0.059	4.82	1.61		6.43
1120	Square box	"	0.114	9.30	5.70		15.00
1140	Box extension	"	0.059	4.82	5.59		10.50
1160	Plaster ring	"	0.059	4.82	3.06		7.88
1180	Cover blank	"	0.059	4.82	1.57		6.39
1190	4-11/16"						
1200	Square box	EA	0.114	9.30	11.50		20.75
1240	Box extension	"	0.059	4.82	12.50		17.25
1260	Plaster ring	"	0.059	4.82	7.61		12.50
1280	Cover blank	"	0.059	4.82	2.82		7.64
1300	Switch and device boxes						
1320	2 gang	EA	0.114	9.30	17.25		26.50
1340	3 gang	"	0.114	9.30	30.25		39.50
1360	4 gang	"	0.160	13.00	40.50		54.00
2000	Device covers						
2020	2 gang	EA	0.059	4.82	13.75		18.50
2040	3 gang	"	0.059	4.82	14.25		19.00
2060	4 gang	"	0.059	4.82	19.25		24.00
2100	Handy box	"	0.114	9.30	4.25		13.50
2120	Extension	"	0.059	4.82	4.00		8.82
2140	Switch cover	"	0.059	4.82	2.12		6.94
2160	Switch box with knockout	"	0.145	11.75	6.38		18.25
2200	Weatherproof cover, spring type	"	0.080	6.51	11.75		18.25
2220	Cover plate, dryer receptacle 1 gang plastic	"	0.100	8.14	1.81		9.95

CONDUCTORS, CONDUIT AND RACEWAYS

ID Code	Component Descriptions	Unit of Meas.	Manhr / Unit	Labor Cost	Material Cost	Equip. Cost	Total Cost
	Descriptions	**Output**		**Unit Costs**			

26 - 05339	**PULL AND JUNCTION BOXES, Cont'd...**						**26 - 05339**
2240	For 4" receptacle, 2 gang	EA	0.100	8.14	3.23		11.25
2260	Duplex receptacle cover plate, plastic	"	0.059	4.82	0.79		5.61
3005	4", vertical bracket box, 1-1/2" with						
3010	RMX clamps	EA	0.145	11.75	8.22		20.00
3020	BX clamps	"	0.145	11.75	8.82		20.50
3025	4", octagon device cover						
3030	1 switch	EA	0.059	4.82	4.82		9.64
3040	1 duplex recept	"	0.059	4.82	4.82		9.64
3105	4", square face bracket boxes, 1-1/2"						
3110	RMX	EA	0.145	11.75	9.81		21.50
3120	BX	"	0.145	11.75	10.75		22.50

26 - 05341	**ALUMINUM CONDUIT**						**26 - 05341**
1010	Aluminum conduit						
1020	1/2"	LF	0.030	2.45	2.21		4.66
1040	3/4"	"	0.040	3.25	2.84		6.09
1060	1"	"	0.050	4.07	3.99		8.06
1080	1-1/4"	"	0.059	4.82	5.33		10.25
1100	1-1/2"	"	0.080	6.51	6.62		13.25
1120	2"	"	0.089	7.23	8.83		16.00
1140	2-1/2"	"	0.100	8.14	14.00		22.25
1160	3"	"	0.107	8.68	18.25		27.00
1180	3-1/2"	"	0.123	10.00	22.00		32.00
1200	4"	"	0.145	11.75	26.00		37.75
1220	5"	"	0.182	14.75	37.25		52.00
1240	6"	"	0.200	16.25	49.25		66.00

26 - 05342	**EMT CONDUIT**						**26 - 05342**
0080	EMT conduit						
0100	1/2"	LF	0.030	2.45	0.60		3.05
1020	3/4"	"	0.040	3.25	1.09		4.34
1030	1"	"	0.050	4.07	1.82		5.89
1040	1-1/4"	"	0.059	4.82	2.92		7.74
1060	1-1/2"	"	0.080	6.51	3.69		10.25
1080	2"	"	0.089	7.23	4.62		11.75
1100	2-1/2"	"	0.100	8.14	9.21		17.25
1120	3"	"	0.123	10.00	10.25		20.25
1140	3-1/2"	"	0.145	11.75	14.50		26.25
1160	4"	"	0.182	14.75	14.00		28.75

CONDUCTORS, CONDUIT AND RACEWAYS

ID Code	Component Descriptions	Unit of Meas.	Manhr / Unit	Labor Cost	Material Cost	Equip. Cost	Total Cost
	Descriptions	**Output**		**Unit Costs**			

26 - 05343 — FLEXIBLE CONDUIT — 26 - 05343

ID Code	Component Descriptions	Unit of Meas.	Manhr / Unit	Labor Cost	Material Cost	Equip. Cost	Total Cost
0080	Flexible conduit, steel						
0100	3/8"	LF	0.030	2.45	0.75		3.20
1020	1/2	"	0.030	2.45	0.85		3.30
1040	3/4"	"	0.040	3.25	1.17		4.42
1060	1"	"	0.040	3.25	2.23		5.48
1080	1-1/4"	"	0.050	4.07	2.79		6.86
1100	1-1/2"	"	0.059	4.82	4.63		9.45
1120	2"	"	0.080	6.51	5.69		12.25
1140	2-1/2"	"	0.089	7.23	6.93		14.25
1160	3"	"	0.107	8.68	12.00		20.75

26 - 05344 — GALVANIZED CONDUIT — 26 - 05344

ID Code	Component Descriptions	Unit of Meas.	Manhr / Unit	Labor Cost	Material Cost	Equip. Cost	Total Cost
1980	Galvanized rigid steel conduit						
2000	1/2"	LF	0.040	3.25	2.82		6.07
2040	3/4"	"	0.050	4.07	3.13		7.20
2060	1"	"	0.059	4.82	4.51		9.33
2080	1-1/4"	"	0.080	6.51	6.24		12.75
2100	1-1/2"	"	0.089	7.23	7.34		14.50
2120	2"	"	0.100	8.14	9.34		17.50
2140	2-1/2"	"	0.145	11.75	17.00		28.75
2160	3"	"	0.182	14.75	17.75		32.50
2180	3-1/2"	"	0.190	15.50	25.75		41.25
2200	4"	"	0.211	17.25	29.25		46.50
2220	5"	"	0.286	23.25	54.00		77.00
2240	6"	"	0.381	31.00	79.00		110

26 - 05345 — PLASTIC COATED CONDUIT — 26 - 05345

ID Code	Component Descriptions	Unit of Meas.	Manhr / Unit	Labor Cost	Material Cost	Equip. Cost	Total Cost
0980	Rigid steel conduit, plastic coated						
1000	1/2"	LF	0.050	4.07	7.06		11.25
1040	3/4"	"	0.059	4.82	8.20		13.00
1060	1"	"	0.080	6.51	10.50		17.00
1080	1-1/4"	"	0.100	8.14	13.50		21.75
1100	1-1/2"	"	0.123	10.00	16.25		26.25
1120	2"	"	0.145	11.75	21.25		33.00
1140	2-1/2"	"	0.190	15.50	32.25		47.75
1160	3"	"	0.222	18.00	40.75		59.00
1180	3-1/2"	"	0.250	20.25	49.75		70.00
1200	4"	"	0.308	25.00	60.00		85.00
1220	5"	"	0.381	31.00	100		130

CONDUCTORS, CONDUIT AND RACEWAYS

ID Code	Descriptions Component Descriptions	Output Unit of Meas.	Output Manhr / Unit	Unit Costs Labor Cost	Unit Costs Material Cost	Unit Costs Equip. Cost	Unit Costs Total Cost
26 - 05347	**STEEL CONDUIT**						**26 - 05347**
7980	Intermediate metal conduit (IMC)						
8000	1/2"	LF	0.030	2.45	2.02		4.47
8040	3/4"	"	0.040	3.25	2.48		5.73
8060	1"	"	0.050	4.07	3.76		7.83
8080	1-1/4"	"	0.059	4.82	4.81		9.63
8100	1-1/2"	"	0.080	6.51	6.02		12.50
8120	2"	"	0.089	7.23	7.86		15.00
8140	2-1/2"	"	0.119	9.71	15.50		25.25
8160	3"	"	0.145	11.75	20.00		31.75
8180	3-1/2"	"	0.182	14.75	23.50		38.25
8200	4"	"	0.190	15.50	26.00		41.50
26 - 05361	**CABLE TRAY**						**26 - 05361**
1010	Cable tray, 6"	LF	0.059	4.82	22.00		26.75
1020	Ventilated cover	"	0.030	2.45	8.89		11.25
1030	Solid cover	"	0.030	2.45	6.93		9.38

MEDIUM-VOLTAGE TRANSFORMERS

ID Code	Component Descriptions	Unit of Meas.	Manhr / Unit	Labor Cost	Material Cost	Equip. Cost	Total Cost
26 - 12001	**MEDIUM-VOLTAGE TRANSFORMERS**						**26 - 12001**
0080	Floor mtd, one phase, int. dry, 480v-120/240v						
0100	3 kva	EA	1.818	150	690		840
1080	5 kva	"	3.077	250	920		1,170
1100	7.5 kva	"	3.478	280	1,240		1,520
1120	10 kva	"	3.810	310	1,550		1,860
1140	15 kva	"	4.301	350	2,070		2,420
1240	100 kva	"	11.594	940	8,340		9,280
1980	Three phase, 480v-120/208v						
2000	15 kva	EA	6.015	490	2,270		2,760
2040	30 kva	"	9.412	770	2,720		3,490
2060	45 kva	"	10.811	880	3,620		4,500
2140	225 kva	"	15.385	1,250	13,010		14,260

SERVICE AND DISTRIBUTION

ID Code	Descriptions	Output		Unit Costs			
	Component Descriptions	Unit of Meas.	Manhr / Unit	Labor Cost	Material Cost	Equip. Cost	Total Cost
26 - 24130	**SWITCHBOARDS**						**26 - 24130**
0580	Switchboard, 90" high, no main disconnect, 208/120v						
0581	400a	EA	7.921	640	3,040		3,680
1000	600a	"	8.000	650	4,710		5,360
1020	1000a	"	8.000	650	5,930		6,580
1040	1200a	"	10.000	810	6,280		7,090
1060	1600a	"	11.940	970	6,900		7,870
1080	2000a	"	14.035	1,140	7,410		8,550
1100	2500a	"	16.000	1,300	7,500		8,800
1520	277/480v						
1540	600a	EA	8.163	660	5,410		6,070
1560	800a	"	8.163	660	5,930		6,590
1580	1600a	"	11.940	970	7,470		8,440
1600	2000a	"	14.035	1,140	7,990		9,130
1620	2500a	"	16.000	1,300	8,510		9,810
1640	3000a	"	27.586	2,250	9,800		12,050
1660	4000a	"	29.630	2,410	11,870		14,280
26 - 24160	**PANELBOARDS**						**26 - 24160**
1500	3 phase, 480/277v, main lugs only, 120a, 30 circuits	EA	3.478	280	1,670		1,950
1510	277/480v, 4 wire, flush surface						
1520	225a, 30 circuits	EA	4.000	330	2,720		3,050
1540	400a, 30 circuits	"	5.000	410	3,690		4,100
1560	600a, 42 circuits	"	6.015	490	7,120		7,610
2000	208/120v, main circuit breaker, 3 phase, 4 wire						
2030	100a						
2035	12 circuits	EA	5.096	410	1,440		1,850
2040	20 circuits	"	6.299	510	1,790		2,300
2060	30 circuits	"	7.018	570	2,640		3,210
2110	400a						
2120	30 circuits	EA	14.815	1,210	5,550		6,760
2140	42 circuits	"	16.000	1,300	6,660		7,960
2180	600a, 42 circuits	"	18.182	1,480	12,950		14,430
2510	120/208v, flush, 3 ph., 4 wire, main only						
2515	100a						
2520	12 circuits	EA	5.096	410	1,020		1,430
2540	20 circuits	"	6.299	510	1,410		1,920
2560	30 circuits	"	7.018	570	2,090		2,660
2610	400a						

SERVICE AND DISTRIBUTION

	Descriptions	Output		Unit Costs			
ID Code	Component Descriptions	Unit of Meas.	Manhr / Unit	Labor Cost	Material Cost	Equip. Cost	Total Cost
26 - 24160	**PANELBOARDS, Cont'd...**						**26 - 24160**
2620	30 circuits	EA	14.815	1,210	4,080		5,290
2640	42 circuits	"	16.000	1,300	5,940		7,240
2680	600a, 42 circuits	"	18.182	1,480	9,260		10,740
26 - 24190	**MOTOR CONTROLS**						**26 - 24190**
0080	Motor generator set, 3 phase, 480/277v, w/controls						
0100	10kw	EA	27.586	2,250	13,490		15,740
1020	15kw	"	30.769	2,500	17,600		20,100
1040	20kw	"	32.000	2,600	19,530		22,130
1100	40kw	"	38.095	3,100	27,490		30,590
1180	100kw	"	61.538	5,010	40,960		45,970
1240	200kw	"	72.727	5,920	93,620		99,540
1280	300kw	"	80.000	6,510	117,020		123,530
2010	2 pole, 230 volt starter, w/NEMA-1						
2020	1 hp, 9a, size 00	EA	1.000	81.00	150		230
2040	2 hp, 18a, size 0	"	1.000	81.00	170		250
2060	3 hp, 27a, size 1	"	1.000	81.00	240		320
2080	5 hp, 45a, size 1p	"	1.000	81.00	240		320
2100	7-1/2 hp, 45a, size 2	"	1.000	81.00	580		660
2120	15 hp, 90a, size 3	"	1.000	81.00	880		960

LOW-VOLTAGE DISTRIBUTION EQUIPMENT

	Descriptions	Output		Unit Costs			
26 - 27268	**RECEPTACLES**						**26 - 27268**
0490	Contractor grade duplex receptacles, 15a 120v						
0510	Duplex	EA	0.200	16.25	1.60		17.75
1000	125 volt, 20a, duplex, standard grade	"	0.200	16.25	12.00		28.25
1040	Ground fault interrupter type	"	0.296	24.00	38.75		63.00
1520	250 volt, 20a, 2 pole, single, ground type	"	0.200	16.25	20.00		36.25
1540	120/208v, 4 pole, single receptacle, twist lock						
1560	20a	EA	0.348	28.25	23.75		52.00
1580	50a	"	0.348	28.25	45.25		74.00
1590	125/250v, 3 pole, flush receptacle						
1600	30a	EA	0.296	24.00	24.00		48.00
1620	50a	"	0.296	24.00	29.75		54.00
1640	60a	"	0.348	28.25	77.00		110
1660	277v, 20a, 2 pole, grounding type, twist lock	"	0.200	16.25	13.00		29.25
2020	Dryer receptacle, 250v, 30a/50a, 3 wire	"	0.296	24.00	18.00		42.00
2040	Clock receptacle, 2 pole, grounding type	"	0.200	16.25	12.00		28.25

LOW-VOLTAGE DISTRIBUTION EQUIPMENT

ID Code	Descriptions — Component Descriptions	Output — Unit of Meas.	Output — Manhr / Unit	Unit Costs — Labor Cost	Unit Costs — Material Cost	Unit Costs — Equip. Cost	Unit Costs — Total Cost
26 - 27268	**RECEPTACLES, Cont'd...**						**26 - 27268**
3000	125v, 20a single recept. grounding type						
3010	Standard grade	EA	0.200	16.25	13.00		29.25
3020	Specification	"	0.200	16.25	15.50		31.75
3030	Hospital	"	0.200	16.25	16.25		32.50
3040	Isolated ground orange	"	0.250	20.25	55.00		75.00
3045	Duplex						
3050	Specification grade	EA	0.200	16.25	13.00		29.25
3060	Hospital	"	0.200	16.25	26.50		42.75
3070	Isolated ground orange	"	0.250	20.25	55.00		75.00
3100	GFI hospital grade recepts, 20a, 125v, duplex	"	0.296	24.00	58.00		82.00

LOW-VOLTAGE CIRCUIT PROTECTIVE DEVICES

ID Code	Component Descriptions	Unit of Meas.	Manhr / Unit	Labor Cost	Material Cost	Equip. Cost	Total Cost
26 - 28130	**FUSES**						**26 - 28130**
1000	Fuse, one-time, 250v						
1010	30a	EA	0.050	4.07	2.77		6.84
1020	60a	"	0.050	4.07	4.68		8.75
1040	100a	"	0.050	4.07	19.50		23.50
1060	200a	"	0.050	4.07	47.25		51.00
1080	400a	"	0.050	4.07	110		110
1100	600a	"	0.050	4.07	180		180
1120	600v						
1140	30a	EA	0.050	4.07	14.00		18.00
1160	60a	"	0.050	4.07	22.25		26.25
1180	100a	"	0.050	4.07	42.00		46.00
1200	200a	"	0.050	4.07	110		110
1220	400a	"	0.050	4.07	230		230
26 - 28161	**CIRCUIT BREAKERS**						**26 - 28161**
0950	Molded case, 240v, 15-60a, bolt-on						
1000	1 pole	EA	0.250	20.25	20.00		40.25
1060	2 pole	"	0.348	28.25	42.50		71.00
1080	70-100a, 2 pole	"	0.533	43.50	120		160
1100	15-60a, 3 pole	"	0.400	32.50	150		180
1120	70-100a, 3 pole	"	0.615	50.00	240		290
1980	480v, 2 pole						
2000	15-60a	EA	0.296	24.00	310		330
2080	70-100a	"	0.400	32.50	390		420
2090	3 pole						

LOW-VOLTAGE CIRCUIT PROTECTIVE DEVICES

ID Code	Component Descriptions	Unit of Meas.	Manhr / Unit	Labor Cost	Material Cost	Equip. Cost	Total Cost
	Descriptions	**Output**		**Unit Costs**			
26 - 28161	**CIRCUIT BREAKERS, Cont'd...**						**26 - 28161**
2100	15-60a	EA	0.400	32.50	390		420
2120	70-100a	"	0.444	36.25	470		510
2140	70-225a	"	0.615	50.00	960		1,010
5000	Load center circuit breakers, 240v						
5010	1 pole, 10-60a	EA	0.250	20.25	21.25		41.50
5015	2 pole						
5020	10-60a	EA	0.400	32.50	43.25		76.00
5030	70-100a	"	0.667	54.00	130		180
5040	110-150a	"	0.727	59.00	280		340
5045	3 pole						
5050	10-60a	EA	0.500	40.75	120		160
5060	70-100a	"	0.727	59.00	180		240
5065	Load center, G.F.I. breakers, 240v						
5070	1 pole, 15-30a	EA	0.296	24.00	160		180
5080	2 pole, 15-30a	"	0.400	32.50	280		310
5090	Key operated breakers, 240v, 1 pole, 10-30a	"	0.296	24.00	100		120
5095	Tandem breakers, 240v						
5100	1 pole, 15-30a	EA	0.400	32.50	35.00		68.00
5110	2 pole, 15-30a	"	0.533	43.50	64.00		110
5120	Bolt-on, G.F.I. breakers, 240v, 1 pole, 15-30a	"	0.348	28.25	150		180
26 - 28164	**SWITCHES**						**26 - 28164**
1080	Fused interrupter load, 35kv, 20a						
1100	1 pole	EA	16.000	1,300	26,000		27,300
1120	2 pole	"	17.021	1,390	28,170		29,560
1250	Weatherproof switch, including box & cover, 20a						
1260	1 pole	EA	16.000	1,300	28,160		29,460
1280	2 pole	"	17.021	1,390	30,330		31,720
5175	Specification grade toggle switches, 20a, 120-277v						
5180	Single pole	EA	0.200	16.25	3.93		20.25
5190	Double pole	"	0.296	24.00	9.43		33.50
5200	3 way	"	0.250	20.25	10.25		30.50
5210	4 way	"	0.296	24.00	31.00		55.00
5495	Switch plates, plastic ivory						
5510	1 gang	EA	0.080	6.51	0.43		6.94
5520	2 gang	"	0.100	8.14	1.01		9.15
5530	3 gang	"	0.119	9.71	1.58		11.25
5540	4 gang	"	0.145	11.75	4.04		15.75

LOW-VOLTAGE CIRCUIT PROTECTIVE DEVICES

ID Code	Descriptions — Component Descriptions	Output — Unit of Meas.	Output — Manhr / Unit	Unit Costs — Labor Cost	Unit Costs — Material Cost	Unit Costs — Equip. Cost	Unit Costs — Total Cost
26 - 28164	**SWITCHES, Cont'd...**						**26 - 28164**
5550	5 gang	EA	0.160	13.00	4.23		17.25
5560	6 gang	"	0.182	14.75	4.99		19.75
5565	Stainless steel						
5570	1 gang	EA	0.080	6.51	3.64		10.25
5580	2 gang	"	0.100	8.14	5.06		13.25
5590	3 gang	"	0.123	10.00	7.76		17.75
5600	4 gang	"	0.145	11.75	13.25		25.00
5610	5 gang	"	0.160	13.00	15.50		28.50
5620	6 gang	"	0.182	14.75	19.50		34.25
5625	Brass						
5630	1 gang	EA	0.080	6.51	6.79		13.25
5640	2 gang	"	0.100	8.14	14.50		22.75
5650	3 gang	"	0.123	10.00	22.50		32.50
5660	4 gang	"	0.145	11.75	26.00		37.75
5670	5 gang	"	0.160	13.00	32.25		45.25
5680	6 gang	"	0.182	14.75	38.75		54.00
26 - 28166	**SAFETY SWITCHES**						**26 - 28166**
0080	Fused, 3 phase, 30 amp, 600v, heavy duty						
1010	NEMA 1	EA	1.143	93.00	240		330
1020	NEMA 3r	"	1.143	93.00	540		630
1040	NEMA 4	"	1.600	130	1,510		1,640
1060	NEMA 12	"	1.739	140	480		620
1070	60a						
1080	NEMA 1	EA	1.143	93.00	330		420
1100	NEMA 3r	"	1.143	93.00	640		730
1120	NEMA 4	"	1.600	130	1,670		1,800
1140	NEMA 12	"	1.739	140	570		710
1150	100a						
1160	NEMA 1	EA	1.739	140	570		710
1200	NEMA 3r	"	1.739	140	990		1,130
1220	NEMA 4	"	2.000	160	3,550		3,710
1240	NEMA 12	"	2.500	200	860		1,060
1250	200a						
1260	NEMA 1	EA	2.500	200	840		1,040
1280	NEMA 3r	"	2.500	200	1,370		1,570
1300	NEMA 4	"	2.759	220	4,660		4,880
1320	NEMA 12	"	3.478	280	1,270		1,550

LOW-VOLTAGE CIRCUIT PROTECTIVE DEVICES

ID Code	Descriptions — Component Descriptions	Output — Unit of Meas.	Output — Manhr / Unit	Unit Costs — Labor Cost	Unit Costs — Material Cost	Unit Costs — Equip. Cost	Unit Costs — Total Cost
26 - 28166	**SAFETY SWITCHES, Cont'd...**						**26 - 28166**
2000	Non-fused, 240-600v, heavy duty, 3 phase, 30 amp						
2020	NEMA 1	EA	1.143	93.00	170		260
2040	NEMA 3r	"	1.143	93.00	270		360
2060	NEMA 4	"	1.739	140	1,070		1,210
2080	NEMA 12	"	1.739	140	320		460
2090	60a						
2100	NEMA1	EA	1.143	93.00	220		310
2120	NEMA 3r	"	1.143	93.00	410		500
2140	NEMA 4	"	1.739	140	1,160		1,300
2160	NEMA 12	"	1.739	140	390		530
2170	100a						
2180	NEMA 1	EA	1.739	140	360		500
2200	NEMA 3r	"	1.739	140	570		710
2220	NEMA 4	"	2.500	200	2,340		2,540
2240	NEMA 12	"	2.500	200	550		750
2260	200a, NEMA 1	"	2.500	200	550		750
2680	600a, NEMA 12	"	12.308	1,000	3,080		4,080
26 - 28168	**SAFETY SWITCHES, HEAVY DUTY**						**26 - 28168**
0980	Safety switch, 600v, 3 pole, heavy duty, NEMA-1						
1000	30a	EA	1.000	81.00	210		290
1020	60a	"	1.143	93.00	280		370
1040	100a	"	1.600	130	530		660
1100	200a	"	2.500	200	830		1,030
1120	400a	"	5.517	450	2,140		2,590
1140	600a	"	8.000	650	3,800		4,450
1160	800a	"	10.526	860	8,600		9,460
1200	1200a	"	14.286	1,160	10,680		11,840
26 - 28169	**TRANSFER SWITCHES**						**26 - 28169**
0980	Automatic transfer switch 600v, 3 pole						
1000	30a	EA	3.478	280	2,680		2,960
1040	100a	"	4.762	390	3,550		3,940
1140	400a	"	10.000	810	8,010		8,820
1180	800a	"	18.182	1,480	14,740		16,220
1220	1200a	"	22.857	1,860	24,300		26,160
1280	2600a	"	42.105	3,430	63,670		67,100

POWER GENERATION

ID Code	Component Descriptions	Unit of Meas.	Manhr / Unit	Labor Cost	Material Cost	Equip. Cost	Total Cost
	Descriptions	**Output**		**Unit Costs**			

26 - 32001   GENERATORS   26 - 32001

ID Code	Component Descriptions	Unit of Meas.	Manhr / Unit	Labor Cost	Material Cost	Equip. Cost	Total Cost
0980	Diesel generator, with auto transfer switch						
1040	50kw	EA	30.769	2,500	32,530		35,030
1220	125kw	"	50.000	4,070	48,980		53,050
1320	300kw	"	100.000	8,140	80,230		88,370
1500	750kw	"	200.000	16,280	233,920		250,200

BATTERY EQUIPMENT

26 - 33530   UNINTERRUPTIBLE POWER   26 - 33530

ID Code	Component Descriptions	Unit of Meas.	Manhr / Unit	Labor Cost	Material Cost	Equip. Cost	Total Cost
1010	Uninterruptible power systems, (U.P.S.), 3kva	EA	8.000	650	7,750		8,400
1020	5 kva	"	11.004	900	8,690		9,590
1030	7.5 kva	"	16.000	1,300	10,430		11,730
1040	10 kva	"	21.978	1,790	13,040		14,830
1050	15 kva	"	22.857	1,860	15,650		17,510
1060	20 kva	"	24.024	1,960	21,730		23,690
1070	25 kva	"	25.000	2,040	27,820		29,860
1080	30 kva	"	25.974	2,110	28,680		30,790
1090	35 kva	"	27.027	2,200	30,420		32,620
1100	40 kva	"	27.972	2,280	33,030		35,310
1110	45 kva	"	28.986	2,360	34,770		37,130
1120	50 kva	"	29.963	2,440	37,380		39,820
1130	62.5 kva	"	32.000	2,600	44,330		46,930
1140	75 kva	"	34.934	2,840	51,280		54,120
1150	100 kva	"	36.036	2,930	68,670		71,600
1160	150 kva	"	50.000	4,070	104,310		108,380
1170	200 kva	"	55.172	4,490	139,080		143,570
1180	300 kva	"	74.766	6,090	208,620		214,710
1190	400 kva	"	89.888	7,320	312,100		319,420
1200	500 kva	"	109.589	8,920	390,120		399,040

FACILITY LIGHTNING PROTECTION

26 - 41130   LIGHTNING PROTECTION   26 - 41130

ID Code	Component Descriptions	Unit of Meas.	Manhr / Unit	Labor Cost	Material Cost	Equip. Cost	Total Cost
0100	Lightning protection						
0980	Copper point, nickel plated, 12'						
1000	1/2" dia.	EA	1.000	81.00	44.00		130
1020	5/8" dia.	"	1.000	81.00	49.50		130

LIGHTING

ID Code	Component Descriptions	Unit of Meas.	Manhr / Unit	Labor Cost	Material Cost	Equip. Cost	Total Cost
		Descriptions		**Output**	**Unit Costs**		

ID Code	Component Descriptions	Unit of Meas.	Manhr / Unit	Labor Cost	Material Cost	Equip. Cost	Total Cost
26 - 51100	**INTERIOR LIGHTING**						**26 - 51100**
0010	Recessed fluorescent fixtures, 2'x2'						
0015	2 lamp	EA	0.727	59.00	72.00		130
0020	4 lamp	"	0.727	59.00	98.00		160
0030	2 lamp w/flange	"	1.000	81.00	91.00		170
0040	4 lamp w/flange	"	1.000	81.00	110		190
0045	1'x4'						
0050	2 lamp	EA	0.667	54.00	74.00		130
0060	3 lamp	"	0.667	54.00	100		150
0070	2 lamp w/flange	"	0.727	59.00	91.00		150
0080	3 lamp w/flange	"	0.727	59.00	120		180
0085	2'x4'						
0090	2 lamp	EA	0.727	59.00	91.00		150
0100	3 lamp	"	0.727	59.00	110		170
0110	4 lamp	"	0.727	59.00	100		160
0120	2 lamp w/flange	"	1.000	81.00	110		190
0130	3 lamp w/flange	"	1.000	81.00	120		200
0140	4 lamp w/flange	"	1.000	81.00	120		200
0145	4'x4'						
0150	4 lamp	EA	1.000	81.00	370		450
0160	6 lamp	"	1.000	81.00	430		510
0170	8 lamp	"	1.000	81.00	460		540
0180	4 lamp w/flange	"	1.509	120	450		570
0190	6 lamp w/flange	"	1.509	120	560		680
0200	8 lamp, w/flange	"	1.509	120	620		740
0205	Surface mounted incandescent fixtures						
0210	40w	EA	0.667	54.00	110		160
0220	75w	"	0.667	54.00	110		160
0230	100w	"	0.667	54.00	120		170
0240	150w	"	0.667	54.00	160		210
0245	Pendant						
0250	40w	EA	0.800	65.00	90.00		160
0260	75w	"	0.800	65.00	99.00		160
0270	100w	"	0.800	65.00	110		180
0280	150w	"	0.800	65.00	130		200
0287	Recessed incandescent fixtures						
0290	40w	EA	1.509	120	150		270
0300	75w	"	1.509	120	160		280
0310	100w	"	1.509	120	180		300

LIGHTING

ID Code	Descriptions	Output		Unit Costs			
	Component Descriptions	Unit of Meas.	Manhr / Unit	Labor Cost	Material Cost	Equip. Cost	Total Cost
26 - 51100	**INTERIOR LIGHTING, Cont'd...**						**26 - 51100**
0320	150w	EA	1.509	120	190		310
0325	Exit lights, 120v						
0330	Recessed	EA	1.250	100	51.00		150
0340	Back mount	"	0.727	59.00	82.00		140
0350	Universal mount	"	0.727	59.00	86.00		140
0360	Emergency battery units, 6v-120v, 50 unit	"	1.509	120	180		300
0370	With 1 head	"	1.509	120	200		320
0380	With 2 heads	"	1.509	120	230		350
0395	Light track single circuit						
0400	2'	EA	0.500	40.75	44.25		85.00
0410	4'	"	0.500	40.75	52.00		93.00
0420	8'	"	1.000	81.00	72.00		150
0430	12'	"	1.509	120	100		220
0595	Fixtures, square						
0600	R-20	EA	0.145	11.75	45.00		57.00
0610	R-30	"	0.145	11.75	70.00		82.00
0660	Mini spot	"	0.145	11.75	42.75		55.00
26 - 51401	**INDUSTRIAL LIGHTING**						**26 - 51401**
0100	Surface mounted fluorescent, wrap around lens						
0110	1 lamp	EA	0.800	65.00	90.00		160
0120	2 lamps	"	0.889	72.00	130		200
0140	4 lamps	"	1.000	81.00	140		220
0250	Wall mounted fluorescent						
0300	2-20w lamps	EA	0.500	40.75	93.00		130
0320	2-30w lamps	"	0.500	40.75	110		150
0340	2-40w lamps	"	0.667	54.00	110		160
0350	Indirect, with wood shielding, 2049w lamps						
0360	4'	EA	1.000	81.00	110		190
0380	8'	"	1.600	130	140		270
0390	Industrial fluorescent, 2 lamp						
0400	4'	EA	0.727	59.00	72.00		130
0420	8'	"	1.333	110	110		220
0490	Strip fluorescent						
0510	4'						
0520	1 lamp	EA	0.667	54.00	45.50		100
0540	2 lamps	"	0.667	54.00	55.00		110
0550	8'						

LIGHTING

ID Code	Descriptions	Output		Unit Costs			
	Component Descriptions	Unit of Meas.	Manhr / Unit	Labor Cost	Material Cost	Equip. Cost	Total Cost
26 - 51401	**INDUSTRIAL LIGHTING, Cont'd...**						**26 - 51401**
0560	1 lamp	EA	0.727	59.00	66.00		130
0580	2 lamps	"	0.889	72.00	99.00		170
0640	Wire guard for strip fixture, 4' long	"	0.348	28.25	10.25		38.50
0660	Strip fluorescent, 8' long, two 4' lamps	"	1.333	110	140		250
0680	With four 4' lamps	"	1.600	130	170		300
0690	Wet location fluorescent, plastic housing						
0695	4' long						
0700	1 lamp	EA	1.000	81.00	110		190
0720	2 lamps	"	1.333	110	160		270
0730	8' long						
0740	2 lamps	EA	1.600	130	280		410
0760	4 lamps	"	1.739	140	370		510
1000	Parabolic troffer, 2'x2'						
1020	With 2 "U" lamps	EA	1.000	81.00	130		210
1060	With 3 "U" lamps	"	1.143	93.00	150		240
1080	2'x4'						
1100	With 2 40w lamps	EA	1.143	93.00	150		240
1120	With 3 40w lamps	"	1.333	110	150		260
1140	With 4 40w lamps	"	1.333	110	160		270
1180	1'x4'						
1220	With 1 T-12 lamp, 9 cell	EA	0.727	59.00	78.00		140
1240	With 2 T-12 lamps	"	0.889	72.00	88.00		160
1260	With 1 T-12 lamp, 20 cell	"	0.727	59.00	88.00		150
1280	With 2 T-12 lamps	"	0.889	72.00	98.00		170
1480	Steel sided surface fluorescent, 2'x4'						
1500	3 lamps	EA	1.333	110	150		260
1520	4 lamps	"	1.333	110	170		280
2100	Outdoor sign fluor., 1 lamp, remote ballast						
2120	4' long	EA	6.015	490	3,160		3,650
2140	6' long	"	8.000	650	3,800		4,450
2620	Recess mounted, commercial, 2'x2', 13" high						
2640	100w	EA	4.000	330	1,050		1,380
2660	250w	"	4.494	370	1,160		1,530
3120	High pressure sodium, hi-bay open						
3140	400w	EA	1.739	140	460		600
3160	1000w	"	2.424	200	790		990
3170	Enclosed						
3180	400w	EA	2.424	200	740		940

LIGHTING

ID Code	Component Descriptions	Unit of Meas.	Manhr / Unit	Labor Cost	Material Cost	Equip. Cost	Total Cost
	Descriptions	**Output**		**Unit Costs**			
26 - 51401	**INDUSTRIAL LIGHTING, Cont'd...**						**26 - 51401**
3200	1000w	EA	2.963	240	1,030		1,270
3210	Metal halide hi-bay, open						
3220	400w	EA	1.739	140	280		420
3240	1000w	"	2.424	200	580		780
3250	Enclosed						
3260	400w	EA	2.424	200	640		840
3280	1000w	"	2.963	240	610		850
3500	High pressure sodium, low bay, surface mounted						
3520	100w	EA	1.000	81.00	230		310
3540	150w	"	1.143	93.00	260		350
3560	250w	"	1.333	110	290		400
3580	400w	"	1.600	130	360		490
3590	Metal halide, low bay, pendant mounted						
3600	175w	EA	1.333	110	370		480
3620	250w	"	1.600	130	510		640
3660	400w	"	2.222	180	550		730
4000	Indirect luminaire, square, metal halide, freestanding						
4020	175w	EA	1.000	81.00	460		540
4040	250w	"	1.000	81.00	500		580
4060	400w	"	1.000	81.00	510		590
4070	High pressure sodium						
4080	150w	EA	1.000	81.00	830		910
4100	250w	"	1.000	81.00	890		970
4120	400w	"	1.000	81.00	980		1,060
4125	Round, metal halide						
4140	175w	EA	1.000	81.00	960		1,040
4160	250w	"	1.000	81.00	990		1,070
4180	400w	"	1.000	81.00	1,040		1,120
4190	High pressure sodium						
4200	150w	EA	1.000	81.00	910		990
4220	250w	"	1.000	81.00	1,060		1,140
4240	400w	"	1.000	81.00	1,110		1,190
4250	Wall mounted, metal halide						
4260	175w	EA	2.500	200	420		620
4280	250w	"	2.500	200	410		610
4300	400w	"	3.200	260	450		710
4310	High pressure sodium						
4320	150w	EA	2.500	200	390		590

LIGHTING

ID Code	Component Descriptions	Unit of Meas.	Manhr / Unit	Labor Cost	Material Cost	Equip. Cost	Total Cost
	Descriptions	**Output**		**Unit Costs**			

26 - 51401	**INDUSTRIAL LIGHTING, Cont'd...**					**26 - 51401**	
4340	250w	EA	2.500	200	410		610
4360	400w	"	3.200	260	420		680
4480	Wall pack lithonia, high pressure sodium						
4500	35w	EA	0.889	72.00	60.00		130
4520	55w	"	1.000	81.00	76.00		160
4540	150w	"	1.600	130	190		320
4560	250w	"	1.739	140	200		340
4570	Low pressure sodium						
4580	35w	EA	1.739	140	320		460
4600	55w	"	2.000	160	440		600
4610	Wall pack hubbell, high pressure sodium						
4620	35w	EA	0.889	72.00	270		340
4640	150w	"	1.600	130	330		460
4660	250w	"	1.739	140	430		570
4700	Compact fluorescent						
4720	2-7w	EA	1.000	81.00	160		240
4740	2-13w	"	1.333	110	180		290
4760	1-18w	"	1.333	110	220		330
6000	Handball & racquet ball court, 2'x2', metal halide						
6020	250w	EA	2.500	200	580		780
6040	400w	"	2.759	220	690		910
6060	High pressure sodium						
6080	250w	EA	2.500	200	640		840
6100	400w	"	2.759	220	690		910
6120	Bollard light, 42" w/found., high pressure sodium						
6160	70w	EA	2.581	210	970		1,180
6180	100w	"	2.581	210	990		1,200
6200	150w	"	2.581	210	1,000		1,210
8000	Light fixture lamps						
8010	Lamp						
8020	20w med. bipin base, cool white, 24"	EA	0.145	11.75	7.78		19.50
8040	30w cool white, rapid start, 36"	"	0.145	11.75	9.86		21.50
8060	40w cool white "U", 3"	"	0.145	11.75	21.50		33.25
8080	40w cool white, rapid start, 48"	"	0.145	11.75	9.18		21.00
8100	70w high pressure sodium, mogul base	"	0.200	16.25	71.00		87.00
8120	75w slimline, 96"	"	0.200	16.25	21.25		37.50
8130	100w						
8140	Incandescent, 100a, inside frost	EA	0.100	8.14	3.69		11.75

LIGHTING

ID Code	Component Descriptions	Unit of Meas.	Manhr / Unit	Labor Cost	Material Cost	Equip. Cost	Total Cost
	Descriptions	**Output**		**Unit Costs**			
26 - 51401	**INDUSTRIAL LIGHTING, Cont'd...**						**26 - 51401**
8160	Mercury vapor, clear, mogul base	EA	0.200	16.25	64.00		80.00
8180	High pressure sodium, mogul base	"	0.200	16.25	98.00		110
8190	150w						
8200	Par 38 flood or spot, incandescent	EA	0.100	8.14	21.75		30.00
8220	High pressure sodium, 1/2 mogul base	"	0.200	16.25	87.00		100
8230	175w						
8240	Mercury vapor, clear, mogul base	EA	0.200	16.25	39.00		55.00
8260	Metal halide, clear, mogul base	"	0.200	16.25	78.00		94.00
8270	High pressure sodium, mogul base	"	0.200	16.25	87.00		100
8530	250w						
8540	Mercury vapor, clear, mogul base	EA	0.200	16.25	54.00		70.00
8560	Metal halide, clear, mogul base	"	0.200	16.25	78.00		94.00
8580	High pressure sodium, mogul base	"	0.200	16.25	92.00		110
8590	400w						
8600	Mercury vapor, clear, mogul base	EA	0.200	16.25	59.00		75.00
8620	Metal halide, clear, mogul base	"	0.200	16.25	78.00		94.00
8640	High pressure sodium, mogul base	"	0.200	16.25	95.00		110
8650	1000w						
8660	Mercury vapor, clear, mogul base	EA	0.250	20.25	140		160
8680	High pressure sodium, mogul base	"	0.250	20.25	250		270

EXTERIOR LIGHTING

ID Code	Component Descriptions	Unit of Meas.	Manhr / Unit	Labor Cost	Material Cost	Equip. Cost	Total Cost
26 - 56003	**EXTERIOR LIGHTING**						**26 - 56003**
1200	Exterior light fixtures						
1210	Rectangle, high pressure sodium						
1220	70w	EA	2.500	200	330		530
1240	100w	"	2.581	210	340		550
1260	150w	"	2.581	210	360		570
1280	250w	"	2.759	220	490		710
1300	400w	"	3.478	280	550		830
1310	Flood, rectangular, high pressure sodium						
1320	70w	EA	2.500	200	240		440
1340	100w	"	2.581	210	280		490
1360	150w	"	2.581	210	260		470
1400	400w	"	3.478	280	320		600
1420	1000w	"	4.494	370	540		910
1430	Round						

EXTERIOR LIGHTING

ID Code	Component Descriptions	Unit of Meas.	Manhr / Unit	Labor Cost	Material Cost	Equip. Cost	Total Cost
		Output		**Unit Costs**			
26 - 56003	**EXTERIOR LIGHTING, Cont'd...**						**26 - 56003**
1440	400w	EA	3.478	280	600		880
1460	1000w	"	4.494	370	940		1,310
1470	Round, metal halide						
1480	400w	EA	3.478	280	670		950
1500	1000w	"	4.494	370	990		1,360
1980	Light fixture arms, cobra head, 6', high press. sodium						
2000	100w	EA	2.000	160	360		520
2021	150w	"	2.500	200	570		770
2060	250w	"	2.500	200	600		800
2080	400w	"	2.963	240	620		860
2090	Flood, metal halide						
2100	400w	EA	3.478	280	600		880
2120	1000w	"	4.494	370	820		1,190
6260	1500w	"	6.015	490	1,030		1,520
6270	Mercury vapor						
6280	250w	EA	2.759	220	390		610
6300	400w	"	3.478	280	440		720
6360	Incandescent						
6380	300w	EA	1.739	140	91.00		230
6410	500w	"	2.000	160	160		320
6420	1000w	"	3.200	260	180		440
26 - 56004	**ENERGY EFFICIENT EXTERIOR LIGHTING**						**26 - 56004**
1000	Solar Powered, led area light, 100 Watt, Zone 4						
1010	Min.	EA	1.333	110	1,190		1,300
1020	Ave.	"	1.600	130	1,330		1,460
1030	Max.	"	2.000	160	1,450		1,610
1040	Zone 2						
1050	Min.	EA	1.333	110	1,570		1,680
1060	Ave.	"	1.600	130	1,630		1,760
1070	Max.	"	2.000	160	1,690		1,850
1080	Zone 4DD						
1090	Min.	EA	1.333	110	1,800		1,910
1100	Ave.	"	1.600	130	1,930		2,060
1110	Max.	"	2.000	160	2,060		2,220
1120	Zone 2DD						
1130	Min.	EA	1.333	110	1,990		2,100
1140	Ave.	"	1.600	130	2,150		2,280

EXTERIOR LIGHTING

ID Code	Component Descriptions	Unit of Meas.	Manhr / Unit	Labor Cost	Material Cost	Equip. Cost	Total Cost
	Descriptions	**Output**		**Unit Costs**			
26 - 56004	**ENERGY EFFICIENT EXTERIOR LIGHTING, Cont'd...**						**26 - 56004**
1150	Max.	EA	2.000	160	2,300		2,460

DIVISION 27
COMMUNICATIONS

VOICE COMMUNICATIONS TERMINAL EQUIPMENT

ID Code	Component Descriptions	Unit of Meas.	Manhr / Unit	Labor Cost	Material Cost	Equip. Cost	Total Cost
	Descriptions	**Output**		**Unit Costs**			

27 - 32001 — TELEPHONE SYSTEMS — 27 - 32001

ID Code	Component Descriptions	Unit of Meas.	Manhr / Unit	Labor Cost	Material Cost	Equip. Cost	Total Cost
0480	Communication cable						
0490	25 pair	LF	0.026	2.10	0.98		3.08
0520	100 pair	"	0.029	2.32	4.67		6.99
0560	400 pair	"	0.044	3.61	16.50		20.00
0700	Cable tap in manhole or junction box						
0800	25 pair cable	EA	3.810	310	6.81		320
1020	100 pair cable	"	15.094	1,230	27.50		1,260
1100	400 pair cable	"	61.538	5,010	110		5,120
2000	Cable terminations, manhole or junction box						
2020	25 pair cable	EA	3.756	310	6.81		320
2060	100 pair cable	"	15.094	1,230	27.50		1,260
2140	400 pair cable	"	61.538	5,010	85.00		5,100

AUDIO-VIDEO SYSTEMS

27 - 41005 — TELEVISION SYSTEMS — 27 - 41005

ID Code	Component Descriptions	Unit of Meas.	Manhr / Unit	Labor Cost	Material Cost	Equip. Cost	Total Cost
0100	TV outlet, self terminating, w/cover plate	EA	0.308	25.00	5.95		31.00
0120	Thru splitter	"	1.600	130	13.00		140
0140	End of line	"	1.333	110	10.75		120
0480	In line splitter multitap						
0490	4 way	EA	1.818	150	21.75		170
0520	2 way	"	1.702	140	16.25		160
1000	Equipment cabinet	"	1.600	130	54.00		180
1010	Antenna						
1020	Broad band uhf	EA	3.478	280	110		390
1040	Lightning arrester	"	0.727	59.00	33.00		92.00
1060	TV cable	LF	0.005	0.40	0.49		0.89

DIVISION 28
SAFETY & SECURITY

ELECTRONIC

ID Code	Component Descriptions	Unit of Meas.	Manhr / Unit	Labor Cost	Material Cost	Equip. Cost	Total Cost
		Descriptions			**Output**		**Unit Costs**

28 - 16005	**SECURITY SYSTEMS**						**28 - 16005**
1000	Sensors						
1020	Balanced magnetic door switch, surface mounted	EA	0.500	40.75	160		200
1040	With remote test	"	1.000	81.00	210		290
1060	Flush mounted	"	1.860	150	150		300
1080	Mounted bracket	"	0.348	28.25	11.50		39.75
1100	Mounted bracket spacer	"	0.348	28.25	10.25		38.50
1120	Photoelectric sensor, for fence						
1140	6 beam	EA	2.759	220	16,860		17,080
1160	9 beam	"	4.255	350	20,620		20,970
1170	Photoelectric sensor, 12 volt dc						
1180	500' range	EA	1.600	130	500		630
1190	800' range	"	2.000	160	550		710
1195	Capacitance wire grid kit						
1200	Surface	EA	1.000	81.00	140		220
1220	Duct	"	1.600	130	100		230
1240	Tube grid kit	"	0.500	40.75	170		210
1260	Vibration sensor, 30 max per zone	"	0.500	40.75	210		250
1280	Audio sensor, 30 max per zone	"	0.500	40.75	220		260
1290	Inertia sensor						
1300	Outdoor	EA	0.727	59.00	160		220
1320	Indoor	"	0.500	40.75	100		140
2000	Ultrasonic transmitter, 20 max per zone						
2020	Omni-directional	EA	1.600	130	120		250
2040	Directional	"	1.333	110	130		240
2050	Transceiver						
2060	Omni-directional	EA	1.000	81.00	130		210
2080	Directional	"	1.000	81.00	140		220
2560	Passive infra-red sensor, 20 max per zone	"	1.600	130	890		1,020
3020	Access/secure unit, balanced magnetic switch	"	1.600	130	550		680
3040	Photoelectric sensor	"	1.600	130	910		1,040
3060	Photoelectric fence sensor	"	1.600	130	940		1,070
3080	Capacitance sensor	"	1.739	140	1,090		1,230
3100	Audio and vibration sensor	"	1.600	130	960		1,090
3120	Inertia sensor	"	1.600	130	1,280		1,410
3160	Ultrasonic sensor	"	1.739	140	1,470		1,610
3200	Infra-red sensor	"	2.000	160	910		1,070
4020	Monitor panel, with access/secure tone, standard	"	1.739	140	620		760
4040	High security	"	2.000	160	910		1,070

ELECTRONIC

ID Code	Component Descriptions	Unit of Meas.	Manhr / Unit	Labor Cost	Material Cost	Equip. Cost	Total Cost
	Descriptions	**Output**		**Unit Costs**			
28 - 16005	**SECURITY SYSTEMS, Cont'd...**						**28 - 16005**
4060	Emergency power indicator	EA	0.500	40.75	370		410
4070	Monitor rack with 115v power supply						
4080	1 zone	EA	1.000	81.00	520		600
4100	10 zone	"	2.500	200	2,640		2,840
4120	Monitor cabinet, wall mounted						
4140	1 zone	EA	1.000	81.00	800		880
4160	5 zone	"	1.600	130	1,320		1,450
4180	10 zone	"	1.739	140	2,880		3,020
4200	20 zone	"	2.000	160	4,010		4,170
4240	Floor mounted, 50 zone	"	4.000	330	4,170		4,500
5000	Security system accessories						
5020	Tamper assembly for monitor cabinet	EA	0.444	36.25	100		140
5040	Monitor panel blank	"	0.348	28.25	13.75		42.00
5060	Audible alarm	"	0.500	40.75	120		160
5080	Audible alarm control	"	0.348	28.25	490		520
5090	Termination screw, terminal cabinet						
5100	25 pair	EA	1.600	130	350		480
5120	50 pair	"	2.500	200	550		750
5140	150 pair	"	5.000	410	900		1,310
5150	Universal termination, cabinets & panel						
5160	Remote test	EA	1.739	140	81.00		220
5180	No remote test	"	0.727	59.00	58.00		120
5220	High security line supervision termination	"	1.000	81.00	400		480
5240	Door cord for capacitance sensor, 12"	"	0.500	40.75	13.75		55.00
5260	Insulation block kit for capacitance sensor	"	0.348	28.25	65.00		93.00
5280	Termination block for capacitance sensor	"	0.348	28.25	14.00		42.25
5360	Guard alert display	"	0.615	50.00	1,470		1,520
5380	Uninterrupted power supply	"	8.000	650	1,490		2,140
5390	Plug-in 40kva transformer						
5400	12 volt	EA	0.348	28.25	59.00		87.00
5420	18 volt	"	0.348	28.25	39.25		68.00
5440	24 volt	"	0.348	28.25	27.75		56.00
5520	Test relay	"	0.348	28.25	89.00		120
5580	Coaxial cable, 50 ohm	LF	0.006	0.49	0.40		0.89
6010	Door openers	EA	0.500	40.75	100		140
6015	Push buttons						
6020	Standard	EA	0.348	28.25	23.00		51.00
6030	Weatherproof	"	0.444	36.25	34.50		71.00

ELECTRONIC

ID Code	Component Descriptions	Unit of Meas.	Manhr / Unit	Labor Cost	Material Cost	Equip. Cost	Total Cost
	Descriptions	**Output**		**Unit Costs**			

28 - 16005　　SECURITY SYSTEMS, Cont'd...　　28 - 16005

ID Code	Component Descriptions	Unit of Meas.	Manhr / Unit	Labor Cost	Material Cost	Equip. Cost	Total Cost
6040	Bells	EA	0.727	59.00	88.00		150
6045	Horns						
6050	Standard	EA	1.000	81.00	92.00		170
6060	Weatherproof	"	1.250	100	170		270
6070	Chimes	"	0.667	54.00	140		190
6080	Flasher	"	0.615	50.00	96.00		150
6090	Motion detectors	"	1.509	120	400		520
6100	Intercom units	"	0.727	59.00	92.00		150
6110	Remote annunciator	"	5.000	410	4,150		4,560

FIRE SAFETY

28 - 31001　　FIRE ALARM SYSTEMS　　28 - 31001

ID Code	Component Descriptions	Unit of Meas.	Manhr / Unit	Labor Cost	Material Cost	Equip. Cost	Total Cost
1000	Master fire alarm box, pedestal mounted	EA	16.000	1,300	7,460		8,760
1020	Master fire alarm box	"	6.015	490	3,830		4,320
1040	Box light	"	0.500	40.75	130		170
1060	Ground assembly for box	"	0.667	54.00	110		160
1080	Bracket for pole type box	"	0.727	59.00	140		200
1090	Pull station						
1100	Waterproof	EA	0.500	40.75	68.00		110
1110	Manual	"	0.400	32.50	51.00		84.00
1120	Horn, waterproof	"	1.000	81.00	96.00		180
1140	Interior alarm	"	0.727	59.00	64.00		120
1160	Coded transmitter, automatic	"	2.000	160	980		1,140
1180	Control panel, 8 zone	"	8.000	650	2,250		2,900
1200	Battery charger and cabinet	"	2.000	160	750		910
1240	Batteries, nickel cadmium or lead calcium	"	5.000	410	570		980
2500	CO2 pressure switch connection	"	0.727	59.00	110		170
3000	Annunciator panels						
3020	Fire detection annunciator, remote type, 8 zone	EA	1.818	150	380		530
3100	12 zone	"	2.000	160	490		650
3120	16 zone	"	2.500	200	610		810
4000	Fire alarm systems						
4010	Bell	EA	0.615	50.00	120		170
4020	Weatherproof bell	"	0.667	54.00	75.00		130
4030	Horn	"	0.727	59.00	68.00		130
4040	Siren	"	2.000	160	690		850
4050	Chime	"	0.615	50.00	85.00		140

FIRE SAFETY

ID Code	Component Descriptions	Unit of Meas.	Manhr / Unit	Labor Cost	Material Cost	Equip. Cost	Total Cost
		Descriptions	**Output**	**Unit Costs**			

28 - 31001	**FIRE ALARM SYSTEMS, Cont'd...**						**28 - 31001**
4060	Audio/visual	EA	0.727	59.00	130		190
4070	Strobe light	"	0.727	59.00	110		170
4080	Smoke detector	"	0.667	54.00	180		230
4090	Heat detection	"	0.500	40.75	32.00		73.00
4100	Thermal detector	"	0.500	40.75	29.75		71.00
4110	Ionization detector	"	0.533	43.50	150		190
4120	Duct detector	"	2.759	220	500		720
4130	Test switch	"	0.500	40.75	85.00		130
4140	Remote indicator	"	0.571	46.50	53.00		100
4150	Door holder	"	0.727	59.00	180		240
4160	Telephone jack	"	0.296	24.00	3.46		27.50
4170	Fireman phone	"	1.000	81.00	450		530
4180	Speaker	"	0.800	65.00	91.00		160
4185	Remote fire alarm annunciator panel						
4190	24 zone	EA	6.667	540	2,340		2,880
4200	48 zone	"	13.008	1,060	4,690		5,750
4205	Control panel						
4210	12 zone	EA	2.963	240	1,590		1,830
4220	16 zone	"	4.444	360	2,090		2,450
4230	24 zone	"	6.667	540	3,200		3,740
4240	48 zone	"	16.000	1,300	5,970		7,270
4250	Power supply	"	1.509	120	370		490
4260	Status command	"	5.000	410	10,120		10,530
4270	Printer	"	1.509	120	3,230		3,350
4280	Transponder	"	0.899	73.00	160		230
4290	Transformer	"	0.667	54.00	230		280
4300	Transceiver	"	0.727	59.00	320		380
4310	Relays	"	0.500	40.75	130		170
4320	Flow switch	"	2.000	160	420		580
4330	Tamper switch	"	2.963	240	250		490
4340	End of line resistor	"	0.348	28.25	18.00		46.25
4350	Printed circuit card	"	0.500	40.75	160		200
4360	Central processing unit	"	6.154	500	11,060		11,560
4370	UPS backup to c.p.u.	"	8.999	730	20,260		20,990
8020	Smoke detector, fixed temp. & rate of rise comb.	"	1.600	130	320		450

DIVISION 31
EARTHWORK

SITE CLEARING

ID Code	Component Descriptions	Unit of Meas.	Manhr / Unit	Labor Cost	Material Cost	Equip. Cost	Total Cost
	Descriptions	**Output**		**Unit Costs**			

31 - 11001   CLEAR WOODED AREAS   31 - 11001

ID Code	Component Descriptions	Unit of Meas.	Manhr / Unit	Labor Cost	Material Cost	Equip. Cost	Total Cost
0980	Clear wooded area						
1000	Light density	ACRE	60.000	3,730		3,330	7,050
1500	Medium density	"	80.000	4,970		4,430	9,410
1800	Heavy density	"	96.000	5,970		5,320	11,290

SELECTIVE TREE AND SHRUB REMOVAL AND TRIMMING

31 - 13005   TREE CUTTING & CLEARING   31 - 13005

ID Code	Component Descriptions	Unit of Meas.	Manhr / Unit	Labor Cost	Material Cost	Equip. Cost	Total Cost
0980	Cut trees and clear out stumps						
1000	9" to 12" dia.	EA	4.800	300		270	560
1400	To 24" dia.	"	6.000	370		330	710
1600	24" dia. and up	"	8.000	500		440	940
5000	Loading and trucking						
5010	For machine load, per load, round trip						
5020	1 mile	EA	0.960	60.00		53.00	110
5025	3 mile	"	1.091	68.00		60.00	130
5030	5 mile	"	1.200	75.00		67.00	140
5035	10 mile	"	1.600	99.00		89.00	190
5040	20 mile	"	2.400	150		130	280
5050	Hand loaded, round trip						
5060	1 mile	EA	2.000	120		150	270
5065	3 mile	"	2.286	140		170	310
5070	5 mile	"	2.667	170		200	370
5080	10 mile	"	3.200	200		240	440
5100	20 mile	"	4.000	250		300	550
6000	Tree trimming for pole line construction						
6020	Light cutting	LF	0.012	0.74		0.66	1.41
6040	Medium cutting	"	0.016	0.99		0.88	1.88
6060	Heavy cutting	"	0.024	1.49		1.33	2.82

EARTHWORK, EXCAVATION & FILL

31 - 22130   ROUGH GRADING   31 - 22130

ID Code	Component Descriptions	Unit of Meas.	Manhr / Unit	Labor Cost	Material Cost	Equip. Cost	Total Cost
1000	Site grading, cut & fill, sandy clay, 200' haul, 75 hp dozer	CY	0.032	1.98		2.40	4.38
1100	Spread topsoil by equipment on site	"	0.036	2.20		2.66	4.87
1200	Site grading (cut and fill to 6") less than 1 acre						
1300	75 hp dozer	CY	0.053	3.31		4.00	7.31
1400	1.5 cy backhoe/loader	"	0.080	4.97		6.00	11.00

EARTHWORK, EXCAVATION & FILL

ID Code	Component Descriptions	Unit of Meas.	Manhr / Unit	Labor Cost	Material Cost	Equip. Cost	Total Cost
		Descriptions — **Output** — **Unit Costs**					

ID Code	Component Descriptions	Unit of Meas.	Manhr / Unit	Labor Cost	Material Cost	Equip. Cost	Total Cost
31 - 23131	**BASE COURSE**						**31 - 23131**
1019	Base course, crushed stone						
1020	3" thick	SY	0.004	0.33	3.19	0.44	3.96
1030	4" thick	"	0.004	0.35	4.29	0.47	5.12
1040	6" thick	"	0.005	0.38	6.43	0.51	7.33
1050	8" thick	"	0.005	0.44	8.58	0.58	9.60
1060	10" thick	"	0.006	0.47	10.75	0.62	11.75
1070	12" thick	"	0.007	0.55	12.75	0.73	14.00
2500	Base course, bank run gravel						
3020	4" deep	SY	0.004	0.34	3.02	0.46	3.83
3040	6" deep	"	0.005	0.37	4.62	0.50	5.50
3060	8" deep	"	0.005	0.41	6.10	0.55	7.06
3070	10" deep	"	0.005	0.44	7.64	0.58	8.66
3080	12" deep	"	0.006	0.50	9.13	0.67	10.25
4000	Prepare and roll sub base						
4020	Minimum	SY	0.004	0.33		0.44	0.77
4030	Average	"	0.005	0.41		0.55	0.96
4040	Maximum	"	0.007	0.55		0.73	1.28
31 - 23132	**BORROW**						**31 - 23132**
1000	Borrow fill, F.O.B. at pit						
1005	Sand, haul to site, round trip						
1010	10 mile	CY	0.080	6.62	22.75	8.80	38.25
1020	20 mile	"	0.133	11.00	22.75	14.75	48.50
1030	30 mile	"	0.200	16.50	22.75	22.00	61.00
3980	Place borrow fill and compact						
4000	Less than 1 in 4 slope	CY	0.040	3.31	22.75	4.40	30.50
4100	Greater than 1 in 4 slope	"	0.053	4.41	22.75	5.86	33.00
31 - 23137	**GRAVEL AND STONE**						**31 - 23137**
0120	F.O.B. PLANT, material only						
1000	No. 21 crusher run stone	CY					33.00
1100	No. 26 crusher run stone	"					33.00
1140	No. 57 stone	"					33.00
1150	No. 67 gravel	"					33.00
1180	No. 68 stone	"					33.00
1220	No. 78 stone	"					33.00
1235	No. 78 gravel, (pea gravel)	"					33.00
1250	No. 357 or B-3 stone	"					33.00
1260	Structural & foundation backfill						

EARTHWORK, EXCAVATION & FILL

ID Code	Component Descriptions	Unit of Meas.	Manhr / Unit	Labor Cost	Material Cost	Equip. Cost	Total Cost
	Descriptions	**Output**		**Unit Costs**			
31 - 23137	**GRAVEL AND STONE, Cont'd...**					**31 - 23137**	
1400	No. 21 crusher run stone	TON					24.50
1500	No. 26 crusher run stone	"					24.50
1600	No. 57 stone	"					24.50
2160	No. 67 gravel	"					24.50
2210	No. 68 stone	"					24.50
2220	No. 78 stone	"					24.50
2280	No. 78 gravel, (pea gravel)	"					24.50
3240	No. 357 or B-3 stone	"					24.50
31 - 23163	**BULK EXCAVATION**					**31 - 23163**	
1000	Excavation, by small dozer						
1020	Large areas	CY	0.016	0.99		1.20	2.19
1040	Small areas	"	0.027	1.65		2.00	3.65
1060	Trim banks	"	0.040	2.48		3.00	5.48
1200	Drag line						
1220	1-1/2 cy bucket						
1240	Sand or gravel	CY	0.040	2.48		2.21	4.70
1260	Light clay	"	0.053	3.31		2.95	6.27
1280	Heavy clay	"	0.060	3.72		3.32	7.05
1300	Unclassified	"	0.064	3.97		3.54	7.52
1400	2 cy bucket						
1420	Sand or gravel	CY	0.037	2.29		2.04	4.34
1440	Light clay	"	0.048	2.98		2.66	5.64
1460	Heavy clay	"	0.053	3.31		2.95	6.27
1480	Unclassified	"	0.056	3.50		3.12	6.63
1500	2-1/2 cy bucket						
1520	Sand or gravel	CY	0.034	2.13		1.90	4.03
1540	Light clay	"	0.044	2.71		2.41	5.13
1560	Heavy clay	"	0.048	2.98		2.66	5.64
1580	Unclassified	"	0.051	3.14		2.80	5.94
1600	3 cy bucket						
1620	Sand or gravel	CY	0.030	1.86		1.66	3.52
1640	Light clay	"	0.040	2.48		2.21	4.70
1660	Heavy clay	"	0.044	2.71		2.41	5.13
1680	Unclassified	"	0.046	2.84		2.53	5.37
1700	Hydraulic excavator						
1720	1 cy capacity						
1740	Light material	CY	0.040	2.48		2.21	4.70

EARTHWORK, EXCAVATION & FILL

ID Code	Component Descriptions	Unit of Meas.	Manhr / Unit	Labor Cost	Material Cost	Equip. Cost	Total Cost
	Descriptions	**Output**		**Unit Costs**			
31 - 23163		**BULK EXCAVATION, Cont'd...**				**31 - 23163**	
1760	Medium material	CY	0.048	2.98		2.66	5.64
1780	Wet material	"	0.060	3.72		3.32	7.05
1790	Blasted rock	"	0.069	4.26		3.80	8.06
1800	1-1/2 cy capacity						
1820	Light material	CY	0.010	0.82		1.10	1.92
1840	Medium material	"	0.013	1.10		1.46	2.57
1860	Wet material	"	0.016	1.32		1.76	3.08
1880	Blasted rock	"	0.020	1.65		2.20	3.85
1900	2 cy capacity						
1920	Light material	CY	0.009	0.73		0.97	1.71
1940	Medium material	"	0.011	0.94		1.25	2.20
1960	Wet material	"	0.013	1.10		1.46	2.57
1980	Blasted rock	"	0.016	1.32		1.76	3.08
2000	Wheel mounted front-end loader						
2020	7/8 cy capacity						
2040	Light material	CY	0.020	1.65		2.20	3.85
2060	Medium material	"	0.023	1.89		2.51	4.40
2080	Wet material	"	0.027	2.20		2.93	5.14
2100	Blasted rock	"	0.032	2.64		3.52	6.16
2200	1-1/2 cy capacity						
2220	Light material	CY	0.011	0.94		1.25	2.20
2240	Medium material	"	0.012	1.01		1.35	2.37
2260	Wet material	"	0.013	1.10		1.46	2.57
2280	Blasted rock	"	0.015	1.20		1.60	2.80
2300	2-1/2 cy capacity						
2320	Light material	CY	0.009	0.77		1.03	1.81
2340	Medium material	"	0.010	0.82		1.10	1.92
2360	Wet material	"	0.011	0.88		1.17	2.05
2380	Blasted rock	"	0.011	0.94		1.25	2.20
2400	3-1/2 cy capacity						
2420	Light material	CY	0.009	0.73		0.97	1.71
2440	Medium material	"	0.009	0.77		1.03	1.81
2460	Wet material	"	0.010	0.82		1.10	1.92
2480	Blasted rock	"	0.011	0.88		1.17	2.05
2500	6 cy capacity						
2520	Light material	CY	0.005	0.44		0.58	1.02
2540	Medium material	"	0.006	0.47		0.62	1.10
2560	Wet material	"	0.006	0.50		0.67	1.18

EARTHWORK, EXCAVATION & FILL

ID Code	Component Descriptions	Unit of Meas.	Manhr / Unit	Labor Cost	Material Cost	Equip. Cost	Total Cost
	Descriptions	**Output**		**Unit Costs**			

31 - 23163 — BULK EXCAVATION, Cont'd...

ID Code	Component Descriptions	Unit of Meas.	Manhr / Unit	Labor Cost	Material Cost	Equip. Cost	Total Cost
2580	Blasted rock	CY	0.007	0.55		0.73	1.28
2600	Track mounted front-end loader						
2620	1-1/2 cy capacity						
2640	Light material	CY	0.013	1.10		1.46	2.57
2660	Medium material	"	0.015	1.20		1.60	2.80
2680	Wet material	"	0.016	1.32		1.76	3.08
2700	Blasted rock	"	0.018	1.47		1.95	3.42
2720	2-3/4 cy capacity						
2740	Light material	CY	0.008	0.66		0.88	1.54
2760	Medium material	"	0.009	0.73		0.97	1.71
2780	Wet material	"	0.010	0.82		1.10	1.92
2790	Blasted rock	"	0.011	0.94		1.25	2.20

31 - 23164 — BUILDING EXCAVATION

ID Code	Component Descriptions	Unit of Meas.	Manhr / Unit	Labor Cost	Material Cost	Equip. Cost	Total Cost
0090	Structural excavation, unclassified earth						
0100	3/8 cy backhoe	CY	0.107	8.82		11.75	20.50
0110	3/4 cy backhoe	"	0.080	6.62		8.80	15.50
0120	1 cy backhoe	"	0.067	5.51		7.33	12.75
0600	Foundation backfill and compaction by machine	"	0.160	13.25		17.50	30.75

31 - 23165 — HAND EXCAVATION

ID Code	Component Descriptions	Unit of Meas.	Manhr / Unit	Labor Cost	Material Cost	Equip. Cost	Total Cost
0980	Excavation						
1000	To 2' deep						
1020	Normal soil	CY	0.889	56.00			56.00
1040	Sand and gravel	"	0.800	50.00			50.00
1060	Medium clay	"	1.000	63.00			63.00
1080	Heavy clay	"	1.143	72.00			72.00
1100	Loose rock	"	1.333	84.00			84.00
1200	To 6' deep						
1220	Normal soil	CY	1.143	72.00			72.00
1240	Sand and gravel	"	1.000	63.00			63.00
1260	Medium clay	"	1.333	84.00			84.00
1280	Heavy clay	"	1.600	100			100
1300	Loose rock	"	2.000	130			130
2020	Backfilling foundation without compaction, 6" lifts	"	0.500	31.25			31.25
2200	Compaction of backfill around structures or in trench						
2220	By hand with air tamper	CY	0.571	35.75			35.75
2240	By hand with vibrating plate tamper	"	0.533	33.50			33.50
2250	1 ton roller	"	0.400	24.75		30.00	55.00

EARTHWORK, EXCAVATION & FILL

ID Code	Component Descriptions	Unit of Meas.	Manhr / Unit	Labor Cost	Material Cost	Equip. Cost	Total Cost
	Descriptions	**Output**		**Unit Costs**			
31 - 23165	**HAND EXCAVATION, Cont'd...**						**31 - 23165**
5400	Miscellaneous hand labor						
5440	Trim slopes, sides of excavation	SF	0.001	0.08			0.08
5450	Trim bottom of excavation	"	0.002	0.10			0.10
5460	Excavation around obstructions and services	CY	2.667	170			170
31 - 23167	**UTILITY EXCAVATION**						**31 - 23167**
2080	Trencher, sandy clay, 8" wide trench						
2100	18" deep	LF	0.018	1.10		1.33	2.43
2200	24" deep	"	0.020	1.24		1.50	2.74
2300	36" deep	"	0.023	1.42		1.71	3.13
6080	Trench backfill, 95% compaction						
7000	Tamp by hand	CY	0.500	31.25			31.25
7050	Vibratory compaction	"	0.400	25.00			25.00
7060	Trench backfilling, with borrow sand, place & compact	"	0.400	25.00	22.75		47.75
31 - 23168	**ROADWAY EXCAVATION**						**31 - 23168**
0100	Roadway excavation						
0110	1/4 mile haul	CY	0.016	1.32		1.76	3.08
0120	2 mile haul	"	0.027	2.20		2.93	5.14
0130	5 mile haul	"	0.040	3.31		4.40	7.71
0150	Excavation of open ditches	"	0.011	0.94		1.25	2.20
0160	Trim banks, swales or ditches	SY	0.013	1.10		1.46	2.57
0165	Bulk swale excavation by dragline						
0170	Small jobs	CY	0.060	3.72		3.32	7.05
0180	Large jobs	"	0.034	2.13		1.90	4.03
3000	Spread base course	"	0.020	1.65		2.20	3.85
3100	Roll and compact	"	0.027	2.20		2.93	5.14
31 - 23169	**HAULING MATERIAL**						**31 - 23169**
0090	Haul material by 10 cy dump truck, round trip distance						
0100	1 mile	CY	0.044	2.76		3.33	6.09
0110	2 mile	"	0.053	3.31		4.00	7.31
0120	5 mile	"	0.073	4.52		5.45	9.97
0130	10 mile	"	0.080	4.97		6.00	11.00
0140	20 mile	"	0.089	5.52		6.66	12.25
0150	30 mile	"	0.107	6.62		8.00	14.50

EARTHWORK, EXCAVATION & FILL

ID Code	Component Descriptions	Unit of Meas.	Manhr / Unit	Labor Cost	Material Cost	Equip. Cost	Total Cost
			Output		**Unit Costs**		
31 - 23195	**WELLPOINT SYSTEMS**					**31 - 23195**	
0980	Pumping, gas driven, 50' hose						
1000	3" header pipe	DAY	8.000	500		600	1,100
1010	6" header pipe	"	10.000	620		750	1,370
1080	Wellpoint system per job; 150' length of PVC header						
1100	6" header pipe, 2"wellpoints, 5' centers	LF	0.032	1.98	60.00	2.40	64.00
1110	8" header pipe	"	0.040	2.48	72.00	3.00	77.00
1120	10" header pipe	"	0.053	3.31	110	4.00	120
1200	Jetting wellpoint system						
1220	14' long	EA	0.533	33.25	82.00	40.00	160
1230	18' long	"	0.667	41.50	94.00	50.00	190
1240	Sand filter for wellpoints	LF	0.013	0.82	3.93	1.00	5.75
2000	Replacement of wellpoint components	EA	0.160	9.94		12.00	22.00
31 - 23336	**TRENCHING**					**31 - 23336**	
0100	Trenching and continuous footing excavation						
0980	By gradall						
1000	1 cy capacity						
1020	Light soil	CY	0.023	1.89		2.51	4.40
1040	Medium soil	"	0.025	2.03		2.70	4.74
1060	Heavy/wet soil	"	0.027	2.20		2.93	5.14
1080	Loose rock	"	0.029	2.40		3.20	5.60
1090	Blasted rock	"	0.031	2.54		3.38	5.93
1095	By hydraulic excavator						
1100	1/2 cy capacity						
1120	Light soil	CY	0.027	2.20		2.93	5.14
1140	Medium soil	"	0.029	2.40		3.20	5.60
1160	Heavy/wet soil	"	0.032	2.64		3.52	6.16
1180	Loose rock	"	0.036	2.94		3.91	6.85
1190	Blasted rock	"	0.040	3.31		4.40	7.71
1200	1 cy capacity						
1220	Light soil	CY	0.019	1.55		2.07	3.62
1240	Medium soil	"	0.020	1.65		2.20	3.85
1260	Heavy/wet soil	"	0.021	1.76		2.34	4.11
1280	Loose rock	"	0.023	1.89		2.51	4.40
1300	Blasted rock	"	0.025	2.03		2.70	4.74
1400	1-1/2 cy capacity						
1420	Light soil	CY	0.017	1.39		1.85	3.24
1440	Medium soil	"	0.018	1.47		1.95	3.42

EARTHWORK, EXCAVATION & FILL

ID Code	Descriptions — Component Descriptions	Output — Unit of Meas.	Output — Manhr / Unit	Unit Costs — Labor Cost	Unit Costs — Material Cost	Unit Costs — Equip. Cost	Unit Costs — Total Cost
31 - 23336	**TRENCHING, Cont'd...**						**31 - 23336**
1460	Heavy/wet soil	CY	0.019	1.55		2.07	3.62
1480	Loose rock	"	0.020	1.65		2.20	3.85
1500	Blasted rock	"	0.021	1.76		2.34	4.11
1600	2 cy capacity						
1620	Light soil	CY	0.016	1.32		1.76	3.08
1640	Medium soil	"	0.017	1.39		1.85	3.24
1660	Heavy/wet soil	"	0.018	1.47		1.95	3.42
1680	Loose rock	"	0.019	1.55		2.07	3.62
1690	Blasted rock	"	0.020	1.65		2.20	3.85
1700	2-1/2 cy capacity						
1720	Light soil	CY	0.015	1.20		1.60	2.80
1740	Medium soil	"	0.015	1.26		1.67	2.93
1760	Heavy/wet soil	"	0.016	1.32		1.76	3.08
1780	Loose rock	"	0.017	1.39		1.85	3.24
1790	Blasted rock	"	0.018	1.47		1.95	3.42
1800	Trencher, chain, 1' wide to 4' deep						
1940	Light soil	CY	0.020	1.24		1.50	2.74
1960	Medium soil	"	0.023	1.42		1.71	3.13
1980	Heavy soil	"	0.027	1.65		2.00	3.65
3000	Hand excavation						
3100	Bulk, wheeled 100'						
3120	Normal soil	CY	0.889	56.00			56.00
3140	Sand or gravel	"	0.800	50.00			50.00
3160	Medium clay	"	1.143	72.00			72.00
3180	Heavy clay	"	1.600	100			100
3200	Loose rock	"	2.000	130			130
3300	Trenches, up to 2' deep						
3320	Normal soil	CY	1.000	63.00			63.00
3340	Sand or gravel	"	0.889	56.00			56.00
3360	Medium clay	"	1.333	84.00			84.00
3380	Heavy clay	"	2.000	130			130
3390	Loose rock	"	2.667	170			170
3400	Trenches, to 6' deep						
3420	Normal soil	CY	1.143	72.00			72.00
3440	Sand or gravel	"	1.000	63.00			63.00
3460	Medium clay	"	1.600	100			100
3480	Heavy clay	"	2.667	170			170
3500	Loose rock	"	4.000	250			250

EARTHWORK, EXCAVATION & FILL

ID Code	Component Descriptions	Unit of Meas.	Manhr / Unit	Labor Cost	Material Cost	Equip. Cost	Total Cost
	Descriptions	**Output**		**Unit Costs**			

31 - 23336 — TRENCHING, Cont'd... — 31 - 23336

ID Code	Component Descriptions	Unit of Meas.	Manhr / Unit	Labor Cost	Material Cost	Equip. Cost	Total Cost
3590	Backfill trenches						
3600	With compaction						
3620	By hand	CY	0.667	41.75			41.75
3640	By 60 hp tracked dozer	"	0.020	1.24		1.50	2.74
3650	By 200 hp tracked dozer	"	0.009	0.73		0.97	1.71
3660	By small front-end loader	"	0.023	1.42		1.71	3.13
3700	Spread dumped fill or gravel, no compaction						
3740	6" layers	SY	0.013	0.82		1.00	1.82
3760	12" layers	"	0.016	0.99		1.20	2.19
3800	Compaction in 6" layers						
3820	By hand with air tamper	SY	0.016	1.00		0.34	1.34
3890	Backfill trenches, sand bedding, no compaction						
3900	By hand	CY	0.667	41.75	23.00		65.00
3940	By small front-end loader	"	0.023	1.89	23.00	2.51	27.50

SOIL STABILIZATION & TREATMENT

31 - 31160 — SOIL TREATMENT — 31 - 31160

ID Code	Component Descriptions	Unit of Meas.	Manhr / Unit	Labor Cost	Material Cost	Equip. Cost	Total Cost
1100	Soil treatment, termite control pretreatment						
1120	Under slabs	SF	0.004	0.27	0.38		0.65
1140	By walls	"	0.005	0.33	0.38		0.71

SOIL STABILIZATION

31 - 32003 — GEOTEXTILE — 31 - 32003

ID Code	Component Descriptions	Unit of Meas.	Manhr / Unit	Labor Cost	Material Cost	Equip. Cost	Total Cost
0060	Filter cloth, light reinforcement						
1180	Woven						
1200	12'-6" wide x 50' long	SF	0.001	0.07	0.34		0.41
1300	Various lengths	"	0.001	0.07	0.51		0.58
1380	Non-woven						
1390	14'-8" wide x 430' long	SF	0.001	0.07	0.18		0.25
1400	Various lengths	"	0.001	0.07	0.26		0.33

SOIL STABILIZATION

ID Code	Component Descriptions	Unit of Meas.	Manhr / Unit	Labor Cost	Material Cost	Equip. Cost	Total Cost
	Descriptions	**Output**		**Unit Costs**			

31 - 32005 — SOIL STABILIZATION — 31 - 32005

ID Code	Component Descriptions	Unit of Meas.	Manhr / Unit	Labor Cost	Material Cost	Equip. Cost	Total Cost
0100	Straw bale secured with rebar	LF	0.027	1.67	7.54		9.21
0120	Filter barrier, 18" high filter fabric	"	0.080	5.01	1.82		6.83
0130	Sediment fence, 36" fabric with 6" mesh	"	0.100	6.26	4.32		10.50
1000	Soil stabilization with tar paper, burlap, straw and stakes	SF	0.001	0.07	0.36		0.43

GABIONS

31 - 36001 — SLOPE PROTECTION — 31 - 36001

ID Code	Component Descriptions	Unit of Meas.	Manhr / Unit	Labor Cost	Material Cost	Equip. Cost	Total Cost
2060	Gabions, stone filled						
2080	6" deep	SY	0.200	12.50	30.25	15.00	58.00
2090	9" deep	"	0.229	14.25	37.00	17.25	68.00
2100	12" deep	"	0.267	16.50	49.00	20.00	86.00
2120	18" deep	"	0.320	20.00	63.00	24.00	110
2140	36" deep	"	0.533	33.25	110	40.00	180

RIPRAP

31 - 37001 — RIPRAP — 31 - 37001

ID Code	Component Descriptions	Unit of Meas.	Manhr / Unit	Labor Cost	Material Cost	Equip. Cost	Total Cost
0100	Riprap						
0110	Crushed stone blanket, max size 2-1/2"	TON	0.533	33.50	35.25	48.25	120
0120	Stone, quarry run, 300 lb. stones	"	0.492	30.75	44.25	44.50	120
0130	400 lb. stones	"	0.457	28.75	46.00	41.50	120
0140	500 lb. stones	"	0.427	26.75	48.00	38.75	110
0150	750 lb. stones	"	0.400	25.00	49.75	36.25	110
0160	Dry concrete riprap in bags 3" thick, 80 lb. per bag	BAG	0.027	1.67	5.96	2.41	10.00

SHORING AND UNDERPINNING

31 - 41160 — STEEL SHEET PILING — 31 - 41160

ID Code	Component Descriptions	Unit of Meas.	Manhr / Unit	Labor Cost	Material Cost	Equip. Cost	Total Cost
1000	Steel sheet piling, 12" wide						
1100	20' long	SF	0.096	7.68	20.00	9.20	36.75
1200	35' long	"	0.069	5.48	20.00	6.57	32.00
1300	50' long	"	0.048	3.84	20.00	4.60	28.50
1400	Over 50' long	"	0.044	3.49	20.00	4.18	27.75

SHORING AND UNDERPINNING

ID Code	Descriptions — Component Descriptions	Output — Unit of Meas.	Manhr / Unit	Labor Cost	Material Cost	Equip. Cost	Total Cost
				Unit Costs			

31 - 41330 — TRENCH SHEETING — 31 - 41330

ID Code	Component Descriptions	Unit of Meas.	Manhr / Unit	Labor Cost	Material Cost	Equip. Cost	Total Cost
0980	Closed timber, including pull and salvage, excavation						
1000	8' deep	SF	0.064	4.00	2.87	5.80	12.75
1200	10' deep	"	0.067	4.22	2.93	6.10	13.25
1300	12' deep	"	0.071	4.45	3.01	6.44	14.00
1400	14' deep	"	0.075	4.71	3.14	6.82	14.75
1600	16' deep	"	0.080	5.01	3.16	7.25	15.50
1800	18' deep	"	0.091	5.72	3.26	8.28	17.25
2000	20' deep	"	0.098	6.16	4.12	8.92	19.00

EXCAVATION SUPPORT AND PROTECTION

31 - 50001 — TRENCH BOX — 31 - 50001

ID Code	Component Descriptions	Unit of Meas.	Manhr / Unit	Labor Cost	Material Cost	Equip. Cost	Total Cost
0100	10' X 10' Steel, 4" Wall, Rental Rate						
0120	4 Hour	EA					150
0140	Day	"					150
0160	Week	"					390
0180	Month	"					1,160
0200	10 x 24 Steel 6" Wall, Rental Rate						
0220	4 Hour	EA					300
0240	Day	"					300
0260	Week	"					740
0280	Month	"					2,230

COFFERDAMS

31 - 52001 — COFFERDAMS — 31 - 52001

ID Code	Component Descriptions	Unit of Meas.	Manhr / Unit	Labor Cost	Material Cost	Equip. Cost	Total Cost
0980	Cofferdam, steel, driven from shore						
1000	15' deep	SF	0.137	11.00	19.25	13.25	43.25
1020	20' deep	"	0.128	10.25	19.25	12.25	41.75
1040	25' deep	"	0.120	9.60	19.25	11.50	40.25
1060	30' deep	"	0.113	9.03	19.25	10.75	39.00
1080	40' deep	"	0.107	8.53	19.25	10.25	38.00
1090	Driven from barge						
1100	20' deep	SF	0.148	11.75	19.25	14.25	45.25
1120	30' deep	"	0.137	11.00	19.25	13.25	43.25
1140	40' deep	"	0.128	10.25	19.25	12.25	41.75
1160	50' deep	"	0.120	9.60	19.25	11.50	40.25

PILES AND CAISSONS

ID Code	Component Descriptions	Unit of Meas.	Manhr / Unit	Labor Cost	Material Cost	Equip. Cost	Total Cost
		Output		**Unit Costs**			

ID Code	Component Descriptions	Unit of Meas.	Manhr / Unit	Labor Cost	Material Cost	Equip. Cost	Total Cost
31 - 62001	**PILE TESTING**						**31 - 62001**
1000	Pile test						
1020	50 ton to 100 ton	EA					20,670
1030	To 200 ton	"					29,160
1060	To 300 ton	"					33,730
1080	To 400 ton	"					39,500
1100	To 600 ton	"					49,380
31 - 62165	**STEEL PILES**						**31 - 62165**
1000	H-section piles						
1010	8x8						
1020	36 lb/ft						
1021	30' long	LF	0.080	6.40	21.75	7.66	35.75
1022	40' long	"	0.064	5.12	21.75	6.13	33.00
1023	50' long	"	0.053	4.26	21.75	5.11	31.00
1030	10x10						
1040	42 lb/ft						
1041	30' long	LF	0.080	6.40	25.50	7.66	39.50
1042	40' long	"	0.064	5.12	25.50	6.13	36.75
1043	50' long	"	0.053	4.26	25.50	5.11	34.75
1060	57 lb/ft						
1061	30' long	LF	0.080	6.40	34.50	7.66	48.50
1063	40' long	"	0.064	5.12	34.50	6.13	45.75
1065	50' long	"	0.053	4.26	34.50	5.11	43.75
1070	12x12						
1080	53 lb/ft						
1081	30' long	LF	0.087	6.98	32.00	8.36	47.25
1083	40' long	"	0.069	5.48	32.00	6.57	44.00
1085	50' long	"	0.053	4.26	32.00	5.11	41.25
1100	74 lb/ft						
1101	30' long	LF	0.087	6.98	44.75	8.36	60.00
1103	40' long	"	0.069	5.48	44.75	6.57	57.00
1105	50' long	"	0.053	4.26	44.75	5.11	54.00
1110	14x14						
1120	73 lb/ft						
1121	40' long	LF	0.087	6.98	44.25	8.36	60.00
1123	50' long	"	0.069	5.48	44.25	6.57	56.00
1125	60' long	"	0.053	4.26	44.25	5.11	54.00
1140	89 lb/ft						

PILES AND CAISSONS

ID Code	Component Descriptions	Unit of Meas.	Manhr / Unit	Labor Cost	Material Cost	Equip. Cost	Total Cost
31 - 62165	**STEEL PILES, Cont'd...**						**31 - 62165**
1142	40' long	LF	0.087	6.98	54.00	8.36	69.00
1144	50' long	"	0.069	5.48	54.00	6.57	66.00
1146	60' long	"	0.053	4.26	54.00	5.11	63.00
1160	102 lb/ft						
1161	40' long	LF	0.087	6.98	62.00	8.36	77.00
1163	50' long	"	0.069	5.48	62.00	6.57	74.00
1165	60' long	"	0.053	4.26	62.00	5.11	71.00
1180	117 lb/ft						
1182	40' long	LF	0.091	7.31	71.00	8.76	87.00
1184	50' long	"	0.071	5.68	71.00	6.81	84.00
1186	60' long	"	0.055	4.38	71.00	5.25	81.00
4010	Splice						
4020	8"	EA	1.333	84.00	110		190
4060	10"	"	1.600	100	120		220
4080	12"	"	1.600	100	160		260
4100	14"	"	2.000	130	200		330
4110	Driving cap						
4120	8"	EA	0.800	50.00	51.00		100
4140	10"	"	1.000	63.00	51.00		110
4160	12"	"	1.000	63.00	51.00		110
4200	14"	"	1.143	72.00	51.00		120
4210	Standard point						
4220	8"	EA	0.800	50.00	80.00		130
4240	10"	"	1.000	63.00	94.00		160
4260	12"	"	1.143	72.00	110		180
4280	14"	"	1.333	84.00	130		210
4290	Heavy duty point						
4300	8"	EA	0.889	56.00	67.00		120
4305	10"	"	1.143	72.00	79.00		150
4310	12"	"	1.333	84.00	100		180
4320	14"	"	1.600	100	130		230
5000	Tapered friction piles, fluted casing, up to 50'						
5002	With 4000 psi concrete no reinforcing						
5040	12" dia.	LF	0.048	3.84	21.50	4.60	30.00
5060	14" dia.	"	0.049	3.93	24.75	4.71	33.50
5080	16" dia.	"	0.051	4.04	29.75	4.84	38.75
5100	18" dia.	"	0.056	4.51	33.50	5.41	43.50

PILES AND CAISSONS

ID Code	Descriptions	Output		Unit Costs			
	Component Descriptions	Unit of Meas.	Manhr / Unit	Labor Cost	Material Cost	Equip. Cost	Total Cost
31 - 62166		**STEEL PIPE PILES**				**31 - 62166**	
1000	Concrete filled, 3000# concrete, up to 40'						
1100	8" dia.	LF	0.069	5.48	24.00	6.57	36.00
1120	10" dia.	"	0.071	5.68	31.00	6.81	43.50
1140	12" dia.	"	0.074	5.90	36.00	7.07	49.00
1160	14" dia.	"	0.077	6.14	39.50	7.36	53.00
1180	16" dia.	"	0.080	6.40	45.00	7.66	59.00
1200	18" dia.	"	0.083	6.67	62.00	8.00	77.00
2000	Pipe piles, non-filled						
2020	8" dia.	LF	0.053	4.26	21.75	5.11	31.00
2040	10" dia.	"	0.055	4.38	27.25	5.25	37.00
2060	12" dia.	"	0.056	4.51	33.25	5.41	43.25
2080	14" dia.	"	0.060	4.80	35.00	5.75	45.50
2100	16" dia.	"	0.062	4.95	40.00	5.93	51.00
2120	18" dia.	"	0.064	5.12	52.00	6.13	63.00
2520	Splice						
2540	8" dia.	EA	1.600	100	97.00		200
2560	10" dia.	"	1.600	100	110		210
2580	12" dia.	"	2.000	130	120		250
2600	14" dia.	"	2.000	130	130		260
2620	16" dia.	"	2.667	170	160		330
2640	18" dia.	"	2.667	170	210		380
2680	Standard point						
2700	8" dia.	EA	1.600	100	130		230
2740	10" dia.	"	1.600	100	170		270
2760	12" dia.	"	2.000	130	180		310
2780	14" dia.	"	2.000	130	200		330
2800	16" dia.	"	2.667	170	250		420
2820	18" dia.	"	2.667	170	360		530
2880	Heavy duty point						
2900	8" dia.	EA	2.000	130	230		360
2920	10" dia.	"	2.000	130	320		450
2940	12" dia.	"	2.667	170	340		510
2960	14" dia.	"	2.667	170	470		640
2980	16" dia.	"	3.200	200	470		670
3000	18" dia.	"	3.200	200	520		720

PILES AND CAISSONS

ID Code	Descriptions	Output		Unit Costs			
	Component Descriptions	Unit of Meas.	Manhr / Unit	Labor Cost	Material Cost	Equip. Cost	Total Cost
31 - 62190	**WOOD AND TIMBER PILES**						**31 - 62190**
0080	Treated wood piles, 12" butt, 8" tip						
0100	25' long	LF	0.096	7.68	18.00	9.20	34.75
0110	30' long	"	0.080	6.40	19.25	7.66	33.25
0120	35' long	"	0.069	5.48	19.25	6.57	31.25
0125	40' long	"	0.060	4.80	19.25	5.75	29.75
0128	12" butt, 7" tip						
0130	40' long	LF	0.060	4.80	21.75	5.75	32.25
0132	45' long	"	0.053	4.26	21.75	5.11	31.00
0134	50' long	"	0.048	3.84	24.75	4.60	33.25
0150	55' long	"	0.044	3.49	24.75	4.18	32.50
0160	60' long	"	0.040	3.20	24.75	3.83	31.75

BORED PILES

ID Code	Descriptions	Output		Unit Costs			
31 - 63135	**PRESTRESSED PILING**						**31 - 63135**
0980	Prestressed concrete piling, less than 60' long						
1000	10" sq.	LF	0.040	3.20	20.75	3.83	27.75
1002	12" sq.	"	0.042	3.33	29.00	4.00	36.25
1004	14" sq.	"	0.043	3.41	30.25	4.08	37.75
1006	16" sq.	"	0.044	3.49	37.25	4.18	45.00
1008	18" sq.	"	0.047	3.74	51.00	4.48	59.00
1010	20" sq.	"	0.048	3.84	70.00	4.60	78.00
1012	24" sq.	"	0.049	3.93	89.00	4.71	98.00
1100	More than 60' long						
1120	12" sq.	LF	0.034	2.74	29.75	3.28	35.75
1140	14" sq.	"	0.035	2.79	32.75	3.34	39.00
1160	16" sq.	"	0.036	2.84	39.25	3.40	45.50
1180	18" sq.	"	0.036	2.89	52.00	3.47	58.00
1200	20" sq.	"	0.037	2.95	70.00	3.53	76.00
1220	24" sq.	"	0.038	3.01	83.00	3.60	90.00
1480	Straight cylinder, less than 60' long						
1500	12" dia.	LF	0.044	3.49	27.00	4.18	34.75
1540	14" dia.	"	0.045	3.57	36.50	4.27	44.25
1560	16" dia.	"	0.046	3.65	44.50	4.38	53.00
1580	18" dia.	"	0.047	3.74	56.00	4.48	64.00
1600	20" dia.	"	0.048	3.84	67.00	4.60	75.00
1620	24" dia.	"	0.049	3.93	83.00	4.71	92.00
1680	More than 60' long						

BORED PILES

ID Code	Component Descriptions	Unit of Meas.	Manhr / Unit	Labor Cost	Material Cost	Equip. Cost	Total Cost
	Descriptions	**Output**		**Unit Costs**			

31 - 63135   PRESTRESSED PILING, Cont'd...   31 - 63135

ID Code	Component Descriptions	Unit of Meas.	Manhr / Unit	Labor Cost	Material Cost	Equip. Cost	Total Cost
1700	12" dia.	LF	0.035	2.79	27.00	3.34	33.25
1720	14" dia.	"	0.036	2.84	36.50	3.40	42.75
1740	16" dia.	"	0.036	2.89	44.50	3.47	51.00
1760	18" dia.	"	0.037	2.95	56.00	3.53	62.00
1780	20" dia.	"	0.038	3.01	67.00	3.60	74.00
1800	24" dia.	"	0.038	3.07	84.00	3.68	91.00
3000	Concrete sheet piling						
3100	12" thick x 20' long	SF	0.096	7.68	31.00	9.20	47.75
3120	25' long	"	0.087	6.98	31.00	8.36	46.25
3130	30' long	"	0.080	6.40	31.00	7.66	45.00
3140	35' long	"	0.074	5.90	31.00	7.07	44.00
3150	40' long	"	0.069	5.48	31.00	6.57	43.00
3200	16" thick x 40' long	"	0.053	4.26	42.25	5.11	52.00
3220	45' long	"	0.051	4.04	42.25	4.84	51.00
3240	50' long	"	0.048	3.84	42.25	4.60	51.00
3260	55' long	"	0.046	3.65	42.25	4.38	50.00
3280	60' long	"	0.044	3.49	42.25	4.18	50.00

CAISSONS

31 - 64001   CAISSONS, INCLUDES CASING   31 - 64001

ID Code	Component Descriptions	Unit of Meas.	Manhr / Unit	Labor Cost	Material Cost	Equip. Cost	Total Cost
1000	Caisson, 3000# conc., 60 # reinf./CY, stable ground						
1020	18" dia., 0.065 CY/ LF	LF	0.192	15.25	17.75	18.50	52.00
1040	24" dia., 0.116 CY/ LF	"	0.200	16.00	28.50	19.25	64.00
1060	30" dia., 0.182 CY/ LF	"	0.240	19.25	43.50	23.00	86.00
1080	36" dia., 0.262 CY/ LF	"	0.274	22.00	61.00	26.25	110
1100	48" dia., 0.465 CY/ LF	"	0.320	25.50	110	30.75	170
1120	60" dia., 0.727 CY/ LF	"	0.436	35.00	180	41.75	260
1140	72" dia., 1.05 CY/ LF	"	0.533	42.75	270	51.00	360
1160	84" dia., 1.43 CY/ LF	"	0.686	55.00	320	66.00	440
1500	Wet ground, casing required but pulled						
1520	18" dia.	LF	0.240	19.25	19.50	23.00	62.00
1540	24" dia.	"	0.267	21.25	31.00	25.50	78.00
1560	30" dia.	"	0.300	24.00	47.50	28.75	100
1580	36" dia.	"	0.320	25.50	66.00	30.75	120
1600	48" dia.	"	0.400	32.00	120	38.25	190
1620	60" dia.	"	0.533	42.75	200	51.00	290
1640	72" dia.	"	0.800	64.00	290	77.00	430

CAISSONS

		Descriptions	Output		Unit Costs			
ID Code		Component Descriptions	Unit of Meas.	Manhr / Unit	Labor Cost	Material Cost	Equip. Cost	Total Cost

31 - 64001   CAISSONS, INCLUDES CASING, Cont'd...   31 - 64001

ID	Component	Unit	Manhr	Labor	Material	Equip.	Total
1660	84" dia.	LF	1.200	96.00	350	110	560
2000	Soft rock						
2020	18" dia.	LF	0.686	55.00	19.50	66.00	140
2040	24" dia.	"	1.200	96.00	31.00	110	240
2060	30" dia.	"	1.600	130	47.50	150	330
2080	36" dia.	"	2.400	190	66.00	230	490
2100	48" dia.	"	3.200	260	120	310	680
2120	60" dia.	"	4.800	380	200	460	1,040
2140	72" dia.	"	5.333	430	290	510	1,230
2160	84" dia.	"	6.000	480	350	580	1,410

DIVISION 32
EXTERIOR
IMPROVEMENTS

PAVING

	Descriptions		Output		Unit Costs			
ID Code	Component Descriptions		Unit of Meas.	Manhr / Unit	Labor Cost	Material Cost	Equip. Cost	Total Cost

32 - 11171 — ASPHALT REPAIR — 32 - 11171

ID Code	Component Descriptions	Unit of Meas.	Manhr / Unit	Labor Cost	Material Cost	Equip. Cost	Total Cost
0010	Coal tar seal coat, rubber add., fuel resist.	SY	0.011	0.71	2.68		3.39
0020	Bituminous surface treatment, single	"	0.008	0.50	2.46		2.96
0030	Double	"	0.001	0.05	3.27		3.32
0040	Bituminous prime coat	"	0.001	0.06	1.65		1.71
0050	Tack coat	"	0.001	0.05	0.80		0.85
0910	Crack sealing, concrete paving	LF	0.005	0.33	1.37		1.70
4000	Bituminous paving for pipe trench, 4" thick	SY	0.160	9.94	15.75	8.86	34.50
6010	Polypropylene, nonwoven paving fabric	"	0.004	0.25	2.02		2.27
6020	Rubberized asphalt	"	0.073	4.55	3.27		7.82
6040	Asphalt slurry seal	"	0.047	2.94	8.08		11.00

PAVEMENT

32 - 12160 — ASPHALT SURFACES — 32 - 12160

ID Code	Component Descriptions	Unit of Meas.	Manhr / Unit	Labor Cost	Material Cost	Equip. Cost	Total Cost
0050	Asphalt wearing surface, flexible pavement						
0100	1" thick	SY	0.016	1.28	4.52	1.53	7.33
0120	1-1/2" thick	"	0.019	1.53	6.82	1.84	10.25
0130	2" thick	"	0.024	1.92	9.09	2.30	13.25
0140	3" thick	"	0.032	2.56	13.75	3.06	19.25
1000	Binder course						
1010	1-1/2" thick	SY	0.018	1.42	6.45	1.70	9.57
1030	2" thick	"	0.022	1.74	8.58	2.09	12.50
1040	3" thick	"	0.029	2.32	12.75	2.78	17.75
1050	4" thick	"	0.032	2.56	17.00	3.06	22.50
1060	5" thick	"	0.036	2.84	21.25	3.40	27.50
1070	6" thick	"	0.040	3.20	25.75	3.83	32.75
2000	Bituminous sidewalk, no base						
2020	2" thick	SY	0.028	1.75	9.84	1.56	13.25
2040	3" thick	"	0.030	1.86	14.75	1.66	18.25

RIGID PAVING

32 - 13130 — CONCRETE PAVING — 32 - 13130

ID Code	Component Descriptions	Unit of Meas.	Manhr / Unit	Labor Cost	Material Cost	Equip. Cost	Total Cost
1080	Concrete paving, reinforced, 5000 psi concrete						
2000	6" thick	SY	0.150	12.00	28.75	14.25	55.00
2005	7" thick	"	0.160	12.75	33.50	15.25	62.00
2010	8" thick	"	0.171	13.75	38.25	16.50	69.00
2015	9" thick	"	0.185	14.75	43.00	17.75	76.00

RIGID PAVING

ID Code	Component Descriptions	Unit of Meas.	Manhr / Unit	Labor Cost	Material Cost	Equip. Cost	Total Cost
		Output		**Unit Costs**			
32 - 13130	**CONCRETE PAVING, Cont'd...**					**32 - 13130**	
2020	10" thick	SY	0.200	16.00	47.75	19.25	83.00
2030	11" thick	"	0.218	17.50	53.00	21.00	91.00
2040	12" thick	"	0.240	19.25	57.00	23.00	99.00
2045	15" thick	"	0.300	24.00	72.00	28.75	130
2050	Concrete paving, for pipe trench, reinforced						
2051	7" thick	SY	0.240	15.00	57.00	13.25	85.00
2052	8" thick	"	0.267	16.50	62.00	14.75	93.00
2053	9" thick	"	0.300	18.75	66.00	16.50	100
2054	10" thick	"	0.343	21.25	71.00	19.00	110
2060	Fibrous concrete						
2070	5" thick	SY	0.185	14.75	29.50	17.75	62.00
2080	8" thick	"	0.200	16.00	37.50	19.25	73.00
4000	Roller comp.conc., (RCC), place and compact						
4040	8" thick	SY	0.240	19.25	36.25	23.00	79.00
4060	12" thick	"	0.300	24.00	55.00	28.75	110
8980	Steel edge forms up to						
9000	12" deep	LF	0.027	1.67	1.08		2.75
9020	15" deep	"	0.032	2.00	1.39		3.39
9030	Paving finishes						
9040	Belt dragged	SY	0.040	2.50			2.50
9060	Curing	"	0.008	0.50	0.41		0.91
32 - 13131	**SIDEWALKS**					**32 - 13131**	
6000	Walks, cast in place with wire mesh, base not incl.						
6010	4" thick	SF	0.027	1.67	1.93		3.60
6020	5" thick	"	0.032	2.00	2.61		4.61
6030	6" thick	"	0.040	2.50	3.21		5.71

UNIT PAVING

ID Code	Component Descriptions	Unit of Meas.	Manhr / Unit	Labor Cost	Material Cost	Equip. Cost	Total Cost
32 - 14160	**PAVERS, MASONRY**					**32 - 14160**	
4010	Brick walk laid on sand, sand joints						
4020	Laid flat, (4.5 per sf)	SF	0.089	6.77	4.16		11.00
4040	Laid on edge, (7.2 per sf)	"	0.133	10.25	6.66		17.00
4080	Precast concrete patio blocks						
4100	2" thick						
5010	Natural	SF	0.027	2.03	3.58		5.61
5020	Colors	"	0.027	2.03	4.53		6.56
5080	Exposed aggregates, local aggregate						

UNIT PAVING

ID Code	Component Descriptions	Unit of Meas.	Manhr / Unit	Labor Cost	Material Cost	Equip. Cost	Total Cost
	Descriptions	**Output**		**Unit Costs**			

32 - 14160   PAVERS, MASONRY, Cont'd...   **32 - 14160**

ID Code	Component Descriptions	Unit of Meas.	Manhr / Unit	Labor Cost	Material Cost	Equip. Cost	Total Cost
5100	Natural	SF	0.027	2.03	10.00		12.00
5120	Colors	"	0.027	2.03	10.00		12.00
5130	Granite or limestone aggregate	"	0.027	2.03	10.00		12.00
5140	White tumblestone aggregate	"	0.027	2.03	10.75		12.75
5960	Stone pavers, set in mortar						
5990	Bluestone						
6000	1" thick						
6010	Irregular	SF	0.200	15.25	10.00		25.25
6020	Snapped rectangular	"	0.160	12.25	14.75		27.00
6060	1-1/2" thick, random rectangular	"	0.200	15.25	18.00		33.25
6070	2" thick, random rectangular	"	0.229	17.50	20.50		38.00
6080	Slate						
6090	Natural cleft						
6100	Irregular, 3/4" thick	SF	0.229	17.50	10.75		28.25
6110	Random rectangular						
6120	1-1/4" thick	SF	0.200	15.25	23.25		38.50
6130	1-1/2" thick	"	0.222	17.00	26.25		43.25
6140	Granite blocks						
6150	3" thick, 3" to 6" wide						
7020	4" to 12" long	SF	0.267	20.25	13.25		33.50
7030	6" to 15" long	"	0.229	17.50	8.67		26.25
9800	Crushed stone, white marble, 3" thick	"	0.016	1.00	1.88		2.88

PAVING SPECIALTIES

32 - 17003   GUARDRAILS   **32 - 17003**

ID Code	Component Descriptions	Unit of Meas.	Manhr / Unit	Labor Cost	Material Cost	Equip. Cost	Total Cost
1000	Pipe bollard, steel pipe, concrete filled, painted						
1020	6" dia.	EA	0.667	41.75	280		320
1040	8" dia.	"	1.000	63.00	370		430
1060	12" dia.	"	2.667	170	580		750
2000	Corrugated steel, guardrail, galvanized	LF	0.040	2.48	35.00	2.21	39.75
2020	End section, wrap around or flared	EA	0.800	50.00	94.00		140
2080	Timber guardrail, 4" x 8"	LF	0.030	1.86	40.75	1.66	44.25
3000	Guard rail, 3 cables, 3/4" dia.						
3020	Steel posts	LF	0.120	7.45	20.00	6.65	34.00
3040	Wood posts	"	0.096	5.96	20.00	5.32	31.25
3050	Steel box beam						
3060	6" x 6"	LF	0.133	8.28	82.00	7.38	98.00

PAVING SPECIALTIES

ID Code	Component Descriptions	Unit of Meas.	Manhr / Unit	Labor Cost	Material Cost	Equip. Cost	Total Cost
	Descriptions	**Output**		**Unit Costs**			
32 - 17003	**GUARDRAILS, Cont'd...**						**32 - 17003**
4000	6" x 8"	LF	0.150	9.32	87.00	8.31	100
4010	Concrete posts	EA	0.400	25.00	54.00		79.00
4100	Barrel type impact barrier	"	0.800	50.00	680		730
4200	Light shield, 6' high	LF	0.160	10.00	44.75		55.00
32 - 17004	**PARKING BARRIERS**						**32 - 17004**
1000	Timber, treated, 4' long						
1020	4" x 4"	EA	0.667	41.75	12.50		54.00
1200	6" x 6"	"	0.800	50.00	23.50		74.00
1780	Precast concrete, 6' long, with dowels						
1800	12" x 6"	EA	0.400	25.00	65.00		90.00
1900	12" x 8"	"	0.444	27.75	77.00		100
32 - 17230	**PAVEMENT MARKINGS**						**32 - 17230**
0080	Pavement line marking, paint						
0100	4" wide	LF	0.002	0.12	0.29		0.41
0120	6" wide	"	0.004	0.27	0.29		0.56
0125	8" wide	"	0.007	0.41	0.44		0.85
0140	Reflective paint, 4" wide	"	0.007	0.41	0.60		1.01
0145	Airfield markings, retro-reflective						
0150	White	LF	0.007	0.41	0.99		1.40
0160	Yellow	"	0.007	0.41	1.06		1.47
0165	Preformed tape, 4" wide						
0170	Inlaid reflective	LF	0.001	0.07	2.67		2.74
0190	Reflective paint	"	0.002	0.12	1.82		1.94
0195	Thermoplastic						
0200	White	LF	0.004	0.25	1.12		1.37
0210	Yellow	"	0.004	0.25	1.12		1.37
0220	12" wide, thermoplastic, white	"	0.011	0.71	3.18		3.89
0230	Directional arrows, reflective preformed tape	EA	0.800	50.00	160		210
0240	Messages, reflective preformed tape (per letter)	"	0.400	25.00	80.00		110
0250	Handicap symbol, preformed tape	"	0.800	50.00	33.00		83.00
2000	Parking stall painting	"	0.160	10.00	7.62		17.50

SITE IMPROVEMENTS

ID Code	Component Descriptions	Unit of Meas.	Manhr / Unit	Labor Cost	Material Cost	Equip. Cost	Total Cost
		Descriptions		**Output**	**Unit Costs**		

32 - 31130		**CHAIN LINK FENCE**					**32 - 31130**
0230	Chain link fence, 9 ga., galvanized, with posts 10' o.c.						
0250	4' high	LF	0.057	3.58	7.38		11.00
0260	5' high	"	0.073	4.55	9.87		14.50
0270	6' high	"	0.100	6.26	11.25		17.50
0280	7' high	"	0.123	7.71	12.75		20.50
1000	8' high	"	0.160	10.00	14.75		24.75
1040	For barbed wire with hangers, add						
1050	3 strand	LF	0.040	2.50	2.69		5.19
1060	6 strand	"	0.067	4.17	4.56		8.73
1070	Corner or gate post, 3" post						
1080	4' high	EA	0.267	16.75	86.00		100
1084	5' high	"	0.296	18.50	95.00		110
1085	6' high	"	0.348	21.75	110		130
1086	7' high	"	0.400	25.00	130		160
1087	8' high	"	0.444	27.75	130		160
1089	4" post						
1090	4' high	EA	0.296	18.50	150		170
1091	5' high	"	0.348	21.75	170		190
1092	6' high	"	0.400	25.00	190		210
1093	7' high	"	0.444	27.75	210		240
1094	8' high	"	0.500	31.25	230		260
1100	Gate with gate posts, galvanized, 3' wide						
1102	4' high	EA	2.000	130	95.00		230
1104	5' high	"	2.667	170	120		290
1106	6' high	"	2.667	170	150		320
1108	7' high	"	4.000	250	180		430
1109	8' high	"	4.000	250	190		440
1161	Fabric, galvanized chain link, 2" mesh, 9 ga.						
1163	4' high	LF	0.027	1.67	4.01		5.68
1164	5' high	"	0.032	2.00	4.91		6.91
1165	6' high	"	0.040	2.50	6.87		9.37
1166	8' high	"	0.053	3.34	11.50		14.75
1400	Line post, no rail fitting, galvanized, 2-1/2" dia.						
1410	4' high	EA	0.229	14.25	28.00		42.25
1420	5' high	"	0.250	15.75	30.50		46.25
1430	6' high	"	0.267	16.75	33.25		50.00
1440	7' high	"	0.320	20.00	37.75		58.00
1450	8' high	"	0.400	25.00	42.25		67.00

SITE IMPROVEMENTS

ID Code	Descriptions	Output		Unit Costs			
	Component Descriptions	Unit of Meas.	Manhr / Unit	Labor Cost	Material Cost	Equip. Cost	Total Cost
32 - 31130	**CHAIN LINK FENCE, Cont'd...**						**32 - 31130**
1460	1-7/8" H beam						
1470	4' high	EA	0.229	14.25	34.75		49.00
1480	5' high	"	0.250	15.75	39.00		55.00
1490	6' high	"	0.267	16.75	46.50		63.00
1500	7' high	"	0.320	20.00	53.00		73.00
1510	8' high	"	0.400	25.00	57.00		82.00
1550	2-1/4" H beam						
1560	4' high	EA	0.229	14.25	25.50		39.75
1570	5' high	"	0.250	15.75	31.75		47.50
1580	6' high	"	0.267	16.75	36.25		53.00
1590	7' high	"	0.320	20.00	42.25		62.00
1600	8' high	"	0.400	25.00	49.00		74.00
1980	Vinyl coated, 9 ga., with posts 10' o.c.						
2000	4' high	LF	0.057	3.58	7.98		11.50
2010	5' high	"	0.073	4.55	9.50		14.00
2020	6' high	"	0.100	6.26	11.25		17.50
2030	7' high	"	0.123	7.71	12.50		20.25
2040	8' high	"	0.160	10.00	14.25		24.25
2045	For barbed wire w/hangers, add						
2050	3 strand	LF	0.040	2.50	2.90		5.40
2060	6 Strand	"	0.067	4.17	4.68		8.85
2080	Corner, or gate post, 4' high						
2100	3" dia.	EA	0.267	16.75	99.00		120
2110	4" dia.	"	0.267	16.75	150		170
2120	6" dia.	"	0.320	20.00	180		200
2160	Gate, with posts, 3' wide						
2180	4' high	EA	2.000	130	110		240
2190	5' high	"	2.667	170	130		300
2200	6' high	"	2.667	170	150		320
2210	7' high	"	4.000	250	170		420
2220	8' high	"	4.000	250	190		440
2500	Line post, no rail fitting, 2-1/2" dia.						
2510	4' high	EA	0.229	14.25	26.25		40.50
2520	5' high	"	0.250	15.75	28.50		44.25
2530	6' high	"	0.267	16.75	31.25		48.00
2540	7' high	"	0.320	20.00	35.50		56.00
2550	8' high	"	0.400	25.00	39.50		65.00
2600	Corner post, no top rail fitting, 4" dia.						

SITE IMPROVEMENTS

ID Code	Component Descriptions	Unit of Meas.	Manhr / Unit	Labor Cost	Material Cost	Equip. Cost	Total Cost
	Descriptions	**Output**		**Unit Costs**			
32 - 31130	**CHAIN LINK FENCE, Cont'd...**						**32 - 31130**
2610	4' high	EA	0.267	16.75	140		160
2620	5' high	"	0.296	18.50	160		180
2630	6' high	"	0.348	21.75	180		200
2640	7' high	"	0.400	25.00	200		230
2650	8' high	"	0.444	27.75	210		240
3000	Fabric, vinyl, chain link, 2" mesh, 9 ga.						
3010	4' high	LF	0.027	1.67	3.76		5.43
3020	5' high	"	0.032	2.00	4.59		6.59
3030	6' high	"	0.040	2.50	6.43		8.93
3040	8' high	"	0.053	3.34	10.75		14.00
8000	Swing gates, galvanized, 4' high						
8010	Single gate						
8020	3' wide	EA	2.000	130	200		330
8025	4' wide	"	2.000	130	220		350
8028	Double gate						
8030	10' wide	EA	3.200	200	530		730
8035	12' wide	"	3.200	200	570		770
8040	14' wide	"	3.200	200	590		790
8045	16' wide	"	3.200	200	660		860
8050	18' wide	"	4.571	290	710		1,000
8055	20' wide	"	4.571	290	750		1,040
8060	22' wide	"	4.571	290	830		1,120
8065	24' wide	"	5.333	330	850		1,180
8070	26' wide	"	5.333	330	890		1,220
8075	28' wide	"	6.400	400	950		1,350
8080	30' wide	"	6.400	400	1,010		1,410
8085	5' high						
8088	Single gate						
8090	3' wide	EA	2.667	170	210		380
8095	4' wide	"	2.667	170	250		420
8098	Double gate						
8100	10' wide	EA	4.000	250	570		820
8105	12' wide	"	4.000	250	610		860
8110	14' wide	"	4.000	250	1,050		1,300
8115	16' wide	"	4.000	250	690		940
8120	18' wide	"	4.571	290	710		1,000
8125	20' wide	"	4.571	290	800		1,090
8130	22' wide	"	4.571	290	840		1,130

SITE IMPROVEMENTS

ID Code	Component Descriptions	Unit of Meas.	Manhr / Unit	Labor Cost	Material Cost	Equip. Cost	Total Cost
	Descriptions	**Output**		**Unit Costs**			

32 - 31130 · CHAIN LINK FENCE, Cont'd... · 32 - 31130

ID Code	Component Descriptions	Unit of Meas.	Manhr / Unit	Labor Cost	Material Cost	Equip. Cost	Total Cost
8135	24' wide	EA	5.333	330	880		1,210
8140	26' wide	"	5.333	330	920		1,250
8145	28' wide	"	6.400	400	1,020		1,420
8150	30' wide	"	6.400	400	1,060		1,460
8155	6' high						
8158	Single gate						
8160	3' wide	EA	2.667	170	270		440
8165	4' wide	"	2.667	170	290		460
8168	Double gate						
8170	10' wide	EA	4.000	250	650		900
8175	12' wide	"	4.000	250	740		990
8180	14' wide	"	4.000	250	780		1,030
8185	16' wide	"	4.000	250	840		1,090
8190	18' wide	"	4.571	290	900		1,190
8195	20' wide	"	4.571	290	930		1,220
8200	22' wide	"	4.571	290	1,000		1,290
8205	24' wide	"	5.333	330	1,070		1,400
8210	26' wide	"	5.333	330	1,110		1,440
8215	28' wide	"	6.400	400	1,200		1,600
8220	30' wide	"	6.400	400	1,260		1,660
8225	7' high						
8228	Single gate						
8230	3' wide	EA	4.000	250	330		580
8235	4' wide	"	4.000	250	370		620
8238	Double gate						
8240	10' wide	EA	5.333	330	850		1,180
8245	12' wide	"	5.333	330	930		1,260
8250	14' wide	"	5.333	330	1,000		1,330
8255	16' wide	"	5.333	330	1,070		1,400
8260	18' wide	"	6.400	400	1,140		1,540
8265	20' wide	"	6.400	400	1,210		1,610
8270	22' wide	"	6.400	400	1,270		1,670
8275	24' wide	"	8.000	500	1,370		1,870
8280	26' wide	"	8.000	500	1,460		1,960
8285	28' wide	"	10.000	630	1,540		2,170
8290	30' wide	"	10.000	630	1,760		2,390
8295	8' high						
8298	Single gate						

SITE IMPROVEMENTS

ID Code	Descriptions — Component Descriptions	Output — Unit of Meas.	Output — Manhr / Unit	Unit Costs — Labor Cost	Unit Costs — Material Cost	Unit Costs — Equip. Cost	Unit Costs — Total Cost
32 - 31130	**CHAIN LINK FENCE, Cont'd...**						**32 - 31130**
8300	3' wide	EA	4.000	250	370		620
8305	4' wide	"	4.000	250	400		650
8308	Double gate						
8310	10' wide	EA	5.333	330	970		1,300
8315	12' wide	"	5.333	330	1,030		1,360
8320	14' wide	"	5.333	330	1,100		1,430
8325	16' wide	"	5.333	330	1,210		1,540
8330	18' wide	"	6.400	400	1,260		1,660
8335	20' wide	"	6.400	400	1,300		1,700
8340	22' wide	"	6.400	400	1,380		1,780
8345	24' wide	"	8.000	500	1,530		2,030
8350	26' wide	"	8.000	500	1,580		2,080
8355	28' wide	"	10.000	630	1,680		2,310
8360	30' wide	"	10.000	630	1,850		2,480
8505	Vinyl coated swing gates, 4' high						
8508	Single gate						
8510	3' wide	EA	2.000	130	310		440
8515	4' wide	"	2.000	130	340		470
8518	Double gate						
8520	10' wide	EA	3.200	200	800		1,000
8525	12' wide	"	3.200	200	860		1,060
8530	14' wide	"	3.200	200	880		1,080
8535	16' wide	"	3.200	200	990		1,190
8540	18' wide	"	4.571	290	1,060		1,350
8545	20' wide	"	4.571	290	1,120		1,410
8550	22' wide	"	4.571	290	1,250		1,540
8555	24' wide	"	5.333	330	1,280		1,610
8560	26' wide	"	5.333	330	1,340		1,670
8565	28' wide	"	6.400	400	1,420		1,820
8570	30' wide	"	6.400	400	1,510		1,910
8575	5' high						
8578	Single gate						
8580	3' wide	EA	2.667	170	320		490
8585	4' wide	"	2.667	170	370		540
8588	Double gate						
8590	10' wide	EA	4.000	250	860		1,110
8595	12' wide	"	4.000	250	920		1,170
8600	14' wide	"	4.000	250	990		1,240

SITE IMPROVEMENTS

ID Code	Descriptions Component Descriptions	Output Unit of Meas.	Manhr / Unit	Unit Costs Labor Cost	Material Cost	Equip. Cost	Total Cost
32 - 31130	**CHAIN LINK FENCE, Cont'd...**						**32 - 31130**
8605	16' wide	EA	4.000	250	1,030		1,280
8610	18' wide	"	4.571	290	1,060		1,350
8615	20' wide	"	4.571	290	1,200		1,490
8620	22' wide	"	4.571	290	1,260		1,550
8625	24' wide	"	5.333	330	1,320		1,650
8630	26' wide	"	5.333	330	1,380		1,710
8635	28' wide	"	6.400	400	1,540		1,940
8640	30' wide	"	6.400	400	1,590		1,990
8645	6' high						
8648	Single gate						
8650	3' wide	EA	2.667	170	400		570
8655	4' wide	"	2.667	170	440		610
8658	Double gate						
8660	10' wide	EA	4.000	250	980		1,230
8665	12' wide	"	4.000	250	1,100		1,350
8670	14' wide	"	4.000	250	1,170		1,420
8675	16' wide	"	4.000	250	1,260		1,510
8680	18' wide	"	4.571	290	1,350		1,640
8685	20' wide	"	4.571	290	1,400		1,690
8690	22' wide	"	4.571	290	1,500		1,790
8695	24' wide	"	5.333	330	1,610		1,940
8698	26' wide	"	5.333	330	1,660		1,990
8700	28' wide	"	6.400	400	1,800		2,200
8705	30' wide	"	6.400	400	1,900		2,300
8710	7' high						
8713	Single gate						
8715	3' wide	EA	4.000	250	490		740
8720	4' wide	"	4.000	250	550		800
8723	Double gate						
8725	10' wide	EA	5.333	330	1,270		1,600
8730	12' wide	"	5.333	330	1,400		1,730
8735	14' wide	"	5.333	330	1,500		1,830
8740	16' wide	"	5.333	330	1,600		1,930
8745	18' wide	"	6.400	400	1,700		2,100
8750	20' wide	"	6.400	400	1,810		2,210
8755	22' wide	"	6.400	400	1,910		2,310
8760	24' wide	"	8.000	500	2,050		2,550
8765	26' wide	"	8.000	500	2,190		2,690

SITE IMPROVEMENTS

ID Code	Component Descriptions	Unit of Meas.	Manhr / Unit	Labor Cost	Material Cost	Equip. Cost	Total Cost
		Output		Unit Costs			

32 - 31130   CHAIN LINK FENCE, Cont'd...   32 - 31130

ID Code	Component Descriptions	Unit of Meas.	Manhr / Unit	Labor Cost	Material Cost	Equip. Cost	Total Cost
8770	28' wide	EA	10.000	630	2,300		2,930
8775	30' wide	"	10.000	630	2,640		3,270
8780	8' high						
8783	Single gate						
8785	3' wide	EA	4.000	250	550		800
8790	4' wide	"	4.000	250	590		840
8793	Double gate						
8795	10' wide	EA	5.333	330	1,450		1,780
8800	12' wide	"	5.333	330	1,540		1,870
8805	14' wide	"	5.333	330	1,660		1,990
8810	16' wide	"	5.333	330	1,810		2,140
8815	18' wide	"	6.400	400	1,890		2,290
8820	20' wide	"	6.400	400	1,960		2,360
8825	22' wide	"	6.400	400	2,060		2,460
8830	24' wide	"	8.000	500	2,290		2,790
8840	28' wide	"	8.000	500	2,370		2,870
8845	30' wide	"	10.000	630	2,520		3,150
8900	Motor operator for gates, no wiring	"					5,830
9000	Drilling fence post holes						
9010	In soil						
9020	By hand	EA	0.400	25.00			25.00
9030	By machine auger	"	0.200	12.50		4.25	16.75
9050	In rock						
9060	By jackhammer	EA	2.667	170		57.00	220
9070	By rock drill	"	0.800	50.00		17.00	67.00
9100	Aluminum privacy slats, installed vertically	SF	0.020	1.25	0.99		2.24
9120	Post hole, dig by hand	EA	0.533	33.50			33.50
9130	Set fence post in concrete	"	0.400	25.00	9.68		34.75

32 - 31901   SHRUB & TREE MAINTENANCE   32 - 31901

ID Code	Component Descriptions	Unit of Meas.	Manhr / Unit	Labor Cost	Material Cost	Equip. Cost	Total Cost
1000	Moving shrubs on site						
1020	12" ball	EA	1.000	63.00			63.00
1040	24" ball	"	1.333	84.00			84.00
1220	3' high	"	0.800	50.00			50.00
1240	4' high	"	0.889	56.00			56.00
1260	5' high	"	1.000	63.00			63.00
1280	18" spread	"	1.143	72.00			72.00
1300	30" spread	"	1.333	84.00			84.00

SITE IMPROVEMENTS

ID Code	Component Descriptions	Unit of Meas.	Manhr / Unit	Labor Cost	Material Cost	Equip. Cost	Total Cost
				Unit Costs			

32 - 31901　　　SHRUB & TREE MAINTENANCE, Cont'd...　　　32 - 31901

ID Code	Component Descriptions	Unit of Meas.	Manhr / Unit	Labor Cost	Material Cost	Equip. Cost	Total Cost
2000	Moving trees on site						
2020	24" ball	EA	1.200	75.00		67.00	140
2040	48" ball	"	1.600	99.00		89.00	190
3020	Trees						
3040	3' high	EA	0.480	29.75		26.50	56.00
3060	6' high	"	0.533	33.25		29.50	63.00
3080	8' high	"	0.600	37.25		33.25	71.00
3100	10' high	"	0.800	49.75		44.25	94.00
3110	Palm trees						
3120	7' high	EA	0.600	37.25		33.25	71.00
3140	10' high	"	0.800	49.75		44.25	94.00
3142	20' high	"	2.400	150		130	280
3144	40' high	"	4.800	300		270	560
3148	Guying trees						
3150	4" dia.	EA	0.400	25.00	13.00		38.00
3160	8" dia.	"	0.500	31.25	13.00		44.25

32 - 31902　　　FERTILIZING　　　32 - 31902

ID Code	Component Descriptions	Unit of Meas.	Manhr / Unit	Labor Cost	Material Cost	Equip. Cost	Total Cost
0080	Fertilizing (23#/1000 sf)						
0100	By square yard	SY	0.002	0.12	0.03	0.04	0.19
0120	By acre	ACRE	10.000	630	190	210	1,030
2980	Liming (70#/1000 sf)						
3000	By square yard	SY	0.003	0.16	0.03	0.05	0.25
3020	By acre	ACRE	13.333	840	190	280	1,310

32 - 31903　　　WEED CONTROL　　　32 - 31903

ID Code	Component Descriptions	Unit of Meas.	Manhr / Unit	Labor Cost	Material Cost	Equip. Cost	Total Cost
1000	Weed control, bromicil, 15 lb./acre, wettable powder	ACRE	4.000	250	310		560
1100	Vegetation control, by application of plant killer	SY	0.003	0.20	0.02		0.22
1200	Weed killer, lawns and fields	"	0.002	0.10	0.26		0.36

PLANTING IRRIGATION

32 - 84004　　　LAWN IRRIGATION　　　32 - 84004

ID Code	Component Descriptions	Unit of Meas.	Manhr / Unit	Labor Cost	Material Cost	Equip. Cost	Total Cost
0480	Residential system, complete						
0490	Minimum	ACRE					19,250
0520	Maximum	"					36,630
0580	Commercial system, complete						
0600	Minimum	ACRE					29,220
0620	Maximum	"					46,190

PLANTING IRRIGATION

ID Code	Descriptions — Component Descriptions	Output — Unit of Meas.	Output — Manhr / Unit	Unit Costs — Labor Cost	Unit Costs — Material Cost	Unit Costs — Equip. Cost	Unit Costs — Total Cost
32 - 84004	**LAWN IRRIGATION, Cont'd...**						**32 - 84004**
1000	Components						
1200	Pipe						
1400	Schedule 40, PVC						
1410	1/2"	LF	0.042	2.63	0.43		3.06
1420	3/4"	"	0.044	2.78	0.61		3.39
1430	1"	"	0.046	2.86	0.93		3.79
1450	1-1/4"	"	0.046	2.86	1.23		4.09
1460	1-1/2"	"	0.047	2.94	1.46		4.40
1470	2"	"	0.050	3.13	2.16		5.29
1480	2-1/2"	"	0.053	3.34	3.27		6.61
1490	3"	"	0.057	3.58	4.47		8.05
1500	4"	"	0.067	4.17	6.32		10.50
1510	6"	"	0.080	5.01	11.00		16.00
3000	Fittings						
3200	Tee						
3210	1/2"	EA	0.133	8.35	0.84		9.19
3220	3/4"	"	0.133	8.35	0.97		9.32
3230	1"	"	0.133	8.35	1.75		10.00
3340	1-1/4"	"	0.145	9.11	3.17		12.25
3350	1-1/2"	"	0.160	10.00	3.61		13.50
3360	2"	"	0.178	11.25	5.11		16.25
3370	2-1/2"	"	0.200	12.50	19.25		31.75
3380	3"	"	0.229	14.25	24.75		39.00
3390	4"	"	0.267	16.75	37.50		54.00
3400	6"	"	0.320	20.00	160		180
3450	El						
3460	1/2"	EA	0.123	7.71	0.72		8.43
3470	3/4"	"	0.133	8.35	0.80		9.15
3480	1"	"	0.133	8.35	1.41		9.76
3490	1-1/4"	"	0.133	8.35	2.47		10.75
3500	1-1/2"	"	0.133	8.35	2.82		11.25
3510	2"	"	0.145	9.11	4.23		13.25
3520	2-1/2"	"	0.160	10.00	14.00		24.00
3530	3"	"	0.178	11.25	17.50		28.75
3540	4"	"	0.200	12.50	24.75		37.25
3550	6"	"	0.267	16.75	110		130
3600	Coupling						
3610	1/2"	EA	0.123	7.71	0.53		8.24

PLANTING IRRIGATION

| ID Code | Descriptions | Output | | Unit Costs | | | |
	Component Descriptions	Unit of Meas.	Manhr / Unit	Labor Cost	Material Cost	Equip. Cost	Total Cost
32 - 84004	**LAWN IRRIGATION, Cont'd...**					**32 - 84004**	
3620	3/4"	EA	0.133	8.35	0.72		9.07
3630	1"	"	0.133	8.35	1.25		9.60
3640	1-1/4"	"	0.133	8.35	1.58		9.93
3650	1-1/2"	"	0.133	8.35	1.66		10.00
3660	2"	"	0.145	9.11	2.64		11.75
3670	2-1/2"	"	0.160	10.00	5.99		16.00
3680	3"	"	0.178	11.25	10.50		21.75
3690	4"	"	0.200	12.50	11.25		23.75
3700	6"	"	0.267	16.75	47.75		65.00
3800	45 El						
3810	1/2"	EA	0.123	7.71	1.06		8.77
3820	3/4"	"	0.133	8.35	1.75		10.00
3830	1"	"	0.133	8.35	2.47		10.75
3840	1-1/4"	"	0.133	8.35	3.35		11.75
3850	1-1/2"	"	0.133	8.35	4.04		12.50
3860	2"	"	0.145	9.11	5.27		14.50
3870	2-1/2"	"	0.160	10.00	15.75		25.75
3880	3"	"	0.178	11.25	22.75		34.00
3890	4"	"	0.200	12.50	36.00		48.50
3900	6"	"	0.267	16.75	120		140
4000	Riser, 1/2" diameter						
4010	2" (close)	EA	0.200	12.50	0.60		13.00
4020	3"	"	0.200	12.50	0.72		13.25
4030	4"	"	0.229	14.25	0.88		15.25
4040	5"	"	0.229	14.25	0.97		15.25
4050	6"	"	0.229	14.25	1.25		15.50
4100	3/4" diameter						
4110	2" (close)	EA	0.200	12.50	0.60		13.00
4120	3"	"	0.200	12.50	0.72		13.25
4130	4"	"	0.229	14.25	0.80		15.00
4140	5"	"	0.229	14.25	1.06		15.25
4150	6"	"	0.229	14.25	1.13		15.50
4200	1" diameter						
4210	2" (close)	EA	0.200	12.50	0.88		13.50
4220	3"	"	0.200	12.50	1.13		13.75
4230	4"	"	0.229	14.25	1.32		15.50
4240	5"	"	0.229	14.25	1.66		16.00
4250	6"	"	0.229	14.25	1.73		16.00

PLANTING IRRIGATION

ID Code	Component Descriptions	Unit of Meas.	Manhr / Unit	Labor Cost	Material Cost	Equip. Cost	Total Cost
		Descriptions		**Output**		**Unit Costs**	

ID Code	Component Descriptions	Unit of Meas.	Manhr / Unit	Labor Cost	Material Cost	Equip. Cost	Total Cost
32 - 84004	**LAWN IRRIGATION, Cont'd...**						**32 - 84004**
5000	Valve Box						
5010	Concrete, Square						
5020	12" x 22"	EA	1.000	63.00	86.00		150
5030	18" x 20"	"	1.143	72.00	110		180
5040	24" x 13"	"	1.333	84.00	96.00		180
5050	Round						
5060	12"	EA	0.800	50.00	38.00		88.00
5400	Plastic						
5410	Square						
5420	12"	EA	1.000	63.00	40.00		100
5430	18"	"					150
5500	Round						
5510	6"	EA	1.000	63.00	9.99		73.00
5520	10"	"	1.000	63.00	22.00		85.00
5530	12"	"	1.143	72.00	32.00		100
6000	Sprinkler, Pop-Up						
6100	Spray						
6110	2" high	EA	1.333	84.00	5.93		90.00
6120	3" high	"	1.333	84.00	6.50		91.00
6130	4" high	"	1.600	100	7.06		110
6140	6" high	"	1.600	100	14.75		110
6150	12" high	"	1.600	100	19.00		120
6200	Rotor						
6210	4" high	EA	1.333	84.00	27.75		110
6220	6" high	"	1.600	100	37.00		140
6300	Impact						
6310	Brass	EA	1.333	84.00	37.00		120
6320	Plastic	"	1.600	100	18.50		120
6400	Shrub Head						
6410	Spray	EA	1.333	84.00	11.25		95.00
6420	Rotor	"	1.600	100	27.75		130
6900	Time Clocks						
6910	Minimum	EA	2.000	130	180		310
6920	Average	"	2.667	170	350		520
6930	Maximum	"	4.000	250	3,180		3,430
7000	Valves						
7100	Anti-siphon						
7110	Brass						

PLANTING IRRIGATION

ID Code	Component Descriptions	Unit of Meas.	Manhr / Unit	Labor Cost	Material Cost	Equip. Cost	Total Cost
	Descriptions	**Output**		**Unit Costs**			
32 - 84004	**LAWN IRRIGATION, Cont'd...**						**32 - 84004**
7120	3/4"	EA	1.333	84.00	76.00		160
7130	1"	"	1.333	84.00	94.00		180
7140	Plastic						
7150	3/4"	EA	1.333	84.00	55.00		140
7160	1"	"	1.333	84.00	66.00		150
7200	Ball Valve						
7210	Plastic						
7220	1/2"	EA	1.333	84.00	7.23		91.00
7230	3/4"	"	1.333	84.00	7.89		92.00
7240	1"	"	1.333	84.00	10.50		95.00
7250	1-1/2"	"	1.600	100	21.00		120
7260	2"	"	1.600	100	27.50		130
7270	Brass						
7280	1/2"	EA	1.333	84.00	13.50		98.00
7290	3/4"	"	1.333	84.00	21.50		110
7300	1"	"	1.333	84.00	33.50		120
7310	1-1/2"	"	1.600	100	64.00		160
7320	2"	"	1.600	100	97.00		200
7400	Gate valves, Brass						
7410	1/2"	EA	1.333	84.00	15.75		100
7420	3/4"	"	1.333	84.00	26.25		110
7430	1"	"	1.333	84.00	36.75		120
7450	1-1/2"	"	1.600	100	63.00		160
7460	2"	"	1.600	100	79.00		180
8000	Vacuum Breakers						
8010	Brass						
8020	3/4"	EA	2.667	170	54.00		220
8030	1"	"	2.667	170	74.00		240
8040	1-1/2"	"	2.667	170	150		320
8050	2"	"	2.667	170	210		380
8060	Plastic						
8070	3/4"	EA	2.667	170	66.00		240
8080	1"	"	2.667	170	77.00		250
8090	1-1/2"	"	2.667	170	120		290
8100	2"	"	2.667	170	140		310
8400	Backflow Preventors, Brass						
8410	3/4"	EA	26.667	1,670	320		1,990
8420	1"	"	26.667	1,670	360		2,030

PLANTING IRRIGATION

ID Code	Descriptions Component Descriptions	Output Unit of Meas.	Output Manhr / Unit	Unit Costs Labor Cost	Unit Costs Material Cost	Unit Costs Equip. Cost	Unit Costs Total Cost
32 - 84004	**LAWN IRRIGATION, Cont'd...**						**32 - 84004**
8430	1-1/2"	EA	26.667	1,670	780		2,450
8440	2"	"	32.000	2,000	970		2,970
8600	Pressure Regulators, Brass						
8610	3/4"	EA	0.800	50.00	140		190
8620	1"	"	0.800	50.00	190		240
8630	1-1/2"	"	0.889	56.00	570		630
8640	2"	"	1.000	63.00	680		740
8800	Quick Coupler Valve						
8810	3/4"	EA	1.333	84.00	100		180
8820	1"	"	1.333	84.00	150		230

PLANTING

ID Code	Descriptions	Unit of Meas.	Manhr / Unit	Labor Cost	Material Cost	Equip. Cost	Total Cost
32 - 91191	**TOPSOIL**						**32 - 91191**
0005	Spread topsoil, with equipment						
0010	Minimum	CY	0.080	6.62		8.80	15.50
0020	Maximum	"	0.100	8.27		11.00	19.25
0080	By hand						
0100	Minimum	CY	0.800	50.00			50.00
0110	Maximum	"	1.000	63.00			63.00
0980	Area prep. seeding (grade, rake and clean)						
1000	Square yard	SY	0.006	0.40			0.40
1020	By acre	ACRE	32.000	2,000			2,000
2000	Remove topsoil and stockpile on site						
2020	4" deep	CY	0.067	5.51		7.33	12.75
2040	6" deep	"	0.062	5.09		6.76	11.75
2200	Spreading topsoil from stock pile						
2220	By loader	CY	0.073	6.01		8.00	14.00
2240	By hand	"	0.800	66.00		88.00	150
2260	Top dress by hand	SY	0.008	0.66		0.88	1.54
2280	Place imported top soil						
2300	By loader						
2320	4" deep	SY	0.008	0.66		0.88	1.54
2340	6" deep	"	0.009	0.73		0.97	1.71
2360	By hand						
2370	4" deep	SY	0.089	5.56			5.56
2380	6" deep	"	0.100	6.26			6.26
5980	Plant bed preparation, 18" deep						

PLANTING

ID Code	Component Descriptions	Unit of Meas.	Manhr / Unit	Labor Cost	Material Cost	Equip. Cost	Total Cost
		Descriptions	**Output**		**Unit Costs**		

32 - 91191 **TOPSOIL, Cont'd...** **32 - 91191**

| 6000 | With backhoe/loader | SY | 0.020 | 1.65 | | 2.20 | 3.85 |
| 6010 | By hand | " | 0.133 | 8.35 | | | 8.35 |

TURF AND GRASSES

32 - 92190 **SEEDING** **32 - 92190**

0980	Mechanical seeding, 175 lb/acre						
1000	By square yard	SY	0.002	0.10	0.23	0.03	0.36
1020	By acre	ACRE	8.000	500	930	170	1,600
2040	450 lb/acre						
2060	By square yard	SY	0.002	0.12	0.59	0.04	0.75
2080	By acre	ACRE	10.000	630	2,310	210	3,150
5980	Seeding by hand, 10 lb per 100 s.y.						
6000	By square yard	SY	0.003	0.16	0.66		0.82
6010	By acre	ACRE	13.333	840	2,580		3,420
8010	Reseed disturbed areas	SF	0.004	0.25	0.06		0.31

PLANTS

32 - 93230 **PLANTS** **32 - 93230**

0100	Euonymus coloratus, 18" (Purple Wintercreeper)	EA	0.133	8.35	2.87		11.25
0150	Hedera Helix, 2-1/4" pot (English ivy)	"	0.133	8.35	1.19		9.54
0200	Liriope muscari, 2" clumps	"	0.080	5.01	5.01		10.00
0250	Santolina, 12"	"	0.080	5.01	5.74		10.75
0280	Vinca major or minor, 3" pot	"	0.080	5.01	0.93		5.94
0300	Cortaderia argentia, 2 gallon (Pampas Grass)	"	0.080	5.01	18.25		23.25
0350	Ophiopogan japonicus, 1 quart (4" pot)	"	0.080	5.01	5.01		10.00
0400	Ajuga reptans, 2-3/4" pot (carpet bugle)	"	0.080	5.01	0.93		5.94
0450	Pachysandra terminalis, 2-3/4" pot (Japanese Spurge)	"	0.080	5.01	1.27		6.28

32 - 93330 **SHRUBS** **32 - 93330**

0100	Juniperus conferia litoralis, 18"-24" (Shore Juniper)	EA	0.320	20.00	42.00		62.00
0150	Horizontalis plumosa, 18"-24" (Andorra Juniper)	"	0.320	20.00	44.50		65.00
0200	Sabina tamar-iscfolia-tamarix juniper, 18"-24"	"	0.320	20.00	44.50		65.00
0250	Chin San Jose, 18"-24" (San Jose Juniper)	"	0.320	20.00	44.50		65.00
0300	Sargenti, 18"-24" (Sargent's Juniper)	"	0.320	20.00	42.00		62.00
0350	Nandina domestica, 18"-24" (Heavenly Bamboo)	"	0.320	20.00	28.25		48.25
0400	Raphiolepis Indica Springtime, 18"-24"	"	0.320	20.00	30.25		50.00
0450	Osmanthus Heterophyllus Gulftide, 18"-24"	"	0.320	20.00	32.50		53.00

PLANTS

ID Code	Component Descriptions	Unit of Meas.	Manhr / Unit	Labor Cost	Material Cost	Equip. Cost	Total Cost
		Descriptions		**Output**		**Unit Costs**	

32 - 93330 — SHRUBS, Cont'd... — 32 - 93330

ID Code	Component Descriptions	Unit of Meas.	Manhr / Unit	Labor Cost	Material Cost	Equip. Cost	Total Cost
0460	Ilex Cornuta Burfordi Nana, 18"-24"	EA	0.320	20.00	37.00		57.00
0550	Glabra, 18"-24" (Inkberry Holly)	"	0.320	20.00	34.75		55.00
0600	Azalea, Indica types, 18"-24"	"	0.320	20.00	39.25		59.00
0650	Kurume types, 18"-24"	"	0.320	20.00	44.00		64.00
0700	Berberis Julianae, 18"-24" (Wintergreen Barberry)	"	0.320	20.00	25.75		45.75
0800	Pieris Japonica Japanese, 18"-24"	"	0.320	20.00	25.75		45.75
0900	Ilex Cornuta Rotunda, 18"-24"	"	0.320	20.00	30.50		51.00
1000	Juniperus Horiz. Plumosa, 24"-30"	"	0.400	25.00	28.00		53.00
1200	Rhodopendrow Hybrids, 24"-30"	"	0.400	25.00	75.00		100
1400	Aucuba Japonica Varigata, 24"-30"	"	0.400	25.00	25.50		51.00
1600	Ilex Crenata Willow Leaf, 24"-30"	"	0.400	25.00	28.00		53.00
1620	Cleyera Japonica, 30"-36"	"	0.500	31.25	32.75		64.00
1700	Pittosporum Tobira, 30"-36"	"	0.500	31.25	38.25		70.00
1800	Prumus Laurocerasus, 30"-36"	"	0.500	31.25	71.00		100
1900	Ilex Cornuta Burfordi, 30"-36" (Burford Holly)	"	0.500	31.25	37.50		69.00
2000	Abelia Grandiflora, 24"-36" (Yew Podocarpus)	"	0.400	25.00	25.75		51.00
2100	Podocarpos Macrophylla, 24"-36"	"	0.400	25.00	42.00		67.00
2500	Pyracantha Coccinea Lalandi, 3'-4' (Firethorn)	"	0.500	31.25	24.00		55.00
2520	Photinia Frazieri, 3'-4' (Red Photinia)	"	0.500	31.25	38.00		69.00
2600	Forsythia Suspensa, 3'-4' (Weeping Forsythia)	"	0.500	31.25	24.00		55.00
2700	Camellia Japonica, 3'-4' (Common Camellia)	"	0.500	31.25	42.25		74.00
2800	Juniperus Chin Torulosa, 3'-4' (Hollywood Juniper)	"	0.500	31.25	45.00		76.00
2900	Cupressocyparis Leylandi, 3'-4'	"	0.500	31.25	37.75		69.00
3000	Ilex Opaca Fosteri, 5'-6' (Foster's Holly)	"	0.667	41.75	150		190
3200	Opaca, 5'-6' (American Holly)	"	0.667	41.75	220		260
3300	Nyrica Cerifera, 4'-5' (Southern Wax Myrtles)	"	0.571	35.75	47.75		84.00
3400	Ligustrum Japonicum, 4'-5' (Japanese Privet)	"	0.571	35.75	37.50		73.00

32 - 93430 — TREES — 32 - 93430

ID Code	Component Descriptions	Unit of Meas.	Manhr / Unit	Labor Cost	Material Cost	Equip. Cost	Total Cost
0100	Cornus Florida, 5'-6' (White flowering Dogwood)	EA	0.667	41.75	110		150
0120	Prunus Serrulata Kwanzan, 6'-8' (Kwanzan Cherry)	"	0.800	50.00	120		170
0130	Caroliniana, 6'-8' (Carolina Cherry Laurel)	"	0.800	50.00	140		190
0140	Cercis Canadensis, 6'-8' (Eastern Redbud)	"	0.800	50.00	100		150
0200	Koelreuteria Paniculata, 8'-10' (Goldenrain Tree)	"	1.000	63.00	170		230
0250	Acer Platanoides, 1-3/4"-2" (11'-13')	"	1.333	84.00	230		310
0300	Rubrum, 1-3/4"-2" (11'-13') (Red Maple)	"	1.333	84.00	170		250
0350	Saccharum, 1-3/4"-2" (Sugar Maple)	"	1.333	84.00	300		380
0400	Fraxinus Pennsylvanica, 1-3/4"-2"	"	1.333	84.00	150		230

PLANTS

ID Code	Descriptions		Output		Unit Costs			
	Component Descriptions		Unit of Meas.	Manhr / Unit	Labor Cost	Material Cost	Equip. Cost	Total Cost

32 - 93430　　　TREES, Cont'd...　　　32 - 93430

ID Code	Component Descriptions	Unit of Meas.	Manhr / Unit	Labor Cost	Material Cost	Equip. Cost	Total Cost
0450	Celtis Occidentalis, 1-3/4"-2"	EA	1.333	84.00	220		300
0460	Glenditsia Triacantos Inermis, 2"	"	1.333	84.00	200		280
1000	Prunus Cerasifera 'Thundercloud', 6'-8'	"	0.800	50.00	120		170
1200	Yeodensis, 6'-8' (Yoshino Cherry)	"	0.800	50.00	120		170
1400	Lagerstroemia Indica, 8'-10' (Crapemyrtle)	"	1.000	63.00	200		260
1600	Crataegus Phaenopyrum, 8'-10'	"	1.000	63.00	310		370
1800	Quercus Borealis, 1-3/4"-2" (Northern Red Oak)	"	1.333	84.00	180		260
2000	Quercus Acutissima, 1-3/4"-2" (8'-10')	"	1.333	84.00	170		250
2100	Saliz Babylonica, 1-3/4"-2" (Weeping Willow)	"	1.333	84.00	85.00		170
2200	Tilia Cordata Greenspire, 1-3/4"-2" (10'-12')	"	1.333	84.00	380		460
2300	Malus, 2"-2-1/2" (8'-10') (Flowering Crabapple)	"	1.333	84.00	180		260
2400	Platanus Occidentalis, (12'-14')	"	1.600	100	280		380
2500	Pyrus Calleryana Bradford, 2"-2-1/2"	"	1.333	84.00	220		300
2600	Quercus Palustris, 2"-2-1/2" (12'-14') (Pin Oak)	"	1.333	84.00	240		320
2700	Phellos, 2-1/2"-3" (Willow Oak)	"	1.600	100	260		360
2800	Nigra, 2"-2-1/2" (Water Oak)	"	1.333	84.00	230		310
3000	Magnolia Soulangeana, 4'-5' (Saucer Magnolia)	"	0.667	41.75	130		170
3100	Grandiflora, 6'-8' (Southern Magnolia)	"	0.800	50.00	180		230
3200	Cedrus Deodara, 10'-12' (Deodare Cedar)	"	1.333	84.00	300		380
3300	Gingko Biloba, 10'-12' (2"-2-1/2")	"	1.333	84.00	280		360
3400	Pinus Thunbergi, 5'-6' (Japanese Black Pine)	"	0.667	41.75	110		150
3500	Strobus, 6'-8' (White Pine)	"	0.800	50.00	120		170
3600	Taeda, 6'-8' (Loblolly Pine)	"	0.800	50.00	100		150
3700	Quercus Virginiana, 2"-2-1/2" (Live Oak)	"	1.600	100	270		370

PLANT ACCESSORIES

32 - 94002　　　LANDSCAPE ACCESSORIES　　　32 - 94002

ID Code	Component Descriptions	Unit of Meas.	Manhr / Unit	Labor Cost	Material Cost	Equip. Cost	Total Cost
0100	Steel edging, 3/16" x 4"	LF	0.010	0.62	1.29		1.91
0200	Landscaping stepping stones, 15"x15", white	EA	0.040	2.50	5.83		8.33
6000	Wood chip mulch	CY	0.533	33.50	40.75		74.00
6010	2" thick	SY	0.016	1.00	2.49		3.49
6020	4" thick	"	0.023	1.43	4.70		6.13
6030	6" thick	"	0.029	1.82	7.04		8.86
6200	Gravel mulch, 3/4" stone	CY	0.800	50.00	32.25		82.00
6300	White marble chips, 1" deep	SF	0.008	0.50	0.63		1.13
6980	Peat moss						
7000	2" thick	SY	0.018	1.11	3.46		4.57

PLANT ACCESSORIES

ID Code	Descriptions	Output		Unit Costs			
	Component Descriptions	Unit of Meas.	Manhr / Unit	Labor Cost	Material Cost	Equip. Cost	Total Cost
32 - 94002	**LANDSCAPE ACCESSORIES, Cont'd...**						**32 - 94002**
7020	4" thick	SY	0.027	1.67	6.66		8.33
7030	6" thick	"	0.033	2.08	10.25		12.25
7980	Landscaping timbers, treated lumber						
8000	4" x 4"	LF	0.027	1.67	3.58		5.25
8020	6" x 6"	"	0.029	1.79	8.32		10.00
8040	8" x 8"	"	0.033	2.08	10.00		12.00
32 - 94330	**PREFABRICATED PLANTERS**						**32 - 94330**
1000	Concrete precast, circular						
1020	24" dia., 18" high	EA	0.800	50.00	420		470
1040	42" dia., 30" high	"	1.000	63.00	560		620
2000	Fiberglass, circular						
2040	36" dia., 27" high	EA	0.400	25.00	710		730
2060	60" dia., 39" high	"	0.444	27.75	1,640		1,670
2100	Tapered, circular						
2120	24" dia., 36" high	EA	0.364	22.75	560		580
2140	40" dia., 36" high	"	0.400	25.00	930		960
2200	Square						
2220	2' by 2', 17" high	EA	0.364	22.75	480		500
2240	4' by 4', 39" high	"	0.444	27.75	1,640		1,670
2300	Rectangular						
2320	4' by 1', 18" high	EA	0.400	25.00	530		550

DIVISION 33
UTILITIES

SITE RESTORATION

ID Code	Component Descriptions	Unit of Meas.	Manhr / Unit	Labor Cost	Material Cost	Equip. Cost	Total Cost
		Descriptions	**Output**		**Unit Costs**		

33 - 01101 PIPELINE RESTORATION 33 - 01101

ID Code	Component Descriptions	Unit	Manhr/Unit	Labor	Material	Equip.	Total
0980	Relining existing water main						
1000	6" dia.	LF	0.240	19.25	8.62	23.00	51.00
1020	8" dia.	"	0.253	20.25	9.71	24.25	54.00
1040	10" dia.	"	0.267	21.25	10.75	25.50	58.00
1060	12" dia.	"	0.282	22.50	11.75	27.00	62.00
1080	14" dia.	"	0.300	24.00	12.75	28.75	66.00
1100	16" dia.	"	0.320	25.50	13.75	30.75	70.00
1120	18" dia.	"	0.343	27.50	15.00	32.75	75.00
1140	20" dia.	"	0.369	29.50	16.50	35.50	82.00
1160	24" dia.	"	0.400	32.00	17.50	38.25	88.00
1180	36" dia.	"	0.480	38.50	19.00	46.00	100
1200	48" dia.	"	0.533	42.75	21.25	51.00	120
1220	72" dia.	"	0.600	48.00	27.00	58.00	140
1980	Replacing in line gate valves						
2000	6" valve	EA	3.200	260	970	310	1,530
2020	8" valve	"	4.000	320	1,520	380	2,220
2040	10" valve	"	4.800	380	2,290	460	3,130
2060	12" valve	"	6.000	480	3,970	580	5,030
2080	16" valve	"	6.857	550	9,010	660	10,220
2090	18" valve	"	8.000	640	13,630	770	15,040
2100	20" valve	"	9.600	770	18,740	920	20,430
2120	24" valve	"	12.000	960	26,780	1,150	28,890
2140	36" valve	"	16.000	1,280	73,340	1,530	76,150

TUNNELING, BORING & JACKING

33 - 05231 PIPE JACKING 33 - 05231

ID Code	Component Descriptions	Unit	Manhr/Unit	Labor	Material	Equip.	Total
1080	Pipe casing, horizontal jacking						
1100	18" dia.	LF	0.711	44.50	110	64.00	220
1200	21" dia.	"	0.762	47.75	130	69.00	250
1300	24" dia.	"	0.800	50.00	140	73.00	260
1400	27" dia.	"	0.800	50.00	150	73.00	270
1500	30" dia.	"	0.842	53.00	170	76.00	300
1600	36" dia.	"	0.914	57.00	190	83.00	330
1700	42" dia.	"	1.000	63.00	220	91.00	370
1800	48" dia.	"	1.067	67.00	270	97.00	430

DISTRIBUTION PIPING

ID Code	Component Descriptions	Unit of Meas.	Manhr / Unit	Labor Cost	Material Cost	Equip. Cost	Total Cost
	Descriptions	**Output**		**Unit Costs**			
33 - 11003	**CHILLED WATER SYSTEMS**						**33 - 11003**
0100	Chilled water pipe, 2" thick insulation, w/casing						
1020	Align and tack weld on sleepers						
1030	1-1/2" dia.	LF	0.022	1.35	25.50	1.20	28.00
1040	3" dia.	"	0.034	2.13	41.00	1.90	45.00
1050	4" dia.	"	0.048	2.98	47.00	2.66	53.00
1060	6" dia.	"	0.060	3.72	54.00	3.32	61.00
1070	8" dia.	"	0.069	4.26	76.00	3.80	84.00
1080	10" dia.	"	0.080	4.97	97.00	4.43	110
1090	12" dia.	"	0.096	5.96	110	5.32	120
1100	14" dia.	"	0.104	6.48	160	5.78	170
1120	16" dia.	"	0.120	7.45	200	6.65	210
1200	Align and tack weld on trench bottom						
1210	18" dia.	LF	0.133	8.28	200	7.38	220
1220	20" dia.	"	0.150	9.32	270	8.31	290
2000	Preinsulated fittings						
2050	Align and tack weld on sleepers						
2100	Elbows						
2110	1-1/2"	EA	0.500	43.75	610		650
2120	3"	"	0.800	70.00	770		840
2140	4"	"	1.000	88.00	1,000		1,090
2150	6"	"	1.333	120	1,380		1,500
2160	8"	"	1.600	140	1,960		2,100
2200	Tees						
2210	1-1/2"	EA	0.533	46.75	930		980
2220	3"	"	0.889	78.00	1,320		1,400
2510	4"	"	1.143	100	1,000		1,100
2520	6"	"	1.600	140	2,150		2,290
2530	8"	"	2.000	180	2,870		3,050
2540	Reducers						
2550	3"	EA	0.667	58.00	740		800
2560	4"	"	0.800	70.00	1,170		1,240
2570	6"	"	1.000	88.00	1,580		1,670
2580	8"	"	1.333	120	1,710		1,830
2590	Anchors, not including concrete						
2600	4"	EA	1.000	88.00	390		480
2610	6"	"	1.000	88.00	570		660
2902	Align and tack weld on trench bottom						
2910	Elbows						

DISTRIBUTION PIPING

ID Code	Component Descriptions	Unit of Meas.	Manhr / Unit	Labor Cost	Material Cost	Equip. Cost	Total Cost
	Descriptions	**Output**		**Unit Costs**			
33 - 11003	**CHILLED WATER SYSTEMS, Cont'd...**						**33 - 11003**
2920	10"	EA	1.500	93.00	2,240	83.00	2,420
2930	12"	"	1.714	110	2,680	95.00	2,880
2940	14"	"	1.846	110	3,380	100	3,600
2950	16"	"	2.000	120	3,640	110	3,880
2960	18"	"	2.182	140	4,060	120	4,320
2970	20"	"	2.400	150	4,900	130	5,180
3030	Tees						
3035	10"	EA	1.500	93.00	3,640	83.00	3,820
3040	12"	"	1.714	110	4,620	95.00	4,820
3050	14"	"	1.846	110	4,900	100	5,120
3060	16"	"	2.000	120	5,180	110	5,420
3070	18"	"	2.182	140	5,880	120	6,140
3080	20"	"	2.400	150	6,720	130	7,000
3210	Reducers						
3215	10"	EA	1.000	62.00	2,770	55.00	2,890
3220	12"	"	1.091	68.00	3,360	60.00	3,490
3230	14"	"	1.200	75.00	3,640	67.00	3,780
3240	16"	"	1.333	83.00	4,480	74.00	4,640
3250	18"	"	1.500	93.00	4,900	83.00	5,080
3260	20"	"	1.714	110	5,180	95.00	5,380
3320	Anchors, not including concrete						
3340	10"	EA	1.000	62.00	740	55.00	860
3350	12"	"	1.091	68.00	820	60.00	950
3360	14"	"	1.200	75.00	940	67.00	1,080
3370	16"	"	1.333	83.00	1,320	74.00	1,480
3380	18"	"	1.500	93.00	1,840	83.00	2,020
3390	20"	"	1.714	110	2,490	95.00	2,690
33 - 11004	**DUCTILE IRON PIPE**						**33 - 11004**
0990	Ductile iron pipe, cement lined, slip-on joints						
1000	4"	LF	0.067	4.14	18.25	3.69	26.00
1010	6"	"	0.071	4.38	21.25	3.91	29.50
1020	8"	"	0.075	4.66	27.75	4.15	36.50
1030	10"	"	0.080	4.97	38.00	4.43	47.50
1040	12"	"	0.096	5.96	47.00	5.32	58.00
1060	14"	"	0.120	7.45	59.00	6.65	73.00
1080	16"	"	0.133	8.28	73.00	7.38	89.00
1100	18"	"	0.150	9.32	82.00	8.31	100

DISTRIBUTION PIPING

ID Code	Component Descriptions	Unit of Meas.	Manhr / Unit	Labor Cost	Material Cost	Equip. Cost	Total Cost
	Descriptions	**Output**		**Unit Costs**			

ID Code	Component Descriptions	Unit of Meas.	Manhr / Unit	Labor Cost	Material Cost	Equip. Cost	Total Cost
33 - 11004	**DUCTILE IRON PIPE, Cont'd...**						**33 - 11004**
1120	20"	LF	0.171	10.75	93.00	9.50	110
1190	Mechanical joint pipe						
1200	4"	LF	0.092	5.73	19.75	5.11	30.50
1210	6"	"	0.100	6.21	23.50	5.54	35.25
1220	8"	"	0.109	6.78	31.00	6.04	43.75
1230	10"	"	0.120	7.45	40.75	6.65	55.00
1240	12"	"	0.160	9.94	52.00	8.86	71.00
1260	14"	"	0.185	11.50	65.00	10.25	87.00
1280	16"	"	0.218	13.50	71.00	12.00	97.00
1300	18"	"	0.240	15.00	80.00	13.25	110
1320	20"	"	0.267	16.50	92.00	14.75	120
1480	Fittings, mechanical joint						
1500	90 degree elbow						
1520	4"	EA	0.533	33.50	230		260
1540	6"	"	0.615	38.50	300		340
1560	8"	"	0.800	50.00	430		480
1580	10"	"	1.143	72.00	630		700
1600	12"	"	1.600	100	840		940
1620	14"	"	2.000	130	1,300		1,430
1640	16"	"	2.667	170	1,630		1,800
1660	18"	"	3.200	200	2,450		2,650
1680	20"	"	4.000	250	2,720		2,970
1700	45 degree elbow						
1720	4"	EA	0.533	33.50	200		230
1740	6"	"	0.615	38.50	270		310
1760	8"	"	0.800	50.00	380		430
1780	10"	"	1.143	72.00	540		610
1800	12"	"	1.600	100	660		760
1820	14"	"	2.000	130	1,090		1,220
1840	16"	"	2.667	170	1,300		1,470
1860	18"	"	4.000	250	1,900		2,150
1880	20"	"	4.000	250	2,260		2,510
2000	Tee						
2020	4"x3"	EA	1.000	63.00	320		380
2040	4"x4"	"	1.000	63.00	350		410
2060	6"x3"	"	1.143	72.00	410		480
2080	6"x4"	"	1.143	72.00	420		490
2100	6"x6"	"	1.143	72.00	460		530

DISTRIBUTION PIPING

ID Code	Component Descriptions	Unit of Meas.	Manhr / Unit	Labor Cost	Material Cost	Equip. Cost	Total Cost
	Descriptions	**Output**		**Unit Costs**			

33 - 11004 — DUCTILE IRON PIPE, Cont'd... — 33 - 11004

ID Code	Component Descriptions	Unit of Meas.	Manhr / Unit	Labor Cost	Material Cost	Equip. Cost	Total Cost
2120	8"x4"	EA	1.333	84.00	570		650
2140	8"x6"	"	1.333	84.00	650		730
2160	8"x8"	"	1.333	84.00	610		690
2180	10"x4"	"	1.600	100	760		860
2200	10"x6"	"	1.600	100	840		940
2240	10"x8"	"	1.600	100	870		970
2260	10"x10"	"	1.600	100	980		1,080
2280	12"x4"	"	2.000	130	850		980
2300	12"x6"	"	2.000	130	920		1,050
2320	12"x8"	"	2.000	130	1,000		1,130
2340	12"x10"	"	2.000	130	1,140		1,270
2360	12"x12"	"	2.133	130	1,220		1,350
2380	14"x4"	"	2.286	140	1,490		1,630
2400	14"x6"	"	2.286	140	1,590		1,730
2420	14"x8"	"	2.286	140	1,620		1,760
2460	14"x10"	"	2.286	140	1,670		1,810
2480	14"x12"	"	2.462	150	1,710		1,860
2500	14"x14"	"	2.462	150	1,700		1,850
2520	16"x4"	"	2.667	170	1,930		2,100
2540	16"x6"	"	2.667	170	1,970		2,140
2560	16"x8"	"	2.667	170	1,750		1,920
2580	16"x10"	"	2.667	170	1,780		1,950
2600	16"x12"	"	2.667	170	1,740		1,910
2620	16"x14"	"	2.667	170	1,840		2,010
2640	16"x16"	"	2.667	170	1,880		2,050
2660	18"x6"	"	2.909	180	2,240		2,420
2680	18"x8"	"	2.909	180	2,280		2,460
2700	18"x10"	"	2.909	180	2,330		2,510
2720	18"x12"	"	2.909	180	2,370		2,550
2740	18"x14"	"	2.909	180	2,640		2,820
2760	18"x16"	"	2.909	180	2,610		2,790
2780	18"x18"	"	2.909	180	2,960		3,140
2800	20"x6"	"	3.200	200	2,860		3,060
2820	20"x8"	"	3.200	200	2,880		3,080
2840	20"x10"	"	3.200	200	2,940		3,140
2860	20"x12"	"	3.200	200	2,990		3,190
2880	20"x14"	"	3.200	200	3,080		3,280
2900	20"x16"	"	3.200	200	3,590		3,790

DISTRIBUTION PIPING

ID Code	Component Descriptions	Unit of Meas.	Manhr / Unit	Labor Cost	Material Cost	Equip. Cost	Total Cost
33 - 11004	**DUCTILE IRON PIPE, Cont'd...**						**33 - 11004**
2920	20"x18"	EA	3.200	200	3,750		3,950
2940	20"x20"	"	3.200	200	3,840		4,040
3000	Cross						
3020	4"x3"	EA	1.333	84.00	340		420
3040	4"x4"	"	1.333	84.00	370		450
3060	6"x3"	"	1.600	100	380		480
3080	6"x4"	"	1.600	100	410		510
3100	6"x6"	"	1.600	100	450		550
3120	8"x4"	"	1.778	110	630		740
3140	8"x6"	"	1.778	110	680		790
3160	8"x8"	"	1.778	110	740		850
3180	10"x4"	"	2.000	130	870		1,000
3200	10"x6"	"	2.000	130	920		1,050
3220	10"x8"	"	2.000	130	1,000		1,130
3240	10"x10"	"	2.000	130	1,190		1,320
3260	12"x4"	"	2.286	140	1,110		1,250
3280	12"x6"	"	2.286	140	1,250		1,390
3300	12"x8"	"	2.286	140	1,220		1,360
3320	12"x10"	"	2.462	150	1,410		1,560
3340	12"x12"	"	2.462	150	1,520		1,670
3360	14"x4"	"	2.667	170	1,440		1,610
3380	14"x6"	"	2.667	170	1,630		1,800
3400	14"x8"	"	2.667	170	1,700		1,870
3420	14"x10"	"	2.667	170	1,820		1,990
3440	14"x12"	"	2.909	180	1,960		2,140
3460	14"x14"	"	2.909	180	2,150		2,330
3480	16"x4"	"	3.200	200	1,880		2,080
3500	16"x6"	"	3.200	200	1,930		2,130
3520	16"x8"	"	3.200	200	2,040		2,240
3540	16"x10"	"	3.200	200	2,170		2,370
3560	16"x12"	"	3.200	200	2,270		2,470
3600	16"x14"	"	3.200	200	2,460		2,660
3620	16"x16"	"	3.200	200	2,610		2,810
3640	18"x6"	"	3.556	220	2,420		2,640
3660	18"x8"	"	3.556	220	2,500		2,720
3680	18"x10"	"	3.556	220	2,610		2,830
3700	18"x12"	"	3.556	220	2,750		2,970
3720	18"x14"	"	3.556	220	3,260		3,480

DISTRIBUTION PIPING

ID Code	Component Descriptions	Unit of Meas.	Manhr / Unit	Labor Cost	Material Cost	Equip. Cost	Total Cost
33 - 11004	**DUCTILE IRON PIPE, Cont'd...**						**33 - 11004**
3740	18"x16"	EA	3.556	220	3,480		3,700
3760	18"x18"	"	3.556	220	3,680		3,900
3780	20"x6"	"	3.810	240	2,910		3,150
3800	20"x8"	"	3.810	240	2,990		3,230
3820	20"x10"	"	3.810	240	3,130		3,370
3840	20"x12"	"	3.810	240	3,260		3,500
3860	20"x14"	"	3.810	240	3,430		3,670
3880	20"x16"	"	3.810	240	3,970		4,210
3900	20"x18"	"	4.000	250	4,240		4,490
3920	20"x20"	"	4.000	250	4,490		4,740
33 - 11006	**PLASTIC PIPE**						**33 - 11006**
0110	PVC, class 150 pipe						
0120	4" dia.	LF	0.060	3.72	5.31	3.32	12.25
0130	6" dia.	"	0.065	4.03	10.00	3.59	17.50
0140	8" dia.	"	0.069	4.26	16.00	3.80	24.00
0150	10" dia.	"	0.075	4.66	22.75	4.15	31.50
0160	12" dia.	"	0.080	4.97	33.50	4.43	43.00
0165	Schedule 40 pipe						
0170	1-1/2" dia.	LF	0.047	2.94	1.34		4.28
0180	2" dia.	"	0.050	3.13	1.99		5.12
0185	2-1/2" dia.	"	0.053	3.34	3.01		6.35
0190	3" dia.	"	0.057	3.58	4.09		7.67
0200	4" dia.	"	0.067	4.17	5.78		9.95
0210	6" dia.	"	0.080	5.01	11.00		16.00
0240	90 degree elbows						
0250	1"	EA	0.133	8.35	1.12		9.47
0260	1-1/2"	"	0.133	8.35	2.14		10.50
0270	2"	"	0.145	9.11	3.35		12.50
0280	2-1/2"	"	0.160	10.00	10.25		20.25
0290	3"	"	0.178	11.25	12.25		23.50
0300	4"	"	0.200	12.50	19.75		32.25
0310	6"	"	0.267	16.75	62.00		79.00
0320	45 degree elbows						
0330	1"	EA	0.133	8.35	1.72		10.00
0340	1-1/2"	"	0.133	8.35	3.01		11.25
0350	2"	"	0.145	9.11	3.91		13.00
0360	2-1/2"	"	0.160	10.00	10.25		20.25

DISTRIBUTION PIPING

ID Code	Component Descriptions	Unit of Meas.	Manhr / Unit	Labor Cost	Material Cost	Equip. Cost	Total Cost
		Output		**Unit Costs**			
33 - 11006	**PLASTIC PIPE, Cont'd...**						**33 - 11006**
0370	3"	EA	0.178	11.25	15.75		27.00
0380	4"	"	0.200	12.50	25.50		38.00
0390	6"	"	0.267	16.75	63.00		80.00
0400	Tees						
0410	1"	EA	0.160	10.00	1.48		11.50
0420	1-1/2"	"	0.160	10.00	2.86		12.75
0430	2"	"	0.178	11.25	4.12		15.25
0440	2-1/2"	"	0.200	12.50	13.50		26.00
0450	3"	"	0.229	14.25	18.00		32.25
0460	4"	"	0.267	16.75	29.25		46.00
0470	6"	"	0.320	20.00	98.00		120
0490	Couplings						
0510	1"	EA	0.133	8.35	0.91		9.26
0520	1-1/2"	"	0.133	8.35	1.30		9.65
0530	2"	"	0.145	9.11	2.01		11.00
0540	2-1/2"	"	0.160	10.00	4.42		14.50
0550	3"	"	0.178	11.25	6.91		18.25
0560	4"	"	0.200	12.50	9.02		21.50
0580	6"	"	0.267	16.75	28.50		45.25
1000	Drainage pipe						
1005	PVC schedule 80						
1010	1" dia.	LF	0.047	2.94	2.03		4.97
1015	1-1/2" dia.	"	0.047	2.94	2.46		5.40
1020	ABS, 2" dia.	"	0.050	3.13	3.14		6.27
1030	2-1/2" dia.	"	0.053	3.34	4.47		7.81
1040	3" dia.	"	0.057	3.58	5.26		8.84
1050	4" dia.	"	0.067	4.17	7.17		11.25
1055	6" dia.	"	0.080	5.01	12.00		17.00
1060	8" dia.	"	0.063	3.92	16.00	3.50	23.50
1080	10" dia.	"	0.075	4.66	21.25	4.15	30.00
1100	12" dia.	"	0.080	4.97	34.75	4.43	44.25
1105	90 degree elbows						
1110	1"	EA	0.133	8.35	3.38		11.75
1125	1-1/2"	"	0.133	8.35	4.22		12.50
1135	2"	"	0.145	9.11	5.09		14.25
1145	2-1/2"	"	0.160	10.00	12.25		22.25
1155	3"	"	0.178	11.25	12.50		23.75
1165	4"	"	0.200	12.50	22.25		34.75

DISTRIBUTION PIPING

ID Code	Descriptions — Component Descriptions	Output — Unit of Meas.	Output — Manhr / Unit	Unit Costs — Labor Cost	Unit Costs — Material Cost	Unit Costs — Equip. Cost	Unit Costs — Total Cost
33 - 11006	**PLASTIC PIPE, Cont'd...**						**33 - 11006**
1175	6"	EA	0.267	16.75	48.75		66.00
1200	45 degree elbows						
1210	1"	EA	0.133	8.35	5.50		13.75
1220	1-1/2"	"	0.133	8.35	6.99		15.25
1230	2"	"	0.145	9.11	8.66		17.75
1240	2-1/2"	"	0.160	10.00	16.25		26.25
1250	3"	"	0.178	11.25	17.25		28.50
1260	4"	"	0.200	12.50	32.75		45.25
1270	6"	"	0.267	16.75	76.00		93.00
1300	Tees						
1310	1"	EA	0.160	10.00	3.57		13.50
1320	1-1/2"	"	0.160	10.00	11.50		21.50
1330	2"	"	0.178	11.25	14.00		25.25
1340	2-1/2"	"	0.200	12.50	16.25		28.75
1350	3"	"	0.229	14.25	17.75		32.00
1360	4"	"	0.267	16.75	33.75		51.00
1370	6"	"	0.320	20.00	67.00		87.00
1400	Couplings						
1410	1"	EA	0.133	8.35	2.98		11.25
1420	1-1/2"	"	0.133	8.35	5.09		13.50
1430	2"	"	0.145	9.11	7.50		16.50
1440	2-1/2"	"	0.160	10.00	15.75		25.75
1450	3"	"	0.178	11.25	16.25		27.50
1460	4"	"	0.200	12.50	17.00		29.50
1470	6"	"	0.267	16.75	28.50		45.25
2000	Pressure pipe						
2020	PVC, class 200 pipe						
2025	3/4"	LF	0.040	2.50	0.26		2.76
2030	1"	"	0.042	2.63	0.38		3.01
2035	1-1/4"	"	0.044	2.78	0.64		3.42
2040	1-1/2"	"	0.047	2.94	0.77		3.71
2050	2"	"	0.050	3.13	1.26		4.39
2060	2-1/2"	"	0.053	3.34	1.91		5.25
2070	3"	"	0.057	3.58	2.92		6.50
2080	4"	"	0.067	4.17	5.09		9.26
2090	6"	"	0.080	5.01	10.25		15.25
2100	8"	"	0.069	4.26	19.75	3.80	27.75
2200	90 degree elbows						

DISTRIBUTION PIPING

ID Code	Component Descriptions	Unit of Meas.	Manhr / Unit	Labor Cost	Material Cost	Equip. Cost	Total Cost
33 - 11006	**PLASTIC PIPE, Cont'd...**						**33 - 11006**
2210	3/4"	EA	0.133	8.35	0.84		9.19
2220	1"	"	0.133	8.35	0.93		9.28
2230	1-1/4"	"	0.133	8.35	1.39		9.74
2240	1-1/2"	"	0.133	8.35	1.77		10.00
2250	2"	"	0.145	9.11	2.77		12.00
2260	2-1/2"	"	0.160	10.00	8.44		18.50
2270	3"	"	0.178	11.25	13.00		24.25
2280	4"	"	0.200	12.50	23.50		36.00
2290	6"	"	0.267	16.75	49.50		66.00
2300	8"	"	0.400	25.00	83.00		110
2320	45 degree elbows						
2330	3/4"	EA	0.133	8.35	0.95		9.30
2340	1"	"	0.133	8.35	1.22		9.57
2350	1-1/4"	"	0.133	8.35	1.76		10.00
2360	1-1/2"	"	0.133	8.35	2.13		10.50
2370	2"	"	0.145	9.11	3.00		12.00
2380	2-1/2"	"	0.160	10.00	4.92		15.00
2390	3"	"	0.178	11.25	11.25		22.50
2400	4"	"	0.200	12.50	21.25		33.75
2410	6"	"	0.267	16.75	44.25		61.00
2420	8"	"	0.400	25.00	90.00		110
2500	Tees						
2520	3/4"	EA	0.160	10.00	0.80		10.75
2530	1"	"	0.160	10.00	1.05		11.00
2540	1-1/4"	"	0.160	10.00	1.51		11.50
2550	1-1/2"	"	0.160	10.00	2.10		12.00
2560	2"	"	0.178	11.25	3.09		14.25
2570	2-1/2"	"	0.200	12.50	4.86		17.25
2580	3"	"	0.229	14.25	15.00		29.25
2590	4"	"	0.267	16.75	21.25		38.00
2600	6"	"	0.320	20.00	63.00		83.00
2610	8"	"	0.444	27.75	130		160
2700	Couplings						
2710	3/4"	EA	0.133	8.35	0.49		8.84
2720	1"	"	0.133	8.35	0.73		9.08
2730	1-1/4"	"	0.133	8.35	0.95		9.30
2740	1-1/2"	"	0.133	8.35	1.04		9.39
2750	2"	"	0.145	9.11	1.46		10.50

DISTRIBUTION PIPING

ID Code	Component Descriptions	Unit of Meas.	Manhr / Unit	Labor Cost	Material Cost	Equip. Cost	Total Cost
	Descriptions	**Output**		**Unit Costs**			

33 - 11006 — PLASTIC PIPE, Cont'd... — 33 - 11006

ID Code	Component Descriptions	Unit of Meas.	Manhr / Unit	Labor Cost	Material Cost	Equip. Cost	Total Cost
2760	2-1/2"	EA	0.160	10.00	3.09		13.00
2770	3"	"	0.178	11.25	4.86		16.00
2780	4"	"	0.178	11.25	6.83		18.00
2790	6"	"	0.200	12.50	18.00		30.50
2800	8"	"	0.267	16.75	32.50		49.25

SURFACE WATER SOURCES

33 - 12131 — CORPORATION STOPS — 33 - 12131

ID Code	Component Descriptions	Unit of Meas.	Manhr / Unit	Labor Cost	Material Cost	Equip. Cost	Total Cost
0090	Stop for flared copper service pipe						
0100	3/4"	EA	0.400	35.00	51.00		86.00
0120	1"	"	0.444	39.00	69.00		110
0130	1-1/4"	"	0.533	46.75	190		240
0140	1-1/2"	"	0.667	58.00	220		280
0150	2"	"	0.800	70.00	310		380

33 - 12132 — THRUST BLOCKS — 33 - 12132

ID Code	Component Descriptions	Unit of Meas.	Manhr / Unit	Labor Cost	Material Cost	Equip. Cost	Total Cost
0080	Thrust block, 3000# concrete						
0100	1/4 c.y.	EA	1.333	110	120		230
0120	1/2 c.y.	"	1.600	130	180		310
0140	3/4 c.y.	"	2.667	210	220		430
0160	1 c.y.	"	5.333	430	310		740

33 - 12133 — TAPPING SADDLES & SLEEVES — 33 - 12133

ID Code	Component Descriptions	Unit of Meas.	Manhr / Unit	Labor Cost	Material Cost	Equip. Cost	Total Cost
0080	Tapping saddle, tap size to 2"						
0100	4" saddle	EA	0.400	25.00	71.00		96.00
0120	6" saddle	"	0.500	31.25	83.00		110
0130	8" saddle	"	0.667	41.75	96.00		140
0140	10" saddle	"	0.800	50.00	110		160
0150	12" saddle	"	1.143	72.00	130		200
0160	14" saddle	"	1.600	100	150		250
2000	Tapping sleeve						
2010	4x4	EA	0.533	33.50	860		890
2030	6x4	"	0.615	38.50	1,110		1,150
2050	6x6	"	0.615	38.50	1,130		1,170
2060	8x4	"	0.800	50.00	1,160		1,210
2070	8x6	"	0.800	50.00	1,180		1,230
2090	10x4	"	0.960	60.00	1,880	53.00	1,990
2100	10x6	"	0.960	60.00	2,720	53.00	2,830

SURFACE WATER SOURCES

ID Code	Component Descriptions	Unit of Meas.	Manhr / Unit	Labor Cost	Material Cost	Equip. Cost	Total Cost
33 - 12133	**TAPPING SADDLES & SLEEVES, Cont'd...**					**33 - 12133**	
2120	10x8	EA	0.960	60.00	2,840	53.00	2,950
2130	10x10	"	1.000	62.00	2,900	55.00	3,020
2140	12x4	"	1.000	62.00	2,930	55.00	3,050
2150	12x6	"	1.091	68.00	2,950	60.00	3,080
2160	12x8	"	1.200	75.00	3,020	67.00	3,160
2170	12x10	"	1.333	83.00	3,180	74.00	3,340
2180	12x12	"	1.500	93.00	3,290	83.00	3,470
4000	Tapping valve, mechanical joint						
4010	4" valve	EA	3.000	190	850	170	1,200
4020	6" valve	"	4.000	250	1,020	220	1,490
4030	8" valve	"	6.000	370	1,520	330	2,230
4040	10" valve	"	8.000	500	2,420	440	3,360
4050	12" valve	"	12.000	750	4,280	670	5,690
7980	Tap hole in pipe						
8000	4" hole	EA	1.000	63.00			63.00
8010	6" hole	"	1.600	100			100
8020	8" hole	"	2.667	170			170
8030	10" hole	"	3.200	200			200
8040	12" hole	"	4.000	250			250
33 - 12135	**VALVE BOXES**					**33 - 12135**	
0080	Valve box, adjustable, for valves up to 20"						
0100	3' deep	EA	0.267	16.75	300		320
0120	4' deep	"	0.320	20.00	360		380
0130	5' deep	"	0.400	25.00	420		450
33 - 12161	**GATE VALVES**					**33 - 12161**	
0100	Gate valve, (AWWA) mechanical joint, with adjustable box						
0110	4" valve	EA	0.800	49.75	1,340	44.25	1,430
0120	6" valve	"	0.960	60.00	1,520	53.00	1,630
0130	8" valve	"	1.200	75.00	2,020	67.00	2,160
0140	10" valve	"	1.412	88.00	3,030	78.00	3,200
0150	12" valve	"	1.714	110	4,040	95.00	4,240
0160	14" valve	"	2.000	120	10,120	110	10,360
0170	16" valve	"	2.182	140	13,490	120	13,750
0180	18" valve	"	2.400	150	16,860	130	17,140
3000	Flanged, with box, post indicator (AWWA)						
3010	4" valve	EA	0.960	60.00	1,210	53.00	1,320
3020	6" valve	"	1.091	68.00	1,420	60.00	1,550

SURFACE WATER SOURCES

ID Code	Component Descriptions	Unit of Meas.	Manhr / Unit	Labor Cost	Material Cost	Equip. Cost	Total Cost
	Descriptions	**Output**		**Unit Costs**			

33 - 12161 — GATE VALVES, Cont'd... — 33 - 12161

ID Code	Component Descriptions	Unit of Meas.	Manhr / Unit	Labor Cost	Material Cost	Equip. Cost	Total Cost
3030	8" valve	EA	1.333	83.00	2,020	74.00	2,180
3040	10" valve	"	1.600	99.00	3,030	89.00	3,220
3050	12" valve	"	2.000	120	4,400	110	4,640
3060	14" valve	"	2.400	150	10,110	130	10,390
3070	16" valve	"	3.000	190	13,490	170	13,840

33 - 12193 — FIRE HYDRANTS — 33 - 12193

ID Code	Component Descriptions	Unit of Meas.	Manhr / Unit	Labor Cost	Material Cost	Equip. Cost	Total Cost
0080	Standard, 3 way post, 6" mechanical joint						
0100	2' deep	EA	8.000	500	2,050	440	2,990
0120	4' deep	"	9.600	600	2,200	530	3,330
0140	6' deep	"	12.000	750	2,450	670	3,860
0160	8' deep	"	13.714	850	2,750	760	4,360

33 - 12331 — WATER METERS — 33 - 12331

ID Code	Component Descriptions	Unit of Meas.	Manhr / Unit	Labor Cost	Material Cost	Equip. Cost	Total Cost
0080	Water meter, displacement type						
0090	1"	EA	0.800	70.00	220		290
0100	1-1/2"	"	0.889	78.00	750		830
0190	2"	"	1.000	88.00	1,130		1,220

UTILITY SERVICES

33 - 21130 — WELLS — 33 - 21130

ID Code	Component Descriptions	Unit of Meas.	Manhr / Unit	Labor Cost	Material Cost	Equip. Cost	Total Cost
0980	Domestic water, drilled and cased						
1000	4" dia.	LF	0.480	38.50	30.50	46.00	110
1020	6" dia.	"	0.533	42.75	33.50	51.00	130
1040	8" dia.	"	0.600	48.00	39.50	58.00	150

33 - 31001 — CAST IRON FLANGED PIPE — 33 - 31001

ID Code	Component Descriptions	Unit of Meas.	Manhr / Unit	Labor Cost	Material Cost	Equip. Cost	Total Cost
0100	Cast iron flanged sections						
0110	4" pipe, with one bolt set						
0120	3' section	EA	0.218	13.50	60.00	12.00	86.00
0130	4' section	"	0.240	15.00	83.00	13.25	110
0140	5' section	"	0.267	16.50	110	14.75	140
0150	6' section	"	0.300	18.75	130	16.50	170
0160	8' section	"	0.343	21.25	160	19.00	200
0170	10' section	"	0.480	29.75	230	26.50	290
0180	12' section	"	0.800	49.75	240	44.25	330
0190	15' section	"	1.200	75.00	300	67.00	440
0200	18' section	"	1.600	99.00	370	89.00	560

UTILITY SERVICES

ID Code	Component Descriptions	Unit of Meas.	Manhr / Unit	Labor Cost	Material Cost	Equip. Cost	Total Cost
		Output		**Unit Costs**			

33 - 31001   CAST IRON FLANGED PIPE, Cont'd...   **33 - 31001**

ID Code	Component Descriptions	Unit	Manhr	Labor	Material	Equip.	Total
2080	6" pipe, with one bolt set						
2100	3' section	EA	0.240	15.00	100	13.25	130
2102	4' section	"	0.282	17.50	150	15.75	180
2104	5' section	"	0.320	20.00	190	17.75	230
2110	6' section	"	0.369	23.00	220	20.50	260
2120	8' section	"	0.533	33.25	270	29.50	330
2130	10' section	"	0.600	37.25	380	33.25	450
2140	12' section	"	0.800	49.75	420	44.25	510
2150	15' section	"	1.200	75.00	520	67.00	660
2160	18' section	"	1.714	110	620	95.00	820
2165	8" pipe, with one bolt set						
2170	3' section	EA	0.300	18.75	160	16.50	200
2180	4' section	"	0.343	21.25	230	19.00	270
2190	5' section	"	0.400	24.75	280	22.25	330
2200	6' section	"	0.480	29.75	340	26.50	400
2210	8' section	"	0.686	42.50	430	38.00	510
2215	10' section	"	0.800	49.75	600	44.25	690
2230	12' section	"	1.200	75.00	650	67.00	790
2240	15' section	"	1.600	99.00	810	89.00	1,000
2250	18' section	"	2.000	120	970	110	1,210
3005	10" pipe, with one bolt set						
3010	3' section	EA	0.308	19.00	300	17.00	340
3020	4' section	"	0.353	22.00	490	19.50	530
3030	5' section	"	0.414	25.75	570	23.00	620
3040	6' section	"	0.500	31.00	690	27.75	750
3050	8' section	"	0.727	45.25	910	40.25	1,000
3060	10' section	"	0.857	53.00	990	47.50	1,090
3070	12' section	"	1.333	83.00	1,080	74.00	1,240
3080	15' section	"	1.714	110	1,350	95.00	1,550
3090	18' section	"	2.400	150	1,620	130	1,900
3095	12" pipe, with one bolt set						
3100	3' section	EA	0.333	20.75	370	18.50	410
3120	4' section	"	0.387	24.00	550	21.50	600
3130	5' section	"	0.462	28.75	680	25.50	730
3140	6' section	"	0.545	34.00	820	30.25	880
3150	8' section	"	0.800	49.75	1,090	44.25	1,180
3160	10' section	"	0.923	57.00	1,260	51.00	1,370
3170	12' section	"	1.500	93.00	1,600	83.00	1,780

UTILITY SERVICES

	Descriptions	Output		Unit Costs			
ID Code	Component Descriptions	Unit of Meas.	Manhr / Unit	Labor Cost	Material Cost	Equip. Cost	Total Cost
33 - 31001	**CAST IRON FLANGED PIPE, Cont'd...**						**33 - 31001**
3180	15' section	EA	2.000	120	1,810	110	2,050
3190	18' section	"	2.667	170	2,080	150	2,390
33 - 31002	**CAST IRON FITTINGS**						**33 - 31002**
0100	Mechanical joint, with 2 bolt kits						
0105	90 deg bend						
0110	4"	EA	0.533	33.50	88.00		120
0120	6"	"	0.615	38.50	150		190
0130	8"	"	0.800	50.00	330		380
0140	10"	"	1.143	72.00	500		570
0150	12"	"	1.600	100	760		860
0155	14"	"	2.000	130	1,040		1,170
0160	16"	"	2.667	170	1,200		1,370
0165	45 deg bend						
0170	4"	EA	0.533	33.50	73.00		110
0180	6"	"	0.615	38.50	120		160
0190	8"	"	0.800	50.00	260		310
0200	10"	"	1.143	72.00	390		460
0210	12"	"	1.600	100	660		760
0220	14"	"	2.000	130	810		940
0230	16"	"	2.667	170	1,060		1,230
2000	Tee, with 3 bolt kits						
2010	4" x 4"	EA	0.800	50.00	150		200
2020	6" x 6"	"	1.000	63.00	260		320
2030	8" x 8"	"	1.333	84.00	730		810
2040	10" x 10"	"	2.000	130	910		1,040
2050	12" x 12"	"	2.667	170	1,620		1,790
3000	Wye, with 3 bolt kits						
3010	6" x 6"	EA	1.000	63.00	320		380
3020	8" x 8"	"	1.333	84.00	670		750
3030	10" x 10"	"	2.000	130	960		1,090
3040	12" x 12"	"	2.667	170	1,880		2,050
3045	Reducer, with 2 bolt kits						
3050	6" x 4"	EA	1.000	63.00	140		200
3060	8" x 6"	"	1.333	84.00	230		310
3070	10" x 8"	"	2.000	130	640		770
3080	12" x 10"	"	2.667	170	770		940
6010	Flanged, 90 deg bend, 125 lb.						

UTILITY SERVICES

ID Code	Descriptions — Component Descriptions	Output — Unit of Meas.	Output — Manhr / Unit	Unit Costs — Labor Cost	Unit Costs — Material Cost	Unit Costs — Equip. Cost	Unit Costs — Total Cost
33 - 31002	**CAST IRON FITTINGS, Cont'd...**						**33 - 31002**
6020	4"	EA	0.667	41.75	180		220
6040	6"	"	0.800	50.00	220		270
6060	8"	"	1.000	63.00	310		370
6080	10"	"	1.333	84.00	550		630
6090	12"	"	2.000	130	770		900
6095	14"	"	2.667	170	1,520		1,690
6100	16"	"	2.667	170	2,270		2,440
6115	Tee						
6120	4"	EA	1.000	63.00	280		340
6130	6"	"	1.143	72.00	390		460
6140	8"	"	1.333	84.00	600		680
6150	10"	"	1.600	100	1,100		1,200
6160	12"	"	2.000	130	1,480		1,610
6170	14"	"	2.667	170	3,300		3,470
6180	16"	"	4.000	250	4,960		5,210
33 - 31003	**VITRIFIED CLAY PIPE**						**33 - 31003**
0100	Vitrified clay pipe, extra strength						
1020	6" dia.	LF	0.109	6.78	5.73	6.04	18.50
1040	8" dia.	"	0.114	7.10	6.87	6.33	20.25
1050	10" dia.	"	0.120	7.45	10.50	6.65	24.50
1070	12" dia.	"	0.160	9.94	15.00	8.86	33.75
1090	15" dia.	"	0.240	15.00	27.50	13.25	56.00
1120	18" dia.	"	0.267	16.50	41.25	14.75	73.00
1140	24" dia.	"	0.343	21.25	75.00	19.00	120
1160	30" dia.	"	0.480	29.75	130	26.50	190
1180	36" dia.	"	0.686	42.50	180	38.00	260
33 - 31004	**SANITARY SEWERS**						**33 - 31004**
0980	Clay						
1000	6" pipe	LF	0.080	4.97	9.41	4.43	18.75
1020	8" pipe	"	0.086	5.32	12.50	4.75	22.50
1030	10" pipe	"	0.092	5.73	15.75	5.11	26.50
1040	12" pipe	"	0.100	6.21	25.00	5.54	36.75
2980	PVC						
3000	4" pipe	LF	0.060	3.72	4.05	3.32	11.00
3010	6" pipe	"	0.063	3.92	8.11	3.50	15.50
3020	8" pipe	"	0.067	4.14	12.25	3.69	20.00
3030	10" pipe	"	0.071	4.38	16.25	3.91	24.50

UTILITY SERVICES

ID Code	Component Descriptions	Unit of Meas.	Manhr / Unit	Labor Cost	Material Cost	Equip. Cost	Total Cost
33 - 31004	**SANITARY SEWERS, Cont'd...**					**33 - 31004**	
3040	12" pipe	LF	0.075	4.66	24.25	4.15	33.00
5980	Cleanout						
6000	4" pipe	EA	1.000	63.00	18.00		81.00
6010	6" pipe	"	1.000	63.00	39.75		100
6020	8" pipe	"	1.000	63.00	120		180
7980	Connect new sewer line						
8000	To existing manhole	EA	2.667	170	100		270
8010	To new manhole	"	1.600	100	75.00		180

WASTEWATER UTILITY STORAGE TANKS

ID Code	Component Descriptions	Unit of Meas.	Manhr / Unit	Labor Cost	Material Cost	Equip. Cost	Total Cost
33 - 36001	**DRAINAGE FIELDS**					**33 - 36001**	
0080	Perforated PVC pipe, for drain field						
0100	4" pipe	LF	0.053	3.31	2.71	2.95	8.98
0120	6" pipe	"	0.057	3.55	5.08	3.16	11.75
33 - 36005	**SEPTIC TANKS**					**33 - 36005**	
0980	Septic tank, precast concrete						
1000	1000 gals	EA	4.000	250	1,020	220	1,490
1200	2000 gals	"	6.000	370	2,740	330	3,450
1280	5000 gals	"	12.000	750	9,350	670	10,760
1290	25,000 gals	"	48.000	2,980	53,590	2,660	59,230
1300	40,000 gals	"	80.000	4,970	63,560	4,430	72,970
1310	Leaching pit, precast concrete, 72" diameter						
1320	3' deep	EA	3.000	190	780	170	1,130
1340	6' deep	"	3.429	210	1,370	190	1,770
1360	8' deep	"	4.000	250	1,740	220	2,210

MANHOLES

ID Code	Component Descriptions	Unit of Meas.	Manhr / Unit	Labor Cost	Material Cost	Equip. Cost	Total Cost
33 - 39133	**MANHOLES**					**33 - 39133**	
0100	Precast sections, 48" dia.						
0110	Base section	EA	2.000	120	360	110	600
0120	1'0" riser	"	1.600	99.00	100	89.00	290
0130	1'4" riser	"	1.714	110	120	95.00	320
0140	2'8" riser	"	1.846	110	180	100	400
0150	4'0" riser	"	2.000	120	340	110	580
0160	2'8" cone top	"	2.400	150	220	130	500
0170	Precast manholes, 48" dia.						

MANHOLES

ID Code	Component Descriptions	Unit of Meas.	Manhr / Unit	Labor Cost	Material Cost	Equip. Cost	Total Cost
	Descriptions	**Output**		**Unit Costs**			

ID Code	Component Descriptions	Unit of Meas.	Manhr / Unit	Labor Cost	Material Cost	Equip. Cost	Total Cost
33 - 39133	**MANHOLES, Cont'd...**						**33 - 39133**
0180	4' deep	EA	4.800	300	700	270	1,260
0200	6' deep	"	6.000	370	1,070	330	1,780
0250	7' deep	"	6.857	430	1,220	380	2,030
0260	8' deep	"	8.000	500	1,380	440	2,320
0280	10' deep	"	9.600	600	1,540	530	2,670
1000	Cast-in-place, 48" dia., with frame and cover						
1100	5' deep	EA	12.000	750	630	670	2,040
1120	6' deep	"	13.714	850	830	760	2,440
1140	8' deep	"	16.000	990	1,210	890	3,090
1160	10' deep	"	19.200	1,190	1,410	1,060	3,670
1480	Brick manholes, 48" dia. with cover, 8" thick						
1500	4' deep	EA	8.000	610	670		1,280
1501	6' deep	"	8.889	680	840		1,520
1505	8' deep	"	10.000	760	1,080		1,840
1510	10' deep	"	11.429	870	1,340		2,210
1600	12' deep	"	13.333	1,020	1,680		2,700
1620	14' deep	"	16.000	1,220	2,040		3,260
3000	Inverts for manholes						
3010	Single channel	EA	3.200	240	110		350
3020	Triple channel	"	4.000	300	130		430
4200	Frames and covers, 24" diameter						
4210	300 lb	EA	0.800	50.00	410		460
4220	400 lb	"	0.889	56.00	430		490
4230	500 lb	"	1.143	72.00	500		570
4240	Watertight, 350 lb	"	2.667	170	520		690
4250	For heavy equipment, 1200 lb	"	4.000	250	1,130		1,380
4980	Steps for manholes						
5000	7" x 9"	EA	0.160	10.00	17.25		27.25
5020	8" x 9"	"	0.178	11.25	22.00		33.25
6080	Curb inlet, 4' throat, cast in place						
6100	12"-30" pipe	EA	12.000	750	360	670	1,770
6150	36"-48" pipe	"	13.714	850	400	760	2,010
8000	Raise exist frame and cover, when repaving	"	4.800	300		270	560

MANHOLES

ID Code	Descriptions	Output		Unit Costs			
	Component Descriptions	Unit of Meas.	Manhr / Unit	Labor Cost	Material Cost	Equip. Cost	Total Cost
33 - 41004	**PIPE**						**33 - 41004**
1000	Concrete pipe						
1080	Plain, bell and spigot joint, Class II						
1100	6" pipe	LF	0.109	6.78	7.56	6.04	20.25
1200	8" pipe	"	0.120	7.45	7.89	6.65	22.00
1300	10" pipe	"	0.126	7.85	8.03	7.00	22.75
1400	12" pipe	"	0.133	8.28	10.75	7.38	26.50
1500	15" pipe	"	0.141	8.77	14.50	7.82	31.00
1600	18" pipe	"	0.150	9.32	18.00	8.31	35.75
1650	21" pipe	"	0.160	9.94	21.75	8.86	40.50
1700	24" pipe	"	0.171	10.75	27.50	9.50	47.75
1730	Reinforced, class III, tongue and groove joint						
1750	12" pipe	LF	0.133	8.28	15.50	7.38	31.25
1800	15" pipe	"	0.141	8.77	17.50	7.82	34.00
1850	18" pipe	"	0.150	9.32	19.25	8.31	37.00
1880	21" pipe	"	0.160	9.94	25.00	8.86	43.75
1900	24" pipe	"	0.171	10.75	32.75	9.50	53.00
1950	27" pipe	"	0.185	11.50	38.75	10.25	61.00
1960	30" pipe	"	0.200	12.50	42.50	11.00	66.00
1970	36" pipe	"	0.218	13.50	64.00	12.00	90.00
1980	42" pipe	"	0.240	15.00	87.00	13.25	120
1990	48" pipe	"	0.267	16.50	120	14.75	150
2000	54" pipe	"	0.300	18.75	130	16.50	170
2050	60" pipe	"	0.343	21.25	170	19.00	210
2070	66" pipe	"	0.400	24.75	220	22.25	270
2080	72" pipe	"	0.480	29.75	240	26.50	300
2090	Flared end-section, concrete						
2100	12" pipe	LF	0.133	8.28	70.00	7.38	86.00
2110	15" pipe	"	0.141	8.77	83.00	7.82	100
2120	18" pipe	"	0.150	9.32	98.00	8.31	120
2130	24" pipe	"	0.171	10.75	110	9.50	130
2140	30" pipe	"	0.200	12.50	140	11.00	160
2150	36" pipe	"	0.218	13.50	190	12.00	220
2160	42" pipe	"	0.240	15.00	210	13.25	240
2170	48" pipe	"	0.267	16.50	230	14.75	260
2180	54" pipe	"	0.300	18.75	250	16.50	290
5090	Corrugated metal pipe, coated, paved invert						
5095	16 ga.						
6000	8" pipe	LF	0.080	4.97	11.00	4.43	20.50

MANHOLES

ID Code	Component Descriptions	Unit of Meas.	Manhr / Unit	Labor Cost	Material Cost	Equip. Cost	Total Cost
33 - 41004	**PIPE, Cont'd...**						**33 - 41004**
6010	10" pipe	LF	0.083	5.14	14.75	4.58	24.50
6020	12" pipe	"	0.086	5.32	16.50	4.75	26.50
6030	15" pipe	"	0.092	5.73	20.25	5.11	31.00
6040	18" pipe	"	0.100	6.21	24.00	5.54	35.75
6050	21" pipe	"	0.109	6.78	29.50	6.04	42.25
6060	24" pipe	"	0.120	7.45	35.00	6.65	49.00
6070	30" pipe	"	0.133	8.28	46.00	7.38	62.00
6080	36" pipe	"	0.150	9.32	63.00	8.31	81.00
6090	12 ga., 48" pipe	"	0.171	10.75	110	9.50	130
6095	10 ga.						
6100	60" pipe	LF	0.200	12.50	140	11.00	160
6110	72" pipe	"	0.240	15.00	180	13.25	210
6200	Galvanized or aluminum, plain						
6205	16 ga.						
6210	8" pipe	LF	0.080	4.97	9.24	4.43	18.75
6220	10" pipe	"	0.083	5.14	13.00	4.58	22.75
6230	12" pipe	"	0.086	5.32	14.75	4.75	24.75
6240	15" pipe	"	0.092	5.73	18.50	5.11	29.25
6250	18" pipe	"	0.100	6.21	22.00	5.54	33.75
6260	24" pipe	"	0.120	7.45	33.25	6.65	47.25
6270	30" pipe	"	0.133	8.28	44.25	7.38	60.00
6280	36" pipe	"	0.150	9.32	55.00	8.31	73.00
6290	12 ga., 48" pipe	"	0.171	10.75	100	9.50	120
6300	10 ga., 60" pipe	"	0.200	12.50	140	11.00	160
6400	Galvanized or aluminum, coated oval arch						
6405	16 ga.						
6410	17" x 13"	LF	0.109	6.78	34.00	6.04	46.75
6420	21" x 15"	"	0.120	7.45	45.75	6.65	60.00
6425	14 ga.						
6430	28" x 20"	LF	0.133	8.28	64.00	7.38	80.00
6440	35" x 24"	"	0.171	10.75	96.00	9.50	120
6445	12 ga.						
6450	42" x 29"	LF	0.200	12.50	110	11.00	130
6460	57" x 38"	"	0.240	15.00	170	13.25	200
6470	64" x 43"	"	0.253	15.75	200	14.00	230
6500	Oval arch culverts, plain						
6505	16 ga.						
6510	17" x 13"	LF	0.109	6.78	16.00	6.04	28.75

MANHOLES

ID Code	Component Descriptions	Unit of Meas.	Manhr / Unit	Labor Cost	Material Cost	Equip. Cost	Total Cost
	Descriptions	**Output**		**Unit Costs**			
33 - 41004	**PIPE, Cont'd...**						**33 - 41004**
6520	21" x 15"	LF	0.120	7.45	23.00	6.65	37.00
6525	14 ga.						
6530	28" x 20"	LF	0.133	8.28	42.75	7.38	59.00
6540	35" x 24"	"	0.171	10.75	54.00	9.50	74.00
6545	12 ga.						
6550	57" x 38"	LF	0.200	12.50	87.00	11.00	110
6560	64" x 43"	"	0.240	15.00	110	13.25	140
6570	71" x 47"	"	0.253	15.75	150	14.00	180
6600	Nestable corrugated metal pipe						
6615	16 ga.						
6620	10" pipe	LF	0.083	5.14	12.75	4.58	22.50
6630	12" pipe	"	0.086	5.32	16.00	4.75	26.00
6640	15" pipe	"	0.092	5.73	20.75	5.11	31.50
6650	18" pipe	"	0.100	6.21	24.00	5.54	35.75
6660	24" pipe	"	0.120	7.45	33.75	6.65	47.75
6670	30" pipe	"	0.133	8.28	41.75	7.38	58.00
6680	14 ga., 36" pipe	"	0.150	9.32	48.00	8.31	66.00
9680	Headwalls, cast in place, 30 deg wingwall						
9700	12" pipe	EA	2.000	160	420		580
9740	15" pipe	"	2.000	160	510		670
9750	18" pipe	"	2.286	180	620		800
9760	24" pipe	"	2.286	180	920		1,100
9770	30" pipe	"	2.667	210	1,110		1,320
9780	36" pipe	"	4.000	320	1,200		1,520
9790	42" pipe	"	4.000	320	1,500		1,820
9800	48" pipe	"	5.333	430	1,590		2,020
9810	54" pipe	"	6.667	530	1,800		2,330
9820	60" pipe	"	8.000	640	2,160		2,800
9880	4" cleanout for storm drain						
9900	4" pipe	EA	1.000	63.00	670		730
9910	6" pipe	"	1.000	63.00	810		870
9920	8" pipe	"	1.000	63.00	1,120		1,180
9925	Connect new drain line						
9930	To existing manhole	EA	2.667	170	140		310
9940	To new manhole	"	1.600	100	120		220

DRAINAGE AND CONTAINMENT

ID Code	Component Descriptions	Unit of Meas.	Manhr / Unit	Labor Cost	Material Cost	Equip. Cost	Total Cost
		Descriptions		**Output**		**Unit Costs**	
33 - 44131		**CATCH BASINS**					**33 - 44131**
0100	Standard concrete catch basin						
1021	Cast in place, 3'8" x 3'8", 6" thick wall						
1030	2' deep	EA	6.000	370	540	330	1,250
1040	3' deep	"	6.000	370	730	330	1,440
1050	4' deep	"	8.000	500	950	440	1,890
1060	5' deep	"	8.000	500	1,120	440	2,060
1070	6' deep	"	9.600	600	1,250	530	2,380
1201	4'x4', 8" thick wall, cast in place						
1210	2' deep	EA	6.000	370	580	330	1,290
1220	3' deep	"	6.000	370	810	330	1,520
1230	4' deep	"	8.000	500	1,070	440	2,010
1240	5' deep	"	8.000	500	1,240	440	2,180
1250	6' deep	"	9.600	600	1,370	530	2,500
5000	Frames and covers, cast iron						
5010	Round						
5020	24" dia.	EA	2.000	130	430		560
5030	26" dia.	"	2.000	130	480		610
5040	28" dia.	"	2.000	130	570		700
5080	Rectangular						
5100	23"x23"	EA	2.000	130	380		510
5120	27"x20"	"	2.000	130	460		590
5130	24"x24"	"	2.000	130	450		580
5140	26"x26"	"	2.000	130	490		620
5200	Curb inlet frames and covers						
5210	27"x27"	EA	2.000	130	770		900
5220	24"x36"	"	2.000	130	560		690
5230	24"x25"	"	2.000	130	520		650
5240	24"x22"	"	2.000	130	450		580
5250	20"x22"	"	2.000	130	590		720
9120	Airfield catch basin frame and grating, galvanized						
9140	2'x4'	EA	2.000	130	790		920
9160	2'x2'	"	2.000	130	550		680

STORMWATER MANAGEMENT

ID Code	Component Descriptions	Unit of Meas.	Manhr / Unit	Labor Cost	Material Cost	Equip. Cost	Total Cost
		Descriptions	**Output**		**Unit Costs**		

ID Code	Component Descriptions	Unit of Meas.	Manhr / Unit	Labor Cost	Material Cost	Equip. Cost	Total Cost
33 - 46190	**UNDERDRAIN**					**33 - 46190**	
1480	Drain tile, clay						
1500	6" pipe	LF	0.053	3.31	4.52	2.95	10.75
1520	8" pipe	"	0.056	3.46	7.21	3.09	13.75
1530	12" pipe	"	0.060	3.72	14.50	3.32	21.50
1580	Porous concrete, standard strength						
1600	6" pipe	LF	0.053	3.31	5.14	2.95	11.50
1620	8" pipe	"	0.056	3.46	5.56	3.09	12.00
1630	12" pipe	"	0.060	3.72	7.35	3.32	14.50
1640	15" pipe	"	0.067	4.14	13.25	3.69	21.00
1650	18" pipe	"	0.080	4.97	17.75	4.43	27.25
1800	Corrugated metal pipe, perforated type						
1810	6" pipe	LF	0.060	3.72	7.13	3.32	14.25
1820	8" pipe	"	0.063	3.92	8.43	3.50	15.75
1830	10" pipe	"	0.067	4.14	10.25	3.69	18.00
1840	12" pipe	"	0.071	4.38	14.50	3.91	22.75
1860	18" pipe	"	0.075	4.66	17.75	4.15	26.50
1980	Perforated clay pipe						
2000	6" pipe	LF	0.069	4.26	5.98	3.80	14.00
2020	8" pipe	"	0.071	4.38	8.02	3.91	16.25
2030	12" pipe	"	0.073	4.52	14.00	4.03	22.50
2480	Drain tile, concrete						
2500	6" pipe	LF	0.053	3.31	4.08	2.95	10.25
2520	8" pipe	"	0.056	3.46	6.35	3.09	13.00
2530	12" pipe	"	0.060	3.72	12.75	3.32	19.75
4980	Perforated rigid PVC underdrain pipe						
5000	4" pipe	LF	0.040	2.48	2.10	2.21	6.80
5100	6" pipe	"	0.048	2.98	4.04	2.66	9.68
5150	8" pipe	"	0.053	3.31	6.17	2.95	12.50
5200	10" pipe	"	0.060	3.72	9.43	3.32	16.50
5210	12" pipe	"	0.069	4.26	14.50	3.80	22.50
6980	Underslab drainage, crushed stone						
7000	3" thick	SF	0.008	0.49	0.33	0.44	1.27
7120	4" thick	"	0.009	0.57	0.45	0.51	1.53
7140	6" thick	"	0.010	0.62	0.68	0.55	1.85
7160	8" thick	"	0.010	0.64	0.90	0.57	2.12
7180	Plastic filter fabric for drain lines	"	0.008	0.50	0.50		1.00
9000	Gravel fill in trench, crushed or bank run, 1/2" to 3/4"	CY	0.600	37.25	36.25	33.25	110

ENERGY DISTRIBUTION

ID Code	Component Descriptions	Unit of Meas.	Manhr / Unit	Labor Cost	Material Cost	Equip. Cost	Total Cost
		Descriptions	**Output**		**Unit Costs**		
33 - 51001	**GAS DISTRIBUTION**						**33 - 51001**
0100	Gas distribution lines						
1000	Polyethylene, 60 psi coils						
1010	1-1/4" dia.	LF	0.053	4.67	1.92		6.59
1020	1-1/2" dia.	"	0.057	5.01	2.61		7.62
1030	2" dia.	"	0.067	5.84	3.30		9.14
1040	3" dia.	"	0.080	7.01	6.99		14.00
1045	30' pipe lengths						
1050	3" dia.	LF	0.089	7.79	5.73		13.50
1060	4" dia.	"	0.100	8.77	8.95		17.75
1070	6" dia.	"	0.133	11.75	14.25		26.00
1080	8" dia.	"	0.160	14.00	26.25		40.25
2000	Steel, schedule 40, plain end						
2010	1" dia.	LF	0.067	5.84	5.42		11.25
2020	2" dia.	"	0.073	6.37	9.02		15.50
2030	3" dia.	"	0.080	7.01	13.00		20.00
2040	4" dia.	"	0.160	9.94	15.75	8.86	34.50
2050	5" dia.	"	0.171	10.75	29.75	9.50	50.00
2060	6" dia.	"	0.200	12.50	39.75	11.00	63.00
2070	8" dia.	"	0.218	13.50	49.75	12.00	76.00
5000	Natural gas meters, direct digital reading, threaded						
5050	250 cfh @ 5 lbs	EA	1.600	140	130		270
5060	425 cfh @ 10 lbs	"	1.600	140	320		460
5080	800 cfh @ 20 lbs	"	2.000	180	450		630
5090	1,000 cfh @ 25 lbs	"	2.000	180	1,330		1,510
5130	1,400 cfh @ 100 lbs	"	2.667	230	3,090		3,320
5140	2,300 cfh @ 100 lbs	"	4.000	350	4,300		4,650
5150	5,000 cfh @ 100 lbs	"	8.000	700	6,310		7,010
5500	Gas pressure regulators						
5505	Threaded						
5510	3/4"	EA	1.000	88.00	61.00		150
5520	1"	"	1.333	120	64.00		180
5530	1-1/4"	"	1.333	120	67.00		190
5540	1-1/2"	"	1.333	120	440		560
5560	2"	"	1.600	140	450		590
5565	Flanged						
5570	3"	EA	2.000	180	1,590		1,770
5580	4"	"	2.667	230	2,370		2,600

HYDROCARBON STORAGE

ID Code	Component Descriptions	Unit of Meas.	Manhr / Unit	Labor Cost	Material Cost	Equip. Cost	Total Cost
	Descriptions	**Output**		**Unit Costs**			
33 - 56001	**STORAGE TANKS**						**33 - 56001**
0080	Oil storage tank, underground, single wall, no excv.						
0090	Steel						
1000	500 gals	EA	3.000	190	4,040	170	4,390
1020	1,000 gals	"	4.000	250	5,470	220	5,940
1040	4,000 gals	"	8.000	500	8,380	440	9,320
1060	5,000 gals	"	12.000	750	9,830	670	11,240
1080	10,000 gals	"	24.000	1,490	17,500	1,330	20,320
1980	Fiberglass, double wall						
2000	550 gals	EA	4.000	250	11,370	220	11,840
2020	1,000 gals	"	4.000	250	14,620	220	15,090
2030	2,000 gals	"	6.000	370	15,880	330	16,590
2060	4,000 gals	"	12.000	750	18,440	670	19,850
2080	6,000 gals	"	16.000	990	20,120	890	22,000
2090	8,000 gals	"	24.000	1,490	22,580	1,330	25,400
2095	10,000 gals	"	30.000	1,860	23,150	1,660	26,680
2100	12,000 gals	"	40.000	2,490	25,100	2,220	29,800
2120	15,000 gals	"	53.333	3,310	26,920	2,960	33,190
2140	20,000 gals	"	60.000	3,730	32,980	3,330	40,030
2520	Above ground						
2530	Steel, single wall						
2540	275 gals	EA	2.400	150	2,290	130	2,570
2560	500 gals	"	4.000	250	5,720	220	6,190
2570	1,000 gals	"	4.800	300	7,810	270	8,370
2580	1,500 gals	"	6.000	370	9,960	330	10,670
2590	2,000 gals	"	8.000	500	12,320	440	13,260
2620	5,000 gals	"	12.000	750	14,470	670	15,880
3020	Fill cap	"	0.800	70.00	140		210
3040	Vent cap	"	0.800	70.00	140		210
3100	Level indicator	"	0.800	70.00	220		290

STEAM ENERGY DISTRIBUTION

ID Code	Descriptions / Component Descriptions	Output Unit of Meas.	Manhr / Unit	Unit Costs Labor Cost	Material Cost	Equip. Cost	Total Cost
33 - 63330	**STEAM METERS**						**33 - 63330**
0100	In-line turbine, direct reading, 300 lb, flanged						
0120	2"	EA	1.000	88.00	3,880		3,970
0130	3"	"	1.333	120	4,160		4,280
0140	4"	"	1.600	140	4,570		4,710
0145	Threaded, 2"						
0150	5" line	EA	8.000	700	7,350		8,050
0170	6" line	"	8.000	700	7,490		8,190
0180	8" line	"	8.000	700	7,620		8,320
0190	10" line	"	8.000	700	8,040		8,740
0200	12" line	"	8.000	700	8,180		8,880
0210	14" line	"	8.000	700	8,460		9,160
0220	16" line	"	8.000	700	9,010		9,710
33 - 71160	**UTILITY POLES & FITTINGS**						**33 - 71160**
0980	Wood pole, creosoted						
1000	25'	EA	2.353	190	450		640
1030	40'	"	3.791	310	860		1,170
1060	55'	"	7.547	610	1,340		1,950
1065	Treated, wood preservative, 6"x6"						
1070	8'	EA	0.500	40.75	100		140
1120	16'	"	1.600	130	250		380
1150	20'	"	2.000	160	360		520
1155	Aluminum, brushed, no base						
1160	8'	EA	2.000	160	650		810
1190	20'	"	3.200	260	1,020		1,280
1230	40'	"	6.250	510	3,060		3,570
1235	Steel, no base						
1240	10'	EA	2.500	200	760		960
1250	20'	"	3.810	310	1,110		1,420
1300	35'	"	6.250	510	1,880		2,390
2000	Concrete, no base						
2020	13'	EA	5.517	450	980		1,430
2100	30'	"	12.121	990	2,670		3,660
2180	50'	"	18.182	1,480	5,920		7,400
2220	60'	"	20.000	1,630	7,550		9,180

STEAM ENERGY DISTRIBUTION

ID Code	Component Descriptions	Unit of Meas.	Manhr / Unit	Labor Cost	Material Cost	Equip. Cost	Total Cost
	Descriptions	**Output**		**Unit Costs**			
33 - 71190	**ELECTRIC MANHOLES**						**33 - 71190**
0980	Precast, handhole, 4' deep						
1000	2'x2'	EA	3.478	280	460		740
1020	3'x3'	"	5.556	450	610		1,060
1040	4'x4'	"	10.256	830	1,320		2,150
1060	Power manhole, complete, precast, 8' deep						
1080	4'x4'	EA	14.035	1,140	1,880		3,020
1100	6'x6'	"	20.000	1,630	2,520		4,150
1140	8'x8'	"	21.053	1,710	2,980		4,690
1180	6' deep, 9' x 12'	"	25.000	2,040	3,300		5,340
1980	Cast in place, power manhole, 8' deep						
2000	4'x4'	EA	14.035	1,140	2,230		3,370
2020	6'x6'	"	20.000	1,630	2,880		4,510
2040	8'x8'	"	21.053	1,710	3,200		4,910

DIVISION 34
TRANSPORTATION

BASE COURSES AND BALLASTS

ID Code	Descriptions Component Descriptions	Output Unit of Meas.	Output Manhr / Unit	Unit Costs Labor Cost	Unit Costs Material Cost	Unit Costs Equip. Cost	Unit Costs Total Cost
34 - 11130	**RAILROAD BALLAST, RAIL, APPURTENANCES**					**34 - 11130**	
0080	Rail						
1010	90 lb	LF	0.010	0.59	29.00	0.53	30.00
1020	100 lb	"	0.010	0.59	33.25	0.53	34.25
1030	115 lb	"	0.010	0.59	37.25	0.53	38.25
1080	132 lb	"	0.010	0.59	41.50	0.53	42.50
1090	Rail relay						
1100	90 lb	LF	0.010	0.59	13.50	0.53	14.50
1120	100 lb	"	0.010	0.59	14.75	0.53	15.75
1140	115 lb	"	0.010	0.59	18.00	0.53	19.00
1160	132 lb	"	0.010	0.59	21.75	0.53	22.75
1170	New angle bars, per pair						
1540	90 lb	EA	0.012	0.74	110	0.66	110
1560	100 lb	"	0.012	0.74	120	0.66	120
1600	115 lb	"	0.012	0.74	150	0.66	150
1620	132 lb	"	0.012	0.74	170	0.66	170
1630	Angle bar relay						
1640	90 lb	EA	0.012	0.74	44.50	0.66	46.00
1660	100 lb	"	0.012	0.74	45.50	0.66	47.00
1680	115 lb	"	0.012	0.74	47.75	0.66	49.25
1700	132 lb	"	0.012	0.74	51.00	0.66	52.00
1800	New tie plates						
2020	90 lb	EA	0.009	0.53	14.50	0.47	15.50
2040	100 lb	"	0.009	0.53	15.25	0.47	16.25
2060	115 lb	"	0.009	0.53	16.50	0.47	17.50
2080	132 lb	"	0.009	0.53	17.50	0.47	18.50
2090	Tie plate relay						
2100	90 lb	EA	0.009	0.53	4.56	0.47	5.56
2120	100 lb	"	0.009	0.53	6.41	0.47	7.41
2140	115 lb	"	0.009	0.53	6.41	0.47	7.41
2180	132 lb	"	0.009	0.53	7.90	0.47	8.90
2190	Track accessories						
2250	Wooden cross ties, 8'	EA	0.060	3.72	56.00	3.32	63.00
2260	Concrete cross ties, 8'	"	0.120	7.45	140	6.65	150
2280	Tie plugs, 5"	"	0.006	0.37	6.85	0.33	7.55
2300	Track bolts and nuts, 1"	"	0.006	0.37	5.59	0.33	6.29
2320	Lockwashers, 1"	"	0.004	0.24	1.46	0.22	1.93
2340	Track spikes, 6"	"	0.024	1.49	1.38	1.33	4.20
2360	Wooden switch ties	BF	0.006	0.37	2.37	0.33	3.07

BASE COURSES AND BALLASTS

ID Code	Component Descriptions	Unit of Meas.	Manhr / Unit	Labor Cost	Material Cost	Equip. Cost	Total Cost
		Descriptions	Output		Unit Costs		

34 - 11130   RAILROAD BALLAST, RAIL, APPURTENANCES, Cont'd...34 - 11130

ID Code	Component Descriptions	Unit of Meas.	Manhr / Unit	Labor Cost	Material Cost	Equip. Cost	Total Cost
2380	Rail anchors	EA	0.022	1.35	5.68	1.20	8.24
2400	Ballast	TON	0.120	7.45	17.75	6.65	31.75
2420	Gauge rods	EA	0.096	5.96	42.75	5.32	54.00
2460	Compromise splice bars	"	0.160	9.94	540	8.86	560
2470	Turnout						
3020	90 lb	EA	24.000	1,490	16,940	1,330	19,760
3060	100 lb	"	24.000	1,490	17,850	1,330	20,670
3080	110 lb	"	24.000	1,490	19,200	1,330	22,020
3100	115 lb	"	24.000	1,490	19,650	1,330	22,470
3120	132 lb	"	24.000	1,490	21,460	1,330	24,280
3130	Turnout relay						
3160	90 lb	EA	24.000	1,490	10,840	1,330	13,660
3180	100 lb	"	24.000	1,490	11,970	1,330	14,790
3200	110 lb	"	24.000	1,490	12,430	1,330	15,250
3220	115 lb	"	24.000	1,490	13,100	1,330	15,920
3240	132 lb	"	24.000	1,490	14,230	1,330	17,050
3250	Railroad track in place, complete						
3260	New rail						
3320	90 lb	LF	0.240	15.00	190	13.25	220
3340	100 lb	"	0.240	15.00	190	13.25	220
3360	110 lb	"	0.240	15.00	200	13.25	230
3380	115 lb	"	0.240	15.00	200	13.25	230
3400	132 lb	"	0.240	15.00	210	13.25	240
3410	Rail relay						
3420	90 lb	LF	0.240	15.00	110	13.25	140
3440	100 lb	"	0.240	15.00	120	13.25	150
3450	110 lb	"	0.240	15.00	120	13.25	150
3460	115 lb	"	0.240	15.00	130	13.25	160
3500	132 lb	"	0.240	15.00	130	13.25	160
3510	No. 8 turnout						
3520	90 lb	EA	32.000	1,990	38,610	1,770	42,370
3540	100 lb	"	32.000	1,990	42,930	1,770	46,690
3560	110 lb	"	32.000	1,990	47,030	1,770	50,790
3580	115 lb	"	32.000	1,990	48,060	1,770	51,820
3600	132 lb	"	32.000	1,990	49,090	1,770	52,850
3610	No. 8 turnout relay						
3620	90 lb	EA	32.000	1,990	28,080	1,770	31,840
3640	100 lb	"	32.000	1,990	29,520	1,770	33,280

BASE COURSES AND BALLASTS

ID Code	Component Descriptions	Unit of Meas.	Manhr / Unit	Labor Cost	Material Cost	Equip. Cost	Total Cost
	Descriptions	**Output**		**Unit Costs**			

34 - 11130   RAILROAD BALLAST, RAIL, APPURTENANCES, Cont'd...34 - 11130

ID Code	Component Descriptions	Unit of Meas.	Manhr / Unit	Labor Cost	Material Cost	Equip. Cost	Total Cost
3650	110 lb	EA	32.000	1,990	31,020	1,770	34,780
3660	115 lb	"	32.000	1,990	34,520	1,770	38,280
3700	132 lb	"	32.000	1,990	36,710	1,770	40,470
3800	Railroad crossings, asphalt, based on 8" thick x 20'						
3900	Including track and approach						
4020	12' roadway	EA	6.000	370	910	330	1,620
4040	15' roadway	"	6.857	430	1,070	380	1,880
4060	18' roadway	"	8.000	500	1,250	440	2,190
4080	21' roadway	"	9.600	600	1,400	530	2,530
4100	24' roadway	"	12.000	750	1,580	670	2,990
4200	Precast concrete inserts						
4420	12' roadway	EA	2.400	150	1,450	130	1,730
4440	15' roadway	"	3.000	190	1,740	170	2,090
4460	18' roadway	"	4.000	250	2,080	220	2,550
4480	21' roadway	"	4.800	300	2,680	270	3,240
4500	24' roadway	"	5.333	330	3,240	300	3,870
4600	Molded rubber, with headers						
4820	12' roadway	EA	2.400	150	8,340	130	8,620
4840	15' roadway	"	3.000	190	10,440	170	10,790
4860	18' roadway	"	4.000	250	12,360	220	12,830
4880	21' roadway	"	4.800	300	13,630	270	14,190
4900	24' roadway	"	5.333	330	16,610	300	17,240

DIVISION 41
HANDLING EQUIPMENT

HOISTS AND CRANES

ID Code	Component Descriptions	Unit of Meas.	Manhr / Unit	Labor Cost	Material Cost	Equip. Cost	Total Cost
	Descriptions	**Output**		**Unit Costs**			

ID Code		Unit of Meas.	Manhr / Unit	Labor Cost	Material Cost	Equip. Cost	Total Cost
41 - 22133	**INDUSTRIAL HOISTS**						**41 - 22133**
1000	Industrial hoists, electric, light to medium duty						
1010	500 lb	EA	4.000	330	9,730		10,060
1020	1000 lb	"	4.211	340	10,250		10,590
1030	2000 lb	"	4.444	360	10,700		11,060
1040	3000 lb	"	4.706	380	11,070		11,450
1050	4000 lb	"	5.000	410	11,670		12,080
1060	5000 lb	"	5.333	430	13,990		14,420
1070	6000 lb	"	5.517	450	15,860		16,310
1080	7500 lb	"	5.714	470	17,960		18,430
1090	10,000 lb	"	5.926	480	45,270		45,750
1100	15,000 lb	"	6.154	500	56,790		57,290
1110	20,000 lb	"	6.667	540	67,190		67,730
1120	25,000 lb	"	7.273	590	70,110		70,700
1130	30,000 lb	"	8.000	650	73,180		73,830
1200	Heavy duty						
1210	500 lb	EA	4.000	330	15,770		16,100
1220	1000 lb	"	4.211	340	22,070		22,410
1240	2000 lb	"	4.444	360	24,390		24,750
1250	3000 lb	"	4.706	380	25,290		25,670
1260	4000 lb	"	5.000	410	26,410		26,820
1270	5000 lb	"	5.333	430	26,940		27,370
1280	6000 lb	"	5.517	450	29,180		29,630
1290	7500 lb	"	5.714	470	33,520		33,990
1300	10,000 lb	"	5.926	480	35,760		36,240
1310	15,000 lb	"	6.154	500	43,400		43,900
1320	20,000 lb	"	6.667	540	52,670		53,210
1330	25,000 lb	"	7.273	590	59,110		59,700
1340	30,000 lb	"	8.000	650	65,690		66,340
1450	Air powered hoists						
1460	500 lb	EA	4.000	330	9,130		9,460
1470	1000 lb	"	4.000	330	9,580		9,910
1480	2000 lb	"	4.211	340	9,730		10,070
1490	4000 lb	"	4.706	380	10,620		11,000
1500	6000 lb	"	6.154	500	11,450		11,950
2000	Overhead traveling bridge crane						
2010	Single girder, 20' span						
2030	3 ton	EA	12.000	750	24,920	670	26,330
2040	5 ton	"	12.000	750	28,620	670	30,030

HOISTS AND CRANES

ID Code	Descriptions — Component Descriptions	Output — Unit of Meas.	Output — Manhr / Unit	Unit Costs — Labor Cost	Unit Costs — Material Cost	Unit Costs — Equip. Cost	Unit Costs — Total Cost
41 - 22133	**INDUSTRIAL HOISTS, Cont'd...**						**41 - 22133**
2045	7.5 ton	EA	12.000	750	35,950	670	37,360
2050	10 ton	"	15.000	930	36,250	830	38,010
2060	15 ton	"	15.000	930	44,710	830	46,470
2080	30' span						
2090	3 ton	EA	12.000	750	30,810	670	32,220
2100	5 ton	"	12.000	750	37,310	670	38,720
2120	10 ton	"	15.000	930	51,960	830	53,720
2130	15 ton	"	15.000	930	58,760	830	60,520
2170	Double girder, 40' span						
2180	3 ton	EA	26.667	1,660	48,500	1,480	51,640
2190	5 ton	"	26.667	1,660	51,050	1,480	54,190
2195	7.5 ton	"	26.667	1,660	50,520	1,480	53,660
2200	10 ton	"	34.286	2,130	63,360	1,900	67,390
2210	15 ton	"	34.286	2,130	69,630	1,900	73,660
2220	25 ton	"	34.286	2,130	120,610	1,900	124,640
2230	50' span						
2250	3 ton	EA	26.667	1,660	57,700	1,480	60,840
2260	5 ton	"	26.667	1,660	58,910	1,480	62,050
2265	7.5 ton	"	26.667	1,660	60,570	1,480	63,710
2270	10 ton	"	34.286	2,130	66,310	1,900	70,340
2280	15 ton	"	34.286	2,130	81,560	1,900	85,590
2290	25 ton	"	34.286	2,130	107,620	1,900	111,650
41 - 22135	**JIB CRANES**						**41 - 22135**
0100	Self supporting, swinging 8' boom, 200 deg rotation						
0120	1000 lb	EA	6.667	590	4,640		5,230
0140	2000 lb	"	6.667	590	5,090		5,680
0160	3000 lb	"	13.333	1,180	5,460		6,640
0180	4000 lb	"	13.333	1,180	5,980		7,160
0200	6000 lb	"	13.333	1,180	7,260		8,440
0220	10,000 lb	"	13.333	1,180	10,250		11,430
0230	Wall mounted, 180 deg rotation						
0240	2000 lb	EA	6.667	590	2,470		3,060
0260	3000 lb	"	6.667	590	2,990		3,580
0280	4000 lb	"	13.333	1,180	1,870		3,050
0300	6000 lb	"	13.333	1,180	3,740		4,920
0320	10,000 lb	"	13.333	1,180	7,110		8,290

U.S. Local Multipliers

The costs as presented in this book attempt to represent national averages. Costs, however, vary among regions, states and even between adjacent localities.

In order to more closely approximate the probable costs for specific locations throughout the U.S., this table of Geographic Cost Modifiers is provided in the following few pages. These adjustment factors are used to modify costs obtained from this book to help account for regional variations of construction costs and to provide a more accurate estimate for specific areas. The factors are formulated by comparing costs in a specific area to the costs as presented in the Costbook pages. An example of how to use these factors is shown below. Whenever local current costs are known, whether material prices or labor rates, they should be used when more accuracy is required.

| **Cost Obtained from Costbook Pages** | **X** | **Metropolitan Cost Multiplier Divided by 100** | **=** | **Adjusted Cost** |

For example, a project estimated to cost $1,000,000 using the Costbook pages can be adjusted to more closely approximate the cost in Los Angeles:

$$\$1,000,000 \quad X \quad \frac{133}{100} \quad = \quad \$1,330,000$$

State	Metropolitan Area	Multiplier
AK	ANCHORAGE	130
AL	ANNISTON	77
	AUBURN	75
	BIRMINGHAM	78
	DECATUR	75
	DOTHAN	75
	FLORENCE	75
	GADSDEN	77
	HUNTSVILLE	76
	MOBILE	76
	MONTGOMERY	76
	OPELIKA	75
	TUSCALOOSA	79
AR	FAYETTEVILLE	73
	FORT SMITH	73
	JONESBORO	74
	LITTLE ROCK	77
	NORTH LITTLE ROCK	77
	PINE BLUFF	75
	ROGERS	79
	SPRINGDALE	74
	TEXARKANA	75
AZ	FLAGSTAFF	80
	MESA	80
	PHOENIX	82
	TUCSON	76
	YUMA	76
CA	BAKERSFIELD	130
	CHICO	136
	FAIRFIELD	136
	FRESNO	139
	LODI	139
	LONG BEACH	133
	LOS ANGELES	133
	MERCED	139
	MODESTO	139
	NAPA	136
	OAKLAND	139
	ORANGE COUNTY	133
	PARADISE	136
	PORTERVILLE	132
	REDDING	136
	RIVERSIDE	133
	SACRAMENTO	136
	SALINAS	139
	SAN BERNARDINO	133
	SAN DIEGO	130
	SAN FRANCISCO	139

State	Metropolitan Area	Multiplier
CA	SAN JOSE	139
	SAN LUIS OBISPO	133
	SANTA BARBARA	133
	SANTA CRUZ	139
	SANTA ROSA	136
	STOCKTON	139
	TULARE	132
	VALLEJO	136
	VENTURA	133
	VISALIA	132
	WATSONVILLE	139
	YOLO	136
	YUBA CITY	136
CO	BOULDER	90
	COLORADO SPRINGS	89
	DENVER	90
	FORT COLLINS	86
	GRAND JUNCTION	87
	GREELEY	88
	LONGMONT	88
	LOVELAND	90
	PUEBLO	87
CT	BRIDGEPORT	127
	DANBURY	127
	HARTFORD	122
	MERIDEN	125
	NEW HAVEN	125
	NEW LONDON	122
	NORWALK	127
	NORWICH	122
	STAMFORD	127
	WATERBURY	125
DC	WASHINGTON	102
DE	DOVER	123
	NEWARK	122
	WILMINGTON	114
FL	BOCA RATON	84
	BRADENTON	82
	CAPE CORAL	81
	CLEARWATER	83
	DAYTONA BEACH	81
	FORT LAUDERDALE	85
	FORT MYERS	79
	FORT PIERCE	81
	FORT WALTON BEACH	79
	GAINESVILLE	79
	JACKSONVILLE	79

State	Metropolitan Area	Multiplier
FL	LAKELAND	79
	MELBOURNE	81
	MIAMI	85
	NAPLES	82
	OCALA	80
	ORLANDO	81
	PALM BAY	82
	PANAMA CITY	79
	PENSACOLA	78
	PORT ST. LUCIE	81
	PUNTA GORDA	81
	SARASOTA	81
	ST. PETERSBURG	85
	TALLAHASSEE	80
	TAMPA	84
	TITUSVILLE	94
	WEST PALM BEACH	85
	WINTER HAVEN	85
GA	ALBANY	80
	ATHENS	80
	ATLANTA	77
	AUGUSTA	79
	COLUMBUS	76
	MACON	78
	SAVANNAH	79
HI	HONOLULU	133
IA	CEDAR FALLS	100
	CEDAR RAPIDS	105
	DAVENPORT	111
	DES MOINES	111
	DUBUQUE	104
	IOWA CITY	107
	SIOUX CITY	100
	WATERLOO	100
ID	BOISE CITY	83
	POCATELLO	88
IL	BLOOMINGTON	126
	CHAMPAIGN	121
	CHICAGO	144
	DECATUR	119
	KANKAKEE	126
	NORMAL	126
	PEKIN	123
	PEORIA	123
	ROCKFORD	126
	SPRINGFIELD	119
	URBANA	121

State	Metropolitan Area	Multiplier
IN	BLOOMINGTON	105
	ELKHART	105
	EVANSVILLE	104
	FORT WAYNE	105
	GARY	119
	GOSHEN	105
	INDIANAPOLIS	105
	KOKOMO	105
	LAFAYETTE	105
	MUNCIE	105
	SOUTH BEND	119
	TERRE HAUTE	104
KS	KANSAS CITY	111
	LAWRENCE	109
	TOPEKA	108
	WICHITA	97
KY	LEXINGTON	100
	LOUISVILLE	100
	OWENSBORO	99
LA	ALEXANDRIA	80
	BATON ROUGE	82
	BOSSIER CITY	82
	HOUMA	81
	LAFAYETTE	81
	LAKE CHARLES	81
	MONROE	80
	NEW ORLEANS	81
	SHREVEPORT	82
MA	BARNSTABLE	139
	BOSTON	139
	BROCKTON	134
	FITCHBURG	133
	LAWRENCE	139
	LEOMINSTER	133
	LOWELL	139
	NEW BEDFORD	139
	PITTSFIELD	133
	SPRINGFIELD	125
	WORCESTER	133
	YARMOUTH	139
MD	BALTIMORE	89
	CUMBERLAND	91
	HAGERSTOWN	91
ME	AUBURN	84
	BANGOR	83
	LEWISTON	84
	PORTLAND	84

State	Metropolitan Area	Multiplier
MI	ANN ARBOR	118
	BATTLE CREEK	103
	BAY CITY	105
	BENTON HARBOR	118
	DETROIT	118
	EAST LANSING	108
	FLINT	110
	GRAND RAPIDS	87
	HOLLAND	93
	JACKSON	110
	KALAMAZOO	103
	LANSING	108
	MIDLAND	101
	MUSKEGON	93
	SAGINAW	103
MN	DULUTH	122
	MINNEAPOLIS	122
	ROCHESTER	122
	ST. CLOUD	118
	ST. PAUL	123
MO	COLUMBIA	114
	JOPLIN	97
	KANSAS CITY	115
	SPRINGFIELD	98
	ST. JOSEPH	114
	ST. LOUIS	115
MS	BILOXI	69
	GULFPORT	69
	HATTIESBURG	69
	JACKSON	69
	PASCAGOULA	69
MT	BILLINGS	98
	GREAT FALLS	96
	MISSOULA	98
NC	ASHEVILLE	74
	CHAPEL HILL	71
	CHARLOTTE	72
	DURHAM	71
	FAYETTEVILLE	71
	GOLDSBORO	71
	GREENSBORO	71
	GREENVILLE	71
	HICKORY	72
	HIGH POINT	72
	JACKSONVILLE	74
	LENOIR	74
	MORGANTON	72
	RALEIGH	70

State	Metropolitan Area	Multiplier
NC	ROCKY MOUNT	72
	WILMINGTON	74
	WINSTON SALEM	71
ND	BISMARCK	91
	FARGO	94
	GRAND FORKS	92
NE	LINCOLN	92
	OMAHA	92
NH	MANCHESTER	89
	NASHUA	89
	PORTSMOUTH	90
NJ	ATLANTIC CITY	140
	BERGEN	143
	BRIDGETON	138
	CAPE MAY	138
	HUNTERDON	141
	JERSEY CITY	143
	MIDDLESEX	142
	MILLVILLE	138
	MONMOUTH	127
	NEWARK	143
	OCEAN	138
	PASSAIC	144
	SOMERSET	141
	TRENTON	128
	VINELAND	138
NM	ALBUQUERQUE	81
	LAS CRUCES	81
	SANTA FE	80
NV	LAS VEGAS	128
	RENO	125
NY	ALBANY	116
	BINGHAMTON	113
	BUFFALO	111
	DUTCHESS COUNTY	116
	ELMIRA	114
	GLENS FALLS	114
	JAMESTOWN	110
	NASSAU	116
	NEW YORK	164
	NEWBURGH	116
	NIAGARA FALLS	125
	ROCHESTER	114
	ROME	116
	SCHENECTADY	116
	SUFFOLK	154
	SYRACUSE	112

State	Metropolitan Area	Multiplier
NY	TROY	116
	UTICA	112
OH	AKRON	107
	CANTON	102
	CINCINNATI	103
	CLEVELAND	111
	COLUMBUS	104
	DAYTON	102
	ELYRIA	107
	HAMILTON	103
	LIMA	104
	LORAIN	107
	MANSFIELD	104
	MASSILLON	102
	MIDDLETOWN	102
	SPRINGFIELD	103
	STEUBENVILLE	104
	TOLEDO	107
	WARREN	107
	YOUNGSTOWN	107
OK	ENID	80
	LAWTON	83
	OKLAHOMA CITY	80
	TULSA	82
OR	ASHLAND	103
	CORVALLIS	110
	EUGENE	108
	MEDFORD	103
	PORTLAND	113
	SALEM	110
	SPRINGFIELD	108
PA	ALLENTOWN	118
	ALTOONA	112
	BETHLEHEM	120
	CARLISLE	111
	EASTON	120
	ERIE	110
	HARRISBURG	111
	HAZLETON	115
	JOHNSTOWN	111
	LANCASTER	107
	LEBANON	107
	PHILADELPHIA	133
	PITTSBURGH	110
	READING	119
	SCRANTON	114
	SHARON	110
	STATE COLLEGE	112

State	Metropolitan Area	Multiplier
PA	WILKES BARRE	115
	WILLIAMSPORT	115
	YORK	109
PR	MAYAGUEZ	72
	PONCE	72
	SAN JUAN	72
RI	PROVIDENCE	125
SC	AIKEN	71
	ANDERSON	69
	CHARLESTON	71
	COLUMBIA	71
	FLORENCE	72
	GREENVILLE	70
	MYRTLE BEACH	69
	NORTH CHARLESTON	71
	SPARTANBURG	71
	SUMTER	71
SD	RAPID CITY	78
	SIOUX FALLS	84
TN	CHATTANOOGA	78
	CLARKSVILLE	77
	JACKSON	76
	JOHNSON CITY	78
	KNOXVILLE	75
	MEMPHIS	78
	NASHVILLE	77
TX	ABILENE	74
	AMARILLO	74
	ARLINGTON	73
	AUSTIN	76
	BEAUMONT	76
	BRAZORIA	76
	BROWNSVILLE	70
	BRYAN	75
	COLLEGE STATION	75
	CORPUS CHRISTI	74
	DALLAS	74
	DENISON	74
	EDINBURG	70
	EL PASO	73
	FORT WORTH	73
	GALVESTON	75
	HARLINGEN	70
	HOUSTON	71
	KILLEEN	73
	LAREDO	72
	LONGVIEW	73

State	Metropolitan Area	Multiplier
TX	LUBBOCK	75
	MARSHALL	69
	MCALLEN	70
	MIDLAND	73
	MISSION	70
	ODESSA	73
	PORT ARTHUR	76
	SAN ANGELO	73
	SAN ANTONIO	77
	SAN BENITO	70
	SAN MARCOS	75
	SHERMAN	70
	TEMPLE	73
	TEXARKANA	73
	TEXAS CITY	70
	TYLER	72
	VICTORIA	74
	WACO	73
	WICHITA FALLS	75
UT	OGDEN	77
	OREM	76
	PROVO	76
	SALT LAKE CITY	77
VA	CHARLOTTESVILLE	80
	LYNCHBURG	81
	NEWPORT NEWS	82
	NORFOLK	82
	PETERSBURG	79
	RICHMOND	80
	ROANOKE	83
	VIRGINIA BEACH	82
VT	BURLINGTON	80
WA	BELLEVUE	116
	BELLINGHAM	109
	BREMERTON	111
	EVERETT	115
	KENNEWICK	112
	OLYMPIA	114
	PASCO	112
	RICHLAND	112
	SEATTLE	116
	SPOKANE	93
	TACOMA	116
	YAKIMA	102
WI	APPLETON	112
	BELOIT	115
	EAU CLAIRE	112
	GREEN BAY	111

State	Metropolitan Area	Multiplier
WI	JANESVILLE	115
	KENOSHA	116
	LA CROSSE	112
	MADISON	114
	MILWAUKEE	118
	NEENAH	112
	OSHKOSH	112
	RACINE	117
	SHEBOYGAN	111
	WAUKESHA	118
	WAUSAU	111
WV	CHARLESTON	114
	HUNTINGTON	117
	PARKERSBURG	112
	WHEELING	110
WY	CASPER	85
	CHEYENNE	86

Square Foot Tables

The following Square Foot Tables list hundreds of actual projects for ten building types, each with associated building size, total square foot building cost and percentage of project costs for total mechanical and electrical components. This data provides an overview of construction costs by building type. These costs are for actual projects. The variations within similar building types may be due, among other factors, to size, location, quality and specified components, materials and processes. Depending upon all such factors, specific building costs can vary significantly and may not necessarily fall within the range of costs as presented. The data has been updated to reflect current construction costs.

All prices are updated to January 1, 2020 and are national averages.
For a more in-depth report of any of these buildings or additional case studies contact
Design Cost Data at 800-533-5680, or go to www.DCD.com

501

PROJECT	DESCRIPTION	CITY	STATE	SIZE	$/SF	NOTES
	Commercial					
Bank	School Credit Union Administration Building	Katy	TX	30,700	$211.49	New
	FineMark National Bank & Trust	Fort Myers	FL	20,039	$398.99	New
	Florida Shores Bank	Pompano Beach	FL	11,697	$507.82	New
	Mobiloil Credit Union	Vidor	TX	9,252	$356.14	New
	Beaumont Community Credit Union	Beaumont	TX	3,267	$403.74	New
Office	Allendale Town Center	Allendale	NJ	80,226	$37.27	Addition/Renovation
	Roanoke Electric Cooperative	Ahoskie	NC	52,752	$212.60	New
	Regional Aviation & Training Center	Currituck	NC	39,930	$269.70	New
	Transportation/Warehouse Facility	Monroe	GA	32,400	$187.22	New
	Collection System Operations Facility	Walnut Creek	CA	27,179	$369.86	New
	ULTA - (Shell Only)	Pensacola	FL	10,850	$95.70	Renovation
	Daycare Center	Clawson	MI	4,270	$151.53	Adaptive Reuse
	Campgrounds Office & Retail	Cincinnati	OH	2,300	$331.97	New
Parking	Palm Avenue Parking Garage	Sarasota	FL	287,040	$56.71	New
	Reynolds Street Parking Deck	Augusta	GA	214,000	$67.46	New
	Awty Int. School Parking Structure	Houston	TX	174,582	$59.73	New
Retail	SNG Center - Mixed-Use	Fargo	ND	143,860	$100.38	New
	Roof & Lifeway/Steinmart Renovation	Pensacola	FL	88,299	$35.26	Renovation
	No Frills Supermarket	Omaha	NE	61,000	$107.39	New
	West Oaks Mall Redevelopment	Houston	TX	49,800	$191.11	Renovation
	World of Decor	Deerfield Beach	FL	47,500	$145.86	New
	Sarasota Yacht Club	Sarasota	FL	41,332	$428.57	New
	Karschs Village Market	Barnhart	MO	35,384	$83.71	New
	Fresh Thyme Farmers Market	Fishers	IN	28,784	$183.54	New
	Nashville Hangar Inc.	Nashville	TN	28,702	$192.45	New
	Party Time Plus	Billings	MT	26,000	$97.64	New
	Marshalls - (Shell Only)	Pensacola	FL	25,990	$46.72	Renovation
	Ed Hicks Mercedes-Benz USA	Corpus Christi	TX	25,273	$255.39	New
	Montana Honda & Marine	Billings	MT	22,963	$110.98	Addition
	Fresh Market - (Shell Only)	Pensacola	FL	21,000	$80.31	Renovation
	Theatre Exchange Interior Fit Up	Manitoba	CANADA	19,344	$129.54	Renovation
	DSW Shoes Renovation	Pensacola	FL	18,000	$89.92	Renovation
	Dormans Lighting & Design	Lutherville	MD	15,220	$121.89	Addition
	The Groves Exterior Renovation	Farmington	MI	15,137	$68.91	Renovation
	Don Gibson Theatre	Shelby	NC	13,386	$363.32	Renovation
	Tri Ford Showroom Expansion	Highland	IL	12,881	$118.83	Addition/Renovation
	Fiat of LeHigh Valley	Easton	PA	11,905	$152.17	New
	Sicardi Art Gallery	Houston	TX	6,175	$239.37	New
	Childrens Mercy Hospital Gift Shop	Kansas City	MO	5,010	$301.69	Tenant Build-out
Restaurant	LaMar Cebicheria Peruana Restaurant	San Francisco	CA	11,000	$308.45	Tenant Build-out
	Ulele Restaurant	Tampa	FL	8,905	$747.59	Adaptive Reuse
	Youells Oyster House	Allentown	PA	6,107	$245.41	New
	Mellow Mushroom Highlands Shell	Louisville	KY	5,802	$99.47	New
	Mellow Mushroom Highlands TBO	Louisville	KY	5,802	$164.99	Tenant Build-out
	Mellow Mushroom Pizza	Wilder	KY	5,500	$235.97	New
	Liberty Microbrewery	Plymouth	MI	3,425	$169.78	Addition
	700 South Deli	Linthicum	MD	3,200	$209.19	Tenant Build-out
	New York Pizza Department (NYPD)	Tempe	AZ	2,338	$320.05	Tenant Build-out
	Airport Restaurant Build Out	Eglin Air Force Base	FL	2,320	$275.52	Tenant Build-out

All prices are updated to January 1, 2020 and are national averages.
For a more in-depth report of any of these buildings or additional case studies contact
Design Cost Data at 800-533-5680, or go to www.DCD.com

503

PROJECT	DESCRIPTION	CITY	STATE	SIZE	$/SF	NOTES
		Civic/Government				
Civic Center	Lincoln Center	Fort Collins	CO	38,160	$211.01	Addition/Renovation
	Rockport City Services Building	Rockport	TX	20,062	$218.29	New
	Sinclair Park Community Centre	Manitoba	CANADA	17,007	$309.08	Addition/Renovation
	Mt. Olive City Hall Complex	Mount Olive	IL	14,360	$118.52	New
	Teaneck Municipal Complex	Teaneck	NJ	12,870	$227.13	Addition/Renovation
	Cobb Community Center Additions	Pensacola	FL	5,200	$316.11	Addition/Renovation
	Newtown Municipal Center	Newtown	OH	5,077	$164.48	Adaptive Reuse
	Nederland City Hall	Nederland	TX	4,983	$365.94	New
Correctional	County Sheriffs Office	Morgantown	WV	31,645	$290.03	New
	Nederland Public Safety Complex	Nederland	TX	21,189	$212.00	Adaptive Reuse
	Detention Center & Sheriffs Office	Spencer	IA	16,983	$411.13	New
	Ogle City Sheriff & Coroner Admin	Oregon	IL	15,377	$277.02	New
	Chautauqua City Jail & Sheriff	Sedan	KS	12,257	$292.17	New
Courthouse	Courthouse HVAC System Replacement	Gainesville	FL	101,000	$42.14	Renovation
	Courthouse Renovation & Restoration	Springfield	IL	47,720	$180.13	Renovation
Fire Department	College Station Fire Station #6	College Station	TX	25,133	$341.62	New
	Mt. Orab Fire Station	Village of Mt. Orab	OH	18,170	$176.27	New
	Richardson Fire Station No. 4	Richardson	TX	14,090	$401.09	New
	Willowfork Fire Station No. 2	Katy	TX	13,358	$294.82	New
	Joint Fire & Rescue Station	Newtown	OH	13,125	$190.04	Addition/Renovation
	Little Miami Fire & Rescue	Fairfax	OH	12,316	$225.66	New
	Fire Station No. 11	Fort Smith	AR	12,155	$341.81	New
	Pearisburg Fire Station	Pearisburg	VA	11,818	$220.00	New
	Ponderosa Fire Station No. 62	Spring	TX	11,163	$295.16	New
	El Dorado Hills Fire Station 84	El Dorado Hills	CA	10,869	$444.44	New
	Wayne Fire Department	Goshen	OH	10,000	$96.74	New
	Fire Station No. 40	Jacksonville	FL	9,703	$390.00	New
	Rosenberg Fire Station No. 3	Rosenberg	TX	8,479	$369.70	New
	Little Rock Fire Station No. 23	Little Rock	AR	8,291	$475.64	New
	Cleveland Volunteer Fire Station	Cleveland	MS	6,910	$332.50	New
Government	Council Center For Scouting	Fargo	ND	20,466	$199.41	New
	Camp Crook Ranger Station	Camp Crook	SD	4,880	$492.52	New
	Beaumont Municipal Tennis Center	Beaumont	TX	4,460	$360.38	Addition
	Florence Transit Hub	Florence	KY	3,115	$514.77	New
	Knox Area Rescue Ministries	Knoxville	TN	1,762	$677.95	New
	Entrance Station Lake Mead	Clark County	NV	480	$2,750.55	New
	Vehicle Charging Stations	Denton	TX	6 spaces	$7,057.10	New
Library	Dover Public Library	Dover	DE	46,424	$432.38	New
	Clinton-Macomb Public Library	Clinton Township	MI	24,723	$126.33	Adaptive Reuse
	Crozet Western Albemarle Library	Crozet	VA	23,199	$351.02	New
	Upper Tampa Bay Regional Library	Tampa	FL	13,630	$242.95	Addition/Renovation
	Palmetto Branch Library	Palmetto	GA	11,200	$484.85	New
	Regional Library Expansion	Valrico	FL	10,970	$297.82	Addition/Renovation
Miscellaneous	City of Pampa Animal Welfare	Pampa	TX	13,578	$282.14	New
	Royal Winnipeg Ballet Renovations	Manitoba	CANADA	13,237	$76.12	Renovation
	Senior Services - Kitchen Facility	Batavia	OH	6,000	$120.49	New
	Historical Site Locomotive Shelter	Bismarck	ND	2,100	$161.03	New
Office	Federal Building & Courthouse Modernization	Denver	CO	41,600	$349.17	Renovation
	Brazos County Tax Office	Bryan	TX	13,143	$300.42	New
	Illinois Water District Office	Lincoln	IL	8,974	$156.35	New
	Arkansas River Resource Center	Little Rock	AR	4,926	$574.05	New

PROJECT	DESCRIPTION	CITY	STATE	SIZE	$/SF	NOTES
		Educational				
Athletic Facility	Physical Activity/Sports Science	Morgantown	WV	117,344	$238.37	New
	Indoor Football Practice Facility	Clemson	SC	81,992	$183.94	New
	Jesuit College Locker Room Addition	Dallas	TX	41,673	$219.92	Addition
	Multi-Purpose Gymnasium	Jacksonville	FL	22,844	$291.83	New
College Classroom	New Mexico Tech Geology Building	Socorro	NM	86,813	$317.91	New
	CSU Concourse & Training Room	Fort Collins	CO	53,050	$148.50	Addition/Renovation
	Jack Williamson Liberal Arts Center	Portales	NM	52,480	$238.61	Renovation
	UNLV Literature & Law Building	Las Vegas	NV	44,830	$198.39	Renovation
	Southern State Community College	Mount Orab	OH	43,833	$190.88	New
	SERT Building Iowa Lakes College	Estherville	IA	42,940	$130.82	Adaptive Reuse
Elementary	Cibolo Valley Elementary School	Cibolo	TX	153,130	$258.40	New
	Hill Farm Elementary School	Bryant	AR	88,800	$309.09	New
	CREC International Magnet School	South Windsor	CT	63,923	$424.84	New
	Pineville Elementary School	Pineville	WV	51,650	$226.23	New
	Crownpoint Elementary School	Crownpoint	NM	48,592	$421.53	New
	Janney Elementary School Addition	Washington	DC	10,000	$623.03	Addition
High School	Hmong College Prep Academy	Saint Paul	MN	154,434	$88.47	Addition/Renovation
	HFC High School North Building	Flossmoor	IL	136,555	$216.55	Addition/Renovation
	Somerset Jr. High School	Von Ormy	TX	125,800	$188.08	New
	Takoma Education Campus	Washington	DC	119,000	$232.61	Renovation
	High School Addition & Renovation	Decatur	GA	83,816	$270.08	Addition/Renovation
	Palmer Catholic Academy	Ponte Vedra Beach	FL	34,209	$146.34	New
	Elmwood High School Addition	Elmwood Park	IL	31,630	$362.36	Addition/Renovation
	High School Fine Arts Building	Heber Springs	AR	30,505	$423.22	New
	Alamo Heights High School Fine Arts	San Antonio	TX	25,536	$340.10	Addition/Renovation
	St. Patrick Catholic School	Jacksonville	FL	23,227	$312.16	New
	Springdale School Alteration	Corbett	OR	13,680	$133.18	Renovation
	Goddard School Addition Renovation	Anderson Township	OH	12,489	$88.74	Addition/Renovation
	ISD Outdoor Education Center	Sabine Pass	TX	10,193	$337.25	New
	Indian Mountain School Student Center	Lakeville	CT	9,335	$323.77	Addition
	First Impressions Academy	Fayetteville	NC	7,752	$186.28	New
	High School South Campus Field	Cincinnati	OH	5,580	$249.83	New
Middle School	Timberline Middle School	Waukee	IA	187,375	$167.69	New
	Red Bank Middle School	Chattanooga	TN	158,637	$277.64	New
	Jaime Escalante Middle School	Pharr	TX	156,538	$207.89	New
	Conservatory Green ECE-8 School	Denver	CO	113,616	$185.40	New
	Midland Elementary School Addition	Floral	AR	30,150	$249.31	Addition
Laboratory/Research	Science & Technology Building	Fayetteville	NC	65,048	$525.97	New
	NSU/US Geological Survey	Davie	FL	24,000	$109.30	Tenant Build-out
	Northeast Technology Center	Pryor	OK	11,909	$327.86	New
	Environmental Education Center	Bushkill Township	PA	9,275	$568.43	New
	Research & Education Center	Homestead	FL	5,760	$717.33	New
Multi-Purpose	BGSU Student Rec Center	Bowling Green	OH	179,549	$68.90	Renovation
	Kennedy Center Theatre/Studio Arts	Clinton	NY	96,100	$347.95	New
	Classroom & Administration Building	Houston	TX	65,234	$224.93	New
	NM State U Pete Domenici Building	Las Cruces	NM	53,341	$283.51	Addition/Renovation
	Widener University Freedom Hall	Chester	PA	36,700	$335.59	New
	Alumni Hall, Lincoln Park	Midland	PA	29,027	$273.67	New
	GSU Piedmont North Dining Hall	Atlanta	GA	12,300	$384.22	Addition
	NAU Dining Hall Expansion Phase II	Flagstaff	AZ	10,096	$490.01	New
	Neighborhood Resource Center	Richmond	TX	6,935	$211.53	New
	Heber Springs Cafeteria Remodel	Heber Springs	AR	5,585	$354.46	Renovation

All prices are updated to January 1, 2020 and are national averages.
For a more in-depth report of any of these buildings or additional case studies contact
Design Cost Data at 800-533-5680, or go to www.DCD.com

505

PROJECT	DESCRIPTION	CITY	STATE	SIZE	$/SF	NOTES
					Hotels	
Hotels	Omni Dallas Hotel	Dallas	TX	1,161,450	$432.99	New
	John Ascuagas Nugget Hotel/Casino	Sparks	NV	449,820	$147.72	Addition
	Le Centre On Fourth Embassy Suites	Louisville	KY	408,229	$116.90	Adaptive Reuse
	Minneapolis Marriott West	Minneapolis	MN	237,362	$168.73	New
	Sheraton Centre Park Hotel	Dallas	TX	231,031	$241.47	New
	AmeriSuites	Chicago	IL	191,600	$152.68	Addition/Renovation
	Hampton Inn & Suites Hotel	Chicago	IL	162,000	$166.74	New
	Sheraton Harbor Island Hotel Tower	San Diego	CA	144,126	$203.29	Addition
	Compri Hotel	Los Angeles	CA	110,150	$180.04	New
	Best Western Columbia Hotel	San Diego	CA	108,040	$139.28	New
	Spooky Nook Warehouse Hotel	Manheim	PA	92,726	$132.63	Adaptive Reuse
	The Atrium Motel	Norfolk	VA	75,889	$142.43	New
	Staybridge Hotel At Preston Ridge	Alpharetta	GA	74,607	$182.62	New
	Hampton Inn & Suites	Allentown	PA	71,686	$152.31	New
	Hampton Inn Hotel	Carol Stream	IL	71,000	$187.04	New
	The Inn On Lake Superior	Duluth	MN	65,345	$150.46	New
	The Lancaster Hotel	Houston	TX	64,310	$314.86	Renovation
	Fairfield Inn	Helena	MT	31,009	$147.03	New
	The Edison Hotel	Miami	FL	28,875	$121.89	Renovation
	Western Executive Inn	Billings	MT	21,984	$108.83	New
	Country Hearth Inn	Preston	MN	21,028	$127.78	New
	Lawrence Welk Resort Hotel	Escondido	CA	19,874	$145.75	Addition
	Hanalei Hotel Conference Center	San Diego	CA	8,587	$231.43	Addition
	Summit At Vail, Multi-Purpose Lodge	Vail	CO	6,000	$276.32	New

PROJECT	DESCRIPTION	CITY	STATE	SIZE	$/SF	NOTES
		Industrial				
Manufacturing	Brentwood Industries Manufacturing	Reading	PA	205,000	$42.91	New
	Lee Steel Corporate Plant	Romulus	MI	200,625	$93.33	New
	Siemens Westinghouse Fuel Cell Facility	Munhall	PA	191,090	$101.62	New
	Manufacturing Plant & Headquarters	Lansing	MI	188,975	$98.53	Addition
	Concepts Direct	Longmont	CO	117,900	$120.18	New
	Nypro Inc.	Clinton	MA	102,475	$123.28	Addition
	SWF Industrial	Wrightsville	PA	76,218	$75.95	New
	Headquarters & Manufacturing Facility	Lower Nazareth Township	PA	62,980	$36.38	Renovation
	Aerzen USA (Office/Manufacturing)	Coatesville	PA	40,000	$185.63	New
	Lee Steel Corporate Expansion	Wyoming	MI	34,821	$78.86	New
	Prescott Aerospace	Prescott	AZ	31,400	$113.61	New
	Battery Innovation Center	Newberry	IN	30,080	$443.27	New
	American Steel	Billings	MT	25,957	$82.40	New
	Phillip S. Luttazi Town Garage	Dover	MA	21,913	$141.79	New
	ITT Flygt - Industrial Facility	Milford	OH	16,991	$134.45	New
	Broadmoor Golf Maintenance	Colorado Springs	CO	16,064	$243.73	New
	Cooper B-Line Expansion	Highland	IL	15,290	$172.20	Addition/Renovation
	Robberson Ford Collision Center	Bend	OR	15,089	$141.36	New
	Brown Industrial Building	Truckee	CA	13,345	$139.64	New
	CTC Vehicle Maintenance Shops	Killeen	TX	11,250	$132.04	New
	Storage & Shop Facility	Billings	MT	8,763	$91.12	New
	Central Plant with Equipment Bay	Mesa	AZ	8,500	$939.50	New
Office	Woodlands Business Center	Richmond	VA	48,000	$81.62	New
	Wiregrass Research Center	Headland	AL	9,740	$252.07	New
Office/Warehouse	American Superconductor	Devens	MA	354,000	$173.45	New
	Castcon Stone Inc.	Saxonburg	PA	47,000	$116.18	New
	Minnesota DNR Headquarters	Tower	MN	37,802	$172.05	New
	Office & Warehouse	Miami	FL	14,815	$140.96	New
	DOT Office & Maintenance Building	Hillsboro	OH	10,876	$248.65	New
Warehouse	Distribution Center	Windsor	CT	303,750	$35.37	New
	Zany Brainy Distribution Center	Bridgeport	NJ	250,000	$42.23	New
	Galderma - Warehouse	Fort Worth	TX	70,000	$90.99	New
	Manzana Products Warehouse	Sebastopol	CA	41,395	$67.77	New
	Tactical Equip Maintenance Facility	Fort Campbell	KY	35,290	$244.50	New
	Sonoma Wine Company Canopy	Graton	CA	26,000	$57.52	New
	Administration/Chemical Storage Building	Killeen	TX	23,837	$347.80	New
	DOT Truck Storage Building	Hillsboro	OH	18,400	$94.89	New
	F.I. Storage Facility	Kentwood	MI	13,125	$69.78	New
	50 Columbia Drive Warehouse	Pooler	GA	10,000	$87.57	New
	DOT Salt Storage Building	Hillsboro	OH	9,100	$95.67	New
	Organizational Storage Facility	Fort Campbell	KY	8,040	$145.16	New
	Dwan Maintenance Building	Bloomington	MN	7,240	$196.04	Addition/Renovation
	Maintenance/Storage Building	Batavia	OH	7,200	$84.32	New
	DOT Cold Storage Building	Hillsboro	OH	5,040	$102.01	New
	Job Corp Warehouse	Hartford	CT	3,800	$483.62	New
	DOT Materials Storage Building	Hillsboro	OH	1,920	$114.05	New
	Aerial Vehicle Storage	Fort Campbell	KY	1,800	$217.96	New
	Petrol, Oil, Lubricant Storage	Fort Campbell	KY	640	$304.69	New
	Hazardous Waste Storage Building	Fort Campbell	KY	640	$325.62	New

All prices are updated to January 1, 2020 and are national averages.
For a more in-depth report of any of these buildings or additional case studies contact
Design Cost Data at 800-533-5680, or go to www.DCD.com

507

Medical

PROJECT	DESCRIPTION	CITY	STATE	SIZE	$/SF	NOTES
Clinic	HealthCare Emergency/Trauma Center	Topeka	KS	115,000	$410.95	Addition
	Sadler Clinic (Shell Only)	Conroe	TX	61,599	$127.93	New
	Pinellas County Health Department	Largo	FL	54,965	$266.59	Retrofit
	Sanford Moorhead Clinic	Moorhead	MN	49,250	$261.26	New
	County Health Department	Port Charlotte	FL	47,564	$296.22	New
	Sadler Clinic	Conroe	TX	41,066	$121.20	Tenant Build-out
	PineMed Medical Plaza	The Woodlands	TX	30,398	$135.16	New
	Outpatient Specialty Clinic	Vancouver	WA	20,139	$336.29	New
	Ambulatory Surgery Center	Stroudsburg	PA	19,929	$360.93	Addition/Renovation
	Thundermist Health Center	West Warwick	RI	18,217	$208.11	Adaptive Reuse
	E Texas Community Health Services	Nacogdoches	TX	12,500	$98.56	Retrofit
	North Mobile Health Center	Mt. Vernon	AL	6,765	$294.00	New
Dental Office	Construct Dental Clinic Roseburg	Roseburg	OR	7,750	$511.60	New
	Kitchens Pediatric Dental Clinic	Little Rock	AR	6,068	$307.97	New
	Dental Office Shell & Parking	Olympia	WA	5,302	$174.74	New
	Evans Family Dental	Austin	TX	2,354	$214.16	Tenant Build-out
Hospital	Union Hospital Addition	Terre Haute	IN	492,348	$321.87	Addition
	Regional Medical Center	Lafayette	LA	410,273	$538.69	New
	Houston Medical Pavilion	Warner Robins	GA	180,000	$63.46	Adaptive Reuse
	Langley AFB Hospital Renovation	Langley Air Force Base	VA	160,000	$537.81	Renovation
	Cass Regional Medical Center	Harrisonville	MO	137,524	$378.17	New
	Texas Spine & Joint Hospital	Tyler	TX	115,789	$250.47	Addition/Renovation
	Oktibbeha County Hospital Expansion	Starkville	MS	87,116	$328.20	New
	Childrens Mercy Hospital	Independence	MO	54,682	$316.21	New
	Oktibbeha County Hospital Renovation	Starkville	MS	30,263	$163.81	Renovation
	El Rio Community Health Center	Tucson	AZ	26,998	$241.52	New
	Pondella Public Health Center	Fort Myers	FL	26,400	$300.83	Renovation
	Topeka Ear Nose & Throat	Topeka	KS	24,073	$311.90	New
	Rapha Primary Care	Fayetteville	NC	19,907	$133.90	Renovation
	UNM Hospitals North Valley Center	Albuquerque	NM	16,500	$315.37	New
	El Rio Community Health Center	Tucson	AZ	14,000	$274.20	New
	VA Medical Center Area G Renovation	Houston	TX	12,000	$333.65	Renovation
	Surgical Suite Expansion	Dobbs Ferry	NY	9,000	$380.82	Renovation
	Legacy Emergency Room	Allen	TX	8,432	$631.62	New
	Oral & Maxillofacial Surgery Center	Fayetteville	NC	2,214	$537.42	Renovation
Nursing Home/Rehab	Senior Living Community	Hoschton	GA	56,251	$140.06	New
	Retirement Community	Carlisle	PA	47,075	$157.72	Addition/Renovation
	Assisted Living & Memory Center	Dacula	GA	38,221	$162.91	New
	Homestead Village Nursing Care	Lancaster	PA	28,149	$106.66	Renovation
	Jewish Services For The Aging	Tucson	AZ	24,993	$198.58	New
	Short-Term Rehabilitation	Olathe	KS	13,800	$267.13	Addition
	St. Katharine Retirement Center	El Reno	OK	12,000	$315.71	New/Addition
Office	Orthopedic Hospital/Medical Office	Allentown	PA	79,807	$200.10	Renovation
	Tomball Medical Office Building	Tomball	TX	54,380	$136.06	New
	Olathe Health Education Center	Olathe	KS	50,258	$304.25	New
	Home & Hospice Care	Providence	RI	47,734	$191.92	Renovation
	NE Georgia Medical Plaza 400	Dawsonville	GA	26,997	$267.78	Adaptive Reuse
	VA Medical Center/Pharmacy	Waco	TX	19,171	$155.91	Renovation
	Cancer Specialists of North Florida	Jacksonville	FL	18,654	$284.40	New
	MJHS Hospice Residence	N.Y.C.	NY	12,500	$147.16	Renovation
	Medical Office Building	Pelham	NH	8,399	$264.84	New
	Podiatry Group	Marietta	GA	6,768	$53.85	Renovation
	Marietta Podiatry Group	Marietta	GA	4,400	$245.96	New

All prices are updated to January 1, 2020 and are national averages.
For a more in-depth report of any of these buildings or additional case studies contact
Design Cost Data at 800-533-5680, or go to www.DCD.com

PROJECT	DESCRIPTION	CITY	STATE	SIZE	$/SF	NOTES
		Office				
Office	Restaurant Support Center	Lenexa	KS	186,465	$260.41	New
	5000 NASA Boulevard	Fairmont	WY	132,000	$277.67	New
	Rockford Construction Office	Grand Rapids	MI	71,144	$110.95	Adaptive Reuse
	Woodlawn Office Bldg. (Shell Only)	Louisville	KY	60,000	$140.35	New
	Rosecrance Ware Center	Rockford	IL	44,800	$138.52	Adaptive Reuse
	Professional Center (Shell)	White Marsh	MD	43,025	$176.57	New
	Swan Skyline Office Plaza (Shell)	Tucson	AZ	37,200	$119.09	New
	Infinite Energy Phase IV	Gainesville	FL	36,500	$312.17	New
	Freedom Plaza Building	Cookeville	TN	28,488	$244.07	New
	Landmark Professional Building	Clayton	NC	27,231	$231.42	New
	FC Gulf Freeway Building (Shell)	Houston	TX	24,084	$263.46	New
	White Street Building (Shell Only)	Marietta	GA	23,809	$215.00	New
	Columbia Shores Office Condo	Vancouver	WA	22,574	$178.44	New
	Office & Design Studio	Chicago	IL	20,244	$125.28	Tenant Build-out
	Pinnacle III Office Tenant Finish	Leawood	KS	18,409	$59.64	Tenant Build-out
	Commerce Park (Shell)	Suwanee	GA	17,097	$122.31	New
	PCWA Business Center Interior	Auburn	CA	12,085	$62.04	Renovation
	Tenth Avenue Holdings Offices	N.Y.C.	NY	11,000	$87.08	Tenant Build-out
	Office Park - Building A (Shell)	Fort Collins	CO	10,000	$267.42	New
	Longshoremens Welfare Fund Building	Savannah	GA	8,160	$392.63	New
	Garry Street Office Building	Manitoba	CANADA	7,506	$156.66	Renovation
	Reserve Advisors	Milwaukee	WI	5,300	$50.22	Tenant Build-out
	510 Armory Street Office	Boston	MA	5,100	$96.17	Renovation
	Offices of Bonsall Shafferman	Bethlehem	PA	4,950	$71.13	Tenant Build-out
	FCT Capital Partners	Houston	TX	4,100	$83.21	Tenant Build-out
	Martin Rogers Associates Office	Wilkes-Barre	PA	4,000	$133.15	Addition/Renovation
	Cowan & Kohne Financial	Suwanee	GA	3,713	$125.39	Tenant Build-out
	212 Archer Street Office	Bel Air	MD	3,600	$177.37	New
	Utilities Analyses Inc.	Suwanee	GA	3,513	$116.30	Tenant Build-out
	Visual Lizard Interior Fit-Up	Manitoba	CANADA	2,430	$93.32	Tenant Build-out
	Richardson State Farm	Houston	TX	2,200	$112.83	Tenant Build-out
Mixed-Use	Office/Retail/Parking Mixed-Use	Jackson	MS	228,407	$256.01	New
	Korte & Luitjohan Office & Shop	Highland	IL	26,000	$123.01	New
Medical Office	Evanston Medical Office Building	Evanston	WY	9,157	$281.97	New
	Advanced Medical Group	Suwanee	GA	4,433	$119.73	Tenant Build-out
	Bothell Dental Office Build Out	Bothell	WA	2,203	$198.82	Tenant Build-out
Headquarters	CONSUL Energy Corporation Headquarters	Southpointe, Canonsburg	PA	317,500	$237.46	New
	Fairmont Supply Corporate Headquarters	Southpointe, Canonsburg	PA	75,255	$156.93	New
	Practice Velocity Corporate Headquarters	Machesney Park	IL	64,318	$98.60	Adaptive Reuse
	Enterprise Integration Headquarters	Jacksonville	FL	57,723	$61.35	Renovation
	Linear Technology	Cary	NC	20,000	$318.68	New
	PIPS Technology Inc.	Knoxville	TN	19,884	$253.32	New
	Lee Steel Corporate Offices	Novi	MI	15,781	$168.36	Renovation
	Weaver Cooke Headquarters	Goldsboro	NC	15,464	$302.96	New
	In Capital Holdings	Boca Raton	FL	13,000	$170.26	Tenant Build-out
	ACCION Regional Headquarters	Albuquerque	NM	7,580	$325.94	New
Civic Office	Miss Department of Environmental Quality	Jackson	MS	121,170	$94.95	Renovation
	County Central Office Complex	Pensacola	FL	74,630	$287.77	New
	State of WV Office Building	Fairmont	WV	70,442	$256.40	New
	JAX Chamber of Commerce Renovation	Jacksonville	FL	20,110	$211.70	Renovation

All prices are updated to January 1, 2020 and are national averages.
For a more in-depth report of any of these buildings or additional case studies contact
Design Cost Data at 800-533-5680, or go to www.DCD.com

509

PROJECT	DESCRIPTION	CITY	STATE	SIZE	$/SF	NOTES
			Recreational			
Educational	The Pavilion at Ole Miss	Oxford	MS	235,301	$450.69	New
	University Laker Turf Building	Allendale	MI	137,662	$149.43	New
	CSU Recreation Center	Chico	CA	110,245	$465.00	New
	Intramural Recreation Penn State	State College	PA	59,303	$412.49	Addition/Renovation
	Center For Women's Athletics	Fayetteville	AR	39,183	$367.31	New
	Pickens Recreation Center	Pickens	SC	20,400	$183.36	New
	High School Concessions & Press Box	Loganville	GA	1,506	$471.09	New
Health Club	Brooklyn Yard Fitness Club (Shell)	Portland	OR	63,987	$115.43	New
	Title Boxing Club	Cedar Hill	TX	4,330	$71.56	Tenant Build-out
Recreational	Community Recreation Center	Williston	ND	223,787	$448.64	New
	Spirit Lake Casino & Resort	St. Michael	ND	112,277	$60.85	Renovation
	Phipps Tropical Forest	Pittsburgh	PA	80,000	$327.44	New
	Family Recreation Center	Colonie	NY	70,256	$239.32	New
	Youth Activity Center	Joplin	MO	62,056	$101.35	New
	New Holland Recreational Center	New Holland	PA	51,256	$132.15	Renovation
	Community College Recreation Center	Cedar Rapids	IA	43,500	$166.76	New
	Anderson Recreation Center	Anderson	SC	34,282	$373.90	New
	East Park Community Center	Nashville	TN	33,000	$299.93	New
	Church Family Life Center	Clemson	SC	31,509	$323.66	New/Renovation
	C.K. Ray Recreation Center	Conroe	TX	30,380	$152.75	Addition/Renovation
	St. Raphael Athletic & Wellness Center	Pawtucket	RI	30,268	$264.46	New
	The Forge For Families	Houston	TX	29,860	$249.34	New
	Christian Life Center	Birmingham	MI	26,966	$341.28	Addition
	Children's Sports Center	Woodbury	MN	26,219	$122.05	New
	Trinity River Audubon Center	Dallas	TX	20,791	$941.08	New
	Baptist Church Activity Center	Indianapolis	IN	16,636	$150.90	New
	Boys & Girls Club Syracuse	Syracuse	NY	12,107	$184.43	Addition
	Job Corp Recreational Building	Hartford	CT	11,300	$206.94	New
	Presbyterian Family Life Center	Strawberry Plains	TN	11,236	$168.15	New
	McDaniel Yacht Basin	North East	MD	7,620	$189.38	New
	Bicentennial Park	Cincinnati	OH	4,050	$887.13	New
	Bahosky Softball Complex	Bronx	NY	3,800	$479.76	New
Swimming Center	Resort & Indoor Waterpark	Cortland	NY	175,060	$268.02	New
	The Aquatic Center	Tunica	MS	45,008	$319.35	New
	Spirit Lake Phase 4	St. Michael	ND	26,630	$365.12	Addition/Renovation
	Family Aquatic Center	Beachwood	OH	7,500	$1,186.58	New
	Community Aquatic Park & Center	Billings	MT	6,730	$746.27	New
Theater	Cinema & IMAX Theatre	Lansing	MI	13,750	$225.58	New
	Academy Theater	N.Y.C.	NY	4,593	$229.18	Renovation
YMCA	David D. Hunting YMCA	Grand Rapids	MI	162,966	$205.57	New
	YMCA Recreational Center	Ann Arbor	MI	83,377	$279.80	New
	Floyd Co. YMCA & Aquatic Center	New Albany	IN	82,324	$340.68	New
	Wade Walker Park Family YMCA	Stone Mountain	GA	59,134	$355.59	New
	Alexandria YMCA	Alexandria	MN	55,150	$172.05	New
	Greater Nashua YMCA	Nashua	NH	49,980	$211.77	New
	Lancaster YMCA Harrisburg Ave.	Lancaster	PA	42,502	$360.13	New
	Greater Kingsport Family YMCA	Kingsport	TN	40,007	$257.24	New
	Eastside YMCA	Knoxville	TN	39,984	$255.58	New
	Highland County Family YMCA	Hillsboro	OH	33,228	$152.28	New
	Houston Texans YMCA	Houston	TX	31,628	$361.37	New
	Cypress Creek YMCA	Houston	TX	25,699	$152.41	Addition/Renovation

PROJECT	DESCRIPTION	CITY	STATE	SIZE	$/SF	NOTES

	Religious					
Church	First United Methodist Church	Orlando	FL	121,536	$284.46	New
	Beautiful Savior Lutheran Church	Plymouth	MN	69,700	$116.34	New
	Solid Rock Baptist Church	Berlin	NJ	58,359	$105.19	New
	North Side Baptist Church	Greenville	SC	48,087	$268.63	New
	St. Martha Catholic Church	Porter	TX	46,748	$530.78	New
	Gracepoint Gospel Fellowship Church	Ramapo	NY	46,595	$197.42	New
	Good Shepherd Methodist Church	Odessa	TX	41,003	$314.44	New
	Davisville Church Addition	Southampton	PA	36,090	$185.90	Addition
	Immaculate Catholic Church	Columbia	IL	34,000	$259.95	New
	Keystone Community Church	Ada	MI	29,775	$153.06	New
	Grace Church	Des Moines	IA	29,296	$207.67	New
	Good Shepherd Church	Naperville	IL	27,869	$205.71	Addition/Renovation
	River Hills Baptist Church	Corpus Christi	TX	27,404	$311.43	New
	Good Shepherd Catholic Church	Smithville	MO	24,810	$213.95	New
	Prince of Peace Catholic Church	Chesapeake	VA	24,740	$268.07	Addition/Renovation
	Sanctuary Addition Christian Church	Oklahoma City	OK	23,820	$160.68	Addition
	St. Sylvester Catholic Church	Gulf Breeze	FL	22,000	$421.33	New
	St. Peters Catholic Sanctuary	Fallbrook	CA	20,764	$464.25	New
	Notre Dame Catholic Church	Houston	TX	20,280	$428.28	New
	St Eugene Catholic Church	Oklahoma City	OK	20,000	$469.42	New
	Chapin Presbyterian Church	Chapin	SC	19,900	$342.26	New
	St. Michaels Catholic Church	Glen Allen	VA	19,770	$367.20	New
	Shrine of Holy Spirit	Branson	MO	19,200	$349.44	New
	Wildwood United Methodist Church	Magnolia	TX	19,000	$249.69	New
	Episcopal Church of the Nativity	Scottsdale	AZ	18,288	$124.88	Adaptive Reuse
	Hardin Church of Christ	Knoxville	TN	17,149	$125.54	New
	First United Methodist Church	Crossville	TN	15,816	$491.36	New
	Good Shepherd Episcopal Church	Silver Spring	MD	15,200	$293.18	Addition/Renovation
	Ascension Catholic Church	LaPlace	LA	15,057	$387.01	New
	St. Patrick Catholic Church	Jacksonville	FL	14,139	$276.63	New
	Our Lady of Guadalupe Catholic Church	Rosenberg	TX	12,910	$426.68	New
	St. Timothy's Episcopal Church	Creve Coeur	MO	12,682	$212.71	New/Renovation
	St. Paul Lutheran Church	Pomaria	SC	12,072	$348.27	New
	Covenant Baptist Church	Florida City	FL	10,725	$259.86	New
	First United Methodist Church	Katy	TX	10,503	$315.62	Addition/Renovation
	Lake Ann United Methodist Church	Lake Ann	MI	9,975	$218.10	New
	United Methodist Church	Odenton	MD	8,783	$340.77	New
	Kent R. Hance Chapel at Texas Tech	Lubbock	TX	6,530	$618.57	New
	Haven for Hope Chapel	San Antonio	TX	2,232	$464.61	New
Multi-Purpose	Baptist Church Multi-Purpose Bldg	Maryville	TN	41,656	$115.92	New
	Good Shepherd Parish Center	San Diego	CA	28,752	$159.89	New
	Christian Life Center	Kansas City	MO	26,320	$310.55	New
	Baptist Church Outreach Center	Fort Smith	AR	25,000	$272.67	New
	St Rafael Administration Building	San Diego	CA	24,276	$172.21	New
	Catholic Church Social Hall	Chula Vista	CA	23,596	$286.53	New
	United Methodist Church	West Chester	PA	11,935	$250.56	Addition/Renovation
	Student Ministry Center	Knoxville	TN	11,700	$310.42	New
	Catholic Pastoral Ministries Center	Spring	TX	10,135	$398.54	New
	Christian Renewal Center	Dickinson	TX	8,500	$219.10	New
	Holy Family St Lawrence Parish Center	Essex Junction	VT	7,900	$229.78	New
	Presbyterian Church Addition	Gap	PA	7,414	$263.77	Addition/Renovation
	New Hope Church Addition/Alteration	Saint Louis	MO	5,564	$201.96	Renovation

All prices are updated to January 1, 2020 and are national averages.
For a more in-depth report of any of these buildings or additional case studies contact
Design Cost Data at 800-533-5680, or go to www.DCD.com

511

PROJECT	DESCRIPTION	CITY	STATE	SIZE	$/SF	NOTES
		Residential				
Apartment	Solace Apartments	Virginia Beach	VA	331,681	$102.23	New
	1221 Broadway Lofts	San Antonio	TX	205,137	$144.39	Adaptive Reuse
	Sustainable Fellwood Phase I	Savannah	GA	124,037	$135.07	New
	Kelly Cullen Community	San Francisco	CA	98,385	$559.67	Adaptive Reuse
	Bachelors Enlisted Quarters	Camp Williams	UT	76,253	$254.48	New
	Mockingbird Terrace Homes	Louisville	KY	71,110	$161.74	New
	Homeless Men's Residential	San Antonio	TX	67,908	$268.10	New
	Homeless Women's/Family Residence	San Antonio	TX	60,182	$258.34	New
	Magnolia Place	Lancaster	PA	39,714	$162.92	New
	Elkins First Ward Apartments	Elkins	WV	27,000	$116.96	Adaptive Reuse
	Young Burlington Apartments	Los Angeles	CA	24,399	$209.60	New
	The Lofts at 300 Bowman	Dickson City	PA	23,900	$87.38	Adaptive Reuse
	Peaceful Paths Emergency Svc Campus	Gainesville	FL	22,535	$149.98	New
	Wylie House - Ronald McDonald House	Kansas City	MO	21,885	$190.23	New
	Dogwood Manor Apartments	Oak Ridge	TN	19,975	$172.54	New
	Anderson Village Multi-Family	Austin	TX	12,500	$288.04	New
	Salvation Army Sally's House	Houston	TX	7,812	$251.37	Addition
	Stones River Apartment Complex	Murfreesboro	TN	7,548	$232.45	Addition
	Sunshine Park Apartments Renovation	Gainesville	FL	2,252	$123.21	Renovation
Assisted Living	Kenmore Apartments Senior Housing	Chicago	IL	90,528	$215.52	Renovation
	Country Meadows Retirement	Allentown	PA	53,237	$164.91	New
	Creekside Village Assisted Living	Harrisburg	PA	16,150	$143.32	New
	Landis Homes Retirement Community	Lititz	PA	14,255	$67.74	Renovation
Dormitory	NSU Graduate Student Housing	Davie	FL	203,500	$221.42	Renovation
	Rider University Student Housing	Lawrenceville	NJ	50,500	$238.17	New
	JWU Biscayne Commons Dormitory	Miami	FL	40,048	$261.25	New
	College Residence Dorm	Bloomfield	NJ	25,980	$321.68	Renovation
Single-Family Home	Island Residence	Grosse Ile	MI	19,237	$694.37	New
	MG Residence Restoration	Williamston	MI	9,768	$62.45	Renovation
	Concepcion House	Coral Gables	FL	6,067	$358.11	New
	Leal House	Miami	FL	5,935	$247.40	New/Renovation
	Monserrate Street Residence	Coral Gables	FL	5,885	$447.44	New
	Private Residence	Newburgh	IN	5,566	$356.71	New
	Private Residence	Austin	MN	5,489	$146.97	New
	Private Residence	Lake Wallenpaupack	PA	4,845	$321.87	New
	Island in the Grove	Boca Raton	FL	4,701	$367.94	New
	Private Residence	Benson	AZ	3,660	$179.47	New
	Fairhope Green Home	Fairhope	AL	3,610	$204.33	New
	PATH Concept House	Omaha	NE	3,490	$78.27	New
	Private Residence	La Jolla	CA	3,420	$361.17	New
	Solar House - Private Residence	Fly Creek	NY	3,304	$180.75	New
	Elliott Residence	Fort Collins	CO	3,300	$272.57	New
	Renfrew House	Manitoba	CA	3,206	$195.06	New
	Rosado I Hansen Residence	Tucson	AZ	3,175	$136.07	New
	306 W. Waldburg Residence	Savannah	GA	2,588	$170.63	New
	Nutter Green Home	Milford	OH	2,289	$162.71	New
	Guest House Residence	Ahwatuckee	AZ	1,913	$397.17	New
	Kiwi House	Baton Rouge	LA	1,515	$158.61	New
	Private Residence Renovation	Shavertown	PA	810	$164.87	Renovation

All prices are updated to January 1, 2020 and are national averages.
For a more in-depth report of any of these buildings or additional case studies contact
Design Cost Data at 800-533-5680, or go to www.DCD.com

Other Estimating References from BNi Building News

The latest estimating costbooks for 2020 from BNi Building News, including the *Square Foot Costbook, General Construction, Conceptual Estimator* and more! Each costbook gives you accurate, detailed costs based on actual projects and [Includes a FREE PDF download version you can customize].

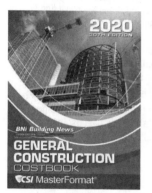

BNi Building News
General Construction
Costbook 2020 with 50-Division CSI MasterFormat

Over 12,000 unit costs provide you with cost coverage for all aspects of construction — from sitework and concrete to doors and painting. The *2020 BNi General Construction Costbook* is broken down into material and labor costs, to allow for maximum flexibility and accuracy in estimating. What's more, you get detailed man-hour tables that let you see the basis for the labor costs based on standard productivity rates.

8½ x 11, $124.95

BNi Building News
PUBLIC WORKS
COSTBOOK 2020

Now you can quickly and easily estimate the cost of all types of public works projects involving roads, excavation, drainage systems and much more.

The *BNi Public Works Costbook 2020* is the first place to turn, whether you're preparing a preliminary estimate, evaluating a contractor's bid, or submitting a formal budget proposal. It provides accurate and up-to-date material and labor costs for thousands of cost items, based on the latest national averages and standard labor productivity rates.

Square-foot tables based on the cost-per-square-foot of hundreds of actual projects — invaluable data for quick, ballpark estimates.

8½ x 11, $135.95

BNi Building News
FACILITIES MANAGER'S
COSTBOOK 2020

The *BNi Facilities Manager's Costbook 2020* is the first place to turn, whether you're preparing a preliminary estimate, evaluating a contractor's bid, or submitting a formal budget proposal. Labor costs are provided and are based on the prevailing rates for each trade and type of work, PLUS man-hour tables tied to the unit costs, so you can clearly see exactly how the labor costs were calculated and make any necessary adjustments. You also get equipment costs — including rental and operating costs, and square-foot tables based on the cost-per-square-foot of hundreds of actual projects.

8½ x 11, $159.95

BNi Building News
ELECTRICAL
COSTBOOK 2020

From meter to duct, conduit to receptacle, The *BNi Electrical Costbook* is the first place to turn, whether you're preparing a preliminary estimate, evaluating a subcontractor's bid, or submitting a formal budget proposal. It puts at your fingertips accurate and up-to-date material and labor costs for thousands of cost items, based on the latest national averages and standard labor productivity rates. What's more, the *2020 BNi Electrical Costbook* includes detailed regional cost modifiers for adjusting your estimate to your local conditions.

8½ x 11, $129.95

BNi Building News
MECHANICAL/ ELECTRICAL
COSTBOOK 2020

From pipe to duct to receptacle, this detailed reference book provides extensive coverage of the most technical aspects of building construction. With thousands of current, reliable mechanical and electrical costs at your fingertips, you can estimate quickly and accurately. Geographic Cost Modifiers allow you to tailor your estimates to specific areas of the country.

8½ x 11, $129.95

BNi Building News
HOME BUILDER'S
COSTBOOK 2020

Here's the easy way to estimate the cost of all types of residential construction projects! Accurate and up-to-date material and labor costs for thousands of cost items, based on the latest national averages and standard labor productivity rates.

Includes detailed regional cost modifiers for adjusting your estimate to your local conditions. Material costs are included for thousands of items based on current national averages (including allowances for transport, handling and storage).

8½ x 11, $110.95

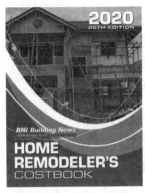

BNi Building News
Home Remodeler's
COSTBOOK 2020

The *2020 BNi Home Remodeler's Costbook* lets you quickly and easily estimate the cost of all types of home remodeling projects, including additions, new kitchens and baths, and much more. The *BNi Home Remodeler's Costbook 2020* is the first place to turn, whether you're preparing a preliminary estimate, evaluating a subcontractor's bid, or submitting a formal budget proposal.

This all-new costbook puts at your fingertips accurate and up-to-date material and labor costs for thousands of cost items, based on the latest national averages and standard labor productivity rates.

8½ x 11, $109.95

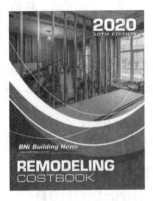

BNi Building News
Remodeling
COSTBOOK 2020

Now you can quickly and easily estimate the cost of all types of home remodeling projects. You'll find yourself turning to the *2020 BNi Remodeling Costbook* again and again, whenever you're preparing a preliminary estimate, evaluating a subcontractor's bid, or submitting a formal budget proposal.

It puts at your fingertips accurate and up-to-date material and labor costs for thousands of cost items. Includes detailed regional cost modifiers for adjusting your estimate to your local conditions.

8½ x 11, $129.95

BNi Building News
SQUARE FOOT
COSTBOOK 2020

In this costbook you'll find over 80 detailed square foot cost studies for projects ranging from civic Government Buildings to Hotels to Industrial and Office Buildings to Residential Buildings and so many more. For each building project you get a detailed narrative with background information on the specific project. In addition, you'll receive unit-in-place costs for nearly 15,000 items and materials used in all types of construction. For each item, you can see man-hours, as well as labor/equipment and material costs, all clearly broken out.

8½ x 11, $109.95

BNi Building News
GREEN BUILDING SQUARE FOOT
COSTBOOK 2020

The new *2020 BNi Green Building Square Foot Costbook* provides you with a comprehensive collection of 57 recent LEED and sustainable building projects along with their actual square foot costs, broken down by CSI MasterFormat section.

For each building, the *2020 BNi Green Building Square Foot Costbook* provides a detailed narrative describing the major features of the actual building, the steps taken to minimize the environmental impact both in its construction and its operation and a square-foot cost breakdown of each building component.

8½ x 11, $109.95

DCR
INTERIORS SQUARE FOOT
COSTBOOK 2020

Unlike other building cost estimating resources, the *2020 DCR Interiors Square Foot Costbook* covers new construction, addition/renovation, adaptive re-use, and tenant build-out.

Each project is broken down by all its interior components presented on a cost-per-square-foot basis. It itemizes the materials used, along with their costs, to assist you in developing a conceptual estimate for interior construction.

8½ x 11, $84.95

DCR
MECHANICAL/ ELECTRICAL SQUARE FOOT
COSTBOOK 2020

Unlike other building cost estimating resources, the *2020 DCR Mechanical/Electrical Square Foot Costbook* breaks down the MEP divisions and itemizes the materials used, along with their costs, in actual projects.

In addition, many of the cost studies in this book feature a variety of "green" technologies, such as hydronic pipe, geothermal heating and cooling, solar water heating, and hybrid ventilation air handlers. It lets you instantly see exactly how MEP costs relate to overall building costs, and how much they can vary from one project to another.

8½ x 11, $84.95

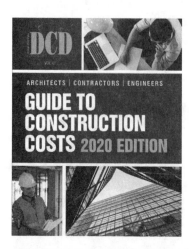

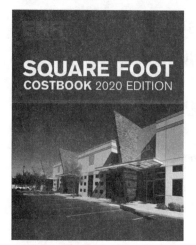

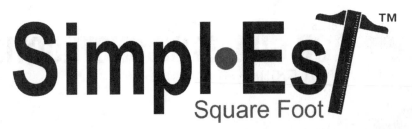

Construction Project Log Book

With *Construction Project Log Book* that task is made as simple as possible.

The 365 Daily Work Log pages let you keep a detailed record for each day of the year. Additional forms such as Accident Reports and numerous checklists help make sure that you're covered.

Document every shipment, machinery rental, delivery, delay, and weather condition — all items that can affect productivity. With the interactive forms you can keep this information on your computer and enter new data daily into the interactive PDF forms.
There are forms that actually do the math for you — eliminating typical mistakes.

7 x 9-1/4, $39.95

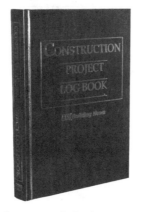

Maintenance Manager's Standard Manual

Since it was first published in 1993, the *Maintenance Manager's Standard Manual* has indeed become the STANDARD reference in the field.

This brand-new Sixth Edition brings it completely up to date, incorporating the latest technology and best practices in all aspects of maintenance management.

Whether you are a facilities manager, engineer, property owner, developer, or anyone else responsible for maintenance operations; not only does it give you all of the essential ingredients for understanding and carrying out successful day-to-day management of maintenance activities, it provides you with an integrated plan for continuous improvement of the maintenance function.

8½ x 11, $99.95

NOTES